In the Minds of Men

In the Minds of Men

Darwin and the
New World Order

by

Ian T. Taylor

Second Edition with Revisions

Ian Taylor November 04.
1988

TFE
PUBLISHING

Canadian Cataloguing in Publication Data
Taylor, Ian, 1931-
In the Minds of Men
Bibliography: p. 468
Includes index.
ISBN 0-9691788-1-6
1. Humanism-Controversial literature. 2. Religion
and science-History of controversy. 3. Civiliza-
tion, Modern-20th century. 4. Life-Origin. I. Title.
CB151. T39   1987   211'.6   C87-094614-5

Editorial/Manthano Enterprises
Design/Fortunato Aglialoro
Typesetting/Trans Canada Graphics
Printed in Canada by T.H. Best Co. Ltd.

TFE PUBLISHING
P.O. Box 5015, Stn. F
Toronto M4Y 2T1 Canada

Contents

Preface to the First Edition

By a curious turn of events I found myself the producer-writer of a documentary film series that examined the ongoing debate between Creation and evolution. Although unrelated to my profession, metallurgical research, the venture turned out to be far more exciting. Viewer response was unexpectedly positive, a surprising development since the most sacred tenets of evolution had been exposed to studio light if not actual daylight. Interestingly, less than five percent of the letters were negative—*hostile* might be a better description. Most of these writers were careful to emphasize their credentials, giving away the fact that their belief system was rooted in a vested commitment to evolution by reason of profession. For the other viewers, among whom were physicians, businessmen, and high school students, there was no such commitment—indeed, I suspect a proper survey would find this to be so for the man in the street today.

The many hundreds of letters showed that public interest in the programs lay beyond mere iconoclasm. Rather, it was due to a deeper and more subtle impact on the human psyche. Basically, the writers expressed the view that although they knew Creation to be somehow "religious", they had always had reservations about the idea of evolution as "scientific". Many indicated that the programs confirmed their suspicion that the education system has not been entirely honest and scrupulous about providing all the facts.

The programs presented sufficient information to enable previously unformulated questions to be properly focused and even sharply honed. The dry-as-dust matter of Charles Darwin's pigeons and fossils took on new significance as the viewer realized their relationship to the great social issues confronting us today. For it became clear that evolution is not now confined to biological evolution, to which Darwin's name is attached, but has become an ideology that extends into virtually every area of human activity, including politics. As the programs continued to reveal further details generally kept from the public, the Creation account as an alternative began to take on the credibility that had been lost in the face of today's orthodox explanation—evolution. In short, armed with all the facts, the viewers were now jury members who could make a proper and personal choice of their worldview.

One thing had become clear: a great need among the ordinary uncommitted people of this world for all the facts and information and not just what has been filtered through the minds of committed humanists, many of whom are educators and members of the media and who thus in a very real though perhaps not conscious way virtually control all that enters the human mind.

In the Minds of Men has been written expressly for the majority of the public, those who feel "uneasy" about evolution and in a broader sense are aware that history, science, religion, and politics must surely share common principles. They do indeed. Although there are books on these individual subjects, so far as is known there is no one volume that combines them all between two covers in such a way that the common evolutionary thread becomes abundantly plain. I have attempted to put together such a volume. Documentation from orthodox scientific sources has been made more than generous so the reader may be as certain as the author that no statement has been taken out of context.

The book may be read on three levels. A reading of the straight text will provide more than enough to whet the appetite of the average reader. The more adventurous reader may delve into the footnotes, in whose depths he will find many gems of information not generally known. And, finally, the appendices will provide the home computer enthusiast with data to play with. But this is not to mention the value of the illustrations. A more diligent approach than using the hackneyed portraits supplied by the picture agencies has brought forth many beautiful engravings not generally seen in this century.

This book would not have been possible but for the help of good friends. My gratitude goes to Robert Simpson ... [and others, and] ... special thanks to Faithe Frew who, good as her name, had sufficient faith in me to keep typing the chapters, notes, the dreary list of references, and the endless rewrites—all in her spare time.

My hope is that through the minds of honest men this work will help make the world a better place.

TORONTO, CANADA

September 1984

Preface to the Second Edition

In a little less than three years, the first edition of *In the Minds of Men* has found many good friends among a wide spectrum of readers in Australia, Canada and the United States. I would particularly like to thank those readers who have sent encouraging letters and have pointed out the inevitable typos and other minor errors. These have been corrected and other helpful suggestions incorporated in this second edition. Any errors that remain are, of course, my responsibility.

It is especially pleasing to know that, in these days of increasing interest in the creation account, *In the Minds of Men* has found full acceptance by the Canadian Public Library system and it is being used in colleges and seminaries as a textbook.

Two noteworthy events have occurred since the first edition was issued: The first concerns the London specimen of that textbook favorite, the *Archaeopteryx* (see page 153), which was all but proved a hoax by a team of scientists; but the reader will have to go to the April 1985 issue of *The British Journal of Photography* for details. The second concerned a 'Stone Age' tribe discovered in the Philippine Islands and reported exclusively by *National Geographic* magazine in August 1972. Nicely supporting Darwin's ascent of man, the affair was exposed as a swindle in the April 12, 1986, issue of the Swiss newspaper *Neue Zeürcher Zeitung*.

I trust that this second edition will prove to be as helpful as the first while any further suggestions and comments from readers are, of course, most welcome.

TORONTO, CANADA
July 1987

Introduction

"In the beginning God created the heavens and the earth." This well-worn opening verse to the book of Genesis has been the answer to man's question How did the cosmos begin? from the beginning of recorded history until recent times. But today, in our computer space-age, can we say that this statement is still relevant? Is this a valid and believable account of our origins? One thing at least will be widely agreed upon about the biblical verse: it relates time, space, and matter in a stunning economy of words, all the more remarkable for the fact that these three most basic entities are not mutually exclusive. That is to say, no one entity can exist without the other two. No matter who the author was in the remote past, it certainly was someone with great wisdom and insight. Taken quite literally, the statement offers the reader a straightforward explanation for the origin of the universe and all it contains, making no apology for the fact that the account involves supernatural creation *ex nihilo*, creation of something from nothing.

Knowledge of the world comes to us either directly or indirectly through our five senses. Man has systematized that knowledge in order to gain an understanding of nature; the exercise is called science and the motivation is usefulness. The discipline of science has generally been in opposition to religion, for the latter claims that there is a further sense beyond the five senses by which man attains true wisdom: divine revelation, acknowledged to be an unprovable concept beyond the natural realm of scientific inquiry and man's understanding. However, because of association with peculiar religious practices, any suggestion of the supernatural is not accepted with enthusiasm by the orthodox scientific fraternity, and history shows that there are good reasons for this rejection. With the progression of scientific understanding and techniques, particularly during this century, the need to appeal to any supernatural explanation has given way, time and time

xv

again, as the light of science has revealed perfectly natural explanations. While it is acknowledged that there are still a great many things for which science as yet has no explanation, it can be said with confidence from the past that it is only a matter of time and research before all of nature's mysteries are revealed. It would appear to be very rational, then, to consign a supernatural account of our origins to that diminishing body of folklore that at one time included wishing wells and fairy rings.

To leave the argument at this point, however, would be to take a superficial approach, especially on the question before us, the origin of the universe.

Harlow Shapley, a professor of astronomy at Harvard University, expressed the modern view of the beginning of the universe when he said, "In the beginning was the Word, it has been piously recorded and I might venture that the word was hydrogen gas" (Shapley 1960, 3). This is the usual scenario presented to the public in imaginatively illustrated popular books, magazines, and even films, such as the ever popular Walt Disney production *Fantasia*. No one has yet proven, however, where the hydrogen or the energy came from in the first place. Statements like Shapley's cannot be taken as an explanation for the very beginning. Some try to get out of this corner by proposing that the universe, in whatever form, has always existed, that there never was a beginning. But this proposal begs the question, and it seems easier to accept a supernatural creation of something from nothing than to try to conceive time without a beginning.

At this point logic brings us to the crux of the matter regarding origins. Once it is recognized that there has to be a beginning, regardless of the explanation for that beginning, we then have to concede that there was timelessness before the beginning. Here we enter a realm quite beyond scientific inquiry or man's comprehension. Whether we like it or not, the argument would seem to force an acknowledgment of a supernatural state of being prior to the familiar natural state that involves time, space, and matter. Perhaps it is possible to express this argument from another viewpoint, considering the extent of space at this present time rather than spacelessness before the beginning.

The popular scientific press speaks about giant radio telescopes reaching to the outer limits of the universe, yet this can surely mean only reaching to the limits of our present-day technology, not to the limits of space itself. Human reasoning tells us that space must continue indefinitely, yet, again, this is like saying there was no beginning to time, and evades the question. The alternative is to concede that there is a limit to the extent of space, but that at the boundary we pass

Harlow Shapley, 1885-1972. A popular public speaker, he was subpeonaed in 1946 for his Communist sympathies and elected president of the American Association for the Advancement of Science the following year. (Author's collection)

from space to spacelessness—and once again we are confronted with passing from the natural to the supernatural realm.

When we consider the origin of matter referred to in the Genesis verse as "the earth", the situation becomes even less clear. The dictionary defines matter as anything that occupies space, so it is evident that space must have existed before matter was created to occupy it. Genesis is thus seen to be set out in the correct logical order. Matter, as we know, consists of ninety-two different kinds of atoms or elements, which in various combinations make up all the material stuff around us: the atmosphere, rocks, and every living thing, including ourselves. Scientists have been working for more than half a century to determine the structure of the atom. They have long since concluded that not only is there design in the hydrogen atom, but energy is necessary to keep it all bound together. And, moreover, that energy had to be expended to put together in the first place what has turned out to be a complex little unit of matter. Greater complexity of design and more energy are, therefore, associated with more complex elements.

To suppose in the face of all this that it all happened by chance, as many scientists do, appeals as much to a supernatural explanation as it does to say that some enigmatic clockmaker designed it all and wound it up at the beginning. The clockmaker argument, by the way, is not new but was presented by William Paley in 1802. Paley, however, took his point of departure from the evidence of design in nature, such as the eye. The argument we are presenting takes us back to the very beginning, to the intelligence directing the energy to assemble the subatomic particles within the nucleus of the atom. Here again we have reached the limits of scientific inquiry and confront the unprovable supernatural.

Professor Shapley's view that "in the beginning...there was hydrogen gas" does express, in a very succinct way, the basis for a belief system that lies entirely within the apparent compass of man's reason. While this naturalistic view scorns the miraculous as an explanation, an element of miracle must nevertheless be involved since the mechanism for bringing order out of disorder is said to be chance. The alternative explanation recognizes that nature is ordered and highly complex, openly concluding that an intelligent Creator was responsible and that miracle was involved. In either case, each view is based on faith, since there were no witnesses to our origins neither can they be repeated in a laboratory; they are essentially the unknowable and unprovable.

The naturalistic explanation for the origins of matter and man did not begin with Charles Darwin in the nineteenth century but appears side by side with the supernatural explanation at the time of the Greeks and undoubtedly goes back even beyond this early period of man's history. An important consequence of this line of thinking follows: by denying an intelligent Creator, or even denying that he is vitally interested in the affairs of man, then men must look to man as the intelligence necessary to run the affairs of the world. This is humanism. Humanism has steadily risen in opposition to theism throughout history, reaching a peak at the time of the French Revolution in 1789. The work of Charles Darwin later provided the scientific foundation for humanism. Since his time, humanistic reasoning has been built upon this foundation until it has become the dominant worldview today.

All this is far from being a dry academic issue since our personal thinking and approach to life are crucially dependent on whichever of the two opposed belief systems we choose to adopt. In a society that claims to be democratic, it would seem only reasonable that every human being be given the opportunity to exercise a free-will choice deciding between the one belief system or the other to provide the anchor point for their particular worldview. The pertinent evidence must therefore be presented and at the same time all the half-truths and speculations cleared away. It is the hope of this book to enable the reader searching for answers to make the decision intelligently.

The first chapter traces the rise of humanism from the Greeks to the French Revolution and attempts to show *why* ideas have arisen rather than simply stating the traditional and often barren list of names and dates. The next few chapters expose the men and their ideas responsible for raising the platform upon which Charles Darwin began his work. By Chapter Five we reach Darwin himself and see a little more of the man and the well-spring of his ideas than is found in the usual biography.

Indeed, vignettes of the lifestyle of many of the other personalities are recounted, not only to show their human side, but also to allow the discerning reader to judge the quality of water in each particular well-spring. From Darwin, the chapters then branch out into some of the most important areas of human endeavor related to our world-view. Most of the controversial issues in the anthropological, biological, and geological sciences are discussed and the chapters continue into medicine, physics, and theology; all have the purpose of exposing not only who said what but, most importantly, why they said it. In the final chapter, the consequences of the step-by-step progression of humanism through the centuries becomes evident in the social sciences. Finally, we see how the entire system becomes justificiation for a new world order under one elitist government.

1

Revelation, Reason, and Revolution

The clearest evidence would be requisite
[required] to make any sane man believe in the
miracles by which Christianity is supported,—
that the more we know of the fixed laws of
nature the more incredible do the miracles
become.
CHARLES DARWIN (1876)
(In Barlow 1958, 86)

The black smoke and flame of the funeral pyre curled about the pallid corpse of what twelve days earlier had been a brave young soldier defending his city in battle. As the bereaved father, Armenius, stared vacantly at the mortal remains of his future hopes, they suddenly stirred to life, and the body of his son leapt from between the flames and shouted, "Don't be afraid, I have much to tell you." He did indeed, and Er's account of how his soul left his body, traveled through another world, and then was sent back to relate what he had seen and heard has been passed down through history and may be found at the end of Plato's great dialogue *The Republic* (1974 ed., 447).[1]

This purported event is clearly miraculous, but it is not isolated; modern examples have been reported by Rawlings (1978), a medical specialist in cardiovascular diseases. He points out that with today's resuscitation techniques, an increasing number of individuals are returning from that clinically gray area between life and death, some to report heavenly experiences while others recount tales of terror. Fascinating though these accounts may be, however, a recitation of the details would be inappropriate in this context. But two observations can be made: First, the experiences reported by individuals alleged to have returned from the dead lie beyond any proof. That is, the experience cannot be repeated and studied in a laboratory. Moreover, the

1

Ancient Egyptian belief in the immortality of the soul: the soul of Ani depicted as the Ba bird visiting his mummified body. (After illustration to spell 89 of the Egyptian *Book of the Dead*; Kathy Stevenson)

experience is not accessible to a second observer. And second, since there can be no proof, the acceptance of such accounts by others becomes a matter of faith and, logically, outright rejection is also a matter of faith since the testimony of the only witness can neither be proved nor disproved. Credibility of the storyteller naturally plays no small part in establishing belief in the minds of those receiving the account. Doubtless, as the story becomes further removed in time and distance from its source, skepticism becomes more the rule than the exception. Nevertheless, the historical record shows that mankind has essentially fallen into two camps consisting of those who are prepared to believe in the unprovable, such as the survival of human personality after physical death, and those who demand proof before belief. The latter camp has generally been in the minority but is somewhat augmented by those of undecided opinion.

Once a position of belief in this unprovable concept has been taken, the matter then becomes more involved. In essence, what is really being admitted by belief is that there is a dimension that is as yet beyond man's reach for inquiry. When pressed further, the accounts, such as the one given by Plato, also make two further important points. The first is that in the other world each soul is held accountable to a Superior Being for actions committed during mortal life. The Zoroastrians of Persia, for example, believed in an existence beyond the grave

Egyptian belief in judgment after death: the judgment scene in this papyrus of Hunefer shows the soul as the heart being weighed against an ostrich feather. (After illustration to spell 30b of Egyptian *Book of the Dead*; Kathy Stevenson)

and spoke of a future resurrection and judgment. The idea of reward and punishment in the next life is not only worldwide but has been very common throughout history (Durant 1954, 1:371). The second important point is that the Superior Being, variously called the Divine Spirit or the Creator, is the great intelligence responsible for the design, creation, and maintenance of the universe, including the earth and its inhabitants. This belief will be recognized as "religion", which has taken on a multitude of forms but which throughout history has been based on faith in such evidence as that offered by individuals returning from a death-like state. Acknowledging that there are many shades of belief, the clear distinction should be made that evidence is not proof; until proof is forthcoming, faith will still be necessary.

The other camp of opinion, which rejects the accounts of life-after-death experiences, usually does so with the argument that since the claims for the supernatural dimension are not open for investigation—that is, are not repeatable and observable—it is better to adopt the safe position of no opinion, or, more boldly, deny the whole issue. The personal accounts are usually rationalized away by claiming the experience to be one of self-generated images under death-like circumstances. But what is really implied is that the whole unprovable notion of a supernatural dimension with a Superior Being having roles of Designer, Creator, and Judge is in fact a delusion. As we shall see in the final chapter, those formally committed to these views have actually made this a statement of creed. The more commonplace principle of design in nature, traditionally seen as evidence for a Designer, is also rationalized by naturalistic explanations according to what are seen as the fixed laws of nature. Charles Darwin expressed this same view and was quite unable to accept the possibility of divine intervention of the fixed laws of nature—that is, of the miraculous. A few before Darwin and many since have held to this same opinion, which ultimately has to reject all the unprovable biblical accounts from the Virgin birth to the supernatural creation of the universe.

Naturalistic explanations are offered to explain away the miraculous but, as we shall see throughout the subsequent chapters, these are often not really explanations at all. For example, a moment's thought given to the popular big-bang theory for the origin of the universe will show that it fails to account for the supposed highly-ordered primordial egg in the first place. Indeed, in the matter of origins, faith in the explanation offered is essential since there were no eye-witnesses to what actually happened nor can the event be repeated in a laboratory. Nevertheless, for those who find the miraculous difficult to accept, the rationalistic explanation provides a measure of intellectual satisfaction.

Revelation and Belief

Once more taking as our example of an unprovable event the accounts of those returning from the near dead state, there is undeniable evidence that our most remote ancestors at the dawn of human history believed in the survival of the personality after death. Neanderthal man buried his dead with flowers and ornaments indicating belief in some kind of after-life. From ancient Egypt to Tibet, from Babylon to China, there has been a committed belief to a life after death and this belief has been carried forward into modern times through the Jewish, Islamic, and Christian faiths. There would seem to be little doubt then that belief in an after-life has been universal since the earliest times.

It is a fair question to ask how this belief came about in the first place and why it is universal, for it must surely have some established basis and not be merely the result of wishful thinking. It is reasonable to suggest that the belief originated and has been reinforced throughout history by individuals returning from the dead, or near-dead state, to tell of their experience. Plato's retelling of Er's account is one such example. If this is true, it can be said then that these reports are revelations of knowledge not available to our natural senses. The Bible, sacred to Jew, Moslem, and Christian, has much to say about the eternal nature of man's soul and actually reports eight cases of resuscitation.[2]

Although this is one of the more spectacular forms of revelation, there are other biblical revelations equally as important, ranging from the origin of the universe and mankind in the first few chapters to our ultimate destiny in the last. All this is revelation of knowledge not available to us by natural means and which must be accepted on faith. The acceptance or rejection of this revealed knowledge has throughout history been one of the root causes of divisions among mankind. It divided the Greek philosophers. It divided Europe at the time of the Reformation. And it is still dividing people today because there will always be those who believe and experience their belief and others who wait in vain for proof that never comes.[3]

Our Greek Heritage

The Greeks contributed a great deal to the corpus of human knowledge in our Western hemisphere and are credited with laying much of the foundation of our heritage. The remainder of the foundation was adopted from the old nation of Israel and forms the Judeo-Christian part of our heritage; more will be said of this later in this chapter. Greek thinkers, rather than, for instance, Arab or Egyptian, have been responsible for our Western mind-set for two principal reasons: First, because the Greeks presented their arguments in what we perceive to be a very rational and logical way, and second, because their records have survived in a readable form. The Egyptian hieroglyphics and the Babylonian cuneiform, for example, were discovered and deciphered only within the last century and a half.

Among the Greeks, Socrates, Plato, and particularly Aristotle stand preeminent as the shapers of the philosophical tradition of the West. Socrates (fifth century B.C.) was a great teacher, using a technique of question and answer that has since become known as the Socratic method. All that is known of him has been related to us through two of his disciples, Plato and Xenophon. He believed profoundly that the universe is under the control of a single Divine Spirit, while the human soul is immortal and meets with judgment and retribution in the other world. His conviction of faith no doubt resulted from his belief that he was the recipient of warnings addressed to him by the Divine Voice (Taylor 1975, 45).[4] However, in teaching his views he raised many awkward questions that challenged the polytheistic (many gods) beliefs of the day. The authorities accused him of corrupting the youth and condemned him to die by hemlock poisoning. In this, he was probably being made the scapegoat for the political ills of the day.

Death of Socrates. Socrates, 469-399 B.C., confounded the vanity of the sophists and the fallacy of their doctrines while he exposed the folly of the many gods the Greeks worshipped. Jacques Louis David, the French painter of this well-known scene, has captured the last moments of Socrates as he discourses to his disciples on the immortality of the soul, absorbed in reflections while the bowl of hemlock is being regretfully offered to him. (Drawn after the painting by W. Cooke, c. 1807; Metropolitan Toronto Reference Library Board)

Attitudes have not changed a great deal since Socrates' time, although an actual cup of hemlock is no longer offered.

As a student of Socrates, Plato was deeply impressed by his teacher's confidence in the certainty of his destiny when faced with the death sentence (Tredennick 1962, 99). Plato's inherited belief in an afterlife was reinforced a decade later during his visit to the Pythagoreans in southern Italy. The Pythagoreans also believed in an afterlife. It is thought that Plato received the account of the young man, Er, from them. In Plato's day, government largely took the form of city-states. From his observations of the general anarchy and corruption, not only in his own city of Athens but also in other countries, Plato concluded that none were working for the common good. He drew up a proposal for an ideal city-state governed by true philosophers (wise men) and set this out in the form of a dialogue in his *Republic*.

What Plato outlined has been taken by some educators to be a model for Utopia. To ensure that future generations are directed towards that noble end, the *Republic* long ago became part of the required reading in liberal arts courses. The atheist philosopher Bertrand Russel (1949, 30) pointed to Soviet Russia as the state most closely run on Platonic principles, while if this is true then Plato's *Republic* advocates slavery for everyone except for the elite few. However, careful reading of the *Republic* shows that the entire hypothetical system hinges on the virtue of its rulers. Plato expressed doubt that his ideal society would ever exist on earth although he felt such a scheme is "laid up as a pattern in heaven" (Plato 1974 ed., 420).[5] He concluded that it would be "better for every creature to be under the control of divine wisdom", that all men may "be friends and equals" (Plato 1974 ed., 418).

Plato's inclusion of Er's account of the immortality of the soul may at first seem incongruous in a dissertation about politics, until it is realized that his temporal *Republic* is only a temporal form of an eternal city-state which he visualized as existing in the other world.[6] His ideal state would then only be possible here and now, with ideal men having the knowledge that each human soul is responsible not simply to itself but to God. Only under these circumstances would virtuous rulers become a possibility. From this it may be seen that Plato is not the left-wing liberal that some advocates of a Utopia on earth would like to believe (Plato 1974 ed., 51).[7]

More than a thousand years before Plato's day, the old nation of Israel also struggled with the concept of rule from above and eventually appointed King Saul (about 1050 B.C.) to be responsible for ruling according to received divine wisdom. This was the beginning of the divine right of kings, or rule by revelation, and was passed on to Judeo-Christianity. Judeo-Christian societies still carry vestiges of this type of rulership. The dismal record shows, however, that the fine dividing line between divine revelation and man's reason, between divinity and dictatorship, has been crossed all too often. In succeeding chapters, the dream of an ideal state using Plato's *Republic* as a model will be found to develop with the rationalist view of science and finally become reality, in name if not in fact, in societies established by revolutions in France, Russia, and China.

Plato founded the first recognizable university, but this arose out of the already existing practice of learned individuals hiring themselves out to teach the young. These teachers were known as "sophists", a word that originally meant "wise-man". But over the years these teachers emphasized the art of winning the argument over finding out if there was any truth to the argument in the first place, with the result that entirely specious arguments were often won purely by the force of rhetoric. The word "sophist" then came to mean "deceiver". Our modern word "sophisticate" is derived from this and conveys a meaning of being "worldly-wise"; root words such as these might lead one to the nagging suspicion that deception and the world's wisdom thus have something in common. Protagoras (fifth century B.C.) was one of the leading sophists of Plato's day. In complete contrast to the views of Socrates or Plato, he could not accept the belief in a supernatural dimension with immortal souls and a Divine Being. For Protagoras, man was the measure of all things, and in an imaginary dialogue between Protagoras and Socrates, Plato (1970 ed.) cleverly played these two opposing beliefs—theistic and atheistic—against each other. The views of Protagoras run as a thread throughout history, and, as we shall see in the final chapter, they eventually mushroom out as twentieth century humanism.

Aristotle had by far the most important influence on Western thought. His early ideas were not unnaturally those of his teacher Plato, with whom he spent twenty years as a student. At this time he believed in the immortality of the soul and a monotheistic (one God) view similar to Plato's belief in a Divine Spirit. Later, when working for Alexander the Great, Aristotle built up an enormous body of knowledge, which he was largely successful in systematizing—after his own fashion. He produced a vast number of works on logic, metaphysics (theology), natural philosophy (today's biological and geological sciences), ethics, politics, and even poetry, all the time rationalizing and fitting everything into his neatly ordered system. During this period of intense rationalism, in the latter half of his life, he began to

Aristotle, 384-322 B.C. Reduced the role of God to that of an absentee landlord. (Engraving by Leroux after the sculpture by Visconti; Academy of Medicine, Toronto)

take on a mechanistic view of the world; his belief in an unproven immortality of the soul diminished and, with it, any idea of divine wisdom and revelation to man.

With growing disbelief in an afterlife, it was but a short step to reason that if the soul were not immortal then it must be mortal and, therefore, would not separate at bodily death but would follow the mortal remains into oblivion. The notions of what constituted oblivion were sketchy and varied among the Greeks but, in any event, could hardly be said to offer any hope. Socrates' belief in a Divine Spirit who was keenly interested in the affairs of nature and men, became for Aristotle merely a prime mover who set everything in motion, and then, like an absentee landlord, left it all to take care of itself. Aristotle recognized that there was great order in the living world, which seemingly graduated as a *scala natura*, or living ladder, from the smallest creature at the bottom to the prime mover at the top. Aristotle (1965 ed.) thus found it difficult to believe that a single great intelligence could direct every day-to-day detail. He reasoned that the Creator had given to every living thing, even to individual organs, a teleological principle, or built-in purpose, so that throughout all time each organ would develop according to a plan. Significantly, liberal commentators such as Balme (1970) deny this and stress that Aristotle appealed to chance, thus reinforcing the historical background to the theory of evolution. A close reading of Aristotle's *Physics*, however, makes it clear that he specifically excluded chance as a factor working for the good of nature (Aristotle 1961). By ascribing a purpose to nature, Aristotle gave nature a characteristic of the deity, and, in a subtle way, this has tended to redirect men's attention towards the complete personification and even deification of nature itself. The historian Hooykaas (1972) has shown that Charles Darwin continually personified nature with remarks such as, "natural selection picks out with unerring skill the best varieties" (p. 18). These remarks even brought a gentle rebuke from his friend Charles Lyell—but all this is a long way from our present subject, the Greek philosophers, and will not be reached until Chapter Fourteen.

Finally, Aristotle's great sense of appeal to reason based on experience of reality and systematic research led him to abandon Plato's concept of knowledge acquired by revelation. In this he was left with the earlier view of the mystic Empedocles (fifth century B.C.), that knowledge is only received through man's five senses—hearing, seeing, touch, taste, and smell. Although this is perfectly logical for the physical world, by its very nature this limits the acquisition of knowledge to the physical world and denies any other dimension. Plato was aware of another channel, an ineffable sixth sense, which was later noted by psychologist William James (1902, 371) as a state of knowledge and yet incommunicable in ordinary language.

Although Aristotle's work appealed to reason, it was based on much speculation and less on his own good advice of observation and experiment. For example, although he was critical of Empedocles' theory that all matter consists of four elements: fire, air, water, and earth and that each of these in turn was supposed to possess two of four basic properties: hot, cold, wet and dry the fact that Aristotle's writings survived led to this nonsense dominating and delaying the progress of science from the 4th century B.C. to the 17th century A.D. In restrospect, it can be seen that this was primarily because his explanations seemed so reasonable at first sight.

Arising from the most remote period of Greek history, sometime in the sixth century B.C., was Democritus, credited as the founder or co-founder with Leucippus of the school of atomistic philosophy. Democritus' view rested on the doctrine that the universe is composed of vast numbers of atoms, mechanically combined. This remarkably modern-sounding atomic concept of the physical universe described the physical universe as operating by chance with no place for supernatural intervention. After this philosophy was established, Epicurus, a contemporary of Aristotle, recognized that chance events could not

The philosophy of Democritus, who was known to have died in 362 B.C. and was probably a contemporary of Leucippus, denied a Creator and gave chance a creative faculty. A man of intellect and wealth, he mocked the less fortunate. (Metropolitan Toronto Reference Library Board)

operate under static conditions. He proposed that movement was a vital factor. In this way, blind chance was given a creative ability. We shall see in later chapters that this movement becomes the process of natural selection in the theory of evolution. Epicurus further claimed that foolish superstition is rooted in the belief in the supernatural and that to banish this belief would at once rid men and society of superstition and notions of divine intervention. Wise conduct of life, he said, was better attained by abandonment of religious beliefs with reliance better placed in evidence attained through the five human senses. Thus began the Epicurean philosophy.

At a later time and in a different place—the Greek empire having collapsed in the meantime—Lucretius Carus (99-55 B.C.), of Rome, eloquently combined the ideas of Democritus and Epicurus in his monumental poem *De Natura Rerum*, that is, *On the Nature of the Universe*. The purely mechanical and atomistic world of Lucretius had no place for a supernatural dimension with an intervening deity. Everything obeyed the inexorable laws of chance and nature. In spite of his apparent denial of the Deity, Lucretius nevertheless began his thesis with a dedicatory prayer to the creative force of nature personified as Venus, goddess mother of the founder of the Roman people (Lucretius 1951 ed., 27). This Latin classic remained as a few treasured scrolls in the hands of the scholars until the invention of the printing press in the fifteenth century. It then became required reading first in Latin; eventually, an English translation followed. Today, it is still required reading in many liberal arts courses.

In summary, the prevailing views among the Greeks, later adopted by the Romans, fell into two camps. The theists, exemplified by Socrates and Plato, believed in supernatural revelation such as the accounts of those returned from the dead. Thus they believed in the immortality of the soul and a Divine Being. Some others, such as Protagoras, were outright atheists, but many, like Aristotle, accepted God but denied revelation and the immortality of the soul (Blackham 1976).[8] In the seventeenth century this latter view became popular among certain Western intellectuals and was known as Deism. These primary beliefs in the nature or even absence of God affected the peripheral views of individuals in each camp and inevitably led to the development of differing views on the creation of the world. Plato (1937 ed.) gave his account of divine creation in his *Timaeus*, while Lucretius summed up the mechanistic view in his *On the Nature of the Universe*. By the time of Lucretius, the Roman and Greek worlds were filled with every cult known to man while the Deist teaching of the inseparability of the body and soul had by then become universal. The Roman poet

Horace (65-8 B.C.) captures this depressing view in these lines to his friend Torquatus:

> Lo! the nude Graces linked with Nymphs appear
>   In the Spring dance at play!
> No round of hopes for us! So speaks the year
>   And time that steals our day.
>
> Yet new moons swift replace the seasons spent;
>   But when we forth are thrust,
> Where old Aeneas, Tullus, Ancus went,
>   Shadow are we and dust.
>
> Once thou are dead, and Minos' high decree
>   Shall speak to seal thy doom—
> Though noble, pious, eloquent thou be,
>   These snatch not from the tomb. (Horace 1911 ed., 101)

Horace expresses the view that unlike the immortals (nude Graces, etc.), man is mortal and has a limited life span. When we die, we return to dust, and no matter how good we may have been in life, nothing can raise us from the dead.

Our Jewish Heritage

In complete contrast to the Greeks and Romans, the descendants of Abraham had an unquestioning faith in one Divine Being and hope of an afterlife in an eternal paradise. The entire structure of Jewish life, whether in Israel or in exile, had always been tightly knit and introspective, with lives regulated daily by the Mosaic rules and regulations, by the priests and the perpetual succession of feast days, intended as reminders of their past. They believed that their laws had been given by the Deity himself to their patriarch Moses and were thus a divine revelation; absolute obedience to the law was essential to ensure a heavenly destiny for their souls and was seemingly a promise made exclusively to the descendants of Jacob. With the promise of this afterlife, and the assurance of the certain loss of it by disbelief and excommunication, belief in the law was self-sustained. Moreover, since they believed the same divinely inspired author had penned the account of the Creation of the earth and the subsequent judgmental Flood, it was not difficult to include this within their belief system.

Then came a certain carpenter from Nazareth. He spoke of the supernatural dimension and the Eternal Being from personal experience and openly demonstrated divine overruling of the natural laws.

Title page to 1743 edition of *On the Nature of the Universe in Six Books* by Lucretius Carus, 99-55 B.C. (Thomas Fisher Rare Book Library, University of Toronto)

The claim to his miraculous birth could be questioned, but his subsequent death and resurrection clearly defied the natural laws. It was the Resurrection that proved to be the greatest stumbling block to the Greeks, but even more upsetting to the Levitical priesthood was his claim to be the Son of God and his criticism of their embellishment of the Mosaic law (Acts 17:31-32). Their very livelihood was threatened when he raised awkward questions about the priesthood before the crowds, so, like Socrates, he was condemned to death, not by a cup of hemlock but by the Roman cross. At the same time there were those who believed that not only was there a more certain way, other than the Jewish tradition, of attaining the eternally blissful life, but also that this was possible without subservience to priests and all their rules and traditions. Vested interests were at stake. The final blow to the orthodox Jewish mind came when it became known that the promised afterlife was not the exclusive preserve of the Jewish lawkeeper but available to everyone (Acts 22:21-22). Clearly, such ideas were a threat to the Jews' community life and even to their nationhood; persecution against the followers of Jesus had to be engineered from within or without—after all, the whole upstart movement was seen to be based on a blasphemy.

Christianity grew out of such beginnings. The first converts were Jews, but within a few years non-Jewish followers were converted. The ancient writings of the Jews, including the Mosaic Creation account, were adopted by the early Christians. For these people, from all walks of life and all nationalities and ages, revelation was something experiential. Miraculous events continued to be a reminder that the deity was pleased to intervene in the affairs of men and often overruled the natural laws to do so. Eventually, the movement became widespread throughout the Roman Empire. Some in high office saw the Christians as responsible for creating public awareness of the corruption in government. The government falsely accused the movement for its own failures and set up a massive persecution of the Christians as a spectacular way to divert public attention from their own mismanagement. Much to the chagrin of the oppressors, victims, like Socrates, had an inner assurance of their destiny and went by the thousands to a fearless death in the Roman Circus.

Christianity and Science

The history of science, which has an all-important place in our lives today, is intimately related to the belief systems of the individuals associated with its various discoveries. During the past two millennia, the greatest scientific achievements have been made in the Western hemisphere, against the background of the Judeo-Christian belief system. The history of science and the history of Christianity thus overlap, and it is important to know something of the one in order to understand the other. For this reason, the rationale behind such topics as Darwin's theory of evolution or space exploration is intimately related to the prevailing historical belief system at the time of their conception.

The presentation of history, particularly in school textbooks, seems intended to be instantly forgotten, with dry lists of names and dates and the who and when but seldom the why. Some more forthright historians, such as Stanley Jaki (1978), have pointed out that one of the failings of their profession is that historians have a tendency to select historical facts to promote their own preconceived views, which are usually antagonistic to Christianity. Jaki gives, as an extreme example, Voltaire's massive universal history, which both ridiculed historic Christianity and glossed over its significance:

> The unscholarly character of Voltaire's account of history can easily be gathered from the fact that he mentioned Christ only once, and by then he was dealing with Constantine's crossing of the Milvian Bridge. Not content with turning Christ into a virtual nonentity, Voltaire was also careful to disassociate Christ from historic Christianity. The fury of his sarcasm would certainly have descended on anyone trying to establish a positive connection between Christian theism and Newtonian science (Jaki 1978, 315).

However, one does not have to reach back to Voltaire to find slanted historical accounts. Young (1974) has recently given unsparing exposure of the fallacies and hypocrisy present in the efforts of two of today's liberal historians, Lynn White and Arnold Toynbee, who blame Christianity for the impending disaster in ecology.[9]

Finally, historians are reluctant to recognize that the explanation of the workings of nature—that is, natural science—coincided with the historical reinstatement of the original Christian belief in divine revelation. Jaki documents, at some length, the connection between community belief system and innovation in science. In an example from a much earlier age, he quotes contemporary science historian Joseph Needham who, in spite of his avowed Marxism, conceded that Chinese science drifted into a blind alley when the Chinese belief in a rational Lawgiver or Creator of the world vanished. "Lacking that belief, the Chinese could not bring themselves to believe that man was able to trace out at least some of the laws of the physical universe" (Jaki 1978, 14). One should therefore approach the history text, academic or popular, with questions about the author's background and beliefs: Is he conservative or liberal, right-wing or left-wing? Many seem to fall into the latter category. In this necessarily brief overview of our Christian and scientific heritage, it is only fair to state that this author makes his approach from the right.

The Latin Church

In its initial stages within the Roman Empire, Christianity suffered constant persecution from the civil authorities. At the same time, the Roman Empire was crumbling from corruption from within. Finally, in A.D. 312 at Milvian Bridge during one of the innumerable battles against the enemies of Rome, emperor Constantine reversed his position against the Christians and formed an alliance to promote their cause—by force of arms if necessary! Constantine ascribed his actions to supernatural intervention.[10] Until this time the church had largely been an underground movement, and the local leaders or bishops had known only spiritual power. Now, one of these bishops in Rome was bequeathed with secular power by Constantine. It turned out to be a curse rather than a blessing. The election of each new head of the church, later called pope, became a matter of power politics, and for the next seventeen centuries papal election was beset with bloodshed, corruption, and intrigue (Martin 1981). Originally, the election of a Christian leader was by consensus of the people; in this way it was believed to be the will of God. The notion was expressed as *vox populi, vox dei*—the voice of the people is the voice of God. It is evident that under Constantine's curse God had very little to say in the voice of the people! Nevertheless, subsequent ideas of democracy in Europe and America have been founded on this principle and have suffered at the hands of those who have sought to control the government and, thus, the people.

The Latin church, now freed from persecution, began full of faith and life, but with growing secular power it began to corrode from the top down. For the most part illiteracy was the greatest problem. Even among the handful of Western scholars, very few could read the Hebrew and Greek of the original Bible, and their knowledge was confined to Jerome's Latin translation. Various fanciful interpretations were made, which eventually became dogmas, while the original message was becoming hopelessly lost to priest and layman among the allegories and traditions. The greatest allegorizer of all was Origen, A.D. 185-254 (Shotwell 1923, 291).[11] The Dark Ages, between A.D. 400 and 1400, were difficult times especially for Europeans, and it is little wonder that there was no scientific progress during this time. Barbarians had swept away the Roman Empire, scholars had been burned together with their books, and, while lawlessness reigned in the countryside, plagues took the lives of millions in the towns and cities. During this time church traditions were introduced, miracles were contrived, and holy relics appeared by the ton in order to maintain the faith (and financial support from the uneducated). Often overlooked, however, is the fact that during this same time the church built hospitals, provided the only education available, and began the universities of England and Europe.

To add to the general misery of the Dark Ages, the Moslem Arabs began a conquest of Europe in A.D. 622. The Arabs within the great Islamic empire became the masters of science, preserving the medical works of the Greek physician Galen (A.D. 130-200) and the scientific works of Aristotle, both of whom had made gross errors that would hinder progress for another thousand years. Not all the Arab scientists of the day were Moslem: many were Christians, Jews, or Persians writing in Arabic. The West is indebted to Islam for certain medical advances, the concept of "zero" in mathematics, and even the numerals we use today; otherwise we might still be struggling with Roman numerals (Edwardes 1971, 52; Goldstein 1980, 97).[12]

Slowly, educated men arose from within the Latin church. By working with Arab scholars, the classical Greek works that had been preserved in Arabic were translated into Latin. By the twelfth century the ideas of the Greeks, and Aristotle in particular, became more widely available and influenced Western thinkers. The old Latin church, full of tradition and superstition though it was, took another turn for the worse.

Architect of the Roman Church

After so many years of intellectual darkness, the more advanced works of Aristotle, such as On the Soul, Physics, and Metaphysics, became available to Western scholars, in A.D. 1200. Aristotle presented a complete explanation of reality, without any reference to a personal God. That is, there was, according to Aristotle, no divine intervention in the affairs of man or nature. In this he challenged Christian and Islamic theology and strained Jewish faith as well.

All these beliefs were based on biblical revelation, which said, for example, that the physical universe had a beginning and it will have an end. Aristotle taught that it was eternal with no end and that history was an endless cycle of existence, striving to be like the "Unmoved Mover" but never reaching its goal. As we have discussed earlier, he also denied the immortality of the soul. Many scholars, Arab, Jewish, and Christian, could see the potential danger of such a belief system and condemned Aristotle's works. On the other hand, his natural philosophies seemed so attractive, like wonderful revelations of truth from a glorious bygone age. The impact of Aristotle's works on the twelfth century mind has been compared with the impact of Darwin's work in the nineteenth century. Both were outwardly attractive, appealing to reason, but both were also at complete variance with scriptural revelation.

Thomas Aquinas, born in Italy, became a Dominican monk, studied in Paris, and spent the rest of his life teaching there and in Italy. Known in his student years as "dumb ox" because of his bulk and slowness, he has since become almost universally known as the sainted theologian.

Thomas Aquinas, 1225-74. Introduced humanism to Christian theology. (Metropolitan Toronto Reference Library Board)

Perhaps to establish that the blessing of heaven rested upon his labors, there is a legend that as he knelt one day before an image of Christ on the cross, the image spoke to him saying, "Thomas, thou has written well concerning me; what price wilt thou receive for thy labour?" This is a typical tradition from the day and raises the interesting theological problem of the deity's purported response to Aquinas doing what had been expressly forbidden *in flagrante delicto*; nevertheless, he had labored well. There is no question that Aquinas was one of history's intellectual giants, and scholars today are impressed by his rigor, complexity, and subtlety of thought. But he was, after all, trying to reconcile the irreconcilable—Aristotle's naturalism and biblical supernaturalism; his efforts for doing so occupy eighteen large volumes (Magill 1963). The result was that Greek philosophy could only be harmonized with biblical theology at the expense of trimming the latter to fit the former. For example, on the question of the origin and destiny of the universe, belief in Aristotle's unending eternity or in the biblically revealed finiteness demands faith for their acceptance in both cases, since there can be no proof for either view. Harmonization inevitably finished up being true to neither and left the door open for bias.[13]

Many of Aquinas's views were not accepted in his own time, but once the door of revelation had been opened to human reason, God became in people's minds removed further from his creation, and man was left to rely on his own intellect. Greek humanism had thus been introduced to Christian theology. Doctrines concerning theology only shift as fast as can be accepted by the cloistered ranks of clerics, and it would be another three centuries before the thoughts of Aquinas were officially adopted at the Council of Trent. It took a further three centuries before posthumous sainthood and Pope Leo XIII's declaration, in 1879, that Aquinas's theology is eternally valid. Aquinas's theological system, known as Thomism, today directs the beliefs and lifestyle of more than 600 million of the world's Roman Catholics.

The Latin Church Divided

From the time of Aquinas in the twelfth century, the old Latin church was headed towards the great schism in Christianity. If dates were to be attached to such events, the Council of Trent, held between 1545 and 1563, marks a convenient formal dividing point. Arising out of the obscurity of the Dark Ages, the scholar John Wyclif, in England, recognized that the people of the Latin church only knew of their faith what had been told them by friar and priest. As a result, all kinds of

John Wyclif, 1324-84. Made handwritten Bibles available to the people and began a revival across Europe. (Metropolitan Toronto Reference Library Board)

abuse had been introduced in the name of eternal salvation. Bibles were the preserve of the monastery priest, rarely read, and when they were, only in Latin. Wyclif translated the Bible into English. Since it would be another century before the invention of the printing press, he had copies written by hand and made available to the people—the beginning of a period in which men began to find out for themselves what the Bible actually said, and did not say, in contrast to what they had been taught. At the same time, Latin copies of the Greek philosophers were becoming available to scholars, and the opposing theological positions began to harden. The church authorities were concerned, not only that awkward questions were being raised but, worse, that coffers were being threatened. To make an example of these "heretics", some were publicly burned at the stake together with their Bibles.[14] Christian persecution was beginning again, and it originated from the same city—popes had merely replaced emperors.

Later in Germany Father Martin Luther, a professor of theology at the University of Wittenburg, grew distressed over his church's teaching of the purported relationship between financial contribution to the church in this life and the destiny of the soul in the next. His reading of the Bible led him to be convinced that God could not be understood with the natural senses and the human reasoning of Aristotle but only by that "sixth sense", that secret the early Christians spoke of as "revelation". Like Wyclif, Luther had his hand on the Reformation door that eventually led to the formation of the Protestant church; the date was 1517.

Martin Luther, 1483-1546. Rejecting all theology based on tradition, he emphasized that God reveals the truth by the reader's faith in the Bible. (Lithograph by Houston; Thomas Fisher Rare Book Library, University of Toronto)

Johann Gutenberg, 1400-68. Gutenberg's new method of printing, introduced in 1446-48, used movable metal type rather than having a hand-carved plate for each page. (Metropolitan Toronto Reference Library Board)

Luther lived after Johann Gutenberg had developed the moveable type printing press, and it was therefore less of an arduous task to get Bibles to the common people in their own tongue. As with Wyclif's revival a century and a half earlier, many came to discover experientially that they could receive knowledge of God and his creation by revelation through the pages of the Bible, but more than that, that they could tell false knowledge from true with absolute certainty. This was a powerful tool in exposing the false teachings of the Latin church. It became painfully evident to the Vatican hierarchy that the Reformation movement could not be extinguished by persecution. Neither the Holy Roman and Universal Inquisition instituted in 1542 nor later the book censorship by the *Index Librorum Prohibitorum* (Index of Forbidden Books) could stem the spread of Protestant Reformation doctrines. A Counter-Reformation movement within the mother church then began, culminating in the Council of Trent. Here, many of the old abuses were cleared away, and a doctrinal position based upon Aquinas's theology was spelled out in detail. This marked the beginning of the Roman church as it is known today and, with it, recognition of the Protestant movement, which had a significantly different doctrinal position. The Roman doctrine was essentially what had grown over the centuries within the Latin church and was based primarily on tradition and the authority of the pope. The Protestant doctrine differed by degrees from the simple nonacceptance of the pope to complete abandonment of all that was not authorized by the Bible.

Liberal historians are often unable to sort out these differences and, as we shall see in the Galileo affair, blame the whole of Christianity from that time to the present for obstructing the pathway of science.

The Galileo Affair

Perhaps the most notable conflict between Christianity and science, and by this we mean the Roman church's hierarchy and the developing humanistic pursuit of knowledge, came to a climax in 1633, at the trial of Galileo Galilei in Rome. Much has been written about this affair, and doubtless more is to come; Bronowski (1973, 214) maintains that the Vatican archives still hold unrevealed documents. In Galileo's day the orthodox view of the cosmos was established according to the science of Aristotle, which had been incorporated into theological doctrine by Aquinas. However, an intervening hand from Egypt had played a part in constructing the medieval portrait of the heavens.

Ptolemy of Alexandria (A.D. 85-165), not to be confused with Egyptian kings of the same name, was a follower of Aristotle and believed that the stationary earth stood at the center of the universe while the

Ptolemy's A.D. 85-165 crystalline spheres of heaven was a notion adopted and taught by the Latin Church to support its biblical interpretation that the earth was fixed in space. (c. 1500; Metropolitan Toronto Reference Library Board)

moon, planets, sun, and all the stars revolved about the earth in a series of inter-nesting spheres. He visualized each hollow sphere as being made of transparent crystal into which was fixed the heavenly bodies; thus, as the spheres revolved, these bodies were transported in their respective circuits. Ptolemy's works were among those inherited from the Arabs and his views came to be adopted by the Latin fathers. Although the Bible is not specific about which revolves about what, they found Scriptures such as, "(The Sun) His going forth is from the end of heaven and his circuit unto the ends of it" (Psalm 19:6), which seemed to offer support for the notion.[15] Eventually, the geocentric or earth-centered view became crystallized into dogma and was held to be as sacred as the Scriptures it was seen to support (Campanella 1639). However, churchmen of that age were not as ignorant as we have sometimes been led to believe. In his criticism of this attitude, C.S. Lewis makes the statement, "You will read in some books that men of the Middle Ages thought the earth was flat and the stars near but that is a lie" (Lewis 1948, 3). Strong talk, but then A.D. White's classic put-down, *A History of the Warfare of Science With Theology in Christendom*, would certainly have inspired Lewis's reaction. Nevertheless, the great crystal spheres were seriously considered by scientists of such stature as Johannes Kepler, who actually wrote music based upon the calculated ratios of the motions of the heavenly bodies. (A more musically successful and lasting attempt survives today in the beautiful Josef Strauss waltz "Music of the Spheres".)

While the notion of Ptolemy's spheres had been ingeniously blended with theology by the poet Dante,[16] others, such as the Polish Latin scholar Nicholas Copernicus, were having serious doubts (Milano 1981). Copernicus had no telescope, but from his observations he concluded that it made more sense to place the sun rather than the earth at the center of our planetary system. He was careful to keep these ideas to himself, but in 1543, near the age of seventy, he published his mathematical description of the heliocentric system—and conveniently died the same year.

Galileo Galilei was a short, active, and very practical man employed as a professor of mathematics in Venice, which at that time was not a romantic tourist spot but the center of the world's arts and commerce. Galileo had read the published work of Copernicus and had built his own small telescope, which had only recently been developed in Holland.[17] In 1610 he was the first man to see the theoretical work of a great scientist of half a century earlier—Copernicus—confirmed by observation, and he naturally wanted to tell the world about it. Unfortunately the world, or rather a few men of the Roman church hierarchy, were

Nicholas Copernicus, 1473-1543.
Refuted Ptolemy's geocentric system and proposed the heliocentric
system we accept today. (Engraving
by Deyerl; Thomas Fisher Rare
Book Library, University of
Toronto)

not yet prepared to accept this news. He was told to keep quiet. Keep
quiet he did. He was no doubt influenced by the memory of fellow
scientist Giordano Bruno's condemnation by the Inquisition to burn at
the stake on the Campo dei Fiori in Rome. Orthodox history has made
Bruno a martyr for science. The truth of the matter is that he was not
condemned for science but rather for occult practices, a common
though infrequently reported activity among the illustrious names of
science (Yates 1964). Galileo waited patiently another twenty-three
years before publishing his findings. The infamous trial took place the
following year in 1633. After making a written recantation of his work,
he was confined to house arrest for the remainder of his days.

Details of the trial can easily be found in other texts. It would seem
fairly evident on the whole that it was a contrived affair, with the
prosecutors fully aware that what the accused was saying was probably
true. The real issue was rather who was making the statement and how.
It is a matter of historical record that additions or deletions to Roman
church doctrine are carefully executed over several generations, the
changes being thus less noticeable than if made quickly. The Roman
church, by adopting Ptolemy, made Aristotle's geocentric system part
of its dogma, but it was becoming evident that geocentricity was in
error (Galileo 1960, 151). However, a layman such as Galileo could not
be allowed to tamper with the public belief in a way that would
seriously undermine priestly credibility. Galileo, therefore, had to be
silenced, not at the stake where history would make him a martyr—
which it has anyway—but in the quietness of house arrest. The public
mind has since been conditioned to tar the whole of Christianity with a
bigot's brush for this incident and leave with the lesson that theologi-

Galileo Galilei, 1564-1642. Not only saw the theoretical work of Copernicus confirmed, but in 1618 saw the notion of Ptolemy demolished when three comets passed effortlessly through the "crystal spheres". (Engraving by Pietro Bettelini; the New York Public Library)

ans should not resist the advances of science. However, it would not do violence to the facts to reverse the moral and point out that if the theologians had not listened to the scientist Ptolemy, they would not have been led astray in the first place.

Renaissance

Renaissance literally means "born again". Webster's dictionary defines it as a transitional movement in Europe between the Dark Ages and modern times, beginning in fourteenth century Italy and lasting into the seventeenth century, adding that the period was "marked by a humanistic revival of classical influence expressed in a flowering of art and literature and by the beginnings of modern science". While this is true, it is really only half the story—the humanistic half. The invention of the printing press about 1465 brought about the Renaissance. For the most part, the printing presses reproduced the Greek works and Bibles, although as might be expected there is evidence of a flourishing little business in pornography.[18] The Greek works were translated into Latin for the scholars and the Bibles began to be translated into the local tongue for the common people. The Greek works reintroduced some positive knowledge but this was generally outweighed by the gross scientific errors of Aristotle and Galen and the dark practices of diabolism from such writers as Hermes Trismegistus.[19] The Bible, on the other hand, brought a spiritual revival, an exodus from the old Latin church, and the eventual schism in Christendom.

Modern science arose from this background. The traditional view holds that it made its advances through the works of humanist thinkers, yet a consideration of the truly great discoveries shows that they were spawned by truly God-fearing men, not humanists. The great laws of motion, thermodynamics and electrical phenomena originated principally in Protestant England and Germany but Catholic France also made some significant contributions. Towards the end of the Renaissance, humanist thinkers, such as Voltaire and Rousseau in

François Marie Arouet-Voltaire, 1694-1778. Exiled from France to England for his outspoken mockery of the Roman Church and the monarchy. (After a painting by Georges La Tour showing Voltaire at forty-two; Metropolitan Toronto Reference Library Board)

France and Locke, Hume, and Mill in England, saw religion as the root of mankind's problems and began to visualize a socialist Utopia where there would be no place for priest or king. Again the printing presses played a major role, in this case spreading the humanist doctrines of Voltaire, who openly mocked all authority, sacred and secular, swaying public opinion by his articles in the very popular Diderot's *Encyclopédie*. However, there was earlier within the Protestant church in England a humanist who not only set out utopian ideals but also devised the scientific method used today.

The Scientific Method

The name Bacon occurs twice in English history. Three centuries elapse between the first and the second, but it is the second who is important in the development of the way we think, and particularly the way scientists think. Francis Bacon was a member of the Church of England and spent his life in law and politics. As an educated man, he had been required to study the classics, which meant reading such authors as Aristotle in the original Greek. Although he was unimpressed with Greek science, and particularly with Aristotle, he was undoubtedly influenced by that philosopher's principles of induction as the proper method for scientific investigation.

The Baconian principles of inductive reasoning consist of making some initial observations and then proceeding, from experiment to

Francis Bacon, 1561-1626. A scientist-philosopher of socialist ideals. (Engraved by H. Wright Smith after an old print by Simon Pass; John P. Robarts Research Library, University of Toronto)

experiment, until, by reasoning, a satisfactory explanation for all the results is obtained. What is implicit in this "art", as Bacon refers to it, is that from the first observation some speculative idea—spoken of more elegantly as "working hypothesis"—is necessary. Then the first experiment is designed to test that idea. For example, by observation the human senses may tell us that heavier objects fall more rapidly than lighter objects. To test this hypothesis, the simplest experiment would be to let two dissimilar objects fall at the same time from a tall tower and see which one reaches the ground first. In fact, both objects would reach the ground at the same time unless one happens to be, for example, a feather, in which case another more elaborate experiment would be required to remove the effect of the air. From such an experiment the theory of gravitation was derived, and, after no exceptions could be found, the theory was declared to be a universal law. It is still valid today.

This is all rather mundane to our twentieth century way of thinking, and we might assume that scientists faithfully follow the Baconian method, but this is not always the case. The problem is a human one; it seems all too often that when experiments are not possible the theory tends to become hardened into fact in the mind of the theorist by the first few observations. Name and reputation become attached to the theory, as in the case of Einstein's theory of relativity or Darwin's theory of evolution; it takes a truly great man to continue to report all the evidence, even contradictory evidence, and thus risk loss of status (Polanyi 1955).[20]

Sir Francis Bacon wrote his best-known work, *Novum Organum*, during his chancellorship under James I of England, in 1620. In the *Novum* he suggested some evolutionary ideas for the origin of species (Bacon 1876, 380). Shortly after the release of the publication, he was dismissed from his position on a charge of bribery and retired to write *New Atlantis*, which appeared posthumously in 1627 (Hesse 1970; Webster 1924).[21] In this utopian work describing the ideal scientific society, he proposed that scientists join together in institutions and pool their work and ideas. This socialist ideal gave birth later to the Royal Society in London, the forerunner to today's research institutions (Crosland 1983).

The French Connection

René Descartes, described as the "father of modern philosophy", was educated by Jesuit teachers and throughout his life remained a Roman Catholic. A first-rate mathematician, his philosophical method was to think rationally from first principles. The worldview of his age had been based largely upon biblical revelation or, in the case of geocentricity, on what was perceived to be revelation. Discoveries in science were beginning to change that worldview, and in the turbulent sea of conflicting beliefs, Descartes chose science as his anchor point. Science, however, relied on the evidence of the human senses, and, while this seemed secure enough at first sight, Descartes began to question if the human senses were reliable for knowing and concluded that they are not. He resolved to doubt everything that could be doubted, and concluded with his famous dictum *Cogito ergo sum*—the most elemental point of self-awareness: "I think therefore I am." Although this statement contains a logical redundancy, it was for Descartes the lowest of all points from which he began to build a rational philosophy (Brown 1977).[22]

Descartes tried to extricate himself from the dilemma of obtaining knowledge through the senses by arguing that since God is good, he would not let man be deceived by his senses when they operate normally. This argument is not without its problems, however. How does

René Descartes, 1596-1650. Descartes, a mathematician and physiologist, searched without success for the human soul and concluded man was merely a mechanism (Engraving after the portrait by Franz Hals; Metropolitan Toronto Reference Library Board)

one know what is normal? Furthermore, his position contains the implication that man is good and therefore not subject to self-deception. But self-deception is caused by preconceived ideas or prejudice and lies at the very root of many problems in science, as we will see in subsequent chapters. Preconception causes us to hear only what we want to hear and to see only what we want to see, sometimes even seeing objects of our expectations, objects that do not exist. All this is well known to researchers today, yet preconception still leads to erroneous interpretations of data.

A rather frightening outcome of Descartes' philosophy began with his *Discourse on Method*, published in 1637. In this he saw the universe as a mechanism governed by mathematical laws. He attempted to formulate these laws, and, as it happened, the formulations were incorrect. But the idea that the universe operated strictly according to mathematical laws was confirmed by the laws of gravitation, discovered and published by Isaac Newton in England in 1687. This was a signal victory, for it encouraged the belief that human inquiry into nature could be made unaided by revelation from Scripture. The pattern was set for others who looked for similar laws governing not only every aspect of nature but also human relationships, society, government, and more recently the human mind. The consequences of finding such laws leaves man with the impression that divine intervention is unnecessary, and that there is no free will, thus reducing the universe, all life, and man himself to mere mechanism. Descartes had actually gone this far in his own thinking, and he had committed these ideas to a thesis, *Traite de l'homme*, written in about 1630. Here he argued that animals and the human body are only mechanisms. Following Galileo's condemnation in 1633, the *Traite* was wisely published posthumously, thus avoiding censure by the church. Nevertheless, this work and all of Descartes' other works were subsequently placed on the Catholic *Index of Forbidden Books*.

Descartes was a follower of Aristotle, generally adopting his views, except for those concerning the soul. Aristotle had maintained that the soul did not separate at death. This view had become common, with the result that the dead were required to be given a Christian burial and the body not defiled for fear of interfering with the "sleeping soul". Knowledge of the existence of the soul is only given by revelation, but to Descartes' rational mind this was not acceptable as a scientific precept. His senses of sight and touch had not found the soul during his extensive work in physiology. Therefore, he reasoned, the soul, like "body humours", was probably mythical. On the other hand, if the Platonic idea of a separable soul had any truth to it, the soul would never be found for study in a dead body.

Descartes couched these thoughts in hypothetical terms in the *Traite*, which proved to be the first cautious step towards modern dualism, the view that the mind and body are entirely separate entities (Fodor 1981).[23] This notion had the effect of both denying and acknowledging the existence of the soul. This may sound very abstract, but it did result in practical changes of viewpoint that allowed human bodies

Jean Jacques Rousseau, 1712-78. Denied the biblical Fall of man and maintained that man would retain his inherent goodness if he lived the simple life. (Pastel portrait by Georges La Tour; Metropolitan Toronto Reference Library Board)

to be dissected with ecclesiastical approval, assuring the progress of medical science. Interestingly, however, modern developments in medicine, such as those pertaining to psychosomatic disorders, have brought the Cartesian view of the soul under general criticism, leaving the profession with the awkward choice of having either to affirm or deny the existence of an entity for which there is not a shred of direct and undeniable scientific proof (Brown 1971).

Jean Jacques Rousseau was born in a Protestant home, converted to Roman Catholicism, then finally renounced Christianity completely, becoming what was popularly known as a "free-thinker" among the intellectual set in Paris (Beer 1972). As a Deist he categorically denied all biblical miracles and relegated God to the role of absentee landlord, in much the same way as had Aristotle and Descartes. In contrast to the tried and established Christian teaching that holds that each man is responsible for his own moral life and must strive to avoid personal evil and sin, Rousseau made himself believe that man is born good and is corrupted only by a bad society. One of the outworkings of this notion was his educational ideal that children should be kept away from the corrupting influences of society and allowed to learn naturally what they want to learn. Not only have Rousseau's speculations no scientific basis, but their author was the least qualified to write about matters such as the education of children: he had abandoned five illegitimate children in a Paris orphanage (Rousseau 1904).[24] Strangely, however, there have since been many who would otherwise pride themselves on their complete rationalism and objectivity, yet who have advocated this type of social change. And so we find that Rousseau has left a lasting mark on modern progressive education.

Another of Rousseau's ideas of far-reaching consequence was the concept of "social contract". Throughout history it has been believed that kings, good or bad, were set up by divine appointment. The belief extends far beyond the Judeo-Christian West, and until World War II, for example, Japanese emperors were considered to be divinely appointed. Nevertheless, man's natural inclination is to rebel against divine rulership for whatever cause, and the first successful confrontation of this age took place in England, in 1215, with the signing of the *Magna Charta*. Here, the monarch of the day was made subject to the law of the land instead of remaining placed above the law. In France, however, kings still exercised their divine rights until the French Revolution, which began in 1789. Rousseau's *Social Contract*, published in 1762, put forward a radical and secular theory of government based on a general will of the people rather than on laws appointed by God, paving the way for the French Revolution and, incidentally, for the

A significant connection between
the American Revolution of 1776
and the French Revolution of 1789
is depicted on this nineteenth century snuff-box lid: Voltaire is
shown on the left, Rousseau in the
centre, and Benjamin Franklin on
the right, wearing a fur hat to hide
his eczema. (The Metropolitan
Museum of Art, New York)

American Revolution, announced by the Declaration of Independence
thirteen years earlier. By removing God from human affairs and declaring man to be inherently good, Rousseau had set the stage for secular
humanism, which, as we shall see, requires the theory of evolution to
maintain the belief that there never has been and never will be any
divine intervention.

Reason's Revolution

As has been shown, the Renaissance period produced a number of
educated men who had become disenchanted with orthodox teachings
based on biblical revelation, that is, the revelation that had been fused
with tradition and a corrupt papacy. It was only natural that this
should breed outright skepticism as found in the free-thinkers such as
Voltaire and Rousseau. The search for the truth turned these men from
revelation to reason as found in the teachings of the classical writers of
Greece and Rome. The Greeks were particularly admired during this
period. The apparently socialist views of Plato were developed, and
even the architecture of the time reflected admiration for the classical
Greek period.

The discovery of the great laws of the universe by the developing
discipline of science gave credence to the view that all of reality conformed rigidly to those laws, and that to understand and discover other
laws through science was the sure promise of power. Moreover, with a
universe under law, there was no place for divine intervention.
Through knowledge man was at last perceived to have gained the
freedom to be master of his own destiny. Thus, the Renaissance marked
the beginning of modern science, the beginning of modern socialism,
and the beginning of secular humanism.

Head office of the East India Company, Leadenhall Street, London, about 1800. An early example of the revival of Greek architecture, which was at its heyday from 1820 to 1840. (Engraving by William Watts; Metropolitan Toronto Reference Library Board)

It does not require great insight to see that power in human society takes the form of a pyramid, in which the mind-set of the general bulk of the structure largely reflects that of the mind at the top. Indeed, contrary to the common impression, modern governments are set up this way, with the apex of the pyramid often a mere figurehead representing the unseen wielders of power immediately beneath it. To control the apex is to control the nation. The Renaissance had produced a handful of idealists with a utopian dream, and while efforts were made to exert their influence on the highest echelons of power in England, the power structure of the Roman church and the nobility in France was evidently too well entrenched to be overthrown purely through connivance. In England, the intellectual approach proved to be more successful, working within the milieu of the Industrial Revolution, but it took the entire nineteenth century and a good part of the twentieth to turn around the mind-set of much of the populace to accept a new social order. In France, at the end of the eighteenth century, more radical means were necessary: a revolution by the people was seen to be the most expeditious means to a noble end and the blood shed but a small price to pay. It was believed that Utopia would be a reality within months once the wheels of revolution were put in motion.

The usual version of the causes of the French Revolution is that a grain shortage triggered rebellion in a people who had long been oppressed by a corrupt nobility and clergy. Many writers have observed, however, that there were other underlying causes, providing ample documentation to make their point. Lord Acton, in his *Essays on the French Revolution*, writes: "The appalling thing in the French Revolution is not the tumult but the design. Through all the fire and smoke we perceive the evidence of calculating organization. The managers remain studiously concealed and masked; but there is no doubt about their presence from the first" (Reed 1978, 136).

It would be inappropriate here to spell out details such as the intrigue that engineered the grain shortage, but the outcome of the revolution, in which many thousands lost their lives not only in riots but especially in the Jacobin reign of terror that followed, was that king and church were swept away and the new socialist state proclaimed a republic. As a nation France had overthrown the rulership of God, no matter how tenuous that rulership was seen to be, by disposing of their divinely appointed king. In his place the revolutionaries elected a committee of godless men to govern by human reason. Historian Walter Scott describes how all this was publicly acted out: In 1793 the Legislative Assembly, in a united voice, renounced unanimously the belief and worship of a deity. Afterwards, a great procession was staged by the National Convention, which was the government of the day, and mounted on a magnificent open wagon was the Goddess of Reason— generally recognized as Demoiselle Candeille, a dancing girl from the opera, fair to look upon but of doubtful virtue—who was paraded from the convention hall to the cathedral of Notre Dame. There she took her place as the deity, by being elevated onto the high altar to receive the adoration of all present. This was followed shortly afterwards by the public burning of the Bible, and the whole scene was reenacted several times throughout the country (Scott 1827, 2:306).

Almost overnight, and by devious means, France had gone from Roman Catholicism to atheism to pagan idolatry; the few who had discovered, as Luther had earlier, that divine revelation was the surer way to the truth, had been banished into exile or lay in the grave. To all outward appearances the small number of idealists, who believed that human reason alone was the pathway to Utopia, were supremely victorious. Having made the radical change in social order, the time was ripe for other radical changes: the traditional weights and measures were replaced by the metric system, which has since moved from country to country, hand-in-glove with socialism. There were even serious moves to metricize time with a ten-hour day and a ten-day week, but, fortunately for the rest of mankind, the long-suffering Frenchman refused to accept this, and it never came into general use.[25]

The socialist victory was, however, short-lived, and by 1815 the monarchy was invited back in and remained for several years. In the meantime the Roman church also reestablished itself, though not with its previous power. It seems that since that infamous day in 1793 when rule by man formally replaced rule by God, there has been in France an uneasy political atmosphere as one republic supersedes another, each slipping ever surely a little more to the left. The utopian experiment, which began in violence, has not had a record of unqualified success. The object of every revolution is to bring about a universal happiness, and this was surely declared in the French revolutionaries' principle of liberty, equality, and fraternity. After almost two hundred years we see the result of their efforts, and they are not enviable. Of liberty, there is not a shred left; of equality, there is scarcely a trace; while of fraternity, there has never been a sign. Yet in spite of such observations and the dismal record of industrial growth of that nation throughout the nineteenth century and for much of the twentieth, the socialist ideal spread throughout Europe and, in its wake, toppled the crowned and mitred heads of authority.

Statue of Liberty presented by the Freemasons of France to the United States in 1886 to celebrate the centenary of the 1776 Revolution. The Revolution was not as successful in its aims as the French and the presentation was late. (Author's collection)

2

Preparing the Ground

Had I been present at the Creation, I would have given some useful hints for the better ordering of the universe.

ALFONSO THE WISE
(thirteenth century A.D.)[1]

T he French Revolution in the eighteenth century had given violent birth to socialist humanism. While it was being acted out in a baptism of blood, a far different kind of revolution was taking place just across the English Channel. The Industrial Revolution in England, a gradual and more carefully orchestrated affair, generally free of violence, provided an intellectual atmosphere that promoted science. In turn, the resultant understanding of the forces of nature offered man power. Quite literally, steam power was the prime mover of the Industrial Revolution. While the nineteenth century capitalist society had its faults, it did nurture every field of the arts. Some of the finest music, literature, architecture, and art was produced during this period.

It is perhaps difficult to appreciate from our point in time that before the Industrial Revolution the average man lived in the country and for the most part lived off the land. Men were very familiar with the flora and fauna around them and unquestioningly saw the divine hand in perfect harmony with nature (which we prosaically refer to today as "ecology").

The Industrial Revolution brought country people into the cities and into awful working conditions where they no longer saw the beauty of nature. Even the sunsets were obscured by the interminable serpents of black smoke from "those dark satanic mills", to use words penned by a poet of the day (Blake 1966, 481).[2] As the first generation of mill workers passed into the second, some, in viewing their squalid and mechanistic surroundings, lost their belief in divine creation.

36

Others experienced an inner yearning to recapture the beauty of nature, and there awoke among the people a tremendous interest in natural history. It was in nineteenth century England, during the long reign of Queen Victoria, that the great public gardens, zoos, and museums were opened. Many of the most popular books of the day were devoted to the wonders of natural history, and it was not uncommon for the working man to be familiar with all the Latin botanical names of many of the common flowers, learned at evening public lectures in natural history. However, it was during the preceding century that much of what was admired by the Victorians as the new science of natural history had been painstakingly researched. Virtually no scientific work at all had been carried out from the time of Aristotle to the eighteenth century, and there is mounting evidence that strongly suggests that a number of the discoveries of science made subsequent to this time were actually rediscoveries of knowledge that had been lost during the previous two thousand years (Price 1975; Salm 1964; Wertime 1973; Zimmerman et al. 1974).[3-6] This chapter will introduce some

London as seen by Gustave Doré in 1872. Living in these surroundings, many lost their appreciation for the beauty of nature as evidence of their creator. (Engraving by Pannemaker after a drawing by Doré; Metropolitan Toronto Reference Library Board)

This small bronze horse had been produced in 450 B.C. by a casting technique rediscovered in the fourteenth century A.D. Suspected as a fake, modern technology has reinstated it as genuine. (The Metropolitan Museum of Art, New York; Fletcher Fund, 1923)

of the key names of those rugged individualists who sought to bring the world of nature within the compass of man's understanding and whose influence is felt even today.

Carl Linnaeus

Carl von Linné was born into a Protestant home in Sweden in 1707. Having developed a consuming interest in flowers, he took a medical degree as the most appropriate training in the natural sciences there was at the time. Eventually he became a professor of medicine and botany at the University of Uppsala, and as was required, he always lectured and wrote in Latin. This was the legacy of the Church of Rome's attempt to impose a universal language upon mankind. At the age of fifty, von Linné adopted the Latinized spelling "Linnaeus", by which he is most commonly known, and remained at the university as a popular lecturer until he died in 1778 (Lindroth 1973).

Linnaeus essentially laid the foundation of natural history by devising a system of classification whereby any plant or animal could be identified and related to an overall plan. He introduced a method of naming each type of living, or once-living, thing that forms the basis of the system used internationally today. Until the time of Linnaeus, common plants and animals were referred to by names that not only differed from language to language but even differed within the same country. To add to the confusion, a common name might be used in different parts of the same country to refer to an entirely different plant or animal. The situation had been a constant problem for the medical profession, which made medicines from herbs; the only sure way of conveying information on herbal cures was to include good illustrations of the actual plants used. Linnaeus was very much aware of the problem, having studied medicine.

Attempts had been made by others before Linnaeus to organize the living world into some kind of order, but the attempts were meager and not universally recognized. The English naturalist John Ray working a century earlier had concluded that each kind or life form was marked by its unchanging appearance from generation to generation (Raven 1942).[7] At least this was a start and it derived from the common belief at that time in the biblical fixity of kinds, each kind having been created separately in the beginning and propagated independently since. Although the biblical concept spoke in rather general terms, it was recognized, for example, that the biblical "cattle" included all of man's domestic animals. Within the "cattle" category would be found the horse kind, the dog kind, the cat kind, and so on, while these were in turn recognized as kinds by their preference for their own mating partner. Dog always bred with dog and cat with cat and in these cases it was a simple matter to assign them as separate kinds. However, there were many other cases, particularly in the plant kingdom, where the distinction was not so clear cut.

The book of Genesis, originally written in Hebrew, used the word "min" which subsequently became translated into English as "kind". Linnaeus, familiar with the Latin Vulgate translation, used the corresponding word "species" in his system of Latin classification. Following the general acceptance of the Linnean system by European science, the time-honored biblical fixity of kinds then became the fixity of species; albeit a very rational one, this was also the first step towards easing the definition away from the biblical concept. As we shall see in Chapter Six, after Darwin the definition of species broadened while the original understanding of what constituted a kind came to be seen as having been too narrow. The result has been an ever greater divergence of meaning that has led to confusion regarding the species and a discrediting of the biblical concept of kinds. It was recognized that permanent new species could not be created, for example, by cross-breeding, and this was seen to be the Creator's way of preventing chaos in nature. The species had been created immutable or fixed, church dogma declared them to be so, and that would be that at least for another century after Linnaeus.

Linnaeus was particularly interested in the plant kingdom and began his work by collecting specimens and ranking them in order of

Carl Linnaeus, 1707-78. The famous botanist at forty-one, from the
frontispiece of the 1748 edition of
his *Systema Naturae*. (Thomas
Fisher Rare Book Library, University of Toronto)

similarity of appearance. As was usual among scientists of his day, he
used Latin descriptive names to identify each class and order, which
were then subdivided again into genera and, finally, species. He
regarded species as the units of creation; for him each species bore the
impression of the original ideas of the Creator, not only in external
form but in anatomical structure, faculties, and functions. In this he
recognized purposeful design and a designer. Today, classification is
made on the same basis, that is by similarity of design features, except
that the word "homology" has replaced the word "design". Undoubtedly, this change of word was done quite innocently but it has had the
effect of making a second important step away from the biblical concept: it avoids all inference to a designer. In the Linnean system every
species was intermediate in appearance between two others but not
fertile with them; members of a species were only fertile one with
another. In the case of the plants his method of determining species
depended upon counting and measuring the sexual parts of the flower
so that distinction was quite positive depending upon the precision of
numbers. His sexual system recognized, for example, that those flowers
with five stamens would not cross with those having six and thereby
assigned them to separate species.

The systematic genius of the Linnean system was not without its
critics, especially as Linnaeus based his method on what he referred to
as the "loves of the plants". Barber says that Linnaeus was inclined to
"overemphasize the metaphorical possibilities of his sexual system".

He referred for example to "Diandria" as two husbands of equal rank (stamens of equal length) in the same marriage, and "Polyandria" as "twenty males or more in the same bed with the female" (Barber 1980, 52). One critic writing in 1736 doubted very much if any botanist would follow the "lewd method" of Dr. Linnaeus (Black 1979, 98).

In Linnaeus's system all organisms formed an ascending scale from the lower organisms to the higher, with man at the summit, but they were not related. Linnaeus took the unusual step for his day of including man, *Homo sapiens*, in his scheme and placing him in the same genus as the orangutan, *Homo troglodytes*. Recognizing that there are much greater differences than first assumed by Linnaeus, the orangutan has since been reassigned to the genus *Pongo*. Nevertheless, in Linnaeus's system this ascending scale was not evolution (phylogeny) but merely a convenient way of classification and identification (taxonomy). Linnaeus believed firmly in Special Creation and the fixity of species and stated, "We reckon as many species as issued in pairs from the hands of the Creator" (Osborn 1929, 187).[8]

Linnaeus introduced his system of plant classification in his *Systema Naturae* in 1735 and in this and subsequent editions there is no hint that one species is related to another through some ancestral form. Himmelfarb claims that in the final edition of his *Systema Naturae* published in greatly expanded form thirty-one years after the first, Linnaeus tentatively suggested that the original number of species created may have been multiplied by interbreeding one species with another (Himmelfarb 1968, 170).[9] However, the most likely explanation was that two extreme variants within a single species had been assigned the status of separate species in error. Linnaeus recognized that variation was possible within a species but was often not sure

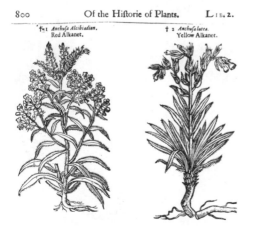

Example from an illustrated herbal of 1633. The text to this woodcut of the Anchusa plant states that the leaves can be used "as a pessary to bring forth the dead birth". (Metropolitan Toronto Reference Library Board)

where one species ended and another began; it would have been a natural temptation to speculate that a new species had been created by crossbreeding when, in fact, it was only a variant within the species. Linnaeus saw some of the more extreme variants as degenerate forms of the perfect archetype that God had created. He remained convinced that the species were immutable. Clark (1948, 39) writes that his belief remained unshaken by anatomical resemblances which he frequently found to exist between animals of different species. In Linnaeus's mind this was simply the designer's use of a common design.

The monumental *Systema Naturae* was internationally accepted by nineteenth century naturalists as the starting point for the modern scientific naming of all organisms. The familiar Latin binomial, that is, the generic and specific names, which are usually found appended to plants and animals in our zoos and museums, are a direct result of classification by Linnaeus. Even today taxonomists occasionally find it necessary to refer back to the works of Linnaeus when checking authorities for names.

After the introduction and establishment of Darwin's theory, taxonomists Engler and Prantl, in 1915, rearranged some of Linnaeus's system to conform to the assumed evolutionary history of the organisms, that is, in accordance with their phylogeny or line of descent from ancestral forms. In contrast to the intentions of Linnaeus, similarity of design had now come to mean relatedness by a common ancestor. The Linnean hierarchy of kingdom (animal, mineral, or vegetable), class, order, genera, and species is still followed today, but with the addition

Comte de Buffon, 1707-88.
Opposed the ideas of Linnaeus and prepared the ground for Charles Darwin. (Engraving after a drawing by A. Pujos, 1776; Metropolitan Toronto Reference Library Board)

of several other divisions and subdivisions such as phylum, family, and sometimes subspecies. The evolutionary term "family" emphasizes the supposed relatedness in a powerful way, and it has become commonplace, for example, to speak of the lion, tiger, panther, etc., as being part of the cat family (Felidae). In very few cases is there sufficient evidence to say that there is any relationship and it is all assumed on the basis of appearance and habits. One notable exception is the Canidae family, that is dogs, wolves, jackals, etc., where enough is now known to be reasonably certain that these are indeed all related and probably had a common, though still dog-like, ancestor. More will be said of this in Chapter Six. In Linnaeus's scheme each species observed was descended more or less unchanged from that created in the beginning.

A final note to the work of Linnaeus: when he died in 1778 all his specimens, books, and letters were sold to a wealthy English collector who founded the Linnean Society of London.[10] This Society soon became the focal gathering point for the world's leading naturalists of the nineteenth century and is an honored institution that still operates today, from Burlington House in the heart of England's capital.

Comte de Buffon

Though he was born within four days of Carl Linnaeus, Georges-Louis Leclerc Comte de Buffon's background was in complete contrast (Roger 1970). Far removed in distance and culture but not in time, Comte de Buffon was born of French nobility and lived during a period when the class into which he was nurtured enjoyed every cultural and financial privilege. Not only did he inherit every social advantage, but he was gifted with a great intellect which he exercised diligently in many fields of endeavor.

Buffon's formative years were spent at a Jesuit college in Dijon, where he showed a natural aptitude for mathematics; in fact, at an early age he not only had a good understanding of Isaac Newton's "Fluxions"—better known today as differential calculus—but he translated that scientist's work into French. Wealthy and successful in every branch of eighteenth century science, the Comte de Buffon spent more than fifty years until the time of his death as director of the Jardin du Roi in Paris; during this time he published his *Histoire Naturelle*, an enormous work of ten volumes. One of Buffon's talents was the ability to communicate to others enthusiasm for his own imaginative ideas, and he quickly became a legend in his own lifetime; this hardly contributed, however, to his sense of modesty. He once declared that there were only five great men in the history of mankind: Newton, Bacon, Leibniz, Montesquieu—and himself.

Buffon was not a religious man. As a youth under Jesuit training, he would have been familiar with the book of Genesis, taught at that time with a literal interpretation. In his earlier years Buffon gave nodding assent to the divine Creator and the fixity of species, but in his later years he rejected the biblical account of Creation and any supernatural attributes entirely. Eventually, his ideas were at complete variance with those of Linnaeus, and, in fact, he became his principal rival and critic.

Buffon did not use the word evolution, but it is nevertheless true that he laid the basis for modern evolution in systematic botany and zoology. He was the first to propose on a broad scale the mutability of species in relation to changes in environment. He proposed the view that over a number of generations and under the influence of the environment, one species could gradually change into another. This was in direct contrast to the fixity of species maintained by the book of Genesis and Linnaeus. He further believed that modifications imparted to a species by the environment are passed on to the offspring. The idea is described as "the transmission of acquired characteristics" today, but Buffon did not express it in these terms. The idea itself, however, was a fertile seed planted in the young mind of Lamarck, one of Buffon's pupils and admirers.

Buffon's work extended over many subjects, including geology. In the late 1700s fossils were becoming objects of interest and were generally acknowledged to be the direct evidence of the Genesis Flood, or Deluge as it was then called. Buffon refused to accept the idea of catastrophes or the biblical Flood and saw fossils to be the result of a former gradual submersion of the continents. He offered no explanation for their reemergence, and, as far as latter-day proponents of the same theory are concerned, a satisfactory explanation for the reemergence of continents is still awaited. In his *Epoques de la nature*, published a decade before he died, Buffon suggested that the earth's beginning took place by a piece being torn out of the sun, which took on a spheroidal shape and a heliocentric orbit to become the earth. The moon was then torn from the earth and became a satellite to it; all this happened 75,000 years ago (Roger 1970, 578). This notion of the moon's origin was resurrected exactly one hundred years later, in 1879, by George Darwin (1879; 1880), son of Charles Darwin. Buffon's speculations were in direct conflict with the orthodox view of the day, which held that the earth was created about four thousand years before the time of Christ. While the Bible itself does not include dates, the time of Creation had been calculated from the lists of genealogies and had by this time become church dogma. Buffon wrote his ideas in a thinly veiled, rhetorical strategem by which he hoped to avoid ecclesiastical censure. The faculty of theology at the Sorbonne was not taken in by this device, however, and he was obliged to recant in writing everything in his works that might be taken to contradict the biblical account of Creation.

Buffon sowed the seeds of the idea of evolution, and these later germinated in the minds of his successors. But the censure he received from the church, together with the towering authority of Cuvier who, succeeded Lamarck, delayed the acceptance of the evolutionary concept by at least half a century. In addition, Buffon's contemporary, the Swede Linnaeus, even though geographically remote from the cultural and intellectual center of Europe, had by sheer genius as an observer and classifier made a much greater impact on the world of science than Buffon. That influence even survived the great revolution brought by Darwin and is still felt today. We see in this a lesson. For a new and revolutionary idea to take root and grow in the collective mind of the people, the seedbed has to be prepared beforehand. This was specifically Buffon's function. His ideas were spread as seeds, then the ground turned over and lay fallow in readiness for the Darwinian springtime.

Jean-Baptiste Lamarck

Buffon was undoubtedly saved from the ignominy of the guillotine by a timely death at the age of eighty-one, just a year before the French revolution. He was survived for a short time by his son, who subsequently lost his life to the guillotine during the Reign of Terror in 1793. The fury of the mob had extirpated king and nobility and silenced the ecclesia; now freed from the shackles of royalty and Rome, they sought to bring into being their utopian government, the republic. The Jardin du Roi—king's garden—which had been under the lordship and tutelage of Buffon for more than half a century, was left somewhat in limbo after his death, due to the uncertainty of the times. Eventually, however, the French revolutionary government, seeking to promote science while reforming society, elected a new director to the Paris institution, which they renamed the Jardin des Plantes; the new director's rather impressive name was Jean-Baptiste Pierre Antoine de Monet, Chevalier de Lamarck.

Lamarck was born in 1744, the youngest of eleven children, into the family of the once distinguished line of barons of Saint-Martin du Picardie. At the time of his arrival, however, the family was quite impoverished. At the age of eleven he went to a Jesuit school to become a priest, but at fifteen left to join the army. At twenty-four he studied medicine for four years in Paris, but drifted from medicine to amateur botany and literary hack-writing. Then in 1779 he published his work

Jean Baptiste Lamarck, 1744-1829.
An unusual portrait showing the
subject blind in his final years.
Lamarck was convinced that physical characteristics acquired by the
present generation could be inherited by the next. Known as
"Lamarckism", the notion is now
totally discredited. (Thomas Fisher
Rare Book Library, University of
Toronto)

French Flowers, which gave him recognition as a botanist. He held
minor posts under Buffon at the Jardin du Roi and eventually became
the director in 1793. The Jardin des Plantes was a small part of the
much larger Museum d'Histoire Naturelle, which later became a world
center under Georges Cuvier.

As a scientist, Lamarck was moderately successful; his personal life
was, however, a continual disaster. At thirty-three he began a liaison
with Marie Delaporte and married her fifteen years and six children
later, as she lay on her deathbed. He married again, and after two
children, his second wife died; his third wife died childless when he was
seventy-five. He was in poor health from sixty-five on and was blind for
the last ten years of his life. When he died at eighty-five, he was
penniless, and his children had to appeal to the state for funeral
expenses. Even his children were not spared: of the five that survived,
one was deaf, one insane, two were single daughters without support,
and only one was successful, as an engineer (Burlingame 1973). Fate
did not spare him even after death; during his life his ideas were
ridiculed in many quarters, while the final blow came with the eulogy
delivered by his superior Cuvier, who pointed out that science had no
use for theories but was far better founded on facts (Thomson 1932,
47).[11] Lamarck died ignored and largely forgotten for at least a generation, after which his ideas were briefly resurrected for, one suspects,
political rather than scientific motives.

Until sometime in the 1790s, he believed in the biblical fixity of species, but then his ideas changed. His biographers are uncertain of the reason, but putting two wives in their graves and marrying a third in a relatively short time may have hardened his mind against the existence of a caring God. After 1800—he was then fifty-five—he abandoned his belief in divine creation and began to advocate his ideas for evolution of life, although he did not use the word evolution. In his *Recherches*, published in 1802, he noted that fossils found in the various rock layers indicated that animals in the past had become extinct, then suddenly appeared again in the fossil record. Having abandoned the idea of Special Creation, he was forced to propose that life had the ability to begin again spontaneously; he did not explain, however, how this came about. Lamarck had been very much influenced by Buffon, and, like his mentor, had a rich imagination. In his *Philosophie zoologique*, published in 1809, he expanded on his theory for the origin of the variety of life forms, past and present. Like others of his time, Lamarck saw living things as forming a hierarchy, from the lowest orders with the least specialization to the highest with the greatest specialization. This was referred to as "the great chain of being"; it would be a long time before such expressions were replaced by the word evolution. He proposed that the shape or size of animal organs was modified according to the circumstances in which the creature might find itself. These slight changes, acquired, for example, because of a changed environment, would then be passed on to the offspring.

Lamarck's proposal, which was developed from Buffon's original idea, is described as "the inheritance of acquired characteristics", today more simply known as "Lamarckism". For Lamarck this was the key mechanism whereby one species, finding itself in a new environment, would develop in the course of many generations, eventually to become a new species, perfectly adapted to the new environment. Lamarck did not state that this happened because of a conscious need on the part of the creature, but as a result of a developed habit, in today's jargon called a "reflex action". In a few classic examples of this view, the giraffe obtained his long neck by browsing on the tall branches of trees, birds who lived in water acquired webbed feet, and moles became blind as a result of living underground. The orthodox explanation was, of course, that these creatures had been specifically designed for each type of environment. Lamarck also made a categorical denial of past catastrophes, referring to the Genesis Flood, and proposed, instead, gradual changes occurring over very long times.

When Lamarck published these ideas in 1809, the Roman church authorities in Paris, who had just a few years before forced Buffon to recant but were now made impotent by the revolution, remained silent.

Lamarckism is one of those explanations for life that at first may seem reasonable and for which supporting evidence can always be found. But closer inspection shows that it is really not a valid theory. The baldness that ran through Darwin's family from grandfather to father, to son, to grandson, and to great-grandsons was an inherited trait and was not acquired by habit. The Jews have practiced circumcision for four thousand years, but August Weismann's (1891, 1:447) statistical work showed that this physical change has never once been inherited.[12] Lamarckism went to the grave with its author, although, strangely, it is resurrected from time to time. For a recent example, see Gorszynski and Steele (1981).[13]

The Lamarckian notion lingered on in the minds of some; however, even Darwin, half a century later, although outwardly he spoke against him, inwardly entertained Lamarckian thoughts as explanations of certain "difficult" steps in evolution. After Darwin published his theory of evolution in 1859, some European countries, perhaps piqued that the key to life's secrets had been discovered on England's shores, erected an alternative evolutionary model called neo-Lamarckism—a new version of Lamarck's theory.

After Darwin died, the intellectual atmosphere surrounding his theory of evolution became a little more liberal, and by the turn of this century Gregor Mendel's genetics were being understood and accepted. The work of August Weismann (1893) on the division of cells then showed that certain germ cells were produced during the embryo stage which were responsible for the characteristics of the next generation. This explained why almost anything could happen to the parent, but as long as the germ cells were not damaged, the offspring would not inherit any defects, such as missing limbs, and so on. Weismann's (1891, 1:444) classic experiment, in which he cut the tails off a total of 901 white mice in five successive generations, showed that each new generation was born with a perfectly normal tail—not a single tail was shorter than usual.[14] This experiment perhaps more than any other finished Lamarckian and neo-Lamarckian ideas, at least in the West, nearly a century ago, although as we will see later in this chapter Lamarck's thinking continued in Russian biological science until the mid-1950s.

Lamarck, as with Buffon before him, had been an apostle of the doctrine of evolution and had proposed a mechanism that was later shown to be illusion rather than fact. However, public consciousness was not yet ready to accept evolution, and the principle lay dormant, waiting for acceptance in the next generation.

Georges Cuvier

The biographies of men such as Linnaeus or Cuvier tend to leave most readers feeling slightly inadequate. Their sheer capacity for work and their expertise in a multitude of areas leave them standing as giants amid the throng of mere mortals of their day. Yet they too were mortal and showed the peculiarities of habit often found among the exceptionally gifted. Georges Cuvier was born into a poor Protestant family in an area of France near the Swiss border. The people in this area were Lutheran, and he was raised in the period just before the French Revolution when Protestants were in constant danger of persecution (Bourdier 1971).

Georges Cuvier, 1769-1832. As father of the science of paleontology and capstone of the French scientific establishment, Cuvier had great influence. His theory of creation withstood the theory of evolution in France for almost the entire nineteenth century. (Engraving from a portrait of Cuvier at fifty-seven; Sigmund Samuel Library, University of Toronto)

By the age of fifteen Cuvier had shown himself to be a very bright student, and a wealthy patron paid for him to go to Caroline University near Stuttgart, Germany. When writing letters home or to his Lutheran minister uncle, Cuvier had to be careful not to say anything pertaining to religious views that could give the French secret police cause to persecute his family. He graduated in medicine at nineteen, having had to learn German while an undergraduate. Good fortune protected him from the turmoil of the revolutionary years. With the return of at least some measure of political stability in France, he came back to Paris to join the newly reorganized Museum d'Histoire Naturelle as a zoologist, in 1795; he was just twenty-one.

Most investigators of the day saw fossil remains as direct evidence of the great Genesis Flood, but as they began to observe further, they saw indications of alternating periods of extinction and reemergence of the species in the rock layers. It looked as if there had been a succession of catastrophes, whereas the Bible spoke of only one; the faith of some began to waver. Cuvier himself became very involved with fossil study and developed a paleontological technique for deducing from a single bone or part of a bone the identity and structure of the entire animal, even those that were extinct. This technique depended on a vast and intimate knowledge of virtually every bone known to zoology. Cuvier soon acquired an international reputation which continued to grow since he was seldom found to be incorrect.

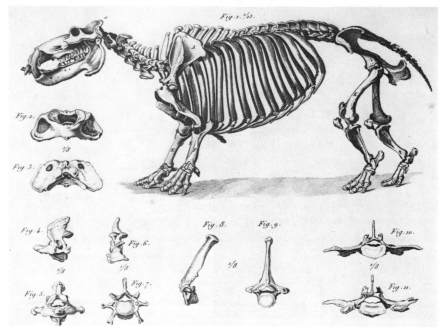

Plate 30 from the atlas to Cuvier's *Recherches sur les ossement fossiles des quadrupedes* showing how isolated fossil bones may be identified from similar structures in living animals; in this case, the hippopotamus. (Sigmund Samuel Library, University of Toronto)

At the age of thirty-five he had achieved success and professional reputation, although his Christian faith had been severely shaken by the fossil record. All the evidence seemed to indicate a great age for the earth rather than the few thousand years of the Mosaic account. At this point he married a Protestant widow with four children, and it is reported that he had a dramatic revival of his faith (Bourdier 1971, 524). Shortly after this he developed a theory for the earth that nicely reconciled geology with Genesis. He made his theory first known in 1812 as part of his massive *Recherches sur les ossement fossiles des quadru-*

pedes, and later more popularly in his *Essay on the theory of the earth*. In this latter he said that in the remote beginning God supernaturally created all species of living things. The earth had subsequently experienced a succession of violent catastrophes that had devastated most of the animal and plant life on earth, but isolated geographical areas had always been spared. The living species propagated themselves anew from these areas. Nordenskiold (1928, 338) says Cuvier expressly included man in this view. The last of these catastrophes was the Genesis Flood, which was worldwide, but in this case the living things had been spared on the ark of Noah. The theory seemed to account for the fossil record and permitted as many years as were required by geology for the catastrophe-repopulation cycles. He explained that God had not provided us with details of the early stages but had simply given the record since the quiet time before the great Flood. The theory was thus an argument from silence and allowed six thousand years or so from the beginning of the Bible record to the present time. He believed in the fixity of species, and that all creatures in the fossil record derived from the original Creation and were not related—that is, there had been no evolution of one species to another (Coleman 1964).[15] Nordenskiold (1928, 338) corrects the common misconception which claims that Cuvier said God recreated all living things after each catastrophe.[16] This misunderstanding is reported in textbook after textbook and leads to the view that God made numerous attempts at Creation and finally got it right on the last occasion. However, this was not Cuvier's position at all. Cuvier's theory was eagerly accepted in England, where many divines of the day were amateur geologists. In Cuvier's scheme the Scriptures were seemingly not violated, leaving the divines to pursue their hobby with a clear conscience.

Cuvier's theory of creation became a kind of dogma that actually dominated French science through the nineteenth century, long after Cuvier had been honored in a state funeral in 1832. It may be appreciated that within any organization, whether it be a nation, a large industry, or a discipline such as natural science, there is a pyramid of power in which the beliefs of the man at the top are reflected all the way down throughout the entire structure. French science under the new socialist government was concentrated in Paris at the Museum d'Histoire Naturelle, and Georges Cuvier was the man at the top.

The situation was no different from any university or government research laboratory of today. The candidate for employment first had to show evidence of conforming to the ideas of the establishment; once accepted, conformity was expected in order to ensure continuation of salary and promotion. The system virtually guarantees maintenance of any theory—regardless of whether the theory is sound or not—held by the man with ultimate authority. Not only that but in a hierarchical system, promotion from within ensures that the theory is perpetuated generation after generation. Cuvier's theory was not sound, but it had become so well entrenched through its founder and followers that it remained and, it is claimed, seriously handicapped French science for almost the entire century, retarding the acceptance of Darwin's theory of evolution at least until the early 1900s.

The folly of the totalitarian hierarchical system, in which a theory or a policy of one human being is maintaind even in the face of contrary evidence, was displayed more recently in Russia. All of Russia's biological and agricultural research efforts until the 1950s were retarded because the director in charge of the Socialist government research organization, Trofim Lysenko, was convinced of the validity of Lamarck's theory of the inheritance of acquired characteristics (Gould 1981a, 14).

In contrast, Cuvier's theory of creation did not remain in the minds of the scientific community in England for very long; in fact, it began to wane with the publication of Charles Lyell's work on geology in the 1830s. It is suggested that the short survival was largely due to the capitalist government in England, which at the time actively fostered new inventions and new ideas as a vital part of the Industrial Revolution. As we shall see in later chapters, men such as Charles Lyell and Charles Darwin, who were the fathers of the new theory of evolution, were independent and wealthy. They were subservient to no research director and were free to develop their theories, and, perhaps more importantly, to publish their ideas. The irony is that under the capitalist system of nineteenth century England, it was possible to publish ideas, whether sound or not, quite freely. Under the socialist government of France, meanwhile, although liberty was proclaimed, at least within the scientific community, the freedom to publish seems to have been entirely lost.

3

Foundations for Darwin's Theory

Progress, far from consisting in change, depends
on retentiveness....Those who cannot remember
the past are condemned to repeat it.
GEORGE SANTAYANA
(1954, 82)

W e now move from the events that led to the violent introduction of socialism in France to the tranquility of England,
where a wary eye was being kept on the activities across the
English Channel. It was, after all, in mid-nineteenth century England
that Darwin introduced his theory of evolution, and it might be asked
why the theory was accepted in Victorian England and not in republican France. In the last chapter we saw that it was the French socialist
government itself, with its centralization of power in each of the
various departments, that militated against the introduction of new
ideas once a paradigm or set of ideas had become established. Cuvier
and his Bible-based Creation theory cast a long and posthumous
shadow over French science for almost the entire nineteenth century
until evolution, as a respectable scientific theory, was finally endorsed
by such men as Marcellin Boule, director of the Institut de paléontol-
ogy humaine and associate of the prestigious Museum d'Histoire Natu-
ralle, Paris.

The situation in England at the end of the eighteenth century was in
complete contrast to that in France. Britain had been a Protestant
country divorced from ties with Rome since the early 1500s. With an
awakening interest in the world about them, adventurous men had set
up trading empires in other lands, while others in the mother country
had sought to change the time-honored ways of manufacturing. New
ideas were free to develop. The Industrial Revolution began in the
1700s and brought great prosperity to a few and a lot of misery to many,

53

but it was at least bloodless, and England became the greatest nation on earth.

Often omitted from history books is the fact that the Industrial Revolution brought in its wake an evangelistic revival in England, led by such notables as John Wesley (1703-91), founder of the Methodist movement. Beginning in the eighteenth century and continuing throughout the nineteenth, many people experienced something that assured them that the Bible was true, and they found no reason to doubt its miracles, including the Creation account in Genesis. So many people were affected that there were difficulties finding accommodation in the established churches for all the people. By the time eighteen-year-old Alexandrina Victoria became queen of England, in 1837, the country had already been "Victorian" for at least twenty years, so much had the Methodist evangelical revival changed the social habits of the country. Gradually, however, the dead hand of tradition and ritual started to creep into the churches, and a cult of respectability and hypocrisy began to replace secular corruption as the sin of the age. Nevertheless, according to many historians, had it not been for the evangelical revival in England, the bloodshed and turmoil of the French Revolution might well have spilled across the English Channel (Bready 1926; Halévy 1937, 10; Lecky 1888, 2:600).[1] In any event, there is no doubt that these revivals later caused much opposition to Darwin and his followers.

John Wesley, 1703-91. Preaching to thousands under the sky, Wesley sparked a revival that prevented the French socialist revolution from spilling over into England. (Painting by N. Hone, 1766; National Portrait Gallery, London)

Benjamin Franklin, 1706-90. Social-ist sympathizer and shuttle diplo-mat, Franklin moved between revolutionaries Voltaire and Rous-seau in Paris and members of the Lunar Society in England. (Engrav-ing after the painting by Alonzo Chappel; Metropolitan Toronto Reference Library Board)

While the French Revolution, and earlier the American Revolution, were acting out their destinies, influential forces at work in England were not only largely responsible for the Industrial Revolution, but were actively sowing the seeds of socialism. It has been acknowledged by Musson and Robinson (1969) and Schofield (1963) that the Lunar Society of Birmingham, which was active from about 1764 to 1800 and never had more than fourteen members, was the most influential group of men in England. This group's influence continued long afterwards under the banner of The Royal Society. In an article on the Lunar Society, Lord Richie-Calder (1982) refers to the men it brought together as a company of "merchants of light",[2] a description used for just such a society in Francis Bacon's *New Atlantis*, written more than a century earlier (Webster 1924).[3] The Lunar Society got its name from the fact that it met monthly at the time of the full moon. Included as its members were such names as Erasmus Darwin, who was Charles Darwin's grandfather; John Wilkinson, a cannon maker; James Watt of steam engine fame; Matthew Boulton, a manufacturer; Joseph Priestly, a chemist; Josiah Wedgwood, founder of the famous pottery business; and Benjamin Franklin, a correspondent in the American colonies. These men recognized that knowledge was power, and by pooling information from various activities and investigations, they were responsible for a number of scientific discoveries that served as the driving force for the Industrial Revolution.

Perhaps equally as important as these noble efforts, however, was the common bond that brought them together. First, six of the members had been educated at Edinburgh University (more will be said of this establishment and these individuals in Chapter Five). Second, it was the socialist ideals of this coterie that bonded them within a royalist society, and it was actually their political views that got them into trouble. Their leanings were definitely on the side of the revolutionaries in the American Revolution of 1776, just as they were on the side of the revolutionaries during the French Revolution in 1789. Benjamin Franklin's role as member of the Lunar Society was that of shuttle diplomat between the French and English Utopian idealists. Erasmus Darwin was an active supporter of the Jacobin cause.[4] James Watt's son had been denounced by Edmund Burke in the British House of Commons as a French agent. Another member, Richard Edgeworth, had collaborated with Rousseau in writing a book on the education of children. Joseph Priestley had been a vigorous supporter of the revolutionary French National Assembly. When fellow member James Keir held a dinner to celebrate the second anniversary of the fall of the Bastille, the Christian community was aggravated to the point that it took matters into its own hands and burned down Priestley's house and his Unitarian meeting hall. Priestley was forced into exile in America (Holt 1931; Huxley 1882; Priestley 1782).[5]

We have already seen in Chapter One that the objectives of the French Revolution were to rid society of church and king, at the root of which stood the Bible, which they ceremonially burned while pro-

Joseph Priestley, 1733-1804. Fiery evangelist for the Unitarian Church, Priestley was exiled to the United States, not for his work as a scientist but for his socialist views. (Engraving by W. Holl after a painting by Gilbert Stewart; Academy of Medicine, Toronto)

claiming reason the goddess of the new republic. With a strong Bible-believing community in England, there was little hope of driving the people to revolution against God and king; however, it may be argued that those who wished to see an English Utopia attempted to bring about the social change in a more subtle way.

Creating doubt and disbelief in long-cherished ideas is a psychological approach used successfully today to introduce new ideas, or new products, to society. The method is as old as mankind. The Bible was recognized as the greatest obstacle to the socialists' aims, and generating disbelief in it was assuredly the most effective way of changing public opinion. Casting doubt on such stories as the Virgin birth and the Resurrection was too blatant, but by reaching into the very foundations of the Bible, the accounts of the Creation and the Flood, more subtle means could be employed. After all, the time frame in which this was alleged to have taken place was so long ago that it was quite beyond any proof. Without proof for a short period of Creation and development and a catastrophe on the magnitude of the Flood, there could also be no proof for a long period producing the same results by natural causes. Thus the expanded time frame would nicely remove the judgmental intervention of God as an explanation, for instance, of the Flood. Whether members of the Lunar Society and lesser lights actually reasoned this way might be worth further research; there is circumstantial evidence that forcefully indicates that this may have been the case. Other revolutionary aspirants in England at the time included Robert Owen (1969) and the Prince of Wales (Webster 1969, 32), each having his own private motives for wishing to see social change. Nevertheless, the historical facts remain undisputed: First, the members of this influential group were on intimate terms with their French socialist contemporaries Voltaire and Rousseau (Richie-Calder 1982, 142). Second, as we shall see later in this chapter, Charles Lyell, writing only thirty years after Voltaire's death, effectively cast doubt on the Genesis account of the Flood by expanding the time frame. Darwin himself commented on these very facts in 1873:

> Lyell is most firmly convinced that he has shaken the faith in the Deluge far more efficiently by never having said a word against the Bible than if he had acted otherwise...I have read lately Morley's *Life of Voltaire* and he insists strongly that direct attacks on Christianity (even when written with the powerful force and vigor of Voltaire) produce little permanent effect; real good seems only to follow the slow and silent side attacks. (Parenthesis in original. Himmelfarb 1968, 387.)[6]

Erasmus Darwin, 1731-1802. Principal member of the secretive Lunar Society and grandfather to Charles Darwin. (Painting by J. Wright, 1770; National Portrait Gallery, London)

Further relevant pieces of information fall into place. The founder of the Lunar Society, Erasmus Darwin, had in 1794 written a book called *Zoönomia* in which he outlined his theory of evolution, anticipating not only Lamarck's ideas but even the theory of natural selection; this book had the distinction of being placed on the Catholic Index;[7] its popularity among independent thinkers was thus assured (King-Hele 1977). Such books as Charles Lyell's *Principles of Geology* (1830-33), Robert Chambers' *Vestiges* (1845), and others throughout the nineteenth century *did* promote evolutionary ideas, and each of these evolutionary works emphasized the expanded time frame. The literal belief in the Genesis account of the Flood and later the Creation *did* decline and socialism *was* introduced, but it took much longer than any conspirators could have anticipated. An actual conspiracy is not being suggested, however, but rather a deeper motivation that lies hidden in the recesses of the human mind and one to which kindred spirits gravitate. Many of the historical characters who were concerned one way or the other with the establishment of Darwin's theory in the nineteenth century were sincere Christians who wanted to harmonize Scripture and the natural sciences. However, there were others, known by their writings, who welcomed any occasion to rid themselves of any obligation to an "ancient Jewish book". The observation that there is within some a deep resentment of the idea that God should intervene in the affairs of men is as old as mankind. This resentment is not always openly admitted but usually manifests itself as a denial of supernaturalism under a cloak of rationalism and science. This resentment forms a common, though usually unspoken, bond, and can be found as often within the church as without.

In this chapter we want to take an enlightened look at some of the individuals who provided the foundation on which the most important theory in modern science rests and to which history has bestowed the credit upon Charles Darwin.

Thomas Robert Malthus

According to Keynes (1933, 99), at the age of three weeks Robert Malthus was kissed by two fairy godfathers, the French radical Jean-Jacques Rousseau and the Scottish skeptic David Hume, who thereby bestowed upon the child their combined intellectual gifts. From Keynes's leftist viewpoint, this act of dedication was the finest thing that could have happened to young Robert. Both Rousseau and Hume were occasional visitors to the Malthus home and were held in great respect by Robert's father, David. The socialist and irreligious influence continued to his teenage years by private education under Gilbert Wakefield, an heretical clergyman who was later imprisoned for supporting the French revolutionaries. Upon entering Cambridge University he found himself under the tutorship of an intimate of Joseph Priestley. It was with this consistency of influence in his formative years that the future "father of social science" grew up.

Graduating from Cambridge with a degree in mathematics, Malthus entered the Anglican Church as a curate. As was often the case at that time, his elected vocation had nothing to do with religious convictions but, as in the case of Charles Darwin almost half a century later, was seen as a secure position from which he could pursue intellectual or sporting interests. He eventually reentered the cloistered halls of Cambridge, emerging when almost forty to be appointed professor of modern history and political economy at the new East India College in Haileybury. His position had the distinction of being the first chair of political economy to be established in England. There he passed a peaceful and uneventful life, lecturing and writing until he died in 1834. Malthus had no connections with the Lunar Society or the Royal Society, but he was in frequent correspondence with the French social reformers.

Malthus would never have had a place in history had it not been for the publication, in 1798, of his *Essay on the Principle of Population* and the expanded version that appeared in five subsequent editions. Apart from the usual textbook explanations (Simpkins 1974),[8] the incident that inspired him to write the *Essay* in the first place is little known. According to Polanyi (1957), Malthus received the following account, ascribed to Townsend by the French mathematician and revolutionary Condorcet. The scene is Robinson Crusoe's island in the

Thomas Robert Malthus, 1766-1834.
Deceived by a story of the goats and
dogs, he laid the foundation for
social Darwinism. (Metropolitan
Toronto Reference Library Board)

Pacific Ocean, off the coast of Chile. On this island Juan Fernandez
landed a few goats to provide meat in case of future visits. The goats
multiplied and became a convenient store of food for the privateers,
mostly English, who were molesting Spanish trade. In order to destroy
the food supply, the Spanish authorities landed a dog and a bitch
which also, in the course of time, greatly multiplied and diminished
the number of goats. "Then a new kind of balance was restored," wrote
Townsend. "The weakest of both species were among the first to pay
the debt of nature; the most active and vigorous preserved their lives."
To which he added: "It is the quantity of food which regulates the
number of the human species." Townsend then applied this principle
to his suggested reform of the Poor Law. The Poor Law in England
was instituted so that the poor should never go hungry, but also that
they should be compelled to work. Townsend pointed out that the
usual legal methods of compelling the poor to work were accompanied
by much trouble, violence, and noise; "hunger will tame the fiercest
animals" and, among the poor, "will teach them civility, obedience
and subjection" while "goading them on to labour" (Polanyi 1957,
112). Fortunately for the British poor, Townsend's reforms were never
introduced, but Malthus became quite enthusiastic with this approach,
as we shall see.[9]

The story of the goats and dogs certainly inspired thinkers like Malthus and later Charles Darwin but, as Polanyi points out, it was only a half-truth. Juan Fernandez duly landed the goats, but there is no record that the dogs were ever landed. Even if dogs had been landed, Polanyi argues, the goats inhabit inaccessible rocks while the beaches were teeming with fat seals—much more engaging prey for wild dogs. Nevertheless, Malthus believed he was in possession of one of nature's secret principles, and he was prompted to reply to the French socialist proposals for a utopian government. One such socialist, Condorcet, maintained that the ideal government was one that provided social and economic equality for all men, because this best suited man's nature and would most quickly lead to universal happiness. Malthus showed in his *Essay* that a Utopia of this sort would be self-defeating, since, with the approach of ideal conditions, the resulting idleness would lead to an unbridled birth rate, and the burden of population would soon outstrip the food supply. He expressed these thoughts in a concise mathematical manner that appears to have a genuine ring of truth about it, yet nature refuses to conform to such simplistic equations. He said: "Population when unchecked, increases in a geometrical ratio. Subsistence increases only in an arithmetic ratio" (Malthus 1878, 6).

Perhaps more effective than the snappy formula were the figures he gave as an example. He suggested that the population was increasing every twenty-five years at the geometrical rate of 1, 2, 4, 8, 16, 32, 64, 128, 256..., while the food supply was increasing during the same time at the rate of 1, 2, 3, 4, 5, 6, 7, 8, 9....The population in this example is seen to double every twenty-five years, while the food supply, expressed in, say, tons of wheat or acres of cultivated land, increases by only a uniform increment each generation. Malthus pointed out that if the process were not interfered with, in three centuries the ratio of population to food supply would be 4,096 to 13 and so on in proportions that any reader could easily deduce for himself (Malthus 1878, 6). The figures rivet the attention, but a moment's thought reveals that Malthus had been too conservative. He had not taken into account the additional mouths to feed in the generations living at the same time, raising the spectre of starving humanity, standing cheek by jowl on every available square foot of dry land.

The figures in the table in Appendix A have been derived from those given by Malthus and show the number of persons to be supported by each unit of subsistence. For example, if the subsistence column is in "cultivated acres", then in the first generation each acre only has to support one person, whereas three centuries later the same acre has to support 315 people.

Three centuries is a very short time in the history of the earth, and Malthus recognized that other powerful factors must be restricting an otherwise unbridled population growth. (More will be said of population growth in Chapter Twelve.) In the first edition of his *Essay*, Malthus proposed that the most important controlling factor was the availability of food, while misery and vice were the natural consequences whenever the family size exceeded the breadwinner's capacity to feed it. He defined misery as nature's way of providing the limitation and included famine and plague as examples. Vice, on the other hand, was man's way of limiting the population, and he included contraception, infanticide, and warfare among the evil outworkings of the human mind. One of the ironies of modern times is that the term "Malthusian" has become a euphemism for those who advocate birth control as one of the principal means of limiting the population, whereas Malthus himself strenuously condemned birth control methods, for "promiscuous intercourse, unnatural affections, violations of the marriage bed and improper arts to conceal the consequences of irregular connections, are preventive checks that clearly come under the head of vice" (Malthus 1878, 8). He rather loosely suggested abstinence by late marriage as the solution to the population problem (Malthus 1878, 396, passim).

Malthus was severely criticized for his very depressing views when they were first published, principally on the grounds that he saw man as a bestial brute whose passions were only kept in check by misery—in short, he had not credited man with any measure of dignity. Accordingly, he collected more data and issued a revised and expanded second edition in 1803, in which he introduced as a major category two other factors, which he called "preventive check" and "positive check": the former limited the birth rate and the latter enhanced the death rate by shortening or removing lives. By "preventive check" Malthus did not mean contraception but moral or self-restraint; this factor, however, had the effect of undermining the very principle with which he had first set out because, regardless of the reasons for "self or moral restraint", a preventive check could and does easily supersede the effect of food supply. The decline in birth rate in times of war or unemployment, for example, is well known. Man was not, therefore, the brutal beast that Malthus had first claimed, although this image of man still remained steadfast in his mind, as is evident from his statements relating to the poor in the sixth edition of his *Essay*:

> Instead of recommending cleanliness to the poor, we should encourage contrary habits. In our towns we should make the

streets narrower, crowd more people into the houses, and court the return of the plague. In the country, we should build our villages near stagnant pools, and particularly encourage settlements in all marshy and unwholesome situations. But above all, we should reprobate [condemn strongly] specific remedies for ravaging diseases; and those benevolent, but much mistaken men, who have thought they were doing a service to mankind by projecting schemes for the total extirpation of particular disorders (Malthus 1878, 412).

Malthus concluded with a recommendation for "positive checks" among the poor:

> We are bound in justice and honour formally to disclaim the right of the poor to support. To this end, I should propose a regulation be made declaring that no child born...should ever be entitled to parish assistance...The [illegitimate] infant is comparatively speaking, of little value to society, as others will immediately supply its place...All children beyond what would be required to keep up the population to this [desired] level, must necessarily perish, unless room be made for them by the deaths of grown persons (Malthus 1878, 411, 430-1).

This somewhat bourgeois approach to social problems coming from an ordained Anglican clergyman may cause surprise today but did not do so in the early years of England's Industrial Revolution. A few moralists raised an eyebrow or two, but there was not the great outcry that might have been expected, especially from the barons of industry who depended on a vast supply of cheap labor.

The second edition of the *Essay*, widely circulated and reproduced in succeeding years, has given Malthus his posthumous reputation as the "pioneer" of the social sciences. His work has been eulogized by the most eminent economists as "the first thorough application of the inductive method to social science". For example, economist Lord Keynes (1883-1946), under whose monetary policies the West has labored since World War II, regarded Malthus as something of a genius; Keynes seemingly adopted him as his alter ego. Darwin and his circle regarded Malthus as the master of logic, and, as we shall see, the principles embodied in the *Essay* form a vital part of Darwin's theory.

So much for Malthusian logic and its acceptance by the weightiest of authorities. Who then would have the temerity to question it? It has, in fact, been questioned many times and perhaps most cogently by Himmelfarb (1955), to whom this section of the chapter is indebted. To return to the jingle once more, it is seen that Malthus contended that there is a discrepancy between the rate at which population multiplies and the rate at which sustenance for that population can increase. When he wrote his *Essay* in 1798 there was no real data to work from; the first national census in Britain was taken in 1801. But even the 1801 census data could not help, since this was a single event and could not be used to determine the *rate* of population growth. Malthus had actually based his vital formula on a selection of population figures taken at random from a variety of unreliable sources. He had made assumptions and approximations and juggled the figures until they came out neatly as the difference between a series of geometric and arithmetic progressions.

The increasing series of numerals, of course, appear very precise and scientific; after all, "figures cannot lie" or, to quote another source, "The mathematical basis for the Malthus argument is as certain as the multiplication table" (Himmelfarb 1955, 55). It was quite impossible for Malthus to estimate how much land was totally or partially uncultivated, how much was fertile, and what it could produce in tons of food per acre, and so on. Even the time between generations was quite uncertain, so that the evidence to support his thesis was extremely speculative; all that can properly be said is that on paper, populations will tend to expand to fill the allotted space. That is not all, however. Not only was the evidence faulty and inconclusive but the very nature of the theory precludes the possibility of obtaining the evidence to prove it. If the population can never exceed the food supply, it can never be known that it is in fact the food supply that checks the population. For instance, other factors could check the population before the limit of the food supply is reached, and Malthus conceded "moral restraint" as one of these factors.

But these problems are minor compared with the internal contradiction in the theory that Darwin and others failed to recognize, although it was discerned by Karl Marx (Padover 1979, 157). In focusing his attention on "population" as the human population, Malthus overlooked the fact that if humans multiply geometrically, then so do all the plants and animals that provide for human subsistence. The whole equation is then seen to be entirely spurious as are all the numbers that at first sight appeared so convincing. In practice, neither men, plants, nor animals multiply geometrically, but their rate of increase depends on the respective checks imposed by the environment on their expansion. The entire ecosystem, including man, is, or was, as we are beginning to find out now, in a very delicately balanced harmony far removed from the depressing "eat-or-be-eaten" struggle for survival envisioned by Malthus. Malthusian "logic" may now be seen to be a pseudoscience, and, not surprisingly, it is a controversial issue in the sense that some will believe it and be blinded to its deficiencies, while others can see it for what it is and are shocked by the excesses to which it leads; population control by legal abortion (a "positive check") is just one example.

We shall see in later chapters that the maxim on which Malthus based his thinking was what later became the "survival of the fittest" theme. The notion can be traced from Condorcet to Malthus, to Spencer, to Wallace, and to Darwin. It eventually mushroomed out to influence men such as Adolf Hitler, but we should be reminded that it all began in the tale of the goats and dogs.

Charles Lyell

In the previous chapter we saw how Georges Cuvier, arising phoenix-like from the fires of the French Revolution, had given the nineteenth century his theory of creation. The great advantage of this catastrophist theory, as it came to be called, was that it was respectable to the church; it appeared not to do violence to the Scriptures, while at the same time it seemed to account for the fossil evidence as it was then known. It allowed, as Cuvier thought, four or five catastrophe-repopulation cycles prior to the catastrophe before the last one—the final catastrophe being the Genesis Flood. This allowed the six thousand or so years for the biblical record, as required by the orthodox view. The overall age of the earth in this theory, however, could be a million years or more, as all the mountain building and repopulation of the earth would seem to indicate from the fossil record.

The catastrophist theory was presented to the world in 1812. In the years following, as further geological evidence accumulated from the Paris basin where Cuvier had suggested four or five catastrophes, it became evident that there had been at least twenty-seven. This began to exercise the credulity somewhat to think that the Creator had erased his creation twenty-seven times in order to get it right on the twenty-eighth time!

And there were other problems. It was becoming difficult to account for all those fossil creatures that disappeared then reappeared with each cycle, then others that appeared only once never to appear again; and why was it that some fossils were found distributed in a great many places and others were only found in a single location? Cuvier died in 1832, and it was about this time that the theory encountered some of these very serious difficulties; fortune declared it to be an opportune moment to introduce a new concept in England at the hand of Charles

Lyell, which, as it turned out, was almost as revolutionary as the theory Darwin announced thirty years later.

Charles Lyell was born the first of ten children to well-to-do orthodox Christian parents in Scotland, in 1797. When he was young, the family moved to Hampshire in the south of England at the insistence of his mother who was concerned about Scottish drinking habits. He went to Oxford University to study the classics and law and was subsequently called to the bar in 1825, when he was twenty-eight. He practiced law for only a couple of years; because of two handicaps, he decided to give up this vocation to pursue his interest as an amateur scientist. Poor eyesight, a slight speech impediment, and a wealthy father who left him financially independent made the decision an easy one.

Lyell joined the Linnean Society and was secretary to the Geological Society (both at Burlington House, London) from 1823 to 1826. During that time he contributed a number of articles to the *Quarterly Review* on the subject of scientific education in England. In 1826, at the age of twenty-nine and with no formal science background, he was elected Fellow of the Royal Society, a somewhat elitist institution, usually the preserve of such intellectual giants as Isaac Newton (who died a Fellow in 1727). Lyell had two qualities which, it is suggested, were of interest to the Royal Society: his ability to write clearly and his interest in evolutionary geology (Eiseley 1959).

Lyell's interest in geology began when he was a student at Oxford where he attended William Buckland's geology lectures. In those days, geology was taught in the context of multiple catastrophes terminating in the Genesis Flood. Lyell's interest heightened when he made a summer trip to Paris and met fellow student Constant Prévost. Prévost had strong Lamarckian views, and since he worked under Cuvier, he could not openly speak of these ideas. But in Lyell he evidently found a willing ear. The following year, in 1824, Prévost visited Lyell, and the two of them went on a geological tour of southwestern England; undoubtedly Lyell learned much of his early geology on this occasion, but it was geology seen through the evolutionary eyes of Lamarck and Prévost (Wilson 1973, 564). Six years elapsed between Prévost's visit and the publication of the first volume of Lyell's great geological treatise, and Lyell spent much of this time traveling around England and Europe. Significantly, during the early part of these travels he read a copy of James Hutton's *Theory of the Earth,* and it was Hutton's evolutionary explanation of the earth that formed the basis for Lyell's work. It can be reasonably assumed then that Lyell's ideas were well formed in principle, if not in detail, *before* he went out to look at the evidence, and that, with a preconceived idea, he was apt to see only the evidence providing support for his theories.

Lyell's Inspiration: James Hutton

James Hutton was born in 1726 and died the year Lyell was born, in 1797. He was a Scotsman of no mean intellect, having graduated from the universities of Edinburgh, Leiden (Holland), and Paris. These were the best universities of their day for the study of science, particularly Edinburgh and Leiden, since they were not under the restraint of a theological affiliation. Although Hutton had a Quaker background, he eventually found that he could not accept the literal interpretation of the Bible and became a Deist, following in the steps of Aristotle, Rousseau, and others. On the matter of origins he argued that the earth's history could best be discovered from the earth itself rather than from questionable Jewish records. He thought that the bent and twisted rock formations and the fossil remains of extinct creatures could be more rationally explained as simply the result of natural processes over a long period of time rather than a catastrophic process all taking but a few months, as taught in the Mosaic record. Waves of the sea erode cliffs and beaches, winds wear away rocks and, it is assumed, whole mountains, given a sufficient length of time. Hutton's *Theory of the Earth* was published in 1795 and provided an expanded time frame that made no appeal to supernatural events for the earth's early history. The theme throughout was that present-day events are

James Hutton, 1726-97. Attempted to expand the time frame of the past by assuming there were no major catastrophes in the earth's early history. Engraving after Sir Joshua Raeburn. (Metropolitan Toronto Reference Library Board)

the key to the past; however, this was not accepted in his own time, and he was charged with atheism by the Royal Irish Academy (Playfair 1970).[10] The charge upset him so that he became ill and actually went to his deathbed two years later, laboring under this odium (Eyles 1972).

Lyell's Geology

Lyell and his wife traveled widely over Europe and the British Isles, gathering geological evidence to support what was really Hutton's theory of the earth. He saw evidence of slow natural processes such as the silting up of a harbor or the erosion of a cliff, and, without the actual measurement of rates, this evidence seemed to confirm the theory. But then there was other evidence such as contorted and upturned rocks, which had the literal appearance of a past catastrophe and could not be ignored. Lyell imposed his imagination on this type of evidence, arguing that it too was really the result of slow processes but only appeared to have resulted from catastrophe because of the imperfection of the geologic record. The appeal to the "imperfection of the geologic record" is rather crucial to the argument and will usually be made anytime evidence appears that does not conveniently support the theory. It was, after all, more convincing to argue from what is observed today than to argue from past catastrophes to which no one was witness. Moreover, conscious of almost certain theological opposition to his expanded time frame for the earth's early history, Lyell found a compromise: rather than deny the biblical Flood outright, which was always held to be worldwide, he claimed that it was probably a local affair and took place somewhere in the Middle East. Lyell had, thereby, made it possible completely to eliminate divine intervention, and for some this was a wholly welcome thesis.

Lyell's geological principles, based on Hutton's dictum that the present is the key to the past, make the assumption that all natural processes have continued as they were from the beginning. This view has been called "Uniformitarianism". Lyell published his work in three volumes entitled *Principles of Geology*, in the years 1830-33, and his principle has since become the foundation of modern geology.

The mind of today's geologist must be able to accommodate a certain ambivalence, because, although classical geology is based on slow-acting processes, it must also be conceded that there have been some cataclysmic events. Mt. Tambora (near Java) exploded in 1815 and to this day remains the greatest volcanic explosion in history, ten times greater than the Krakatoa explosion, which occurred in 1883. In both of these catastrophes, thousands lost their lives and for several years the earth's atmosphere was affected by the dust. Lyell noted the Mt. Tam-

Charles Lyell, 1797-1875. Shown here about 1830, Lyell carried Hutton's banner more successfully than Hutton himself and prepared the foundation for today's geological and biological sciences. (Engraving after George Richmond; Thomas Fisher Rare Book Library, University of Toronto)

bora explosion in his *Principles of Geology* and had to concede that cataclysmic events took place, but in the end convinced himself that they played no significant part in geological history. However, these events did serve to remind geologists of the day that catastrophes are possible. Modern geology does concede that catastrophic events have taken place in the past, but each of these is held to be strictly a local event. The appeal to local events carries with it the assumption of vast spans of time. This is a vital part of the argument, since it is clear that if all local catastrophes occurred within a very short time frame, they would ultimately coalesce into one worldwide catastrophe.[11] However, whether there was one worldwide catastrophe or a succession of local catastrophes becomes a matter of opinion, for there can be no proof for the duration of elapsed time in the distant past (Lyell 1830, 1:80). The sequence of past events is usually not difficult to determine, but the time frame in which they took place is another matter and will be dealt with in some detail in Chapters Eleven and Twelve.

Lyell, Rock Strata, and Fossils

At the beginning of the Industrial Revolution in England, the need for good transportation prompted the building of the great complex of canals and railways. William Smith was a canal engineer and had earned the name "Strata Smith", because he had observed that associated with those rock formations that appear in layers or strata were fossils, which, he came to recognize, usually appeared in a particular vertical order. Smith actually made the first geological map of Great Britain, based on his knowledge of the fossils characteristic of the various strata running throughout the country. Lyell was aware of Smith's observations and of the general assumption that the rock that appeared in layers had previously been sediment formed at the bottom of lakes or seas. The term "sedimentary" is used today to describe rock that generally appears in layers, but it should be borne in mind that the description is based on an assumption and implies that all layered rock was deposited slowly from water. This is not necessarily so, however, since volcanic ash can be ejected in tremendous quantities both beneath water (marine volcanoes) or on land; the ash and water can form hard rock very quickly as evidenced by the preservation of small foot tracks and the impressions of rain drops.[12]

Lyell observed that sedimentary rocks occur most abundantly throughout the world and in some places are thousands of feet thick. Rather than taking this to be the result of catastrophes associated with the Genesis Flood, as was generally thought at that time, he reasoned that the sedimentary deposits could better be explained in terms of the slow sedimentation that could be seen taking place in rivers and lakes of his own day. When extended over a sufficiently long time, even the greatest thicknesses of sedimentary rock could be accounted for by the slow natural processes. Lyell further reasoned that lakes and seas had been emptied in the past by the slow elevation of the land, and the sediment had then dried and become hard rock, containing within it the fossilized life forms that happened to have been living at the time the sediment was being deposited. In order to account for the many different layers of sediment consisting of rock of different chemical or physical composition, he expanded on this theme, proposing that the land sank and was flooded and then elevated and dried in a succession of cycles even hundreds of times, like an enormous trampoline. Unquestionably, some vertical land movements have taken place, but neither Lyell nor his successors have yet provided a satisfactory explanation for the mechanism of repeated elevation and depression.

When Lyell wrote the first edition of his *Principles of Geology*, the word evolution was not yet generally used in the literature but rather the words "mutability", "transmutation", "development", or "progression". Lyell did not want to be involved in the controversial issue of mutability, since by extension of the argument this eventually had to involve man himself; this was too obvious a violation of the Scriptures! In his earlier writings Lyell stuck rigidly to the biblical dogma of the fixity or immutability of species and in this matter was opposed to Darwin's proposal of the mutability of species—that is, that one species could evolve from another. The basic problem facing Lyell was to deny divine judgment, for this meant denying the biblical catastrophist position but at the same time acknowledging that extinction had occurred, which meant invoking divine re-creation of new species. His doctrine of uniformity nicely evaded the judgment by simply stretching out time. But he still had to accept supernatural re-creation of the new species. The sudden appearance of new species in the fossil record was, to Lyell, evidence that re-creation had taken place, while, conversely, the appearance of fossil creatures in several strata and their absence in succeeding strata indicated extinction of that species.

Lyell's Geologic Column

In the first two volumes of his *Principles of Geology*, Lyell dealt at some length with the question of species, which at first sight might appear to be out of place in a book about rocks. The subject is of great importance, however, since it deals with the relationship between fossil remains of once living things and the rocks in which they appear, and it is this aspect that later formed a crucial part of the theory of evolution. Lyell's uniformitarian principle applied to the fossils in rocks is really equally as important as the theory ascribed to Darwin; however, history has somehow managed to allow Darwin's name to eclipse those who went before him.

Lyell had gone as far as he dare go in preparing the ground for Darwin, although at the time the work was first published, the two men did not know each other. He had reasonably assumed that the lowest layer of sedimentary rock had been deposited first, and the fossil life forms these rocks contained were, therefore, the earliest in time; they were generally of "simple" sea creatures. On the other hand, the topmost layers had been deposited last, and it was found that the life forms in these layers appeared to form a scale of increasing complexity from bottom to top. As far as most people were concerned in Lyell's day, the fossils in every layer were the remains of creatures that had all met their death during the year of the Deluge or Genesis Flood. Lyell's expansion of that year to several million now reduced one worldwide flood to dozens of minor inundations; the fossils, claimed by the biblicists to have been contemporary creatures, were now separated from each other by space and time. There was a further subtlety. The rising scale of complexity of fossils was perceived to be an actual record of Aristotle's *scala natura*. Thus, sequential relatedness between these creatures could be imagined more readily than the idea that each descended from a separate creation (Aristotle 1965). However, there were some inconsistencies. The fossil record contained many bothersome gaps in which complex creatures would suddenly appear above—or worse, below—a strata containing relatively simple creatures. Lyell recognized that nowhere in his travels throughout the British Isles and Europe had he found a perfect set of sedimentary rocks containing a gradation of every fossil form, but he suggested that an imaginary column could be put together on paper from the bits and pieces of the entire column that he visualized. This imaginary column, or geologic column, as it is called, is a vital modern tool for such things as oil exploration. Lyell is the acknowledged founder of this branch of science known as stratigraphy. Geologists who use this concept daily in fields of exploration are, for the most part, not the least bit concerned that it appears to do violence to the Mosaic account; after all, the concept works, though not efficiently, and they earn a living by it. These facts cannot be denied, but the uniformitarian interpretation of the facts imposed by Lyell is entirely another matter, as we shall see in Chapter Four. Regarded as a scientific theory, the interpretation leaves a great deal to be desired.

Lyell and Darwin

As we shall see later, it was while Darwin was becoming established as a naturalist that he first met Charles Lyell. Although Lyell was twelve years Darwin's senior, the two men quickly cemented a lifelong friendship. The massive compilation of biological evidence amassed by Darwin in favor of the transmutation or evolution of species eventually persuaded Lyell away from his belief in the fixity of species. It is evident, however, that Lyell struggled with these ideas for some years until 1863, three years after Darwin published his theory, when he finally capitulated, fully accepting Darwin's evolutionary position. It was not a simple matter of changing from a position of immutability to mutability, for it also meant replacing the supernatural recreation process by the naturalistic variation *and* selection process. Lyell spoke of variation *or* selection before he finally realized that both are essential to the theory of evolution. In his final years, Lyell admitted that it had been a severe struggle to renounce the orthodox (Christian) position, and his dilemma must have been one shared by many in his own century as indeed some still face the same dilemma in this century. From the orthodox point of view, to deny the divine judgment (the biblical Flood) was bad enough since it involved so much reinterpretation that it placed doubt on the entire Bible. Denying divine creation was the final step that nullified any need for a Creator and placed within the former believer a sense of being nothing more than a mechanistic organism without purpose and hope. These were undoubtedly the secret thoughts and fears that passed through Lyell's mind in his last years.

Charles Lyell, later Sir Charles, a quiet man with rather poor eyesight and King-maker to Darwin, the acknowledged father of the theory of evolution, died in 1875 and was buried in London's West-minster Abbey.

Alfred Russel Wallace

During the past century, literally hundreds of books have been written about Darwin and his theory of evolution. In providing historic background, authors usually spend some time with Lyell, while only passing mention is made of the *Essay* by Malthus, and very seldom are any details given. Wallace, for instance, is brought in simply as an *agent provocateur* to spur Darwin into publishing his masterpiece. Sometimes Wallace is mentioned by an author as codiscoverer of the theory, which allows the author to extol Darwin's gracious nature in sharing the discovery with an unknown. However, his name is then quickly forgotten; in fact, shortly after its inception as the Darwin-Wallace theory, the name Wallace was dropped, for reasons that will soon become apparent. Thereafter, the theory of evolution has always been associated exclusively with Darwin's name although in recent years there has been a move on the part of some within the scientific establishment to drop Darwin's name and elevate the theory to the "law of evolution" by fiat rather than by facts.[13] Be that as it may, it seems that the theory of evolution, as it was announced to the world by Darwin, is something of an illegitimate brainchild; there appears to be a great deal of doubt about the actual father. Much of this part of the chapter is indebted to Brackman (1980), who has shown that there are very good

Alfred Russel Wallace, 1823-1913. An exceptional naturalist dogged by bad luck. (National Portrait Gallery, London)

reasons for crediting Wallace for the revelation that provided the missing key to unlock the puzzle of evolution. Brackman has patiently outlined the details of a bizarre set of circumstances in which Darwin's friends, Lyell and Joseph Hooker, conspired to secure priority and credit for the theory for Darwin himself. Others have suggested that the key to the puzzle originated with Lyell, who then persuaded Wallace to send it to Darwin with the intention of prompting Darwin to publish.

Whatever the truth of the matter, the theory certainly originated in the muddy waters of intrigue and the confession of a "delicate arrangement"; Darwin's key correspondence that would resolve the doubts is conspicuously absent (Brackman 1980, xi).[14] All these details, however, may be left for others to unravel since their exposure to the light of day does tend to cause true Darwinians to be rather defensive.

Alfred Russel Wallace was the eighth of nine children, born in 1823, in a small town near the Welsh border in England. His parents were devout members of the Church of England, but there is little evidence that he had ever been exposed to the Bible, and later in life he reacted rather strongly against the church. The home atmosphere was one of domestic tranquility and penury; in fact, penury was a fate he seemed to have inherited from his father, and it haunted him throughout his ninety years. Wallace's life history is reminiscent of Lamarck's; both were able men but continually dogged by misfortune and poverty, and both were quickly forgotten after their death. Wallace had a very humble upbringing in contrast to the other natural history notables of his day, yet he became "the greatest tropical naturalist of his time", to quote the late president of the prestigious Linnean society (Brackman 1980, 38). After a brief span of surveying for one of the many new railway lines in England, he set out at the age of twenty-five, with his friend Henry Bates, for the jungles of South America to collect rare beetles and insects for collectors in England; the date was 1848. In nineteenth century England natural history was the great outdoor hobby, and there were many establishments where one could buy butterfly and beetle collections, rock samples, and fossils. After four years in the jungles of South America, alone for most of the time, Wallace returned to England by boat; while en route home, it caught fire and sank, taking his entire four years' work with it!

Undaunted and ever the optimist, Wallace then set out for the Malay archipelago and remained in the Malayan jungles alone, except for his native helpers, for the next eight years, returning to England finally in 1862 at the age of thirty-nine. During his absence the income from his extensive Malayan collections had been parlayed into a modest fortune by his London agent; however, shortly after he returned to settle into married domesticity, he unwisely transferred his investments and promptly lost his entire source of income and security. For the remainder of his life, he never obtained gainful employment but, like Mr. McCawber, was very hopeful that something would turn up. On his fifty-eighth birthday something actually did turn up—a government pension for 200 pounds a year. He was most grateful for this and thanked Darwin who had interceded with the government on his behalf. However, the 200 pounds should be put in perspective; that same year the Darwin household spent 223 pounds just for meat! Brackman has pointed out that Darwin's success in securing the pension for Wallace was an act of expiation for the sordid conspiracy to obtain priority twenty-three years previously (Brackman 1980, 290).

Wallace had been writing and publishing throughout his prolonged unemployment and had acquired a healthy reputation as a great naturalist, but there were two factors that militated against his being completely accepted into the circle of the scientific elite. Class was a very real sociological barrier in nineteenth century England, and Wallace had had the misfortune to have been born on the "the wrong side of the tracks". The university education had become a way of crossing the barrier, but at that time the opportunity was largely a matter of being born into a family of sufficient means and connections. In contrast to Darwin, or even Thomas Huxley who had only just made it across the class barrier, Wallace had none of these attributes.

The second factor had to do with Wallace's "dark side"; he dabbled with spiritism; this activity more than anything else caused him to be alienated from the scientific circle. During his early travels in the Amazon, Wallace had befriended the Indians and had been allowed to enter into some of their black arts. At the time he dismissed much of this activity as heathen superstition. However, upon his return to England he found there was a fashionable interest in the occult and, carried out in the more genteel Victorian setting, he plunged into table-rapping and oui-ja boards with enthusiasm. Many well-known Victorians such as Conan Doyle, John Ruskin, and Lord Tennyson were also involved with spiritism and frequented seances, but Wallace evidently went too far and exposed himself to ridicule by becoming actively involved in the Society for Psychical Research. Colp (1977, 44) notes that Darwin had been introduced to some of the black arts during his five years spent on the Beagle but it seems his involvement was never at the level of that of Wallace and he remained a skeptic to the end of his days.[15] As Wallace's name became more closely associated with society's fringe element it was not politic to leave it associated with the fledgling Darwin-Wallace theory and his name was dropped quickly and quietly; Darwin was surely not displeased to see the theory become his very own. Finally in 1875, Wallace completed his divorce from the scientific camp by his book *Miracles and Modern Spiritism*, in which he confessed experiential reasons for his beliefs. Later his ideas entered further into the realm of the bizarre as he became interested in politics and adopted some extreme Utopian socialist views in which he advocated state ownership of all private property. Wallace was perhaps unwittingly supporting the views of Karl Marx who, at that time, was living out his last days in London.

Alfred Russel Wallace at the turn of the century. Half of his life wasted by his involvement with spiritism, he later adopted extreme socialist views. (Metropolitan Toronto Reference Library Board)

So much for Wallace the man, but what of the part he played in the theory of evolution? Wallace had read Lyell's *Principles of Geology*, which was abundantly furnished with examples illustrating the principles of uniformitarianism. He had read how the fossil evidence implied a succession of life forms, from the simplest in the early ages to the most complex in the more recent ages. Lyell had proposed that the earth was continuing to go through a slow but continual change and that the living things were also going through a slow and gradual change in response to the changing environment. The fossil record had shown that many creatures had become extinct, but those that had survived had continued to diversify into other species becoming more organized, so that there appeared to be a progression of scale into the most recent geological record. Lyell was reluctant to say publicly that one species could become another, but for Wallace, who had no religious convictions concerning the fixity of species by divine creation, it was a relatively simple matter to assume that if sufficient variation occurred in response to, say, a prolonged and drastic change in the climate, then the creatures that responded would become an entirely new species. For example, a primitive mouse might have taken to living in trees, jumping from branch to branch. Over the generations those successors born with loose skin were better able to float through the air and so were selected for survival, eventually to become the flying mouse or bat. Presumably the ones that didn't make it as flyers landed the hard way and became extinct. Darwin, reasoning along these same lines, thought the lemur was the bat's ancestor (Darwin 1859, 181).

During his expedition to Sarawak in the Malay archipelago, Wallace published a paper, in 1855, entitled *On the Law Which Has Regulated the Introduction of New Species*. It was concisely written and enumerated ten facts dealing with such observations as the geographical distribution of species. It also set out the entire theory of evolution, except for *how* the species change. The question of *how* was never far from Wallace's mind as he wrote in his 1855 paper: "To discover how the extinct species have from time to time been replaced by new ones down to the very latest geological period, is the most difficult, and at the same time the most interesting problem in the natural history of the earth" (Brackman 1980, 319).

Wallace's "Sarawak law", as it came to be called, basically said that "every species had come into existence coincident both in time and space (geographic distribution) with a pre-existing closely allied species" (Brackman 1980, 314). This is exactly what the modern theory of evolution teaches in saying, for example, that man has evolved from some ancestral (preexisting) ape. By this time, Charles Lyell and Charles Darwin had become friends. Upon reading Wallace's publication it was evident to both that here was a serious threat to priority of publication of the work that Darwin had been struggling with for more than twenty years.

Exactly three years after writing his Sarawak law, Wallace became ill on the small island of Ternate in the Molaccas between New Guinea and Borneo. The date was February 1858 and, as he recorded in his diary, he had an intermittent fever. One night during his illness he recalled the *Essay* by Malthus, which he had read some years before. Suddenly it all became clear in a moment's revelation:

> It occurred to me to ask the question, Why do some die and some live? And the answer was clearly, that on the whole the best fitted lived. From the effects of disease the most healthy escaped; from

enemies the strongest, the swiftest or the most cunning; from famine the best hunters or those with the best digestion; and so on.

Then I at once saw, that the ever present variability of all living things would furnish the material from which, by the mere weeding out of those less adapted to actual conditions, the fittest alone would continue the race.

There suddenly flashed upon me the *idea* of the survival of the fittest. The more I thought it over, the more I became convinced that I had at length found the long-sought-for law of nature that solved the problems of the Origin of Species (Brackman 1980, 199).[16]

A few days later Wallace wrote out his Ternate paper, which he entitled *On the Tendency of Varieties to Depart Indefinitely From the Original Type*. This was the document that contained the long-sought-for key to the theory of evolution: survival of the fittest was the mechanism, the *how*, by which the process operated (Brackman 1980, 326). The Ternate paper contained, in complete form, what is today known as the Darwinian theory of evolution, and Darwin received a copy from Wallace in June 1858; twelve months later Darwin published the book for which he is best known, *On the Origin of Species*. Even this title was taken from Wallace's Ternate paper, but Wallace's name was only mentioned in three minor places within the text. Brackman (1980) brings together good circumstantial evidence to show that Darwin was guilty of plagiarism, but more will be said of this in Chapter Five.

Before taking a close look at what is really being said as the foundation for Wallace's theory—later known as Darwin's theory—it might be helpful to summarize what has been said so far:

1. *Malthus* saw man as the brute-beast and argued that disease, famine, infanticide, and warfare were legitimate checks on human population and should not be discouraged.

2. *Lyell* rejected catastrophes, including the Genesis Flood, by expanding the time frame for events in the past. In this way what was previously seen as evidence of a single great catastrophe could now be seen as evidence of slow, natural processes working for millions of years. Lyell also said that the fossil record shows an interrupted ascending order of complexity of life forms. He proposed that the rock units be placed in order of their fossil content in an imaginary column—the geologic column.

3. *Wallace* rejected the Genesis fixity of species and adopted Lyell's picture of the ascending order of complexity in the fossil record. He

proposed that in response to Lyell's slowly changing environment, some species would be selected out to survive, whereas others, which either did not respond or faced too much competition for survival, would become extinct. He saw the survival of the fittest principle implied by Malthus as the mechanism for natural selection, whereby the species that adapt favorably to the environment survive to produce the next generation.

As we have seen, Malthus's argument not only contains an internal contradiction but it is not supported by the facts. Man is not the brute-beast but is a moral being and exercises self-restraint. Nature, far from being the bloody battlefield ringing with animal cries of "eat or be eaten", is a delicately balanced harmony that preserves a stable population. Biologists today recognize this and are slightly embarrassed by Tennyson's famous line about "Nature red in tooth and claw" (Tennyson 1974, 105).[17] The fact is that the life of animals shows two major tendencies: one towards aggressiveness and the other towards cooperation, and the cooperative aspect is far more common than we have been led to believe. Kropotkin (1939) has documented a great many cases of mutual aid among animals.

The reasoning in the Lyell-Wallace statements contains a number of assumptions and two tautologies or circular arguments. These will be dealt with in greater detail in Chapters Four and Six, but it would be well to introduce them at this point.

1. It was assumed that processes we see going on today in nature have been going on at a similar rate in the past and that very long times were necessary to accommodate the natural slow-acting processes.

2. It was assumed that the layered rocks were built up slowly by the deposition of sediment from water, and it was further assumed that rising and sinking of the continents took place to account for the multiple layers of sediment.

3. The imperfection of the geologic record was an assumption based on the premise that if it were perfect, the record would clearly show that it had been formed by uniformitarian principles.

4. The ascending fossil order assumes a greater perfection in the human mind and in the pages of textbooks than it does in fact; in practice it is extremely fragmentary and parts are often reversed or missing.

5. It was an assumption that the relatively small variation possible within a species could, with sufficient time, be continued to become a major variation, and cross the boundaries of genera, order, and class.

6. Extending this assumption further, it was assumed that all life forms are related to each other by common ancestors and that life has progressed from the simple to the complex.

The theory of evolution as proposed by Darwin is now seen to stand on a series of assumptions, but that is not all; there are two tautologies. The first states that the ascending fossil order has been caused by evolution, and then, though usually not in the same place, it is said that evolution is shown to be true by the ascending fossil order. This is simply saying the same thing twice and is based on an assumption, because the same fossil evidence could be interpreted in terms of a catastrophe taking place over a short period of time. The second tautology is Wallace's revelation concerning the key to the mechanism of evolution. Darwin had sought in vain for it for more than twenty years, and then it all seemed so simple and obvious: natural selection was caused by survival of the fittest. The argument proposed that the fittest individuals in a population (defined as those who leave the most offspring) will leave the most offspring. There are variants on this theme that are discussed learnedly in the esoteric language of science, but when reduced to simple words all are found to be nothing more than circular arguments.

So much for the principles on which the theory of evolution is founded. It should not be surprising, then, when we find that what was taught as fact yesterday is untrue today. Further, we should not be surprised to learn that there is to this time no agreement on the mechanism for evolution and several quite divergent schools of opinion; this shifting ground is the natural outcome of having a foundation based on assumptions and tautologies. In Chapter Five we will see the part Darwin played in raising this rather shaky structure. First, however, in Chapter Four we will take a close look at some of the earth's features to see just how well the hard evidence supports Lyell's uniformitarian geology.

4

Science and Geology

*Slowness has really nothing to do with the
question. An event is not any more intrinsically
intelligible or unintelligible because of the pace
at which it moves. For a man who does not
believe in a miracle, a slow miracle would be just
as incredible as a swift one.*

G.K. CHESTERTON
(1925, 21)

harles Lyell, author of the theory of uniformity, visited Niagara
Falls in October 1841 (K. Lyell 1881, 2:58).[1] Quite possibly as he
traveled in the horse-drawn coach over the Canadian roads of
the day, he recalled one of his earliest childhood memories that had
been vividly fixed in his mind at the age of four. The event took place
while his family was traveling in two coaches from Scotland to their
new home in England. A short distance from Edinburgh on the narrow
road with a steep hill on one side and a sharp drop on the other, the
horses pulling the first coach were frightened and took off at a gallop.
The coach overturned; there was a broken window though nothing
more serious, and the party was on its way again (K. Lyell 1881, 1:2).

The event made a lasting impression on Lyell's mind, which some
have suggested was the cause of his particular aversion to catastrophes.
This may neatly fit into classical psychoanalytic theory, but the only
fact we can be sure about is that Lyell attempted to explain every
natural rock formation in terms of the very low rates at which we see
changes taking place today—rivers changing their course, cliffs being
eroded by the waves of the sea, and then, during his visit to Niagara, the
rate of recession of the falls (K. Lyell 1881, 2:60).[2]

The Niagara River originally poured over the rim of the Niagara
Escarpment just above the present village of Queenston, Ontario,
carrying the waters of Lake Erie from south to north and emptying into
Lake Ontario. Gradually the waters tumbling over the escarpment

Niagara Falls at about the time of Lyell's visit. Table rock in the foreground and the lighthouse on the opposite side of the Falls have long since disappeared. (Lithograph by F. Salathé after a painting by H.V. Sebron, 1852; Public Archives of Canada, C-2266)

eroded a channel into the bedrock to form a gorge that moved the falls in a southern direction closer to Lake Erie. The present-day Niagara Falls and the seven-mile gorge are thus part of a long-continuing process. Lyell's purpose in visiting this famous landmark was to determine, if possible, how long ago the Niagara River waters began falling over the escarpment.

Lyell talked to a local inhabitant and was told that the falls retreat about three feet a year. He assumed that this was an exaggerated claim and concluded that one foot a year would be a more likely figure (Lyell 1867, 1:361). On the basis of this guess, it was then a simple matter to equate 35,000 feet, or seven miles, as 35,000 years that the falls had taken to cut the gorge from the escarpment to the place it occupied in the year of his visit, which is how he arrived at the figure that he announced to the scientific world.[3] The principle was sound enough, but his method can hardly be called scientific or even honest (Bailey 1962, 149).[4]

In recent years the estimate has been revised downward, but in the mid-nineteenth century it had a most significant impact on the common man's beliefs. Lyell's *Principles of Geology*, as already mentioned, was published in 1830-33, and although it was met with opposition at first, it eventually became the standard work on the subject for the next fifty years, running to twelve editions. Charles Lyell became Sir Charles in 1848, principally because of his Scottish landholdings. To the Victorian mind, this title gave his name and books tremendous credibility and authority; in a similar way today, the news media seek out a scientist with a legitimate Ph.D. when they want an authoritative scientific opinion. Lyell's figure of 35,000 years for the cutting of the Niagara gorge was thus accepted as an actual measurement made by a gentleman of integrity and quite beyond dispute. For the next few generations this estimate served wonderfully to demolish any credence in Archbishop Ussher's date of creation and made the attempt to finish once and for all the orthodox belief in the Mosaic Flood, which was alleged to have occurred a mere four-and-half thousand years ago.

Measurement of the rate of recession of Niagara Falls has been made periodicially since 1841, the date of Lyell's visit, and these published figures show that, far from exaggerating, the local inhabitant was too conservative. A rate of four or five feet a year is closer to the facts (Tovell 1979, 16).[5] Assuming as Lyell did that the rate of recession had always been the same, this measured value reduces the age of the falls to between seven and nine thousand years. Had it been honestly reported in the first place, this would not have been regarded as a refutation but rather a near confirmation of the Mosaic Flood!

Today's geologist prefers to adopt a cautious figure of twelve thousand years, made on the basis of radiometric tests carried out on some pieces of buried wood discovered in the blocked St. David's gorge, which was part of the original Niagara spillway (Tovell 1979, 17). However, the blocked gorge of Niagara is a story beyond the present purposes, which are to illustrate how a preconception in the mind of

Niagara Falls today showing part of the seven mile gorge that has, until recently, been cut at a rate of four or five feet a year. Dotted lines show position of Falls at time of Lyell's visit in 1841. (Ontario Ministry of Tourism and Recreation)

one man, Charles Lyell, contributed significantly to the subsequent complete change of mankind's worldview.

Lyell's View of the Earth

Lyell's concept of uniformity had four components. First, he quite reasonably assumed that the natural laws are constant. Scientific inquiry of any kind is impossible if we cannot assume that, for example, the laws holding the planets in orbit or the laws of chemical affinity have not been constant. Implicit in this assumption is the belief that God has never at any time violated those laws by intervention. Second, Lyell assumed that the earth's geological features were caused entirely by processes we see taking place today. Again, this is reasonable but excludes the possibility of large-scale catastrophic events, whether or not they were divinely originated. Third, he assumed that the geological changes are always slow, gradual, and steady; modern geology, however, has conceded that this assumption is too rigid and that some catastrophes have occurred but have been relatively small, local events. Fourth, although Lyell could not accept until quite late in life that species could gradually change from one to another, he proposed that the fossil record represented but one part of a "great year" or grand cycle, where the ichthyosaur and pterodactyl might return once more to inhabit the earth.

In spite of all its sophisticated equipment and techniques, modern geological interpretation is firmly founded on Lyell's first two uniformity assumptions, has modified the third, and has rejected and graciously forgotten the fourth. In addition, since Darwin's day the assumption has been added that life evolved from the simple to the complex, from the single cell to man, and that the remains of the various life forms have been buried in the sediments of lakes and seas and preserved as fossils. It is worth noting that the Lyellian term "sedimentary" is applied to the most important class of rocks found throughout the earth and derives from his belief that they all originated as sediment slowly deposited from bodies of water but occasionally deposited by wind and ice. In the last two decades, however, it is being cautiously conceded that at least some sedimentary rocks originated by an entirely different mechanism (Ronov 1959).[6] It has been observed that volcanic eruptions can very quickly dump millions of tons of ash, distinct from lava, either on open ground, such as the Mount St. Helen's disaster, or underwater, producing a cement-like sediment trapping life within it in a matter of hours rather than centuries (Kennet and Thunell 1975; Worzel 1959).[7] Indeed, the volcano as the agent of destruction of life and subsequent preservation of the forms as fossils was suggested as early as 1841 by Miller, who wrote concerning millions of fossilized fish: "The thought has often struck me that calcined lime, cast out as ashes from some distant crater, and carried by the wind, might have been the cause of the wide-spread destruction to which the organs testify" (Miller 1841, 236). Whatever mechanism was responsible, the fossils and the sedimentary rocks in which they are formed are key elements in the whole chain of nineteenth century Lyellian and Darwinian reasoning.

About Fossils

Fossils occasionally make the news, especially if they happen to be human, and inquiry will often show that they become the focal point of academic controversy, but the public is seldom made aware of just what passions are aroused by those with a personal or vested interest and with reputations at stake. However, the controversies do not attract the public interest they did in the middle to late nineteenth century when the battle for evolution was being fought. Even composer Camile Saint-Saëns was captivated by this issue and included the fossils, following the lions and the elephants, in his popular "Carnival of the Animals", written in 1886.

Fossils are the remains of once living things: perhaps part of a plant, insect, fish, bird, mammal, or, in very rare instances, the bones of man. Usually it is only the hard, boney parts that are preserved. More often than not, however, much of the skeleton will be missing so that the complete assemblies, especially of large animals, that we see on display in museums are usually the composite result of fossil bones from different sources. In instances where they are found, human remains are often unique, and the museum display will invariably be a plaster copy of the original.

Almost everyone is familiar with the skeletal remains of dinosaurs, which generally take pride of place in any museum. On occasion it is possible for a visitor to acquire a little more information about these huge fossil bones by touching them: they are stone rather than bone and, of course, very heavy. The question arises how did a carbon compound, which is the essential component of bone, change into a silicon compound—the "mineralized" component—and still retain not only the same outward appearance but the same internal structure and, in the case of fossilized wood, even the same color? The truthful answer is that since the mineralization process has never been duplicated in the laboratory, no one can be absolutely sure of the exact mechanism; the explanations proposed are largely speculative, all making the assumption that vast lengths of time were involved.

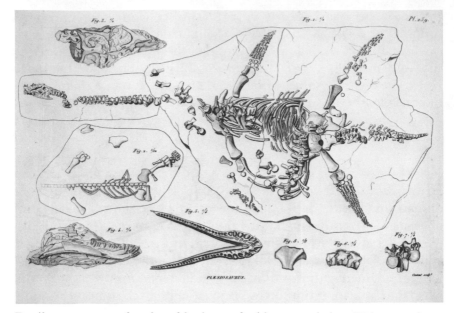

Fossil creatures are often found broken and with parts missing. This example from the atlas to Cuvier's *Recherches* is typical and shows the *Plesiosaurus* or sea-dwelling dinosaur (1836 edition, plate 259; Sigmund Samuel Library, University of Toronto)

The *Plesiosaurus* reconstructed from fossil remains in a painting prepared for the Museum of Natural History, Stuttgart, by Fraas. The original work was destroyed in 1943 and has been restored in this drawing by Mary Wardlaw.

The common textbook explanation for the mineralization process is that mineral-containing water has seeped into interstices in the fossil, dissolving the bone and at the same time depositing the silica-based minerals from the water—a molecule-by-molecule replacement process (Schuchert and Dunbar 1950, 38). This may sound plausible, but a moment's consideration shows what any physical chemist knows: such a process is self-stifling; once even the thinnest silica film has been formed, this glass-like material prevents further diffusion of both the mineral-containing water inwards or the dissolved carbonaceous material outwards. The problem is seen most clearly in the case of agates. These egg-shaped stones are formed, it is believed, by deposition of silica from ground water seeping into gas cavities in volcanic lava.

Polished section through an egg-shaped agate stone. The layers of silica appear as concentric rings, each being made visible by varying impurities producing slightly different colors. Entry and exit channels for the water were not evident in this four-inch long sample.

The theory requires that the "egg" grows in concentric layers beginning at the outside and finishing at the centre. However, to quote Webster, an authority on gem stones, "It is the absence of the feeding canals in many agates that the main objection to the theory lies" (Webster 1970, 183). Plainly, the fossilization process is still a mystery.

When an animal dies or is killed, the body very quickly decomposes; bacterial action and scavengers are all part of nature's economy. If this were not so, we would find ourselves stumbling about in dead bodies hundreds of feet deep. Rapid burial to exclude bacteria and scavengers, then, is one of the first requirements of the fossilization process. As Lyell observed, sediment forms at the bottoms of lakes and the ocean, and it is said that for the fossils to be found in sedimentary rocks, they must have fallen to the bottom and been covered over with sediment in some unexplained, rapid way. This is the textbook explanation; the authors then typically point out that such events were likely to be rare, but the vast number of fossils found are explained by the millions of years available to accumulate these numbers.

Exploration of the ocean bed has been carried out since 1872 when the British ship HMS Challenger took part in a four-year scientific expedition (Murray 1880-95).[8] The depth of sediment as determined seismographically in a more recent expedition varied from none at all to more than thirteen thousand feet,[9] while the samples examined contained only the countless millions of tiny shells of the single-celled protozoa such as the microscopic radiolaria and the foraminifera (Pettersson 1950, 44). Occasionally, sets of shark's teeth are found, since these are virtually insoluble in sea water, but the ocean bottom is never found littered with dead bodies waiting to be fossilized.

The parlor aquarium was introduced to England during the 1850s and became a popular part of Victorian life. Had Lyell and his supporters been keepers of goldfish, they would have been well aware that expired individuals are not found on the bottom of the tank. When a living creature dies, internal bacterial action produces gas that, if the body is in water, keeps it from sinking, and in the case of a large animal, the body may remain suspended for weeks. During this time it is picked clean by scavengers and begins to fall, but by then the sea water has started to dissolve the bones. Dissolution in sea water or even fresh water is more rapid than burial on land. One can thus appreciate that fossil formation by the falling of sediment over the body on the ocean bottom must have been rare indeed.

Museum Displays

When we see the rather spectacular fossil finds on display in museums, we might wonder how it was that not only have the bones been preserved but in many cases they are all in place; there are clear

Fossil *Ichthyosaur* preserved in the act of feeding, or perhaps giving birth to her young. (Stuttgart Museum für Naturkunde; courtesy C. McGowan, Royal Ontario Museum)

impressions of the skin, muscles, and even feathers in a few bird specimens. Delicate bat wings and insects have even been preserved as impressions (Brues 1951, 56).[10] We know, for instance, that dinosaurs were not covered with hair but had reptile-like skin, because on occasion impressions of their skin have been left in the sedimentary rock. We also know that at least certain types of dinosaurs laid eggs, because clutches of fossilized eggs have been found and the fossilized embryo is seen inside (Andrews 1926, 229-31).[11] Presumably, dinosaurs did not lay their eggs under water. It is conjectured that it was probably wind-blown sand that caused the rapid burial, but this same explanation has to serve for the dinosaurs as well since these were found in the same area. The Stuttgart Museum of Natural History in Germany contains a fossilized *ichthyosaur*, or sea-dwelling dinosaur, fossilized at the moment of feeding her young. In the Ludwigsburg Museum of Natural History in Germany, there is an even more spectacular specimen of an *ichthyosaur* fossilized in the process of giving birth with the young clearly visible in the birth canal. In the Princeton Museum of Natural History there is a perch fossilized in the act of swallowing a herring. In each of these examples, the creatures were sea-dwelling, and their burial under fine sediment and subsequent fossilization had to have been sufficiently rapid to leave no trace of decomposition.

Some have pointed out that, occasionally, pregnant whales are beached; they die and the gases of decomposition build up sufficient internal pressure to expel the dead fetus. If this can happen to whales, then it could also have happened to the ichthyosaur—*in partum mor-*

Fossil perch preserved in the act of swallowing a herring. Found in the Eocene varves of Fossil Lake in Wyoming, where it is assumed that a foot of rock took two thousand years to form; it would seem that rapid burial must have occurred to preserve the details in the specimens. (Princeton Museum of Natural History)

tis. Whether in fact the ichthyosaur gave live birth, which seems most probable, or gave birth after death, the carcass and fetus, according to this explanation, had then to be rapidly and deeply buried in place on the beach and under a fine sediment that later hardened into the limestone where they were found. The fine details preserved in both German specimens, each of which is almost six feet long, show no signs of decomposition, and the natural explanations proposed, without the appeal to a catastrophe, are strained to say the least.

Fossil Evidence of Catastrophe

In England, one of the largest sedimentary rock deposits covering thousands of square miles is known as the Old Red Sandstone, and it contains many millions of fossilized fish in contorted positions indicating that they died in agony (Chambers 1887, 56; Miller 1841, 232).[12] In some of the Sandstone quarries the fossil fish are so densely packed it is estimated there are more than a thousand per cubic yard. There is a similar sedimentary rock deposit extending for hundreds of square miles on the California coast and containing millions of fossil herring; again, all appear to have died in paroxysms of agony. The famous fossil bird, *Archaeopteryx*, found in the Solnhofen Limestone, east of Stuttgart, Germany, and which appears in most school biology textbooks, died with its neck contorted backwards. In the Drumheller fossil beds of Alberta, there are millions of fossil clams in a layer three feet thick and packed together with each pair of shells tightly closed. Normally, clams do not live packed together, and when a clam dies, the muscle holding the shells in a closed position relaxes, and the shells spring open. This fossil evidence indicates that these clams were buried alive; a similar fossil bed is found in Texas. These few examples, which are by no means isolated, can all be better explained in terms of a massive catastrophe in which deep ocean sediments were suddenly brought up, entrapping sea life, then encroaching the lowlands and drowning and entombing dinosaurs with their eggs. If the evidence seems to support a massive disturbance in the oceans, what evidence is there that the ocean waters swept inland covering even high ground?

In the suburbs of Los Angeles may be found the well-known asphalt pit of Rancho La Brea, where thousands of animal bones mixed with clay and sand are found in the bituminous deposit; the black tarry substance has beautifully preserved the bones. The site began to be "mined" for asphalt for roofing and paving in San Francisco more than a century ago, and the bones were reported at that time. Since 1906 the University of California has been collecting these fossil skeletons, which are crowded together, and, for the most part, disassembled. The

The Rancho La Brea tar pits according to the textbook interpretation and conceived in this painting by Charles R. Knight for the American Museum of Natural History. (American Museum of Natural History, New York)

best known animal skeleton found at La Brea is the saber-toothed tiger (*Smilodon*), having curved canine teeth more than ten inches long and, fortunately, now extinct. Many of the world's museums display this fierce creature with the original fossil material since hundreds of saber-toothed tiger skulls have been recovered (Page 1983).[13] A great many other animals are recognized among the La Brea fossil remains including wolves (three-thousand individuals), bison, mammoths, camels, horses, some birds, and the separated bones of a human skeleton, the skull of which was said to be no different from the human skull of today (Boule and Vallois 1957, 478).[14] This last item is not an isolated case; the jawbone of a young child was recently found by Irving in an

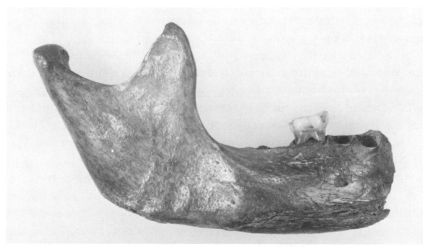

Jaw-bone of a child eleven or twelve years old, discovered in an animal graveyard in the Yukon in 1976. The investigators are hesitant to attach an age to it. (B.F. Beebe, University of Toronto)

animal graveyard in the permafrost of the Yukon Territories (Irving and Harington 1973).[15]

The usual explanation given in geology textbooks and in the popular Time-Life books for these masses of animal bones at La Brea (there are a similar bituminous deposits in Peru and in Poland) is as follows:

> Throughout the ages the volatile parts of the escaping oil have evaporated, leaving behind the sticky residue of asphaltum, which formed a death trap for the prehistoric animals of southern California. Animals coming to the seeps for water, or attempting to cross soil-covered patches of asphalt, were trapped...their death cries attracted carnivores and scavengers which in turn became engulfed. Their bones lie beautifully preserved— although all in a jumble—in the asphalt deposits, from which they have been recovered by the hundreds of thousands (Schuchert and Dunbar 1950, 44).

This is typical of the explanation usually given, while what the public normally sees are nicely reconstructed skeletons or imaginative reconstructions, such as the painting by Charles R. Knight in the American Museum of Natural History in New York. This sort of explanation might be satisfying were it not for further facts that somehow are seldom commented on by textbook authors. Lull, for example, mentions that "the asphalt tends to work so that the bones are pulled apart and one never finds a skeleton in articulation [connected together]" (Lull 1935, 28). This is pure speculation since there is no evidence that the asphalt is in a state of motion and, in any case, this would not explain the disconnected bones found mashed together at other locations where there is no asphalt. The disconnected skeletons and broken bones are more easily explained by a catastrophe, such as turbulent flood waters of tidal dimensions sweeping up fleeing animals in their path and dashing bodies against rocky ravines and gorges. Possibly, at La Brea, there was an oil seepage that subsequently permeated the smashed remains; this is speculation, but it would better satisfy the facts than the conventional textbook explanation.

Typical of a fossil grave site not associated with asphalt is the Agate Spring Quarry, Nebraska, which contains a fossil-bearing deposit up to twenty inches thick and containing as many as one hundred bones per square foot. Thousands of animals are represented at this site, most of which are extinct; again, the skeletons are disconnected and the bones smashed and broken, all of which indicates that the animals were caught up in a violent cataract of water, sand, and gravel and driven into the common grave in which they are found today.

Sinking Continents

Although it might be possible to concede that all this evidence could be the result of violent but local floods, there is also the type of evidence that Lyell used to support his contention that the continents have sunk beneath the ocean waters and risen again. Fossil sea shells and marine creatures are found in the tops of hills and mountains throughout the world. In several places fossil whales have even been found in hilltops, and Laverdière (1950) has reported examples in the Montreal-Quebec City area where a fossil whale was found in the Laurentide Hills at more than five hundred feet above sea level.[16] Whether the land sank beneath sea level here, as Lyell maintained, or the sea level rose above the land, the result would be the same—a flood.

Plainly, evidence is provided of vertical and upward movement on a massive scale by the upturned sedimentary rocks containing marine fossils in mountain ranges. There is, however, less spectacular evidence of vertical movement but no indication of the direction, that is, whether up or down, in the raised beaches that are often found to be tilted from the horizontal along their length. One such tilted beach runs the complete length of the north shore of Lake Ontario and is seen as prime evidence that the entire continent sank beneath the present sea level and then reemerged but not quite uniformly. It is assumed that the weight of the ice during the ice age was the cause of the downward movement of the continent, but then this Lyellian argument also requires vertical movement for large areas such as Arizona, where it is acknowledged that there was no ice. Furthermore, repeated inunda-

Raised beach runs around the north shore of Lake Ontario and is tilted from end to end indicating some vertical movement of the land. First beach hidden by trees across the center of the photograph; today's beach in the foreground. (Photo by D. Cox)

tions are often called for to account for the various sedimentary layers, but no one really knows the mechanism by which whole continents are said to have sunk then risen again (Hallam 1963).[17]

In point of fact, in a raised beach the only hard evidence for vertical movement is the difference in elevation between the highest and lowest parts of the beach; nothing can be said about which end went down and/or which end went up. Further, it is really going beyond the limits of the evidence to claim that the entire continent sank hundreds of feet, which is what would be necessary to bring it all beneath the present sea level, on the basis of the relatively short distance evidenced by the raised beaches. So whether we would believe that the entire continent sank or the present sea level rose to provide the flood as witnessed by the marine fossils, scientists acknowledge the difficulty of finding the mechanism responsible for the vertical movement of either the land in the one case or the sea in the other.

Back to Niagara Falls

The discovery of the fossil whale near Montreal brings us full circle back to Niagara Falls, since these two locations are roughly in the same geographical area. Lyell's followers have maintained that this area of Canada sank below sea level under the great weight of the ice during the last ice age; ice assumed to be several miles thick is required by the argument in order to cause the land to sink, and it was further assumed that the land remained submerged for some time after the retreat of the ice. This extended period of submersion is necessary in order to account for marine fossils such as the whale; it is reasonably assumed that the creature was not carried by the ice, neither did it walk over dry land. Having the Laurentide Hills beneath sea level somewhat less than thirty-five thousand years ago, according to Lyell's estimate for the last ice age, is perhaps sufficiently remote in time to be believable. How-

ever, now that the estimates for the cutting of the Niagara gorge and the last ice age have been reduced to twelve thousand years, while the measured rates indicate seven to nine thousand years, that is asking us to believe that the Laurentide Hills only rose from beneath the sea some five or six thousand years ago. At this point it is almost possible to believe that it was the Genesis Flood that left the area four-and-a-half thousand years ago!

One of the principles of scientific inquiry is to adopt the simplest explanation possible, and here, without any appeal to numerous ice ages and the assumption that ice of sufficient weight depressed the land, the one flood would seem to qualify as the simpler explanation. Moreover, the Flood requires a mechanism to raise the sea level but once, whereas Lyell's assumption requires a mechanism that will raise and lower the solid earth many times.

What About the Ice Age?

The name of Louis Agassiz is intimately associated with the idea that at some time in the earth's geological past the climate changed and huge glaciers pushed their way down from the polar regions. Later, when the climate became warm again the glaciers retreated to where they are found in their diminished form today.

Agassiz was born in 1807 in Switzerland. During hikes into the Swiss mountains he noticed that as the glaciers moved down the mountain valleys, the stones and rocks carried within the ice scratched the underlying bedrock leaving score marks parallel to the direction of ice flow. Following his emigration to America in 1856, Agassiz, by that time famous as a professor and popularizer of natural history, saw in his travels flat beds of rock with similar scratch marks that usually ran in a north-south direction. He suggested that glaciers had at one time pushed their way down from the north and then retreated, leaving not only the score marks as evidence for their once having been in the area but also many erratic boulders and stones scattered about at random as they were released from the melting ice.

The idea of the ice age was accepted cautiously at first and then with enthusiasm, as it provided a mechanism for much of what Lyell had difficulty in otherwise explaining, such as the extinction of so many animals that had by then been discovered as fossils. However, Agassiz saw the ice age as something catastrophic, whereas Lyell accepted it in his usual manner, as a gradual change of the earth's climate. He believed heavier snowfalls each season around the earth's poles built up the assumed thickness of ice.

One proposed mechanism for the ice age was that extra volcanic

Louis Agassiz, 1807-73, studied
under Cuvier in Paris and later
emigrated to become one of
America's most popular naturalists.
He never gave up his belief in the
biblical account of Creation.
(Engraved by J. Sartain from a
photograph by Whipple and Black
when Agassiz was fifty; Metropolitan
Toronto Reference Library Board)

activity had produced a dust cloud in the upper atmosphere that had reduced the sunlight reaching the earth, but no one was sure what caused the extra volcanic activity. Whatever the actual mechanism, and geology is still undecided, the scenario of the gradually increasing snowfall was acceptable to the Lyellian doctrine of uniformity, and this is what we are given to believe today. Moreover, not one but four ice ages were eventually proposed, because it was imagined that sufficient weight of ice, perhaps a mile or more in thickness, would conveniently provide the needed mechanism for the depression of the continents beneath sea level on at least four of the most recent occasions. Modern geological opinion, however, is now inclined to concede one ice age rather than four, which, if nothing else, at least simplifies the rationalization.

To the man in the street far removed from the frozen wastes of the Arctic and even more remote from Antarctica, the ice age, as described, is perhaps believable. After all, there is perpetual ice and snow at the poles now as evidence. And, if scientists say that there have been four ice ages then that must be so, just as long as we are not told to expect the fifth in our own lifetime! And yet there are some things that do not fit the orthodox view that the ice age was a snowflake-by-snowflake affair. First, the moisture for all that snow had to get into the atmosphere before it fell, and the only way known for that to happen is by evaporation of water, which requires heat. The volcanic dust theory would tend to cut off the source of radiant heat from the sun and reduce rather than promote evaporation, so that this mechanism plainly cannot be correct. Secondly, there is evidence that the earth's polar regions were at one time a lot warmer than they are today. During his Antarctic expedition in 1907-9, Shackelton (1909, 2:314) found seven seams of coal, each between three and seven feet thick,[18] while preserved remains of warm-water coral have been found at the watery northern pole within the Arctic Circle. In both cases the evidence indicates that these areas were not at one time snow and ice-covered, which of course they are now, and this tells us that there was an "ice age", but how thick the ice was and how far it extended towards the equator is conjectural. Further, it is believed that there is evidence that the beginning of the ice age was not gradual but—it seems almost heresy to say it— catastrophic.

Frozen Mammoths

Ever since the late 1700s when men began to return with travelers' tales of some of the more remote parts of the earth, there have been intriguing accounts of animals buried and preserved whole in the frozen wastes of northern Siberia and Alaska. Unlike the other fossil graveyards where only broken bones are found in confusion, the vast cemetery of the north teems with complete animals, wolves, bears, elephants, rhinoceroses, and the woolly mammoths with their beautiful tusks of ivory (Whitley 1910).[19] There are many of these animals preserved with their bones fresh and not at all mineralized, and, since Roman times, ivory "mining" has been a steady and lucrative trade (Farrand 1961; Lippman 1962).[20] The Chinese, renowned for their ivory carving, use mammoth tusks from Siberia, and it is estimated that

Sorting mammoth tusks at an ivory auction yard in Siberia about 1920. Ivory mining has been continuous since Roman days and surely represents many thousands of buried mammoths. (Metropolitan Toronto Reference Library Board)

northern Siberia has provided more than half the world's ivory for such items as billiard balls and piano keys. While Darwin played his game of billiards or listened to his wife play the piano, the ivories involved may well have come from the Siberian mammoths whose extinction he admitted was an insoluble problem to Lyell's principle of gradual changes and his own theory of evolution (Colp 1977, 65; Whitley 1910, 56).[21]

The year 1901 provided a unique opportunity to make a first-hand scientific study of a mammoth that had then recently been exposed on the banks of the Beresovka River in northeastern Siberia and sixty miles inside the Arctic Circle (Digby 1926; Dillow 1981; Pfizenmayer 1939; Sanderson 1960).[22] The mammoth was found frozen in a sitting position in what is technically referred to as muck and located in the middle of an ancient landslide. The flesh and even the eyeballs were so well preserved that the expedition's sled dogs had plenty of fresh meat to eat. Death must have come to this specimen very quickly, because the blood still contained some oxygen and was preserved sufficiently well to establish the relationship to the blood of today's Indian elephant, although distinct anatomical differences would not necessarily classify them as the same species. There was well-preserved food in the mouth and twenty-four pounds of undissolved and identifiable plants in the stomach. One interesting and unexpected feature reported by Herz (1904, 623) was an erect male genital.[23] Now all these details were soberly reported in the scientific journals of the day, including the annual report of the Smithsonian Institution for 1903, yet geology textbooks still insist on the uniformitarian explanation that the unfortunate creature—as if it were the only one—must have stumbled and died where it fell amid the snow-covered wasteland.

Imaginative paintings of the woolly mammoth by such artists as Burian invariably show these animals in a winter landscape, yet the reported analysis of the stomach contents shows more than fifty varieties of herbs, grasses, and mosses, some of which today only grow in temperate climates (Dillow 1981, 371-80). The buttercups that were found (actually just the seeds), for example, will only grow when the temperature is well above 40°F. The ripe fruits of the sedges and grasses fix the time of death during the second half of July or the beginning of August.

All these and many more details of the mammoth have been available in English to anyone willing to make inquiry at even a modest university library. Yet for most of those who actually do so and who popularize the mammoth mystery, prejudice causes them to omit many little details, such as the erect genital, that cry out as evidence of an

The erect genital of the Beresovka mammoth appears at the bottom of the
picture to the left, while the tail is above. The connection strip of hide has been
turned through 180° for the photograph. (Smithsonian Institution, photograph
number 83-2243)

extremely rapid catastrophe on a major order. Fortunately, there are
still some with genuinely open minds, and Dillow has described a
fascinating piece of research in cooperation with scientists specializing
in heat transfer at the Bird's Eye Division of General Foods Corpora-
tion, New York. Preliminary experiments were conducted with gladi-
oli and carnation flowers in a prepared solution of stomach acid to find
out the minimum rate of temperature decrease required in order to
preserve parts of the flowers such that they would still be identifiable.
Then, from the dimensions of the mammoth and the known rates of
heat transfer (heat loss) through fur, skin, fat, flesh, etc., an outside
temperature was computed that would reduce the stomach temperature at the previously determined rate in order to preserve the buttercup
flowers. The staggering conclusion was that the mammoth, and presumably all the tens of thousands of other frozen animals in the north,
was overcome in midsummer by a cold blast with temperatures lower
than minus 150°F (Dillow 1981, 396). The lowest recorded temperatures on earth have never reached this extreme, while the temperatures
in these polar regions today have never since recovered to the point
where buttercups will grow again.

We do not know what caused the ice age that seems from these few examples so obviously to have been a catastrophe. One theory that takes all the very rapid freezing rates into account supposes that the earth passed through the icy tail of a comet, and the ice particles at the temperature of outer space were caught up in the earth's gravitational and magnetic fields and were dumped on the magnetic north and south poles (Gow 1972; Pattern 1976; Sears 1979).[24-25] There could have subsequently been some glaciation at the edges of the instantly formed ice field, while the ice might also have been some thousands of feet in thickness. The ice-dump theory could also account for a number of other features, such as Canada's permafrost, ice caves between lava rocks (Pattern 1976, 120), and the Ross sea-bed core evidence which indicates that Antarctica only became ice-covered as recently as six thousand years ago (Hough 1950).[26] None of these facts can be adequately explained—and the Beresovka mammoth least of all—by the nineteenth century hypothesis of the falling snowflakes.

What Kind of Rock Is That?

For those who have been visitors to the Grand Canyon in Arizona and have stood at the canyon rim with a clear drop into the abyss below, the view is not only breathtaking—words are really inadequate to describe it—but there is also a sense of wonder mixed with frustration as unanswered questions flood through the mind. Nature has permitted man to see at this unique spot a cross section through about a mile of the earth's crust. The United States Parks Service, fully aware of the visitor's feelings, provides geology lectures at popular spots along the south rim of the canyon; they also post geological explanations beside each type of rock formation on the well-beaten trails to the Colorado River, which winds its way along the very bottom of the canyon. Most spectacular are the various layers of rock quite sharply delineated by color and texture that line the canyon walls, winding a layer-cake pattern in and out of minor canyons throughout the two hundred mile length of what is really a major fissure in the earth's surface. By the time the visitor leaves the canyon, his mind is reeling with names such as Kaibab, Toroweap, Permian, Devonian, and Cambrian, while all the millions of years involved are just too staggering to comprehend.

By what divination does the geologist conclude from the examination of a piece of rock its name, its age, and its history in relationship to other rocks in the same area? The situation can be reduced to something relatively simple when it is appreciated that there are basically only three types of rock that may receive names from two sources. The rock types may be igneous, which means that at one time such a rock was hot and liquid—lava from volcanoes, basalt, and granite are common examples. Or the rock may be sedimentary, meaning that it usually originated as a fine sediment and settled to the bottom of a body of water. Limestone, sandstone, shale, and clay are examples, although the clay is really a sediment at the stage before it has hardened into rock. The third type is called metamorphic rock and may have been either igneous or sedimentary in origin, but in some way, as yet unknown, it has crystallized and become very hard. Marble is thought to be metamorphosed limestone, while anthracite is believed to have come from bituminous coal, which is technically a sedimentary rock. That is not too difficult, and anyone can make a good start at identifying the three types of rock by a visit to a local cemetery.

The names of rock strata come from two sources: First, there is the local geographical name, such as Kaibab, Toroweap, and Coconino, which are, for example, names used to identify the various strata at the Grand Canyon. These same strata will also be catalogued under one of the geological age names, which is the second source of names for rocks. Geological age names are just that, the name indicating its assigned age according to a scheme worked out by Lyell and others in the nineteenth century.

Naturalists such as Cuvier and Deshayes, working in Paris a few years before Lyell was born, discovered that there were strata containing marine fossils and that the uppermost beds contained many species of shell-bearing mollusks, such as clams, that still live today. Successively lower groups of strata were found to contain fewer and fewer living species. Lyell saw this as a principle and proposed a classification based on the percentage of still-living shelled invertebrates, the clams for example, and coined age names for rocks based upon this arbitrary division. Thus, he said that those rocks containing 50-90 percent of modern species would be called Pliocene, from the Greek meaning "more recent". Rocks containing 20-40 percent of the fossils represented by modern species would be called Miocene, meaning "less recent", while those containing less than 5 percent would be called Eocene, meaning "dawn". Lyell had made his proposal in the 1830s, *before* the rocks of the world had been studied. It is now conceded that the percentage of living species found in rocks of a given date varies from region to region, so that Lyell's method is not a satisfactory basis for correlation. Nevertheless, followers of Lyell quickly elaborated on his scheme, subdividing and extending further backwards in time and assigning ages to each geological era. In spite of the deficiency of Lyell's method, certain fossils came to be recognized as typical of each age, while some juggling of the various fossil forms was necessary to fit the assumed upward gradation of complexity into proper chronological sequence; these particular fossils—mostly small sea creatures—became the "index" fossils for the system. The existence of a particular index fossil found in a rock sample then immediately associates that particular strata with an age name and, of course, with the age that has been assigned to it (Dunbar 1960, 352).

The ages of the various geological eras were determined by a combination of guesswork and calculation. It was noticed, for example, that a river deposited a sediment each year when in flood; by estimating the depth of sediment deposited in one year and knowing the total depth of sediment by drilling a hole, the age of the river system could be calculated. Often the annual rate was a fraction of an inch, and with a total depth of sediment of hundreds of feet, great ages were assigned to that particular layer of sediment. This, however, was based on the assumption that the deposition rate had been uniform throughout the entire time. The assigned ages, particularly for the earliest forms of life, seem to have been put on a sliding scale that increases in direct proportion to our understanding of the complexities of the living cell. In Lyell's day, for example, the beginning of life was thought to have occurred about 200 million years ago, but this estimate has since escalated to 2,000 million years, just ten times longer, which suggests that this is more speculation than science. Even the radiometric methods, considered by many to be foolproof independent checks, are themselves based on a number of critical assumptions that leave a certain amount of uncertainty to the whole idea of age names. More will be said of this in Chapter Eleven.

Age Names and the Geologic Column

Based on Lyell's system, the index fossils have been arranged on paper in a vertical column representing every possible stratum—all in order from the least complex at the bottom to the most complex, including man, at the top. Such a column is known as the geologic column and is a key tool for the geologist. Although index fossils do appear in a rough order, in practice there often are overlapping zones with two index fossils together; sometimes they appear in reverse order even on a massive geographical scale,[27] while throughout it is always possible to find a fossil totally out of place (Pierce 1957). When this happens with human remains, there tends to be controversy (Corliss 1978).[28] It seems that scientific literature did contain reports of out-of-place human fossils until about 1859, the time Darwin introduced his theory of evolution. For instance, a human skull was found in a coalbed near Freiberg, Germany, and reported in detail by Karsten in 1842.[29] At this date, however, Lyell's geologic column was not established dogma and the paper was reported by a reputable scientific journal of the day. A similar finding today, however, would stand very little chance of being published because it would either call into question the whole of geology as a science, or it would have to be concluded, as in the case of the Freiberg skull, that a human being appeared 100 million years before his time!

The geologic column is a theoretical and abstract device, but nowhere on earth will there be found a series of rock strata representing every age name in the column; in fact, the most that can be expected are a few strata together representing only a very small part of it. However, the column is claimed to be a useful device when drilling exploration holes for oil, and so on, and is sometimes sufficient to indicate whether it is worthwhile to continue drilling further.

The age names such as Cambrian, with the subdivisions of upper, middle, and lower that are given to rock strata, depend then on the fossils found and have nothing to do with color, texture, chemical composition, or any other characteristic. For example, a layer of limestone at one point, of shale at another, and of sandstone at a third might all be called *Cretaceous* and assigned an age of 130 million years or so if they all happen to contain the same index fossil.

The order of the geological age names is, therefore, the supposed order of a set of index fossils, based on the assumed order of the evolution of life, while evidence of the evolution of life is then said to be shown by the order of index fossils. This is circular reasoning and can in no way be called science.

For some years now an increasing number of reputable geologists have begun to realize this and question the whole principle. Writing in the *American Journal of Science*, O'Rourke has stated: "The intelligent layman has long suspected circular reasoning in the use of rocks to date fossils and fossils to date rocks. The geologist has never bothered to think of a good reply, feeling the explanations are not worth the trouble as long as the work brings results. This is supposed to be hard-headed pragmatism" (O'Rourke 1976, 54).[30] Now there is nothing wrong with using the names in the geologic column to identify strata containing the same kind of fossil. However, associating each of these names with vast spans of time is not in the best interests of impartial science but, rather, seems to have theological motives, since it has been responsible for very effectively replacing one belief system by another. For example, the long periods of time preclude any possibility of the individual fossil creatures confined within each age name of having been contemporaneous.

Lyell's principle of stretching the time frame of the Genesis account of Creation has, at a stroke, replaced one catastrophic flood with a series of tranquil inundations to produce what is essentially the same evidence. This one master stroke has also since permitted it to be argued that evolution has provided all the diversity of life forms from a common ancestor and thus neatly removes the need to appeal to supernaturalism. When all is said and done, it matters not in the least to the mining engineer whether a rock is four million years old or four thousand, as long as his work brings profitable results, and the only possible reason the ages steadfastly remain attached to the names is that this is the foundation for the theory of evolution. The geologic column with all the associated ages is thus a major article in the canon of faith that every student of geology is obliged to commit to memory.

The Problem of Bent Rocks

It has already been mentioned that Lyell had to exercise great imagination to explain what appeared to be evidence of catastrophe in terms of slow processes. Just as an example, there are in many places throughout the world layers of sedimentary rocks that have been buckled into more or less regular folds; some are small scale, but many are on a huge scale covering many miles. The upward crests of the folds are called anticlines, and the downward folds are called synclines. At these locations the solid rock is bent into acute angles. To quote Longwell,

Syncline, Trinity Bay, Newfoundland. The absence of cracks in these layers of sedimentary rock indicates that they were formed quickly and bent while plastic: evidence of a massive and violent catastrophe in the past. (Geological Survey of Canada, Ottawa; photograph number 108185)

Knopf, and Flint (1950), a popular North American textbook on geology: "It is cause for some wonder that strong brittle rocks be bent into sharp folds" (p. 246). The authors then go on to explain how that is possible without the rock cracking: "If there is sufficient time for adjustment the most brittle rocks under strong confining pressure can be forced to bend as if they were soft and plastic" (p. 248).[31]

The student of geology and ultimately the public are asked to accept this statement entirely without proof, as indeed for the very long times proposed there can be no proof. Lyell was a lawyer by profession and had received no training in mechanics or the strength of materials. Had he consulted any engineer of the day, the very elementary fact would have been pointed out to him that crystalline materials such as rock or concrete have great compressive strength but virtually no strength in tension; while in a fold or bend, for every layer of rock in compression, there must be an equal and opposite layer of rock in tension. In an anticline the bent outside layers of the rock were in tension but are found to be generally unfractured and in many places not even cracked. The modern theory of fracture mechanics cannot account for this fact, yet, before abandoning the theory, the alternative explanation, which Lyell rejected, should be considered.

Lyell and modern geology acknowledge that the rock layers were first formed as flat sediments, which were soft and plastic in their early stages. With time and, it is said, pressure, these sediments crystallize (metamorphose) and become hard solid rock. Lyell required long times, but it is just those long times that worked against his theory by causing the sediment to harden *before*, or certainly during, bending. He made the *a priori* assumption that the natural laws operating today have not changed, but then because of the obvious problem of bending solid rock, he had to make an appeal to time as a factor that somehow changes the laws by which rocks crack when their tensile strength is exceeded; this is a contradiction of his own principle of uniformitarianism. All this difficulty would have been avoided if Lyell's mind-set could have accepted the most obvious explanation, that the rocks were bent in the early stages when the sediments were pliable and before metamorphosis took place. This would easily satisfy all the facts but would require the process to have taken place over a short period of time, say a few months; but, of course, it would be difficult to escape the conclusion that a major catastrophe was involved.

Those Anomalous Fossils

Geology surely loses credibility as a science when it is discovered, for example, that a fossil life form declared to be extinct millions of years ago suddenly appears alive in a fisherman's net. It is usually claimed that the supposedly extinct creatures survived for millions of years in some isolated ecological niche, but this assumes absolute uniformity of conditions, which, it is admitted, is extremely unlikely.

The famous *Coelacanth*, known only from its fossil and allegedly extinct for 50 million years, suddenly turned up in a fisherman's net off the coast of Madagascar in 1938, and since then a dozen more specimens have been caught (Mackal 1980; Millot 1955).[32]

Imaginative reconstruction of a sea-serpent from fishermen's accounts. (Engraving produced in 1860; Thomas Fisher Rare Book Library, University of Toronto)

Of all the fossil creatures, the dinosaur is the largest and probably best exemplifies the prehistoric age. It is perhaps only remotely possible, but should a live dinosaur be discovered, this would cause the most heated controversy; its very being would challenge Lyell's geologic column and the theory of evolution. Some hint of the arguments likely became evident in April 1977, when a Japanese fishing vessel caught a 4,000 pound dead creature in its nets off the east coast of New Zealand. From photographs, sketches with careful measurements, and flipper samples for tissue analysis, it had every appearance of being a plesiosaur, or sea-dwelling dinosaur, which has until now only been known by its fossils. Unfortunately, the fishermen had to return the dead creature to the sea to save their fish cargo, but the evidence, such as the tissue analysis, showed that it was clearly not a mammal. Meanwhile, the measurements of the head and neck and the absence of a dorsal fin discounted the possibility of its being a basking shark. Nevertheless,

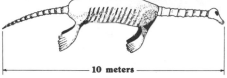

Dead creature caught by Japanese fishermen near New Zealand in 1977. A qualified zoologist on board the vessel recorded all the pertinent data possible. (Taiyo Fishery Company, Japan). His sketch of the dead creature has been redrawn for this publication. (See also pages 86 and 426)

Western scientists insisted that it was either a sea lion (mammal) or a shark, but most of the Japanese scientific community was convinced that it was indeed a plesiosaur (Koster 1977).[33]

We are repeatedly told in newspaper articles, magazines, and textbooks that 70 million years ago, at the end of the Cretaceous period and the beginning of the Tertiary period, three quarters of all the known species of animals living in the water and on the land became extinct. This included all the dinosaurs, while the reason for their extinction has been the cause for dozens of theories. The latest, by Alvarez et al. (1980), suggests that the earth was hit by some giant meteorite from space.[34] Not that a catastrophe is being suggested here, of course, but by some convolution of mind a "slow catastrophe", perhaps taking a million years, is proposed! Such speculation will no doubt continue to fill the pages of professional journals in the future as they have in the past; Arctic spillover as proposed by Gartner and McGuirk (1979), is another example.

According to the geologic column, man did not enter the primeval scene until a million years ago—quite recent in geological terms—and with a gap of at least seventy million years between the extinction of the dinosaur and the emergence of man. Evidence that suggests that man and dinosaur were contemporaneous would tend to upset the concept of the geologic column, especially since it is so precariously balanced on a series of assumptions. In the limestone bed of the Paluxy River near the little town of Glen Rose, Texas, there are some magnificent dinosaur foot tracks. Running parallel to and between are what appear to be human foot tracks—five toes, ball and heel, spaced apart—left foot, right foot. These were described by Roland Bird of the American Museum of Natural History, New York, in 1939.[35] In 1940, the American museums removed large sections of the dinosaur tracks from the river bank, which have since been on display at the Smithsonian and other museums, but no mention is ever made of the human-like tracks, which were carefully excluded. In the May 1954 issue of *National Geographic* magazine, Bird had a full-length article on the dinosaur tracks at the Paluxy River, but, again, no mention was made of the human-like tracks.[36] Some have claimed that these tracks were carved by the local inhabitants, which is possible, since good money was being paid for curios. However, in 1969 a documentary film was produced in which fresh tracks were exposed by damming the river. With earth-moving equipment, part of the limestone bank was removed to follow existing tracks. Good quality prints were exposed and a number of geologists invited for their opinion. Their recorded reactions were interesting, but in the end, they defended the theory and rejected the evidence. True science is supposed to apply inductive reasoning; if the evidence does not fit the theory, the evidence is verified, and, if found to be valid, the theory is then questioned.

Recently, more human-like tracks have been found in the limestone strata of the Paluxy River, together with dinosaur tracks.[37] Again scientists were invited to inspect these fossil impressions. The opinion was that the impressions were made by the dinosaur's "elbow", and it was asserted that the toes were "added" recently by being carved in the rock. The impressions are real enough, while the carving, or at least scratch marks, may well be likely. It might be asked, however, who would go to this much trouble? It can be appreciated that for those with a vested interest in the orthodox geological view to add scratch marks to existing toe impressions with the intention of discrediting genuine evidence is far easier and the motive more compelling than it would be for those with an interest in an alternate view actually to carve the toe impressions and risk all credibility. Many more human-like tracks

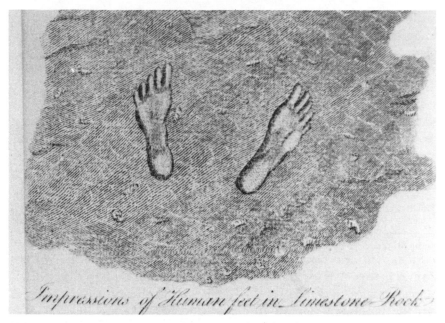

Impressions of Human feet in Limestone Rock

This engraving showing human feet impressions in Limestone rock near St. Louis, Missouri, was published with a descriptive text by Henry Schoolcraft in *The American Journal of Science* for 1822. Apart from the questions the picture invites, it is notable that it was reported at all in a professional journal of that date. Reports of similar findings would not be accepted by any reputable journal today. (Science and Medicine Library, University of Toronto)

have been discovered all over the United States (Schoolcraft 1822) and Ingalls (1940) has pointed out that they cannot all have been carvings.[38]

The evidence at Glen Rose, which would challenge Lyell's nineteenth century geology, needs to be seen firsthand since it is unfortunately ephemeral in the sense that it is being dissolved by acid rain, is difficult to record on film, and is in constant danger of vandalism.

An Alternative View

A quarter of a century ago Velikovsky (1955) produced a massive indictment against Lyell's uniformitarian doctrine of geology with evidence from all over the earth of past catastrophes of a worldwide nature. DeGrazia (1966) has exposed and censured the intemporate attacks made on Velikovsky by the natural scientists, and it is evident that the published facts posed a threat to the established belief system. Not insignificantly, many were those with vested interests in the textbook market. We do not necessarily have to accept Dr. Velikovsky's interpretation of the evidence—in fact, some of his interpretations have since been disproven—but it is surely not in the spirit of true science to sweep the evidence under the carpet just because it does not support the nineteenth century ideas of Lyell. Yet, it is just these geological princi- ples of Lyell, based on the greatly expanded time frame for the early history of the earth, that form the foundation for Darwin's theory and its subsequent variations.

In Chapter Twelve evidence for a young earth is presented and, if accepted, completely refutes the expanded time frame, while, of course, evolution of any kind under these conditions would be impossible. However, the outcome of contracting the time by almost a million times in order to fit the young-earth evidence leaves little alternative but to adopt the biblical model of the single, worldwide Flood. For instance, the marine fossils on mountain tops still have to be accounted for.

Trying to reconcile the Genesis account of the Flood with the actual fossil record and doing so without appeal to miracle is far from a simple matter. For example, the account requires a rapid regrowth of plants, grasses, and trees on salt-laden sediment (not soil) in order to provide habitation for all the creatures after leaving the ark. The account makes no claim for a miraculous re-creation, but to say that this is what happened can with some justification be called a "cop- out". Yet, ironically, many who would argue cop-out are quite pre- pared to accept the Virgin birth and the Resurrection as bona fide, one-shot miraculous events.

The early nineteenth century geologists, such as William Buckland, went out with the intention of finding geological evidence to support the Genesis account. These men were neither fools nor knaves, yet they came away from all they saw converted to the idea of long ages; some had a partial conversion to the doctrine of evolution, while others eventually went so far as to deny supernaturalism altogether. Since that time there have been small armies of geologists accumulating facts for more than a century with an evolutionary view of the earth's early history. One is then faced with the problem of reinterpreting all this data in terms of a single flood which, according to the record, took place over a twelve month period and occurred only five or six thousand years ago. Obviously, the task of reinterpretation is enormous, and small armies of geologists open-minded enough to perform such a task are not available. Nevertheless, some attempts have been made in the light of much knowledge that has become available since the nineteenth cen- tury, and some alternative views, although very tentative, are presented below with the purpose of giving some balance to this chapter.

The biblical description of the Flood states that it began with an unprecedented rainfall for forty days and that the sea level then rose continuously for five months until every mountain was entirely covered with water. Many of the mountains that are familiar to us today have evidently been uplifted since the Flood; the water level need not have risen 30,000 feet to cover Mount Everest—possibly only a few thousand feet were necessary. Within the general turmoil, volcanoes would have been very active, spewing out vast quantities of ash, which would become underwater a sort of cement-like slurry. Superimposed on all the general turmoil of the Flood would be the effect of the moon's gravitational pull on the worldwide ocean. At the present time the moon pulls up a "bulge" of water, and as the earth rotates beneath it, this bulge is seen as the tide coming in; however, the waters today never go beyond their prescribed limits. In the Genesis Flood, the bulge remained and was not dissipated at the shorelines so that the earth, continuing to spin beneath it, would cause a buildup of tremendous currents. The velocity of the water traveling over the submerged earth could have been hundreds of miles per hour directly beneath the bulge but taper off to nearly zero towards the poles of the earth's axis. The process would produce great quantities of sediment and lead to a complex but, nevertheless, organized imposition of forces upon the deposition rates of sediment and suspended matter.

Whitcomb and Morris (1961) propose two possible mechanisms: The first suggests that the Flood buried the living creatures in their habitat, thus we would expect to find oysters at the bottom of the column, fish above this, then reptiles on the low-lying land and finally man near the top as he sought the high ground (Morris 1961, 273). This explanation has its problems, however, and only explains the first appearance of life forms. The second mechanism seems more likely and is based upon hydraulic sorting. In rapidly moving water, suspended solid particiles tend to settle slowly; the most dense, such as clams and trilobites, would settle first and finish in the lowest stratum, whereas birds and hairy ungulates would remain suspended longer and finish near the top of the stratum. In 1982 Morton proposed the ingenious reproduction-repopulation model.

In Morton's model the Genesis Flood was a catastrophe of such tremendous magnitude that it obliterated virtually all evidence of life and human artifacts prior to this event. Moreover, the erosion was so great that in most places the continental surfaces were eroded down to crystalline bedrock, and enormous volumes of suspended sediment were produced. The only life to survive was that in the ark and some marine life in the relatively quiet waters around the earth's poles. The biblical account says the waters returned to ocean basins; these had presumably been formed by the shifting of the land masses. Twelve months after entering the ark, the occupants emerged onto dry land, and the earth was repopulated by these survivors. However, the account then focuses on the personalities of the descendants and says nothing specific about subsequent land movements, mountain building, and catastrophic local floods.

The reproductive-repopulation model appeals to these local floods to provide most of the fossil record in today's geologic column. It is proposed that marine life migrated from near the poles, while animal and vegetable life fanned out from Mount Ararat to repopulate the earth, which may not necessarily have had the familiar continental features that we know today. Morton proposed that the rate of migration of a given species depended on its rate of reproduction. It turns out that, in general, small creatures reproduce at a much greater rate than larger creatures, while the marine invertebrates have the most prolific reproduction rates of all. Oysters, for example, which produce more than 100 million eggs per spawning, would migrate from their ocean source most quickly. The migration of rapidly reproducing creatures in the sea, as on the land, would be accelerated in the early stages, since they would migrate to areas ahead of slower-breeding predators, and their survival rates would be higher. These small sea creatures would then be the first to repopulate the earth and, in local marine catastrophes such as undersea volcanoes, be the first to appear at the bottom of the geologic column. However, they would also appear in later periods as local inundations of land by the sea occurred. Amphibians are the next prolific reproducers, and frogs, for example, produce about two thousand eggs per year, while salamanders produce only forty eggs per year. Interestingly, frogs first appear in the Triassic period, while salamanders first appear in the Jurassic, which is slightly later in the geologic column and confirms what might be expected from their respective reproduction rates. Reptiles produce fewer offspring than amphibians, and the numbers range from ten to two hundred, while mammals are the slowest reproducers of all with an average of five to twenty offspring per year; man averages less than one per year and so would be expected to be rare and found mostly at the top of the geologic column.

The reproduction-repopulation model explains the geologic column as it is found today in terms of first appearance, subsequent reappearance, and even total extinction. It also explains why the small creatures (invertebrates) are found at the bottom and the general tendency for life forms to become larger as the column is ascended. The interpretation is that this is a function of reproduction rates and migration over a few centuries rather than evolution of one species into another over millions of years. It also provides an answer to the philosophical problem that bothered Darwin concerning the apparent wastefulness of nature, examples of which filled the whole of chapter three of his *Origin*.

Morton's explanation would argue that it was precisely these seemingly wasteful rates of reproduction that were necessary to repopulate the earth and which have subsequently provided the fossil evidence that has been misinterpreted as evidence for evolution. However, the Morton model should be regarded as tentative. It is quite possible that elements of both the Whitcombe and Morris models and the Morton model were in operation during the Genesis Flood, but as yet, there is no completely satisfactory working model.

Lyell's Geology Has Its Problems

Very seldom are the unsolved problems of conventional geology brought to the public attention, but in 1973 Derek Ager, a well-respected professor at University College of Swansea, published a small compendium of these problems, intended to stimulate fellow geologists into finding solutions.[39] The overriding constraint, however, was that the canon of faith in the millions of years demanded by the theory of evolution should not be violated. The result has been that the problems remain unsolved! However, even without this constraint, many of these problems actually become evidence for the universal Flood. One example given by Ager and known as the "persistence of facies", will be considered (Ager 1973, 1-14). Facies are described as sedimentary rocks having similar characteristics, and, when found on a worldwide scale, are referred to in orthodox geology as "persistence of facies". Ager describes the unusual white chalk deposits containing black flint stones like currants in a pudding and which also contain the small identifying marine fossils *Micraster* and *Echinocorys*. This very specific kind of sedimentary rock is found to extend in a band from western Australia to Texas, Arkansas, Alabama, and Mississippi, then to northern Ireland through England to become the famous white cliffs of Dover, to northern France, Denmark, northern Germany, southern Scandinavia, to Poland, Bulgaria, and eventually Georgia in the Soviet Union, and the south coast of the Black Sea. This phenomenon, which, Ager points out, occurs with several other types of rock formation, has never been adequately explained by Lyell's geology in which each rock formation is believed to have been deposited separately in time and space. However, the "persistence of facies" is exactly the kind of evidence that would be expected from a single universal flood having a complex but organized imposition of forces on the deposition of sediment and suspended matter.

Orthodox geology is more and more beginning to acknowledge that there have been local catastrophes in the past, and the positions of orthodoxy and those who hold to the literal biblical view with subsequent floods may in time begin to coalesce (Cowen and Lipps 1975).[40] Certainly the flood model suggested can better explain the fossils that are occasionally found in drill cores and recognized as being "out of order"; it must be remembered, however, that they are only out of order so far as the evolutionary interpretation is concerned. The alternative model can also account for human artifacts reported from time to time in the lower strata of the geologic column and that become surrounded by controversy if they are reported at all. The fossils out of order on a massive scale, such as those that identify the entire top of the Matterhorn or the fossil trees found standing upright traversing "several million years" of strata, can all be better explained in terms of successive catastrophes over a few centuries (Lyell 1845, 2:155).[41] There are many other geological anomalies of this type, which may be resolved more simply by the universal flood model, which is not based on circular arguments or a chain of assumptions, and it is suggested that science should be free to explore this or any other model. After all, it was precisely the same lack of freedom to explore under Cuvier that retarded scientific progress in the French republic for more than half a century.

Polystrate fossil tree found at Kingston, Ontario. The trunk passes vertically through multiple layers of limestone, suggesting that these layers were deposited rapidly. Similar polystrate fossil trees occur at Joggins, Nova Scotia, and were seen by Charles Lyell. (Author)

5

Charles Darwin, M.A.

Tell me what company thou keepest, and I'll tell
thee what thou art.
MIGUEL DE CERVANTES
(Don Quixote)

A t the time of writing this chapter, *Bowker's Subject Guide to Books in Print for 1983-84* (Bowker 1983) listed more than seventy titles related in one way or another to the biography of Charles Darwin. Many of these titles were reprints of books published earlier in this century and a surprising number from the previous century. It might be wondered, first, Why reprint books first published a century ago? and second, What new thing could possibly be said about the man at this time? The answer to both questions is believed to be the same answer that would be given to the question, Why produce yet another commentary on the Bible? Basically, because people are interested. Many of the biographies, especially the more popular shorter versions, are little less than eulogies to the great scientist, and it has been only recently that some of the more "human" aspects of Darwin's life have come to the surface; the conspiracy to secure priority over Wallace has already been mentioned. Part of the reason for these latter-day revelations is the fact that a vast quantity of Darwin's correspondence still remains unpublished at the Cambridge University library. A further reason is the fact that Darwin's autobiography, written in 1876, and the published Darwin correspondence, was edited by his son, Francis, at the insistence of his widowed mother, Emma Darwin. It was not until 1958, when the unexpurgated edition of the autobiography was published by Darwin's grand-daughter, Lady Barlow, that it became evident that Francis Darwin had expunged some six thousand words that were claimed might embarrass the Darwin name.[1] In addition, there had always been a critical gap in Darwin's otherwise meticulously kept correspondence for the vital years 1856-59 but in 1961 notebooks relating to this correspondence were discovered among the papers of Sir Charles Lyell (Brackman 1980, 32).[2] Both the completed autobiography and the missing correspondence reveal Darwin to be less of a saint than his biographers had previously been led to believe.

Finally, there is a tendency on the part of many biographers to dismiss quickly the kind of Christian upbringing Darwin had as a child and youth and the subsequent influence of his wife's beliefs. Prior to Darwin's birth and throughout his formative years, England was experiencing an evangelical revival. Very few were not, in one way or another, exposed to this influence. It is reasonable to suppose that the young Darwin was included in or at least aware of this movement. There was, however, an opposing influence close to his own family that would certainly have discouraged any association or inquiry into evangelical Christianity. That influence was the Unitarian Church.

The Unitarian Church

From the beginning of Christendom there have always been those individuals within it who have found it not only difficult to believe certain parts of the faith but who have actively and openly spoken out against it. Arius, in the third century A.D., could not accept the idea of three Gods within one, that is, the Trinity, and in those early days he and his followers were branded as heretics. In the Middle Ages those who expressed such disbelief were burned at the stake, but later within the Protestant Lutheran church, disbelief of this kind led to exile. England and the Americas were the recipients of some of these exiles, principally from Hungary and Poland, and from the sixteenth century their ideas began to spread among the liberal members of the established Protestant churches.

This disbelief eventually multiplied but always centered on certain crucial areas involving the supernatural: denial of the Trinity, the Virgin birth of Christ, the Resurrection, Hell and eternal punishment; all the purely miraculous events were rationalized in one way or another. These are the views of the Unitarian Church today. With all this denial it may be wondered what they regard as their purpose in meeting; inquiry shows that their principal concerns are humanitarian and social issues.

John Biddle (1615-62) is regarded as the founder of English unitarianism, and it remained confined to individuals at first, among whom are claimed poet John Milton, philosopher John Locke, and scientist Isaac Newton. In the rationalistic atmosphere of the eighteenth century, many were converted through active Unitarian missionary efforts and teachings by men of such intellectual caliber as the founder of modern chemistry, Joseph Priestley, in England, and Ralph Waldo Emerson, in America. The first Unitarian church building was opened in London by a liberal defector from the Anglican Church in 1773. King's Chapel in Boston was the first Unitarian church opened in America about a decade later. Soon after this, however, the famous divinity school of Harvard University, founded in 1816, became the center of Unitarian thought. Although there were divisions within the Unitarian church caused by the level of disbelief the organization would sanction among individuals, it has since coalesced under the name of the Unitarian-Universalist Church and is a quietly influential group behind today's humanist activities; it has no connection with the Unity School of Christianity or the Unification Church of Sun Myung Moon, although all of these organizations depart so far from the orthodox and entire biblical teaching that they can in no way be considered Christian.

The Creation account and the great Flood in the book of Genesis are supernatural events. Individuals whose minds found it difficult to accept the New Testament miracles, which were supernatural events on a local scale, warmly welcomed evolutionary ideas, which seemed to rationalize away the supernatural on the grand scale. As we shall see, the Unitarian Church's teachings played a small, though, it is believed, vital part in influencing the mind of Charles Darwin, and its teachings continue to do so today within orthodox churches, where it is found that many liberal intellectuals are Unitarian in belief even though they may stand in orthodox church pews and pulpits.

Darwin's Youth
Charles Robert Darwin was born in 1809, the second youngest of six children, four of whom were girls. The Darwin family home was in Shrewsbury, a market town on the English side of the Welsh border.

The source of family income, which was not inconsiderable, derived from the ills of the local populace since the father, Dr. Robert Darwin, had one of the most successful medical practices in provincial England. Dr. Darwin had married the daughter of the Unitarian Josiah Wedgwood, but she died when Charles was five, and until he was eight he was educated at home by his elder sister, Caroline. From his eighth to ninth years, he attended his first day school, kept by a Unitarian minister, and then went to Dr. Butler's famous Shrewsbury grammar school for the next seven years, where virtually the entire curriculum was given over to Latin and Greek. Darwin later said of this purely Dickensian part of his education: "Nothing could have been worse for the development of my mind than Dr. Butler's school.... The school as

Josiah Wedgwood, 1730-95. Staunch Unitarian and founder-owner of the famous pottery company. Wedgwood had a posthumous but significant influence on Charles Darwin's religious views. (After the painting by George Stubbs; Metropolitan Toronto Reference Library Board)

a means of education to me was simply a blank" (Barlow 1958, 27). Mercifully, he was removed from the school at sixteen, and since his interests appeared to lean towards science rather than the arts, he was sent to join his elder brother, Erasmus, at Edinburgh University to study medicine.

Charles was brought up among physicians so this was not an unexpected venture. His paternal grandfather, Erasmus, had been a famous physician. A paternal uncle, also named Charles Darwin, and, of course, father Robert, and eventually an older brother Erasmus were all physicians, so that things medical were not foreign to Charles Darwin in his developing years. In fact, before going to Edinburgh he had often helped his father compound the medicines, and he had learned how to follow and observe symptoms. Ironically, although he never became a physician, he was to be concerned with these techniques for the greater part of his life (Colp 1977, 3-8).

After two years at medical school and having been present at two gruesome operations—there were no anesthetics in those days—Charles found that he didn't have the stomach for medicine as a vocation. Many people today can identify with Charles's stomach problem, those for whom upsetting thoughts or sights go straight to the bowels. Darwin expressed it in a letter to his sister Caroline when he said: "The noodle (his head) and the stomach are antagonistic powers" (Colp 1977, 15). Headaches, gastric upsets, cardiac palpitations, vomiting, and diarrhea eventually became a way of life for the poor man, and one of his life's preoccupations was to find a remedy, which eventually only came with old age. However, as a young man fond of fun and the outdoor life, health problems were not yet to be a part of his daily regimen.

Dr. Darwin was sympathetic to his son's reaction to the seamier side of medicine and sent him to Christ's College, Cambridge, to spend three years as a pre-divinity student. The change from medicine to theology was not entirely without rationale on the part of Robert Darwin, even though his son's aptitude for language was abysmal—he managed to forget most of the seven years of Greek he had learned at Dr. Butler's school in his two years at Edinburgh and had to be specially tutored for entrance to Cambridge, beginning again with the Greek alphabet. Dr. Darwin's opinion of his son's potential as a creditable heir to the family name was not high. In this early part of Victorian society, becoming a member of the clergy when all else failed was seen by many fathers as a convenient route for otherwise wayward sons and was, above all, to be part of a respectable profession. There was a further reason in the back of the good doctor's mind: as a young man he had joined the Freemasons, and he could see the possibilities for advancement into a secure and comfortable position within the church for his son by suitable words at the right time in the appropriate episcopal ear (Barlow 1958, 30).[3]

Charles passed his B.A. examination in 1831. At the age of twenty-two he was all set, at least on paper if not entirely in spirit, to become Rev. Charles Darwin in some Anglican country church—he had specified a country church so that he could still enjoy some hunting and shooting. Had he acquired either the title Doctor or Reverend, there is little doubt that the world would never have heard of Charles Darwin. But as fate would have it, circumstances conspired in a most unexpected way and he found himself on board the HMS Beagle as official scientist, then called naturalist, to set sail on a voyage of exploration around the world that would last five years; the date of sailing was December 1831. This momentous voyage would change Darwin's way of thinking and eventually that of most of mankind. It is for this reason that so much has been written on the subject.

Darwin and the Bible

Some of the more popular biographers, such as William Irving, like to say that Darwin began his famous voyage as a Bible-believer and finished up five years later convinced of evolution (Irving 1955, 51); however, Himmelfarb more diligently shows that this impression is not true, pointing out that Darwin's thoughts on evolution did not begin until July 1837, nine months after his return (Himmelfarb 1968, 65, 147). As we shall see later from what is known of Darwin's early life it is not difficult to discern that the statement about being a Bible-believer is very much an open question; it is evident that he never understood the Bible in the first place and was little wiser after three years at Cambridge.

Charles Darwin never actually knew his paternal grandfather, Erasmus Darwin, as he died seven years before Charles was born. However, the liberal and evolutionary ideas of Erasmus undoubtedly influenced the young Darwin. Erasmus was a physician, something of a poet, an instrument of the Industrial Revolution, and author of a massive two-volume work *Zoönomia* (1794-96); this work contained within it the essence of the theory that his grandson would announce to the world half a century later.[4] Charles always had a great respect for his grandfather and in spite of the latter's evident racey lifestyle—he acknowledged two illegitimate daughters—he had a German biography translated, thus perpetuating the memory of his grandfather among English readers (Krause 1879, 61).[5]

Robert Darwin, Charles's father, was even less orthodox in his faith than his grandfather Erasmus. Although very secretive about his disbelief, he nevertheless felt it necessary to have his children brought up in an orthodox Anglican fashion to allay public suspicion of his own irreligious nature (Barlow 1958, 22).[6] Robert's disbelief extended to the borders of atheism, which may be inferred from his statement that he had only known three women who were genuinely enlightened, one of whom was his sister-in-law, Kitty Wedgwood, and of her he was convinced that "so clear-sighted a woman could not be a [Bible] believer" (Litchfield 1915, 1:164).[7] Doctor Darwin's authority in the Darwin family was patriarchal, even awesome, at six feet two inches and 328 pounds; when he was present, every conversation had to be exactly pleasing to the master's ear; under these conditions, it is extremely unlikely that there would have been any "Bible-talk" in the Darwin home.

The period in life that a young man may spend away at university is very crucial and often serves to establish what are only half-formed ideas learned earlier in the home. Darwin's first real foray into the alien world beyond his Shrewsbury home began when his father sent him to join his elder brother, Erasmus, at the medical school of Edinburgh University. At that time the universities of Oxford and Cambridge were dominated by theological interests, so that even the earth sciences were circumscribed by Archbishop Ussher's dating of Creation in 4004 B.C. Edinburgh, on the other hand, was open to all faiths, and with what inevitably results, professed belief in none. The young Darwin met several geologists, zoologists, and botanists of his own age whose discussions were keenly Lamarckian. It was during this period that he found time to read his grandfather's then widely read *Zoönomia*.

This, then, was the intellectual atmosphere in which Darwin found himself during two of his most formative years. Interestingly, grandfather Erasmus, Unitarian Joseph Priestly, and geologist James Hutton had all attended the same university in their youth and, it can be concluded from their writings, had abandoned any belief they had ever had in the orthodox Christian faith.

Finally, it might be thought that Darwin, having taken a B.A. at Cambridge and now ready as a young clergyman-to-be, would surely have some knowledge of the Bible. In fact, there is no record that he ever cracked a Bible open during his days as a pre-divinity student nor was there any requirement to do so.[8] A B.A. consisted of three subjects: classics, mathematics, and theology. For theology there were two required works to be studied, Paley's *Evidences of Christianity* and Paley's *Moral and Political Philosophy*. Darwin did rather poorly in classics and worse in mathematics, even with a private tutor, but he enjoyed Paley so much that he read another of Paley's works, *Natural Theology*, even though it was not required reading.

Paley's influence was deep and lasted him throughout his life,[9] while from the point of view of his attitude towards the Bible, Paley no doubt contributed to the loss of even the little faith he had. Paley was a liberal for his day and had published an anonymous work decrying the need as a lecturer in divinity at Cambridge to subscribe to the thirty-nine articles of faith (Clarke 1974, 20).[10] Before going to Cambridge Darwin had studied these articles to acquaint himself with the Anglican doc-

William Paley, 1743-1805. As a senior Anglican clergyman and writer, Paley was influential. An early liberal, Paley's God was Aristotle's God—a master designer but now remote from his creation. (Painting by George Romney, 1789; National Portrait Gallery, London)

trine, which he had happily accepted, concluding that he did not "in the least doubt the strict and literal truth of every word in the bible" (Barlow 1958, 57). Writing his autobiography half a century later, he looked back on this occasion and remarked, "It never struck me how illogical it was to say that I believed in what I could not understand and what is in fact unintelligible" (Barlow 1958, 57).

A further and final indication of the total absence of his understanding of even the basic elements of salvation comes from a passage that was deleted from his autobiography, written when he was nearly seventy. He cites the "damnable doctrine" that would condemn all unbelievers to everlasting punishment, protesting that "this would include my father, brother and almost all my best friends" (Barlow 1958, 87). This statement was made after having been married to a Unitarian for more than thirty years, and it is fairly certain that at this point in his life even the unorthodox denial of hell had been pressed upon his mind.

Such were the wells of unbelief from which he slaked his youthful thirst for truth. As a university graduate of twenty-two about to embark on the greatest adventure of his life, he had by this time imbibed of unbelief deeply, yet it seems Providence was to offer him an opportunity to make a free-will choice: rationalism or Scripture as pathways to the truth.

The Beagle Voyage

It seems that in bringing together the assortment of seventy-four souls that would be locked together on the Beagle for the five-year voyage, providence had arranged for Darwin's mind to be encouraged by hearing the Bible read on a regular basis; he may even have read it for himself, since he had a copy among the books he had selected to accompany him on the journey around the world. Captain Robert FitzRoy was a deeply religious man who believed every word in the Bible and, with a passionate fundamentalism, personally conducted each Sunday service on board the Beagle throughout the entire five years. Attendance was mandatory. Although the official object of the voyage was to map and explore the coast lines, FitzRoy had his private motives, one of which was to discover minerals of commercial value, and the other, perhaps less clearly defined, to substantiate the book of Genesis.

As the naturalist, these were Darwin's assigned tasks. It is reported he agreed with enthusiasm, although there is good reason to believe that he probably had little real knowledge of theology, on the one hand, or geology, on the other. In any event, Darwin, over the next five years, apparently did become a convinced believer in the Genesis account and on one occasion was quite shocked when a member of the crew was heard to flatly deny the Flood of Noah. He even got involved in some of FitzRoy's evangelistic schemes to Christianize the natives of Tahiti and other heathen ports of call and was a supporter of a missionary society until his dying day.

Charles Darwin's real love had always been the study of nature, and it seems he had been presented with an opportunity such as few men have ever had before and which no man will ever have again, to study the unspoiled natural world and have about him men—there was also a missionary on board—who believed the Creation account and were enthusiastic to find factual evidence for its support.

Darwin was traveling at the leisurely pace of the sailing ship, feeling every nuance of the elements and going, not as a common traveler, but with the express purpose of exploring the unexplored world of the nineteenth century. He could wonder at the brilliance and majesty of a tropic starlit night above or marvel at the microscopic life forms teeming in the ocean waters below. He had taken a microscope and could study the plankton and radiolaria as easily as throwing a bucket on a rope over the ship's side. He wandered through the virgin rain forest, explored unusual rock formations, climbed volcanoes, studied strange birds and beasts, and observed the customs of peoples unaffected by Western culture. And throughout it all he saw the immense diversity of life, every living thing perfectly fitted to its habitat. Were all these inanimate and animate things the work of the Creator's hands— the master Designer that Paley spoke of—or was there some other explanation? This question undoubtedly passed through his mind, yet at that time there was really no alternative, there was no completely worked out theory of evolution that one could adopt should the supernatural creation account be found too difficult to accept.

There were some negative aspects to the five-year voyage: it hardly had the comforts of a luxury cruise, and it actually circumnavigated the earth's lower hemisphere almost one-and-a-half times. Although Fitz-Roy was only twenty-six, four years older than Darwin, he was an exceptionally competent captain. He did, however, have some peculiarities that must have made life in the close quarters of the little ship somewhat strained at times. FitzRoy was, as we would say today, in a condition of being permanently "uptight"; he was a man of almost manic-depressive moods and demanded absolute obedience from all. In many ways he was a hard man after the breed of Captain Bligh, although in the days of the sailing ship, some of this attitude was undoubtedly necessary. Darwin was a likeable and easygoing individual and, even though he shared a cabin with FitzRoy, managed to survive his moods and tempers. The thought may have occurred to Darwin that if there was any relationship between the captain and his faith then the latter should be approached as the former—rather cautiously. As it was, poor FitzRoy did have a mental problem; years later, shortly after Darwin had published his *Origin*, he committed suicide.

Apart from seasickness, which he endured for the entire five years along with FitzRoy's moods, it might be wondered what it was that eventually turned Darwin's mind around from belief to disbelief in the Creation account. The books he had taken with him on the voyage consisted of a few to study French, Spanish, mathematics, and the classics, a copy of Milton's *Paradise Lost*, Humboldt's *Personal Narrative*, a Bible, and the first volume of Charles Lyell's *Principles of Geology*, which had left the publishers just a few months before the Beagle set sail; the second volume was sent on and reached him in Montevideo. Since one of his main tasks was to study the geology of the places visited and since he had had no formal training in the subject, it is fairly reasonable to assume that Darwin spent considerable time reading Lyell's books. Lyell, it will be recalled, proposed that the natural processes we see going on today have been slowly and quietly working away for millions of years and are responsible for all the earth's geological features. Lyell's books probably stood on the cabin's little bookshelf side by side with the very book they denied. The Bible said that there had been a cataclysmic judgment by water—a flood destroying everything some time in the past near the beginning of man's recorded history. Rather than millions, it happened only a few thousand years ago. As they sailed, day after day, Darwin saw the South American coastline where the rocky continent rose vertically two or three hundred feet above the surface of the ocean and remained at this level for hundreds of miles. He also saw how the wave action steadily eroded the rock-strata. Was all this the result of a great flood a few thousand years ago or has this been here for millions of years with the continent rising and falling below the water to build a new sedimentary layer on each occasion? When on land, he saw the great diversity of life each day: new species of insects, new kinds of animals and birds, thousands of different trees and flowers, and in his mind's eye the ark of Noah must have become impossibly crowded. Yet, for all we know, he said little or nothing about these thoughts but returned from the voyage outwardly a believer in Genesis but inwardly a secret doubter. He had departed a boy and returned a man, matured by the experience and with much of that experience recorded in notebooks that would serve him for the remainder of his life.

He spent the two years following his return to England in 1836 writing the narrative of the Beagle's voyage in his *Journal and Remarks* (1839). He also wrote papers for the Geological Society during this period, and there is evidence from his notes that it was during the organization of his thoughts for these written works that disbelief took firmer hold in his mind. The steps taken in this mental process are not difficult to retrace. They are well-worn steps taken by others before him and a great many since; they begin, typically, with doubt in the supernatural. Darwin himself confirmed this years later when speaking of the Gospels; he thought that the miracles were not credible to any "sane man" and that the fixed laws could explain everything (Barlow 1958, 86). There are many today who hold these same views privately, if not openly.

The Genesis Flood was a supernatural event, and with Lyell's *Principles of Geology* before him, Darwin had the choice to interpret what he saw as the result of natural forces over a long period of time or as the result of supernatural forces acting over a short period of time, and comparatively recently. Reporting what he saw was a simple matter. Providing a rational explanation, however, required a decision, and he chose to reject the supernatural account and adopt Lyell's naturalistic explanation. Having rationalized what orthodox science of the day held to be evidence of the Flood, the next step was to find a naturalistic explanation for another key belief: what was claimed to be the divine creation of each species.

Darwin was an avid reader, and, as Eiseley (1959) has pointed out, during this period of meditation on the species problem, he read Patrick Matthew's *Naval Timber and Arboriculture*. A title unlikely to quicken the pulse, yet Darwin evidently found the appendix of sufficient interest to lift the author's expression "this natural process of selection", change it slightly to "natural means of selection", and incorporate it in his first essay written in 1842. Matthew had published his work in 1831, before Darwin set sail on the Beagle. In 1844 Darwin wrote a second essay and contracted the expression further to "natural selection".

Darwin's extensive reading had also included Edward Blyth's work, published in 1835 and 1837, on the species question, and, again, Eiseley remarks on the similarities of ideas in the essays with those of Blyth.[11] Darwin acknowledged neither Matthew nor Blyth in his *Origin*, nor in his essays, which were not published until 1909, by which time Darwin's claim to priority was well-established. Eiseley was not alone in pointing out that the idea of natural selection did not originate with Darwin and questioned the enormous body of myth that has obscured the truth underlying the origin of a theory to which history has bestowed the dubious credit on Charles Darwin.

During this period of reading other men's ideas about species, Darwin began to keep his "secret" notebooks on the transmutation of species. The date he started these notebooks is known precisely, July 1837, which coincides nicely with the publication of Blyth's articles in the then popular *Magazine of Natural History*. Darwin knew that the idea of transmutation, that is, the imagined change of, for example, a reptile into a bird over a great many generations, ran counter to every other scientist of that day. He was no doubt also aware that what he was thinking was shocking and, in a sense, blasphemous by virtue of his removal of God the Creator further and further away from his Creation. For the next several years, Darwin confided all his thoughts on the subject of "transmutation" to his notebooks, and it wasn't until 1844 that he confessed to his friend Dr. Hooker that "at last gleams of light have come, and I am almost convinced (quite contrary to the opinion I started with) that species are not (it is like confessing a murder) immutable" (F. Darwin and Seward 1903, 1:41). Many commentators have pointed out that the "murder" he spoke of was in effect the murder of God—Darwin's theory would eventually attempt to remove entirely the idea of God the Creator from man's mind, just as if he had been murdered.

The Darwin Family

At the time the disbelief was becoming established in his mind, Darwin married Emma Wedgwood, his maternal father's youngest grand daughter. The Darwin family was intimately associated with the Wedgwood family, the same family of Wedgwood pottery fame today. Old Josiah Wedgwood was a Unitarian and friend of Darwin's grandfather Erasmus, while the chemist Dr. Joseph Priestley (a Unitarian of missionary zeal) was included in this circle of friends. Josiah's oldest daughter, Susannah, had married Robert, the son of Erasmus, and was thus Charles Darwin's mother. Thus, Charles married his mother's niece. On the eve of the marriage Darwin's father had counseled him to conceal from his future wife his religious doubts and beliefs, since he had found by experience that a husband seldom managed to convert his wife to skepticism (Barlow 1958, 95). Darwin dutifully kept this advice and extended it in principle to his writings where he later admitted, "Many years ago I was strongly advised by a friend [it was Lyell] never to introduce anything about religion in my works, if I wished to advance science in England" (Himmelfarb 1968, 383). As we have seen, the principle was even carried beyond his mortal life for references to his irreligion were posthumously removed from his autobiography at the insistence of his widow.

One of the Wedgwood boys had married Charles's eldest sister Caroline, so that the Darwin family, who had no commitment to a faith, were now well married into a family with a fairly strong commitment to the Unitarian faith.

It is reasonable to ask why Darwin brought a Wedgwood girl all the way from Shrewsbury when London had more than a few likely women to offer an eligible bachelor. Times have changed, but class distinction was important to Victorian England and especially so to the Darwins and the Wedgwoods who recognized in each other all the qualities of "superior" people. More than that, however, was a principle that many writers have observed runs right throughout Darwin's work and might be described as latent Lamarckism. Lamarck, in the previous century, contended that characteristics acquired by the present generation will tend to be inherited by the next. Lamarck's thinking had been discredited in Darwin's own day, but the theme continued then, as it still does today, in the collective unconscious and appeared several times in Darwin's writings. Thus, reasoning that thoroughbred animals or plants are produced by selection, conditioned Darwin to select a mate from closely related "superior" stock. In most countries today a first-cousin marriage, such as made by the Darwins, would not be allowed by law.

Another cousin of Darwin, Francis Galton, wrote extensively on this principle and openly advocated selective breeding programs for the creation of tomorrow's elite ruling class (Galton 1869, 24).[12] We now know, of course, that inbreeding of this sort is positively dangerous because of the likelihood of expressing mutant genes, resulting in physical and mental disorders of the offspring. Highly inbred animals are known to be temperamental and prone to sickness.

Darwin's idea of inbreeding to produce superior stock can be seen to be a complete disaster in the case of his own ten children. Of the ten, one girl, Mary, died shortly after birth; another girl, Anne, died at the age of ten years; his eldest daughter, Henrietta, had a serious and prolonged breakdown at fifteen in 1859. Three of his six sons suffered such frequent illness that Darwin regarded them as semi-invalids while his last son, Charles Jr., was born mentally retarded and died in 1858, nineteen months after birth.

Darwin's Illness

Darwin began to suffer ill health soon after returning to England, and Emma became his lifelong and devoted nurse, his companion, and, of

Charles Darwin, 1809-82. Taken by
society photographers Maul and
Fox in 1854, this is the suffering
Darwin shortly before he wrote his
Origin of Species. (Metropolitan
Toronto Reference Library Board)

course, mother of his ten children. The subject of Darwin's illness has
been much discussed particularly in medical circles and more especially perhaps because he kept extensive notes on his symptoms, medi-
cations, and treatments; however, there does not appear to be concerted
agreement on the exact cause of his problem. Dr. J.H. Winslow, for
example, believes that he suffered from cumulative arsenic poisoning.
There was nothing sinister about this; it was merely thought to be the
effect of having taken Fowler's solution beginning in his teens and
continuing throughout his life—Fowler's solution contained a small
quantity of arsenic and was a popular Victorian tonic (Colp 1977, 132).
Others have speculated that it was his addiction to nicotine, which he
regularly took as snuff (powdered tobacco) and preferred to cigarettes;
he confined his smoking to part of a daily ritual in which he smoked
one cigarette while his wife read to him or played the piano. Professor
Saul Adler, on the other hand, believes that Darwin suffered from
Chagas' disease, which he had contacted in Argentina by being bitten
by "the great black bug of the Pampas", thought by Adler to be
Triatoma infestans; Chagas' disease was not known until about 1909;
Darwin's several physicians would not have been familiar with the
disease or its treatment (Colp 1977, 126). And then there are all the
psychoanalytic and psychoneurological theories based on the apparent
relationship between the mental activity of working on the theory of
evolution and his physical health—a mind-body relationship about
which there is still much to be learned.

Colp has recently produced one of the most exhaustive surveys of
Darwin's illness and includes a critical analysis of all the theories. He

concludes that psychological stresses were the most probable causes of his illness, as there were even indications of this in his youth. Most remarkable, however, is the simultaneous occurrence of the beginning of his thinking about evolution (around July 1837) and the beginning of his illness, and later, the cessation of his evolutionary thoughts and the lessening of his illness (Colp 1977, 142).

The illness was exacerbated with every psychologically disturbing event, such as the death of his father, the suicide of FitzRoy, and the severe criticism he received on the publication of the *Origin* in 1859. The stressful situations were never quite consistent; most times they seemed to lead to stomach upsets but, at other times, to heart palpitations and, less frequently to eczema; it was very probably the anxiety over the reception of the *Origin* that caused the eczema on his facial skin and prompted him to grow the famous beard at this time. In his introduction Colp points out that Darwin's illness cannot be understood without understanding two attributes of Darwin the man: his determination to win acceptance for his evolutionary theory and his anxieties over the difficulties of proving his theory and its ideological consequences (Colp 1977, xiii).

The commentaries on Darwin's illness seem to fall into two camps: On the one hand, there are those, such as Sir Gavin de Beer and Sir Peter Medawar, who have a deep commitment to evolution and who claim that Darwin's illness was purely organic, with no psychic overtones (Brackman 1980, 7). In the opposing camp, there are those who probably accept the theory of evolution but have no commitment to it; they see Darwin's illness as psychic in origin. There is as yet no

Rear view of the Darwin home in the village of Downe, southeast of London. His study is on the left and the servants' quarters on the right—clearly the residence of a wealthy man. The house has been preserved as a national shrine and still appears today as in this picture of 1887. (Metropolitan Toronto Reference Library Board)

conclusive diagnosis of his illness, but, as so often happens where there is no proof, investigators will draw conclusions from the evidence according to their presuppositions, for a hero with a psychiatric disorder is something of a suspect, but a hero with an incurable disease is a martyr.

Darwin and his wife moved to Down House in the village of Downe in Kent, just south of London, and he remained there raising his family, made more or less a recluse by his illness, which became a way of life until his dying day. He was something of a hypochondriac with all the medical treatments, but the illness did seem to serve one useful purpose: it became a convenient crutch by which he could avoid meeting people, avoid confrontation, and even terminate difficult interrogation by some who did manage to visit. His entire time was spent working on his theory, experimenting with plants, breeding pigeons, and writing letters all over the country for information that would substantiate his ideas. The work eventually developed into an obsession. It is a fact that he was tortured by obsessional thoughts: first, to find the mechanism by which evolution occurred; second, to establish the theory by proof; and third, to maintain a claim to the theory as his own.

The Origin of Species

Darwin's twenty years of work on the subject of natural selection culminated in the publication, in 1859, of the book that was to make his name both famous and infamous. However, the events leading to the book's being written and published have been reinvestigated recently by Brackman (1980), whose conclusions deserve to be reiterated at this juncture.

Darwin received Wallace's "Sarawak" paper in 1855, which came as a shock, because he realized that someone else was as close as he was himself to the answer to life's riddle. His friend and mentor, Charles Lyell, persuaded him to begin writing a book immediately on all that he had thus far discovered. Three years later, in 1858, he received a bigger shock when Wallace's "Ternate" paper arrived, giving the entire theory complete with the elusive "key", the survival-of-the-fittest as the mechanism by which selection took place and caused one species to *diverge* to another. Darwin was now persuaded by his friends, Lyell and Hooker, to stop work on the "big book" and prepare instead an abstract, a shorter version, for publication as quickly as possible. In what was described as a "delicate arrangement", Lyell and Hooker then conspired to present to the Linnean Society meeting on 1 July 1858 Darwin's 1844 sketch (which did not mention divergence), fol-

Charles Lyell, 1797-1875   *Joseph Hooker, 1817-1911*

Authors and managers of the "delicate arrangement" to launch the theory of evolution under Darwin's name and credible reputation. (Lyell: engraving by Stodart about 1860; Hooker: photograph by Wallich about 1870; Thomas Fisher Rare Book Library, University of Toronto)

lowed by Darwin's copy of his letter to Asa Gray of 5 September 1857 (which purportedly did mention divergence), then finally Wallace's "Ternate" paper of March 1858.

Asa Gray was in the United States, and Wallace was safely out of the way in the Malayan jungle; Darwin's priority was thus established by presenting the documents in a chronological but unorthodox order. The protocol of science would dictate that, as a "paper", Wallace's presentation should have been made first. Correspondence for the period just prior to the July meeting is mysteriously missing, and there seems to be no record of the actual letter received by Gray. All of Gray's replies to Darwin for this crucial period are also missing. Moreover, Darwin admitted editing his copy of the letter for the Linnean Society. All told, a great cloud of suspicion hangs over Darwin's claim of priority to the vital divergence principle. Darwin was embroiled in a disease-ravaged household at the time of the meeting and did not attend, so that he did not in fact present a preliminary joint paper with the Wallace paper and "with a fineness of character" share the priority with Wallace, as it is commonly reported. It would, in fact, be another year before Darwin made his formal disclosure in his now famous *Origin of Species* (Brackman 1980, 58; J.L. Gray 1939; Sarton 1930).[13-15]

Darwin's "abstract" actually contained 490 pages and was entitled

*On the Origin of Species by Means of Natural Selection or the Preserva-
tion of Favoured Races in the Struggle for Life,* which has been
popularly contracted to simply the *Origin.* The first edition of 1,250
copies appeared in November 1859, and the second quickly followed in
January 1860. In Darwin's lifetime, six editions were published, each
revised from the previous edition as critics pointed out deficiencies and
as new information was obtained; Darwin lived to see the last edition
translated into nine major languages, and it has since been translated
into at least twenty-four. The expression "survival-of-the-fittest" originated in the writings of Herbert Spencer, a contemporary of Darwin's,
and did not appear in the *Origin* until the fifth edition, while the word
"evolution" did not appear until the sixth edition in 1872. Darwin
never did complete his "big book" of which the *Origin* was only an
abstract (Freeman 1965; Peckham 1959).

It might be inferred from this account of multiple editions and
translations that it was a popular book, but its success was brought
about principally through notoriety rather than literary excellence. In
fact, it was rather badly written and hard to follow, while even Huxley,
writing in 1888, complained, "I have read... the *Origin* for the sixth or
seventh time, becoming confirmed in my opinion that it is one of the
most difficult books to exhaust that ever was written" (L. Huxley 1900,
2:193). The book caused a public uproar, scathing newspaper articles
appeared, and it was soundly denounced from virtually every pulpit;
nevertheless, it is notable that neither the *Origin* nor the *Descent of
Man* ever appeared on the Catholic *Index.* This is surprising since
Charles Darwin's work was more damning to Christian orthodoxy
than his grandfather's *Zoönomia.* Placed on the index in 1817, *Zoönomia* was still there when the final edition of the index was published in
1948. It is evident, then, that a radical change in policy with regard to
origins had occurred within the Vatican sometime between 1817 and
1859.

The *Origin* contained a great many examples to show how breeders
carefully selected offspring of domestic animals or plants having
desired characteristics, in order to produce in subsequent generations
an animal or plant more useful to man. This was artificial selection,
and Darwin reasoned that if this could happen by intelligent guidance
over a few generations, then it could also happen by random chance in
nature over a much greater length of time. Lyell's new geology had
provided vast spans of time that were vital to Darwin's theory but at the
same time precluded laboratory confirmation. The main thrust of the
Origin was what Darwin saw as the evidence of the mechanism, that is,
natural selection by which one species, when isolated and subjected to a

changing environment, diverged over many generations to become an entirely separate species. By extension of this principle, Darwin saw all living forms related in a great continuum from the most simple speck of life to the most complex; however, he stopped short of saying that a certain mammal, namely the ape, diverged to become man. In fact, the origin of man had been skillfully and deliberately avoided, but the theological bloodhounds could sniff out a heresy or even the makings of one just as they had almost thirty years earlier when Lyell had published his *Principles of Geology.*

The establishment of the theory of evolution was an uphill battle but one in which Darwin took no part. He was lampooned and caricatured by the popular press, hooted at and called "reprobate" by the villagers. But in this kind of persecution there was no question of his losing his position or security; financial independence had left him accountable to no man. He had shrewdly invested in stocks and multiplied his inheritance to more than a quarter of a million pounds at the time of his death, and this is the vital distinction between Darwin as a scientist with a new vision and the scientist today with an idea that runs counter to the establishment (Keith 1955, 231).[16]

Darwin's Other Books

Between continuing bouts of illness and days when he could only work for an hour or so, Darwin continued to write. During his lifetime he managed to produce a surprising number of monographs and books dealing with such subjects as coral reefs, volcanic islands, barnacles, insects, and orchids. Apart from the *Origin,* for which he is best known, there are two other works that deserve mention.

In 1871 he published *The Descent of Man, and Selection in Relation to Sex.* This was in two volumes and contained much of the data not included in the *Origin,* namely sexual selection as one of the agencies through which evolution could be explained. Observing the mating of animals, Darwin claimed that the special structures, such as the peacock's train and deer's antlers, assist in natural selection by sexual attractiveness; he also dealt with sexual selection in man. The simple conclusion of this work, which did not arouse nearly as much public controversy as might be expected, was that "man is descended from an hairy, tailed quadruped...an inhabitant of the Old World...the progenitor of the...New World monkeys" (Darwin 1871, 2:389). Why the placid acceptance of this notion? Most likely because the greater part of the energy of the religious opponents of the theory of evolution had been expended during their attacks on the *Origin.* Ironically, the *Descent* met the approval of very few natural scientists of the day, and even Lyell had only just turned to accept the logical outcome of Darwin's theory that man was included in the hierarchy of life.

The most serious claim implicit in the *Descent* had to do with man's moral and mental faculties. It was one thing to point out the physical affinities between man and ape, but quite another to extend this reasoning to man's mind. Although this flatly contradicted the scriptural statement that Adam had received his soul from the breath of God, there was no great outcry from the church on this point, at least not at the level that might be expected. The secular press did pick up the implication from the *Descent*, however, pointing out that not only were Darwin's ideas unscientific but that, should they ever gain wide acceptance, "morality would lose all elements of stable authority." The London *Times* (8 April, 1871) went on to say that Darwin was exploiting the "authority of a well-earned reputation" to advance the "disintegrating speculations of this book" and that having done so on the basis of cursory evidence and hypothetical arguments was not only unscientific but positively reckless. We today are able to look back and perhaps appreciate the prophetic nature of these newspaper comments.

If the notion of the evolution of man's mental faculties was implicit in the *Descent*, it became explicit the following year, in 1872, when Darwin published *The Expression of the Emotions in Man and Animals* in which he moved into an area that today would be considered essentially psychological. Darwin is, in fact, considered to be the "father of psychology" by the faithful (Zusne 1975, 112);[17] a moment's reflection on, for instance, Freudian psychology will show it to be strictly based on Darwinian principles. Darwin had for many years closely observed his ten children and his pets, making notes on the different ways emotions were facially expressed. Certain facial muscles, he said, are used to indicate a particular state of mind. As an evolutionary example, Darwin gave that of the snarling of a man, even though he no longer has large canine teeth with which to follow through the threat (Darwin 1965, 247-52).[18] Darwin's book thus completely rejected the concept maintained by a near contemporary, Sir Charles Bell, after whom the palsy is named, that the facial muscles of expression in man were a special divine endowment (Bell 1844, 131).[19]

Darwin's Death

Darwin died in April 1882 at the age of seventy-three, worn out with the struggle of his work in the midst of ill health for almost half a century. The clamor over his evolutionary idea had died down significantly by this time, and many in high places had been completely won over. Instead of being buried in the Anglican churchyard in the village of

The memorial statue of Charles Darwin on the day of its unveiling in the most prominent location within the British Natural History Museum. T.H. Huxley is reading the dedication. (Metropolitan Toronto Reference Library Board)

Downe, he was buried, by request of a parliamentary petition, in Westminster Abbey, where he lies today near the tomb of Sir Isaac Newton. He was soon to be followed by his evolutionary friend Sir Joseph Hooker; Sir Charles Lyell was already placed at the Abbey. (Thomas Huxley, the great champion of Darwin's ideas, did not make it to the Abbey, presumably because he had ruffled too many episcopal feathers; however, he did receive secular sanctification if not sacred.)

The British Natural History Museum had virtually deified Darwin by having a marble image of the man carved twice life-size and seated

The statue of Charles Darwin today. Located obscurely behind the main stairway, it is evidently on its way out. Ultimately science is no respecter of persons. (Author)

pensively on a huge marble throne; for many years the image took pride of place in the central hall of the museum at the head of the stairway. When chief apostle Huxley died in 1895, a similar image was produced and raised to be seated on the right hand of his master. In recent years both images have been quietly removed to a small antechamber behind the main staircase. Man's glory is, indeed, but short-lived.

Emma Darwin, 1807-96. Engraving from a photograph by M.I. Schaen of Darwin's widow aged eighty-eight. The evidence points to Emma as the anonymous author of the Lady Hope story. (Thomas Fisher Rare Book Library, University of Toronto)

There is a sequel without which even this brief story of Darwin's life would not be complete, and acknowledgment must be made to Dr. Wilbert Rusch for the details. From time to time pamphlets and tracts appear containing a little homily about a certain Lady Hope, a Christian worker who visited the partially bedridden Darwin shortly before he died. The scene is set in "one of those glorious autumn afternoons", and the account describes him as "a dying man reading his Bible" and regretful at having rejected in his youth its early chapters. The conclusion piously calls all those believing in evolution to repentance and points out that even the father of the theory recognized his error just in time to save himself from damnation.[20]

So much for the alleged testimony of Lady Hope, which is usually dressed in the flowery language of the nineteenth century; the question is, Is there any truth to it? The story can be traced back to at least 1915, and there were probably earlier versions, but one of the obvious difficulties is that of the dying man on the glorious autumn afternoon— Darwin died in the spring! Even supposing the alleged visit had taken place in the autumn of the previous year, this leaves an interval of at least six months prior to his death in April. Fortunately, Darwin's letters for this critical period of time are available and have been since 1903 when they were first published. Taking just one example, an excerpt from a letter written less than two months before he died (28 February 1882), we find the following statement written by Darwin in the context of spontaneous generation of organic life from nonlife: "If it is ever found that life can originate on this world, the vital phenomena will come under some general law of nature. *Whether the existence of a conscious God can be proven from the existence of the so-called laws of nature* [i.e. fixed sequence of events] *is a perplexing subject, on which I have often thought, but cannot see my way clear*" (F. Darwin and Seward 1903, 2:170. Emphasis added).

In 1876 Darwin wrote that in 1836-39 he had come to see that "the Old Testament was no more to be trusted than the sacred books of the Hindoos" (Barlow 1958, 85), and in another place he had described how he lost his faith in the Bible: "Disbelief crept over me at a very slow rate, but was at last complete. The rate was so slow that I felt no distress, and have never since doubted even for a single second that my conclusion was correct" (Barlow 1958, 87). Darwin was at one time visited by Dr. Aveling, Karl Marx's son-in-law, who claimed that Darwin's religious views were essentially the same as his own, that is, atheistic. Darwin objected on the grounds that his own views were in no way aggressive, and that, therefore, he had a preference for the views of the agnostic (F. Darwin 1887, 1:317).

All these statements of Charles Darwin are utterly incompatible with the picture drawn by Lady Hope, who is, incidentally, a figure about whom an extensive search has failed to reveal any information.[21] Who, then, did originate the story of "Darwin's last hours"? This is likely to remain one of those unsolved mysteries, yet there are some possible clues. Emma Darwin survived her husband by fourteen years and died in 1896. Although she did not subscribe to all the views of the Unitarian Church of today, she was a Unitarian attending the Anglican Church and very antipathetic to the idea that all human morality had "grown up by evolution". The theory of evolution was not widely accepted by the general population in her day, and she was anxious to avoid any suspicion that Darwin regarded spiritual beliefs as no "higher" than their animal origins (Tax 1960, 1:12). Emma Darwin, it should be remembered, persuaded her son Francis to delete certain passages from his father's autobiography before its posthumous publication in 1887, and it is evident that as early as 1885 she made efforts to maintain a good and proper image of the family name (Barlow 1958, 93).[22] It seems quite possible, then, that a person who would be prepared to delete certain pages from history might equally well be prepared to add pages to it. The suspicion thus points to Emma Darwin herself as the author of the "last hours" story.

6

The Species Question

*Nobody can imagine how nothing could turn
into something. Nobody can get an inch nearer to
it by explaining how something could turn into
something else.*

G.K. CHESTERTON
(1925, 21)

Kimball's (1965, 539) popular high-school biology textbook makes the opening statement that Charles Darwin's *Origin of Species* "ranks second only to the Holy Bible in its impact on man's thinking". This is quite probably true, while the rank of biblical status has recently been achieved by the publishing of Barrett's (1982) concordance to the *Origin*. The nature of each book's impact, particularly on our Western culture, is another question conveniently beyond the scope of the high-school biology class. Both books are frequently affirmed and denied, extolled and maligned, and requoted and misquoted without actually having been read. Whatever psychoanalytical meanings may be attached to them, both books can certainly be said to excite the human passions.

In contrast to the Bible's lofty opening statements concerning the cosmological events at the beginning of time, the opening chapter of Darwin's magnum opus is concerned with more earthly matters. It is about pigeons. As we shall see later, Darwin's pigeon-breeding experiments were exemplary. The results clearly showed that a pigeon will always be a pigeon, but Darwin's interpretation of the results was that the pigeon had derived from something else. It was not difficult for him to arrive at this conclusion. First, as was noted in Chapter Five, he had made his mind up as early as July of 1837 that transmutation of the species, that is, evolution, did occur. Second, Linnaeus's classification system, then already in universal use, required very little imagination to make transmutation a believable process. Chapter Two showed that Linnaeus based his classification system on similarity of design, subse-

138

quently referred to as homology. Darwin saw classification based on the presence of organs of similar design as a classification based on kinship. He felt that all creatures sharing homologous organs are related to one another, having inherited their homologous organs from a common ancestor. From Darwin's viewpoint, then, the pigeons were related to all the other birds, and their early ancestors were, in turn, related to yet earlier ancestors derived from the reptiles, and so on. There was no proof for this but it seemed eminently reasonable.

What Is a Species?

Those of us who live in larger cities have a tendency to forget that the variety of birds in the world today extends much beyond the sparrows and pigeons. The fact is that the variety of all living things, including birds, is so enormous that the work of classification begun over two centuries ago is still continuing. Undoubtedly some species of plant and animal are becoming extinct without even being discovered. To complicate matters, the variation is often so great that it has been natural to mistake two variants within a species as two separate species; the crucial question for Darwin, as it still is for biologists and zoologists today, is not only to know, When is a species not a species? but indeed, What is a species? Naturalists such as Ray and Linnaeus working in the seventeenth and eighteenth centuries and many others well into the nineteenth century firmly believed in the immutability of species, each biblically fixed by an impenetrable barrier of sterility. They had before them the example of the horse and ass or donkey. These familiar domestic animals, although similar in appearance, were seen to be derived from separately created kinds and were thus classified as separate species in the same genus, *Equus caballus* and *Equus asinus*, respectively. Although the horse and ass are interfertile, that is, fertile with each other, the mule, which results from this union, is sterile (dysgenic hybrid); this was the barrier of sterility that prevented mules from producing a second generation after their own kind. As it has been said, the mule is without pride of ancestry or hope of posterity. The ancient Israelites, obedient to the letter of the law, were careful not to let "their cattle gender with a diverse kind" (Leviticus 19:19); accordingly they always bought their mules from Gentile neighbors. In this example of the horse and the ass, there is an interesting confirmation of the biblical injunction for each to produce "after his kind"; the masculine pronoun is used in the Hebrew "after their kind" (Genesis 1:11-25). Male mules are always sterile but on rare occasions a female will be fertile, and, if bred with a stallion will produce a normal horse (Willoughby 1974, 390). In the minds of the Bible-believing naturalists of

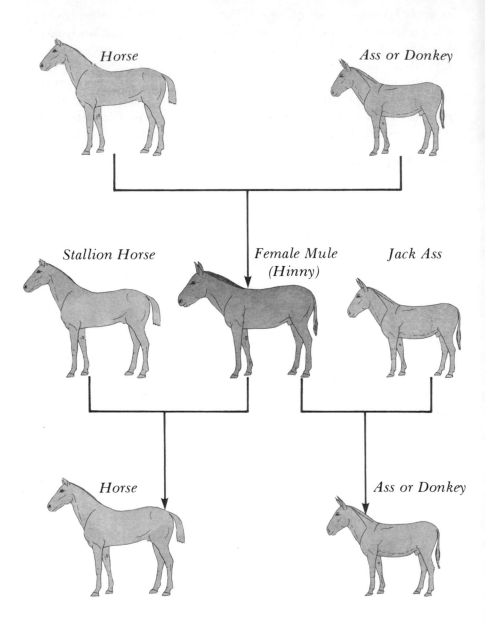

The Genesis "after his kind" clearly demonstrated in the rare case of the fertile female mule.

the eighteenth century, God was thus seen to have provided a sterility barrier between separately created kinds, preventing chaos in nature.

The principle was extended to man himself with the irresistible syllogism that because all animals capable of producing fertile offspring are of the same species and since all men are also capable of producing fertile offspring, then all men are of the same species. Those who subscribed to this reasoning (monogenists) did so from a theological viewpoint, because it nicely supported the biblical account of mankind originating from one mating pair (Adam and Eve), but it was admittedly difficult to explain the origin of the black, white, and yellow races of man. The more liberal school (polygenists) argued that man originated from four or five mating pairs and were prepared to read into Scripture more than was said to justify their position. The need was to explain the various races but this presented the difficulty of then explaining the widespread interracial fertility. Today, with a much greater awareness of the complexity of the biochemistry of reproduction, it transcends all rational credulity to believe that man could have evolved at four separate locations and be interfertile, yet this remains as part of the current belief system.[1]

Entitled "The Creation", this massive sculpture was unveiled in October 1982 at the Washington Episcopalian Cathedral. It is said to convey the instant when humankind emerges from the void, and shows four couples. The Genesis account has openly been abandoned in favor of an anthropological interpretation to which there is no universal agreement. (Religious News Service Photo)

With the rise of science and the age of exploration, particularly in the early nineteenth century, a number of discoveries upset the neat compartmentalizing of the species on the basis of the ability to reproduce. First, naturalist explorers such as Joseph Hooker, Alfred Wallace, and Henry Bates returned to England with literally thousands of new and often exotic species of flora and fauna which were presented to an eager and curious public in the great Victorian museums and zoos. Some of these trophies included the gorilla discovered in 1847 while hundreds of extinct creatures were represented in the growing fossil collections. Each of the living things was sufficiently different to be seen as having derived from a separate creation, and, in the minds' eye of the Christian public, the ark of Noah was becoming impossibly crowded. Secondly, the impenetrable sterility barrier between creatures given by common assent to be separate species was found to have loop-holes. It came to be recognized that interfertility was possible though not usual between the dog and the wolf, between the hare and rabbit, goat and sheep (offspring called chabeins), and the camel and dromedary; but worse, unlike the horse and the ass, these unions produced fertile offspring capable of interbreeding among themselves (eugenic hybridity). The example of the cat and rabbit combination, which lingers on in the public mind, was merely the result of a well-publicized hoax.

These are known exceptions among the domestic animals, and others such as the cow and the buffalo have since been added. Armed with these domestic examples, scientists were faced with the question of who was related to whom among the undomesticated. The task of finding out by breeding experiments was not only impossible from the numbers involved, but wild animals in captivity are notoriously uncooperative in matters of breeding. These apparent exceptions to the rule of sterility were, however, turned to advantage by the biblicists who saw the possibility of reducing the cargo of the ark; for example, one mating pair of dogs would have been sufficient not only to provide for every dog variation known today, but also for every variation of wolf. By this same reasoning all the other dog-like animals such as the dingo, coyote, jackal, fennec, and fox were candidates as descendants of the same ancestral pair. Early in the 1800s there was lack of actual evidence that they were interfertile with the domestic dog or with each other but by 1890 it was known that the entire *Canidae* family are interfertile (Mivart 1890, viii). This is not commonly known among the public to this day while it does mean that all these dog-like animals and their variants can claim to be descendants of a single mating pair. Whether the ancestral pair was on the ark or evolved by some evolutionary quirk in the Oligocene era is a pertinent question in the creation/

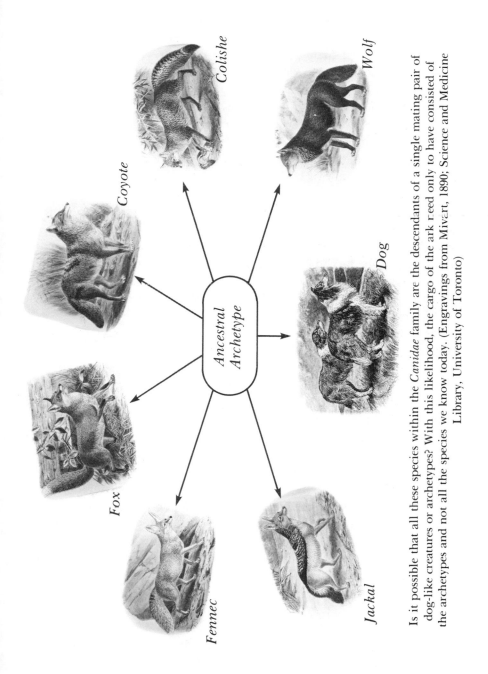

Is it possible that all these species within the *Canidae* family are the descendants of a single mating pair of dog-like creatures or archetypes? With this likelihood, the cargo of the ark reed only to have consisted of the archetypes and not all the species we know today. (Engravings from Mivert, 1890; Science and Medicine Library, University of Toronto)

evolution debate today, but the choice of belief is only possible if extremely long time periods are involved.

As in the case of the *Canidae* family there is now sufficient information about the *Equus* family, in which, for example, the horse and the zebra are interfertile, suggesting that there was a common horse-like ancestor. Controlled breeding experiments of animals commonly accepted to be separate species have in the past been difficult but are now made easier by clinical techniques. Normally, animals in the wild will not breed with any except their own kind and candidates for controlled breeding experiments had first to be reared together. When the offspring from two species are fertile the parents are seen to be of the same kind but often the hybrid is somewhat unstable and in successive inbreeding tends to revert back to one of the parent species. It seems almost as if nature has conspired to make it impossible to define a species because there is often no clear-cut sterility barrier as was thought at one time. Even worse, so far as man's attempt to classify is concerned, is the fact that sometimes filial descendants, that is brother and sister, are intersterile although they are clearly of the same species. All this may be disturbing for the scientist, but the animals seem to know who belongs to whom.

So far as the human race was concerned, anthropologists were beginning to report instances of sterility between some varieties. Broca reported sterility between certain Negro males and Caucasian females but, oddly, fertility when the sexes were reversed. The explanation, however, was admitted to be a matter of mechanics rather than genetics (Broca 1864, 28). Seemingly more convincing was the reported sterility between the aboriginal females and the Caucasian male convicts of Australia. Again, this was later found to be due to social causes and not genetic. Nevertheless, the polygenist took this evidence to demonstrate that mankind had more than one origin and was *converging* to form a single species. The monogenists, on the other hand, saw in such evidence the possibility that a single species, such as man, when separated by time and distance, could *diverge* and so lose their interfertility. This is, however, now considered to be highly unlikely. The question then became one of faith, since there was no way of telling whether two similar species were converging to become one or were a single species diverging to become two. The monogenist view was supported by the classic work of Boas early in the following century, who showed that by simply moving to a different geographical location, the shape of the human cranium in the succeeding generation could change significantly (Boas 1912, see chapter fifteen). If it was possible for heads to change shape, it seemed equally possible for the skin to change color and perhaps even for interfertility to shift by degrees to sterility. Such effects are now well known among the animal species and it is quite acceptable to give the divergent line a separate species name, but there has always been a great reluctance to do this in the case of man. To this day, mankind the world over is regarded as the single species, *Homo sapiens* and is completely interfertile while, if the facts be known, those reported cases of sterility are likely to be from causes other than genetic. But we are getting beyond our point in history.

At the time Darwin wrote his *Origin* the species question was in a state of flux and confusion, with monogenists and polygenists having opposite interests in the slavery issue, arguing mostly from hearsay. Darwin summarized the situation so far as the animal species were concerned as follows:

> No one definition has as yet satisfied all naturalists; yet every naturalist knows vaguely what he means when he speaks of a species. Generally the term includes the unknown element of a distinct act of creation. The term "variety" is almost equally difficult to define; but here community of descent is almost universally implied, though it can rarely be proved.... Hence, in determining whether a form should be ranked as a species or variety, the opinion of naturalists having sound judgment and wide experience seems the only guide to follow (Darwin 1859, 44-7).

Darwin did not provide a definition of species in his *Origin of Species,* which may appear to be quite unscientific. There could have been wisdom in this, however, as it then left him free to use contrary arguments to support his theory. His appraisal of the lack of agreement on the definition of species in his own day is ironically very similar to the situation today, the major difference being that whereas formerly it was based on a belief in the creation account, today the definitions, and there are several, are based on belief in the theory of evolution. In the former case, any opportunity to lump the species together provided support for the biblical account, particularly that concerning the cargo of the ark of Noah. In the latter approach there is a tendency to split or multiply the species and, although this may be convenient for classification, it unwittingly tends to provide evidence for evolution in action.

There has always been a division within the ranks of those who classify the living things, the taxonomists, the two camps being known among the initiates as "lumpers" and "splitters". While both camps today are committed to the theory of evolution, the "lumper" will realistically see great variation possible within a species, while the

The common chickadee seems to
have a "language" barrier within
its kind.

"splitter" tends to see the slightest variation as evidence of divergence
and the variant qualify as a separate species. There is some circularity
here since divergence is seen as evidence of evolution but by applying a
separate species name, this tends to confirm that evolution has taken
place. As an example of splitting, the Carolina Chickadee (*Parus
carolinus*) and the black-capped Chickadee (*Parus atricapillus*) are two
look-alike birds that breed together and produce fertile offspring but
are classified as separate species because they sing a different song (Ross
James, pers. com. 1982). By this same reasoning, the English and the
French peoples should be classified as separate species because they
speak a different language! Knowing how much variation is possible
before declaring the variant to be a separate species is therefore a very
subjective exercise and has led to different definitions of what is meant
by a species. It is little wonder students become confused. A popular
modern textbook has lamented the confusion and gives the following
definition: "A genetical or biospecies is a population or group of
populations of actually or potentially interbreeding animals that are
reproductively isolated from other such groups" (Buettner-Janusch
1973, 35). It is what is understood to be the means of isolation that
constitutes the gray area. A geographical barrier is most commonly
accepted but as we descend to details concerning habits or even song in
the case of the Chickadee, opinions divide. The London socialite and
the Swahili warrior seldom meet and mate. There are geographical and
social barriers yet they are acknowledged to be a single species. It would
seem only reasonable that animals have similar preferences for their
own kind. Giving separate species names is then merely a convenient
means of identification. However, it should be clearly recognized that
the multiplicity of species generated by shifting the definition is not
evidence for evolution of amoeba to man.

Interestingly, the same textbook author points out that some of
today's scholars have turned to the typological concept of species. This
concept supposes that there were ideal archetypes from whom all living

forms have descended by divergence which they see as imperfections from the original (Buettner-Janusch 1973, 36). This concept is a perfectly logical outcome of what is observed in nature and is known as the cladistic system of classification.

Cladistics supposes that rather than the gradual and steady Darwinian evolution of one life form to another, there have been sudden jumps from one ancestral form to another and what is seen today are the descendants from those archetypal ancestors. In contrast, the creation account begins with ancestral forms and does not recognize unprovable jumps. Cladistics thereby only substitutes one set of miracles by another; nevertheless, both the American Museum of Natural History and the British Museum have adopted the method and, while there has been controversy, there is little doubt the trend will continue.

The arguments within the cloistered halls of science have even taken on political overtones as some see the evolutionary jumps as providing evidence to support Marxist doctrines! (Wade 1980). Nevertheless, what is even more disturbing for some, is that the admission of ancestral archetypes comes perilously close to supporting the creationist position; after all, what are called archetypes today were once called "kinds". Perhaps the much maligned ark was not so crowded after all.

Finches and Pigeons

The species question plagued Darwin's mind when he returned from his five-year voyage on H.M.S. Beagle. While visiting the Galapagos Islands he observed the variations in the shape and size of the beak of some rather drab-looking finches found only on this group of islands, more than six hundred miles from the mainland of South America. On some islands these little birds had adapted to seed eating and had large heavy beaks, while on other islands the birds fed on insects and had small sharp beaks and so on. It was also evident that where the different varieties of this bird met on the same island, they were careful to mate only with their own kind. Darwin reasoned that at some time in the past a high wind carried a mating pair of these birds from the mainland to this remote spot in the Pacific. Since that event the descendants of the original pair adopted different ecological niches and in doing so had diverged, or become differentiated.

Darwin's explanation is most probably true, but since his time enthusiasts have claimed that the original species has differentiated into fourteen separate species (Lack 1968).[2] More cautious workers concede that the finches are merely in process of becoming separated. A human analogy would be the Negro Pygmy and Masai tribes who probably exhibit greater physical differences than the finches, are separated geographically and socially, and yet are still regarded as one species. Nevertheless, the finches (Geospizinae) will be found today in museums and textbooks as prime evidence for evolution in action—proof that divergence led to the fish becoming a reptile, the reptile becoming a mammal, and the mammal becoming man. Darwin was more cautious and in 1839 described these birds in his *Journal of Researches* (Darwin 1845, 380), though he did not claim that they were separate species and did not mention them as evidence in his *Origin*.[3]

As we have seen, at the time he was working on his theory (1840-60), the general concept of a species was based on the biblical fixity of species. Darwin would naturally have considered it necessary to conduct breeding experiments on the finches to tell if a sterility barrier had developed by divergence, although he was very unclear about divergence at the time. If this were so, he reasoned, it would prove that one species could derive from another; having taken that first step, human imagination was free to see a chain of relationships over countless intermediate species back to the original spark of life. This was Darwin's vision but unfortunately he had not brought any live finches back for breeding experiments. The inspiration came to him quite early, however, that even better than the finches were the pigeons

The common pigeon occurs in these widely variant forms but is acknowledged to be a single species.

Darwin's finches are not common, vary comparatively slightly, and yet are claimed to represent fourteen separate species.

available on his own doorstep and, better yet, the local people offered lots of breeding experience for the asking. He joined two pigeon-fanciers clubs and hob-nobbed among their gin palaces.

Pigeon breeding was very popular in Victorian England, as it still is in some parts, and it became evident that pigeons can be bred to produce the most astonishing variety of shapes. In Darwin's experiments he carefully observed the differences in the various types of pigeon, counting their feathers and noting coloration and habits. When their use in life had been fulfilled, he studied their inward parts, counting vertebrae and ribs and measuring bones. He found that there were seven basic varieties of pigeon, but since every combination of cross between varieties was fertile, he had to conclude from the understanding of the day that they were all variants within a single species. This may have been somewhat disappointing since it implied that the finches were almost certainly still a single species. Evidence that one species could become another—that is, that the barrier of biblical fixity could be broken—had not been provided. Writing fourteen years after the publication of the *Origin* Darwin confessed to his friend Bentham:

> In fact the belief in Natural Selection must at present be grounded entirely on general considerations [faith?]... When we descend to details, we can [not] prove that no one species has changed... nor can we prove that the supposed changes are beneficial, which is the groundwork of the theory. Nor can we explain why some species have changed and others have not" (F. Darwin 1887, 3:25).

To this day, the situation is no different since much of what is offered as evidence has been provided by simply expanding the definition.

The pigeon experiment further showed that they had all descended from the common rock pigeon, *Columba livia*, which is the sort that decorate our park statues. Darwin correctly drew this conclusion because the off-spring would often revert back to the rock pigeon's characteristics. He was not familiar with the genetic theory as it is known today so was unaware of the reason, but the reversion he observed was well known among animal breeders and represented the limits to variation possible within a species. In practical terms, this means that there are definite built-in limits to, for example, the size of dogs or the running ability of race-horses, etc., and Darwin found the limits of fancy shape possible within the pigeon species. Having recognized that in the breeding experiments variants can only go to certain limits, it then occurred to him that under natural conditions over much longer periods of time, the species barrier might be broken. Fortunately, Charles Lyell's geology provided all the time, vast ages of it, but so far as proof was concerned, it was precisely those long times that placed experimental proof far beyond the human life span. The notion could neither be proved nor disproved; Darwin recognized this but suggested that perhaps evidence could be found in the fossil record (Darwin 1859, 172, 279).

Darwin found that between one variety of pigeon and another the number of ribs and vertebrae could vary.

From Species to Species Among the Fossils

When making the study on the pigeons, Darwin observed that between one variety and another the vertebrae could vary in number as could the number of ribs, and if this could be so in a live species, then it was also possible among the extinct, which, of course, are only known from their boney remains (Darwin 1859, 22). He believed that there would be found in the fossil record creatures that once existed at every stage of variation, not only as one species became another but as one major group became another. At the time he published the first edition of the *Origin*, not one fossil of these "missing-links" or transitions had been found, but there was great hope as it seemed reasonable that the rocks should be full of fossil creatures of this type. It was surely only a matter of time before transitional creatures—for example, between fish and amphibious reptiles or between reptile and mammal, which was the expected order of evolution—showed up.

Dinosaurs

The absence of any evidence of the transitional forms, either among the living or the dead, the latter being, of course, the fossil record, was one of the most damaging arguments that faced Darwin and his followers. A massive effort began among the proponents of the theory to excavate fossils, particularly of the vertebrates, with the hope of finding transitional forms to provide the badly needed confirmation. The excavation efforts were made with great vigor in the 1860-80 period and have continued with somewhat diminishing energy into the present century. Many of the classical "missing-links" between man and ape were discovered in this period, but as we shall see in later chapters, most of these have now fallen into disrepute. The great dinosaurs were given special attention because they grew to be so large and specialized in form that it was thought they must have had an especially long line of transitions, thereby providing a better chance for their being discovered. There was also a slight commercial motive because the dinosaurs were a potent source of attraction to the museums. The *Stegosaurus* is a good example of the specialized nature of the dinosaurs. This eight-to-ten-ton reptilian had two sets of bone plates extending vertically from the backbone and four large spikes on the tail. These features are unique—no other creature has them—and it was expected that some transitional forms would be found showing the gradual development of the plates and spikes. So far, after more than a century of searching, no transitional creatures leading to the *Stegosaurus* have been found, and the same dismal truth pertains to all the other highly specialized creatures in the fossil record. In every case, the creatures appear abruptly in the record, and so far as can be told from the fossil bones, each creature is in perfected form. The absence of transitions was a continuing problem for Darwin, as it still is to the paleontologists today (Darwin 1859, 280; Kitts 1974, 467).[4-5]

The Field Museum of Natural History has one of the largest collections of fossil specimens in the world, representing, it is said, about 20 percent of all known fossil species. Dr. David Raup, curator of geology at this museum, is probably in as good a position as any to sum up the present position regarding the evidence of transitions in the fossil record. In a recent issue of the *Field Museum Bulletin* he wrote:

> We are now about 120 years after Darwin and the knowledge of the fossil record has been greatly expanded. We now have a quarter of a million fossil species but the situation hasn't changed much. The record of evolution is still surprisingly jerky and ironically, we have even fewer examples of evolutionary transition than we had in Darwin's time. By this I mean that some of the classic cases of Darwinian change in the fossil record, such as the evolution of the horse in North America have had to be discarded or modified as a result of more detailed information (Raup 1979, 25).

Raup also goes on to say that all the major extinctions such as those of the dinosaurs are still very puzzling. Certainly it seems that never a month goes by without there being some new theory in the popular press to account for the disappearance of the dinosaur (Russell 1982).[6]

The Horse

In the nineteenth century many parents would name their children after good Bible characters, seemingly in the hope that the blessed life would somehow be perpetuated in the latter-day namesake. Othniel C. Marsh was born of such parents in the days of pioneering America. Although he became one of the greatest fossil hunters, it is very doubtful that his pious parents' expectations were realized, particularly since he ended up in a national scandal. His paleontological claim to fame rested on his discovery of thirty different kinds of fossil horse in Wyoming and Nebraska during the 1870s. He reconstructed and arranged these fossils in an evolutionary series and put them on display at Yale University, where they remain to this day. It was said that this was the series of skeletons depicting the evolution of the horse that convinced T.H. Huxley of the reality of evolution. Copies of this series are to be found in every major museum, and, visually, it does look very convincing as proof of the transition from the little three-toed animal to the modern single-toed horse. All is not as simple and clear-cut as it is made out to be, however, since the actual evolutionary sequence will differ from one authority to another. Not only that, but the sequence of mounted specimens differs from one museum to another, all of which indicates there is a great deal of uncertainty and speculation about the whole thing. For example, the number of the rib bones does not follow the supposed sequence, and the creatures are not always found in the expected sequence in the fossil record; that is, sometimes the smallest creature is found in the higher strata. Even the name of the first specimen in the series, sometimes called *Eohippus*, or dawn horse, has been in dispute for some years. When it was first found it was called *Hyracotherium* because it was like the *Hyrax*, or rock badger, of today; from this it was believed that the early horses climbed trees.

When all is said and done, however, a row of look-alike fossils cannot be proof that one species changed into another; we cannot be sure that the little rock badger of long ago changed into *Orohippus*, since it is just as likely that they have always been separate species, one still living, one extinct. Some of the fossil horses in the series could simply have been variants within a single species, just as the pigeons were having different numbers of vertebrae and ribs; this can never be known with extinct creatures, but with living pigeons science can be sure. To put the argument another way, if horses and donkeys were only known by their fossils, they might well be classified as variants within a single species, but the experience of breeders shows that, in

All that we know of the *Archaeopteryx lithographica*, to give its full name, is contained within five pieces of limestone rock, each of which is split into two mating halves. Shown is the better half of the Berlin specimen. (Courtesy of Chris McGowan, Royal Ontario Museum)

fact, they are separate species. Acknowledging all the enormous amount of work that men such as Henry F. Osborn and G.G. Simpson have put into the horse series, the sad fact remains that what has actually been done is to select the fossil data to fit the theory, and this cannot be considered scientific proof. It is little wonder, then, that Raup (1979) makes the comment that the evolution of the horse in North America has to be discarded or modified.

From Reptile to Bird

The high-quality limestone deposits at Solnhofen in Germany had long been used to provide material for lithographic plates used in the printing industry. From time to time, finely preserved fossil fish were discovered, and these provided an additional source of revenue for the quarry owners. In 1861 a small fossilized feather, quite perfect in detail, was found and later proved to be of great interest (Augusta and Burian 1961, 41; Feduccia and Tordoff 1979). According to Lyell's system of dating rocks, this particular limestone had been previously dated by other fossils as being from the Jurassic period, long before birds were supposed to have evolved, so the feather was something of an enigma. Shortly after this, a fossil bird, with the head and neck missing, was discovered in the same area, and from the previously found feather the name had already been given as *Archaeopteryx*, which means "early wing". The specimen was believed to be an intermediate between reptiles and birds since it had features common to both and was a triumph for Darwin, perfectly confirming his theory. The timing and nature of this discovery was of great significance, and after a rather large sum of money changed hands, the specimen took pride of place in the British museum (Augusta and Burian 1961, 43). In 1877 a second *Archaeopteryx* was discovered in a location quite near the first, but this was a much better specimen complete with neck and head, while to everyone's surprise the creature had thirteen teeth in sockets in each jaw. Again, the highest bidder won the day, and this time the specimen finished up in the Berlin museum (Augusta and Burian 1961, 49). This specimen is so well preserved that it is usually shown in biological textbooks as a transitional creature and is taken to be prime evidence for the theory of evolution.

Counting the feather, there are five specimens of *Archaeopteryx*. In addition to the well-known London and Berlin specimens, a very poor example was found in 1956 and a questionable re-indentification of a fossil in the Teyer Museum was made in 1970. Feathers are really quite complex and are the identifying mark of a true bird. For this reason, the *Archaeopteryx* is acknowledged to be a bird (Feduccia and Tordoff 1979). However, it does have teeth and "fingers" on the leading edge of the wing, which give it reptilian features, and is thus thought to be in the last stages of transition from a reptile. There are a number of difficulties, not the least of which is that, unlike the feathers, the reptilian features are not definitive; that is, some reptiles, such as the turtle and the tortoise, do not have teeth while some birds, such as the baby hoatzin from South America and the ostrich, do have the little "fingers" on the wing. None of these living creatures, the turtle, the hoatzin, or the ostrich, has ever been considered to be transitional because of the presence or absence of these features. It may be suspected that the *Archaeopteryx* is only considered a transition because it is extinct; as a living creature more would be known about it.

The fossil record normally only preserves the hard bony parts, and it is often argued that much of the transition from one species to another actually took place in the soft tissues, which, as a rule, are non-fossilizable. Although the *Archaeopteryx* feather is quite exceptional, the transitional sequence of reptile scale to bird feather falls into this "non-fossilizable" category, and it should be clearly understood that this entire argument is one from silence (Regal 1975). Perhaps reluctant to use this device, both Wallace (1980, 325) and later Darwin (1859, 182) cited the living example of the penguin, which uses its wing as a flipper or flapper for swimming.[7] Some enthusiasts of evolution are still using the penguin's flipper as an example of a transition in "action" and brought about by adaptation to a new environment. The transitional feature is believed to be the true feathers on the trailing edge of the flipper and what appear to be scales on the leading edge with a gradation of structures in between. However, ornithologists candidly admit that some definitive work needs to be done in this area since there are serious doubts about the scales being true scales (Allen Baker, pers. com. 1982). Even so, true scales and true feathers on the same creature, such as are found on a bird's legs, are not proof, or even evidence, of evolution but only mean that similar design features or homologues have been incorporated within separate species; that is, scales are found on both reptiles and on some bird's legs.

The *Archaeopteryx*, in spite of its appearance in practically every biological textbook as the perfect transition, has been the subject of continuing debate, especially as fossils of true birds have since been reported by Jensen in the Jurassic Limestone beds of Utah (Jensen 1977). It would appear that if true birds lived in the same geological period, then the *Archaeopteryx* would not necessarily have been their ancestor. All that can truthfully be said about the *Archaeopteryx* is that it is a true but extinct bird having some features that provide circumstantial evidence for believing it to be a transition.

An early reconstruction of the *Archaeopteryx* showing feather detail from Romanes 1897. About as big as a pigeon, the reconstructed versions vary slightly from textbook to textbook. (Thomas Fisher Rare Book Library, University of Toronto)

How the Reptile Became a Mammal

There is a principle that says that the more fragmentary the evidence, the greater will be the claims made for it. Surely there could be no better demonstration of this principle than the sheer magnitude of effort centered on the alleged reptile to mammal transition. One of the fundamental differences between a reptile and a mammal from the point of view of the bone structure, and this is generally all that remains in the fossil, is the construction of the ear and the lower jaw. The major reason for focusing on this particular difference is that, very often, only the lower jaw and some parts of the skull are available for study.

The mammal has two bones in the lower jaw, the reptile has six; these bones are fused by sutures so that the assembly in each case appears as a single jawbone. The mammal has three tiny bones in the ear, the reptile has one, and it is claimed that in evolving from the reptile, two bones from each side of the reptile jaw migrated into the ear to provide the full complement of bones found in the mammal ear and account for the diminished number in the mammal jaw (Colbert 1949; Manley 1972).[8] Now the general public is not usually made aware of these assertions. The reluctance to test public credulity is understandable, and since this work is reported in the esoteric language of the scientist in obscure specialist publications, it is considered worthwhile to bring to the reader just some of the details on which the claims are made. It should be borne in mind that when fossils of these extinct creatures are found, it is usually just the teeth and jaw and only sometimes the entire skull, but in virtually every case the bones are broken and disarticulated.

In 1973 Kermack and others reported finding what they refer to as the *Morganucodon*, which they claim is the transition that has passed beyond the stage of the *Cynodont*, that is, beyond the true reptile stage. Earlier (1968) the same investigators had described a similar creature they named the *Kuehneotherium*. Several sets of *Morganucodon* fossil parts were found in China and in Wales, which would seem to indicate that the same transition evolved twice on opposite sides of the earth and at approximately the same time. The investigators acknowledged that the *Morganucodon* had a fully reptilian lower jaw with all six bones, but the claim for its being a transition was based on an inferred assembly of the jaw hinge. Bones in the assembled condition were not actually found. Digging through some of the minutia of a monumental eighty-eight page report relating just to the lower jaw of this creature, it became apparent that this item ranged from one-half to three-quarters of an inch long, which would make *Morganucodon* about as big as a rat if the entire skeleton had been available. Detailed drawings of both the *Morganucodon* and *Cynodont* jaws appeared in the Kermack (1973) paper, and although both were drawn to the same size for comparison, the drawings were actually on different scales. It turns out the *Cynodont* was in fact eighteen times larger than the *Morganucodon*. We are now faced with the reality of this notion, which is saying that a mammal-like reptile the size of a rat evolved from a true reptile the size of a large pig.

There are many other difficulties associated with the claims that these fossil remains are evidence for a transition joining two great classes into an evolutionary relationship. For example, according to the normal geological interpretation, these mammal-like reptiles appeared at the beginning and not at the end of the great reptile age. This being so, it would then appear that they arrived 100 million years too early. However, this is the evidence such as it is, and it has been generously described here as "fleeting". By this it is meant that, like the *Archaeopteryx*, the evidence is not ironclad and is very much subjective; some will accept it, others will not, but we are reminded that it is upon such stuff as this that the framework for today's belief in the theory of evolution rests.

Popular Claims for Transitions

A final word on the transitions concerns the unsubstantiated textbook and popular press claims giving the impression that the fossil record with all the transitions is now virtually complete. Richard Leakey's statement made in the same year that David Raup made his statement in the *Field Museum Bulletin* quoted earlier will serve as an example: "New fossil finds since Darwin's day have smoothed out much of the abruptness of the fossil record. Fossil finds have now closed the gaps between fish and land vertebrates and between reptiles and mammals" (Leakey 1979, 15). Evidently there are two diametrically opposed opinions being represented by these experts, and, unfortunately, Leakey's more liberal view is the one found in the popular press, while the more conservative and authoritative view is confined to the relative obscurity of the Field Museum's own publication.

In the first place, it should be noted that in the wide-sweeping liberal claims of Leakey, no mention is made of closing the gap between the invertebrates and the vertebrates. Leakey begins with the fish that have backbones and are thus vertebrates, but life is supposed to have begun with the invertebrates, which have no backbone. The evolution of the backbone is the first major gap, but Leakey makes no mention of this problem. This transition from an unknown invertebrate to the vertebrate is believed to have taken 100 million years, but so far there is not one shred of evidence for it. When it comes to gaps within the evolution of the vertebrates, such as that between the reptile and the bird, there is the fleeting evidence of the *Archaeopteryx* previously described, and then there is the gap between the reptiles and the mammals—but, again, the evidence is fleeting. However, this is the textbook evidence such as it is and it may be noted that while this is confined to the animal kingdom, nothing is ever mentioned about transitional evidence from the plant kingdom.

Natural Selection

Darwin entitled his famous abstract *The Origin of Species by Means of Natural Selection*, which is really a concise summary of his entire theory. Over the twenty years or so that he had worked on it he had written hundreds of letters to animal and plant breeders all over the country soliciting replies to questions. He drew extensively from their experience. Breeders selected those variants or varieties having characteristics of commercial value for breeding, while less promising varieties were denied opportunities to breed. Artificial selection of this type produced cows giving greater quantities of milk, horses of greater running ability, and so on. Darwin believed that, in a similar way, nature selected out those variants among the species that were best fitted for the environment. However, selection under natural conditions was known to be very conservative; that is, offspring tended to be like the parents, and anything too far from the normal would breed back to the basic type, a fact Darwin was fully aware of from his work with the pigeons. He acknowledged all this but then argued that natural selection becomes a force for change when the environment changes. He believed that variation was going on all the time within a species, but that only those variants most closely adapted tended to survive. He said that a change in the environment would, in the course of many generations, produce gradual changes and eventually lead to a separate species. This required dynamic conditions of continuous and random variation within the species and a changing environment. One other feature of Darwin's natural selection was sexual attraction. He pointed out that in the courtship rituals of animals, the males compete for the females in tests of strength, and the strongest or the swiftest victors have the opportunity to reproduce; the losers tend to have much less opportunity and so would eventually die out. In the case of birds, the males display their plumage, and the hen bird chooses the most sexually attractive mate according to her standard of beauty. Darwin did not explain why sexual selection applied only to the males and not the females, nor why blind nature should be concerned with the preservation of beauty (Darwin 1859, 89).

Throughout the *Origin*, and from one edition to the next, Darwin was never entirely clear in his own mind about "end purpose". In the case of artificial selection, man intelligently controls the breeding to produce an improved end result. Under natural conditions, Darwin appealed to blind chance, which could have no innate intelligence, but there was a dilemma: the theory said that life began as a simple organism and evolved into more complex organisms, which implies an intelligent directing force, but he wanted at all costs to avoid any kind of inference to the supernatural. To circumvent the dilemma, he steadfastly avoided using the terms "lower" and "higher" forms of life[9] and spoke rather of "change", which allowed him greater freedom for argument when discussing specific cases (F. Darwin and Seward 1903, 1:114; Mayr 1972).[10] However, his most artful device was use of the word "descent", which he introduced in the first edition of the *Origin* and continued to use throughout his writing to his *Descent of Man*, published in 1873. Unlike the word "ascent", which in the context of a sequential process implies purposeful direction, the word "descent" has rather the connotation of the blind laws of nature, such as water "finding its own level". In other words, "descent" does not imply purposeful design or a Designer. Darwin did allow himself use of the word "perfection", in the sense that the organism progressed towards perfect adaption to its environment.

This, then, is classical Darwinism, which died a slow death more than half a century ago. The theory was facile, tidy, and convinced many, including Thomas Huxley, who, after reading the *Origin*, confessed how stupid he was not to have thought of the theory himself (L. Huxley 1900, 1:170). Lyell's geology had provided all the time thought to be necessary for evolution to take place and at the same stroke had precluded any possibility of proving the theory by laboratory experiment. There were many unanswered questions. Do animals really change in a changing environment or are they more likely to migrate or simply die out? Then again, what if the environmental change was too rapid for the proposed adaptation from random variation to keep up?

Overriding all these and other questions was the total absence of any fossil evidence. Nevertheless, the theory was superficially convincing for those who wanted an alternative to the traditional supernatural explanation. It was this version of the theory, with all its deficiencies and assumptions, that challenged theological dogma in the last half of the nineteenth century and the beginning of this century. More will be said of this confrontation in Chapters Thirteen and Fourteen, but in the meantime the shifting grounds for the theory need to be traced into this present decade.

Mendel and Genetics

At about the time Darwin began to write his *Origin,* a Czech monk began working on the problem of heredity using garden peas. Johann Mendel had entered a religious order to obtain an education and was sent to the University of Vienna. He was not a very proficient student and failed the course, coming away with nothing more than a change of name; the order had renamed him Gregor Mendel. He was sent back to Czechoslovakia to the small monastery of Brunn, where he spent the remainder of his life, eventually becoming the abbot, and he died in 1884 at the age of sixty-two.

Until Mendel's work became known, nineteenth century thinking held that offspring from crossing varieties within a species would have intermediate characteristics. For example, it was believed that children of intermediate height would result from a tall father and a short mother. Darwin went to his grave believing this, although if it were true, any interbreeding population would quickly finish up all looking exactly alike.

Mendel's work with garden peas eventually swept aside nineteenth century thinking and provided the foundation for our understanding of inheritance today. He began his work about 1856, and it took him eight years—not a long time to breed a number of generations of peas, note their characteristics, and formulate a law. It has always been a source of mystery and speculation by students of the history of science to know how Mendel designed his experiment and got the whole thing right the first time. Some would claim this as divine revelation, and it certainly seems more than coincidental that he chose to study seven different characteristics of the pea without knowing first that the pea had seven pairs of chromosomes to provide those characteristics.

The time he began to experiment was also particularly fortunate, five or six years *before* he became aware of Darwin's theory, which he read in the German edition of the *Origin,* published in 1860. Had he not begun the work when he did, it is possible that he may never have done it at all, because he later became oriented towards the evolutionary views of Darwin. He published his results in 1865 in the *Journal of the Brünn Society for the Study of Natural Science,* where it remained totally ignored by the rest of the scientific community until its discovery in 1900 (Mendel 1959). Gregor Mendel, a rather overweight, cigar-smoking monk, had, it seems, one mission in his otherwise obscure life.

He performed that mission humbly and effectively and is honored today by his name being attached not to a theory but rather to the law of genetic inheritance.

The reason most frequently given for Mendel's work's being ignored for a generation is that it was published in an obscure journal, but this is not true. The journal was distributed to 120 libraries, including some in England and eleven in the United States. Mendel's work was even mentioned in the ninth edition of the *Encyclopaedia Britannica* (1892, 12:426). In 1865 when Mendel's work was published, Darwin's theory had been accepted by many influential academics.

Since Mendel's genetics challenged the Darwinian idea of natural selection, it is just possible that any interest shown in his work was actively discouraged. This would not be unusual. For example, as we shall see in the next chapter, Louis Pasteur met with opposition when he demonstrated the impossibility of the spontaneous appearance of life from nonliving matter in 1862 (For more recent examples of prejudice in science, see Mahoney 1976; Peters and Ceci 1980; and this work, Chapter Fifteen, note 23). Pasteur's work, as we shall see in the next chapter, was a severe blow to Darwin and his followers, but Mendel did not have the scientific stature of Pasteur and could safely be ignored.

By 1900 Darwin's theory of natural selection was found to be deficient, principally because there was absolutely no evidence that one species could become another by the accumulation of minute variation. Breeding experiments had shown time after time that the species barrier could not be permanently crossed. The appeal to untold millions of years simply evaded the possibility of proof, while the abundant evidence expected in the fossil record turned out to be conspicuously absent. It was evident that Darwinian evolution was now even more difficult to explain in terms of Mendel's genetics. And as the principles of inheritance were beginning to be understood by the new generation of scientists, the time was ripe for another theory to explain the mechanism of evolution.

Mutation: For the Worse or for the Better?

About the turn of the century, a Dutch botanist named Hugo de Vries proposed his mutation theory as the mechanism of evolving one species into another. However, de Vries' theory was short-lived and by 1914 was discredited by Jeffrey (1914) who showed that all he had discovered in his experiments with primroses was a previously unknown variety within the species.[11] He thought that the new variety was a "mutant" or

Hugo de Vries, 1848-1935. Discovered an unknown variety of primrose and launched the theory of mutation: an essential part of the canon of faith in the theory of evolution. (*Journal of Heredity*. Washington, D.C. 1935, 26:288)

new species, but the idea of "mutations" did set the stage for further work.

During the 1920s it was discovered that emissions from radioactive substances, such as radium, X rays, and even ultraviolet light, sometimes caused mutant offspring when the parents had been exposed to this kind of radiation. The word "mutant" in this sense usually meant a change for the worse; de Vries, however, used the word "mutant" to mean a change for the better. A number of scientists saw this as a possibility for producing new species and set about to prove this using the common fruit fly, *Drosophila melanogaster*, which reproduces fairly rapidly and enables mutants to be studied over many generations in a relatively short time. After half a century of work on fruit flies bombarded with all kinds of radiation, many mutant types have been produced with different colored eyes, with different sizes of eyes, with no eyes, and with variations in the wings, but throughout, the creatures have steadfastly remained fruit flies. No new species has ever been produced, while the mutants have invariably been deformed or in some way are less than normal. This is perhaps not too surprising when one thinks of the lead-shield protection given to our reproductive organs when we have an X ray examination, since this is specifically to prevent mutant or damaged offspring. There is a tendency in biological textbooks to make supposition appear as fact by suggesting that some mutations have been for the better by increased wing muscles, etc., and the reader should be careful to understand what has, in fact, been observed and what is being supposed.

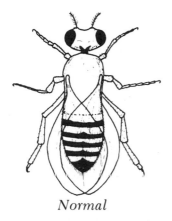

Normal

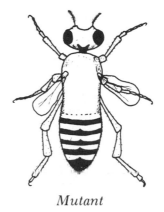

Mutant

Experimentation with fruit flies began in the 1920s with Thomas Hunt Morgan and today is still a minor "industry" among researchers. The stubborn fruit fly has endured every genetic indignity possible, but so far not one has ever produced anything except another fruit fly.

Neo-Darwinian or Synthetic Theory

By the 1930s the classical Darwinian theory was being supplanted by the neo-Darwinian theory in which it was thought that mutant genes of a favorable type played a decisive part. The mutant genes were believed to be produced by radiation such as cosmic rays rather than X rays. In 1942 Julian Huxley coined the term modern synthesis for the same idea, and it is the neo-Darwinian theory or synthetic theory that has dominated evolutionary thinking for the past forty years. The elder apostle today is Ernst Mayr (1963, 586). Essentially, the synthetic theory recognizes that natural variation within a species is too narrow, too conservative, and in any case always tends to revert back to the basic type. The theory proposes that there is the infrequent appearance of a mutation where by chance the individual is more favorably suited to its environment. While admitted to be rare, the mutant then finds an exactly matching mate; since they are slightly better fitted to the environment, it is supposed they tend to have more offspring than the normal variants. This chance process is repeated over countless generations, and the small mutant changes accumulate and eventually lead to the appearance of an entirely new species.

There are in fact a number of different schools of thought centered on this theme, which is a fairly reasonable indication that there is no definite proof for any one of these ideas; if there were, the authorities would be agreed (Kimura 1979; Szent-Gyorgyi 1977).[12]

Behind the scenes, scientific theories tend to be dominated by one individual, and often the winds of change only blow as a requiem to that individual's demise. However, when the individual has gathered about himself a band of disciples, it may take a whole generation to bring about the change. The classical Darwinian theory implied there was a continuous modification of the species, and it was not until the past few decades that that view became challenged by the acknowledgment that stability of the species is the norm, and modification only occurs in response to a change in environment. This was an important and radical change in thinking which has led to the cladistic method of classification discussed earlier and, as we shall now see, to a new theory for the mechanism of evolution proposed by Eldredge and Gould of Harvard University.

The neo-Darwinian school began to have its dissenters in the 1960s. The feeling at the time was marked by the Wistar Institute Symposium held in Philadelphia, in April 1966, where the chairman, Sir Peter Medawar, made the following opening remarks: "The immediate cause of this conference is a pretty widespread sense of dissatisfaction about what has come to be thought as the accepted evolutionary theory in the English-speaking world, the so-called neo-Darwinian theory" (Medawar 1967, xi). By 1980 the neo-Darwinian theory was struggling for survival in the battle of belief against a rising new theory for the mechanism of evolution. The new and latest theory is the brainchild of paleontologists Eldredge and Gould, which they call "punctuated equilibria".

Punctuated Equilibria

One of the greatest weaknesses of classical Darwinism and, subsequently, of neo-Darwinism, is the absence of fossil evidence for the alleged transitional forms. If the origin of new species was really by gradual and continuous change of existing species, the rocks should be packed full of every possible kind of transition, not only between the species that we know today but also between all the extinct species.

Richard Goldschmidt (1940) of the University of California recognized this deficiency and proposed his saltation theory, in which no transitional forms were necessary. This theory stated that evolution occurred by mutational jumps of a sudden and large order instead of the slow accumulation of small changes. This was an echo of the formerly discredited de Vries theory. Goldschmidt's idea was more popularly referred to as the "hopeful monster theory" where, for example, a reptile laid an egg and some "brown furry thing" hatched out of it (Gould 1977a). Chance would dictate that the "brown furry thing" found a mate exactly like itself and that the pair would then find themselves perfectly fitted to some new environment. The theory evidently lay beyond the bounds of scientific credulity of the day and was soundly rejected.

In 1972 Eldredge and Gould resurrected Goldschmidt's saltation theory and added a little twist of their own; they called the new theory "punctuated equilibria" (Eldredge and Gould 1972, 82). As a well-respected paleontologist, Gould was fully aware of the lack of fossil evidence for gradual change and was forthright enough to declare this in the May 1977 issue of *Natural History*. The entire context of his original statement is worth reading since it is essentially an open confession that, although evolutionary trees are displayed in every textbook, it was a "trade secret of paleontology" that these were based on inference and not on fossil evidence (Gould 1977b, 14).[13] Gould pointed out that Darwin had wagered his entire theory of evolution on the absence of these fossils and to emphasize the fact quoted from Darwin himself: "The geological record is extremely imperfect and this fact will to a large extent explain why we do not find interminable varieties [transitions] connecting together all the extinct and existing forms of life by the finest graduated steps. He who rejects these views on the nature of the geological record will rightly reject my whole theory" (Darwin 1859, 342). Gould then continued to comment that paleontologists have paid an enormous price for Darwin's theory of natural selection and adds, "We never see the processes we profess to study" (Gould 1977b, 14). This criticism of natural selection is but an echo of the same cries that were made from nineteenth century pulpits; however, Gould's motives were hardly theological but rather a preamble to introduce his own theory. Interestingly, these statements from a qualified paleontologist are in complete contrast to Leakey's sweeping claim made in the popular press only a year earlier that "other fossil finds have closed the gaps" (Leakey 1979, 15).

By "punctuated equilibria", Gould and Eldredge (1977) mean that for long periods of time there is equilibrium, or stasis, in which a species only exhibits the normal variation, but then a series of favorable mutations occurs by which certain members of the species suddenly change to become another species. The "sudden" nature of the event is meant in the geological sense involving, for example, a period of 50,000 years. This time is not enough in the overall evolutionary picture to leave any fossil remains since this is thought to have happened only rarely, but it is still long enough to be acceptable to the geneticist, and no doubt there was the hope that the proposal would not do too much violence to the orthodox neo-Darwinian view. Lyell's stratagem of changing the time frame of past events may be recognized here, where time for the evolution of a new species was at first stretched to accommodate classical and neo-Darwinian views, was collapsed completely by Goldschmidt and then was stretched again, though only slightly, by Eldredge and Gould. Punctuated equilibria will also be recognized as an argument based on the silence of the fossil record, and again, the time frame precludes any possibility of proof.

In 1980 an historic conference was held in Chicago's Field Museum and attended by 160 of the world's top paleontologists, anatomists, evolutionary geneticists, and developmental biologists. The content of the conference directly challenged the uncertain position of the neo-Darwinian theory, which had dominated evolutionary biology for the previous four decades (Adler 1980). However, unlike the Wistar Institute symposium of fourteen years earlier, no verbatim record of the proceedings marked the event (Lewin 1980). From the insight into the minds of the men behind today's evolutionary science given by the Wistar proceedings, this absence of verbatim record seems a great pity, though doubtless there was very good reason for not making this public knowledge. The most important outcome of the meeting on which most were agreed was that the small changes from generation to generation within a species can in no way accumulate to produce a new species. This was a radical and major departure from the faith and, in principle, as much a departure as the Vatican's Second Council (1962-65) decision to allow Roman Catholics to eat meat on Friday! Yesterday, a man could fail an exam or lose a job for not subscribing to the neo-Darwinian mechanism. Today that unbelief is no longer worthy of excommunication. The punctuated equilibria theory took a rather prominent position at this conference and, although not accepted by the die-hard neo-Darwinists, was generally well received and will undoubtedly occupy tomorrow's textbooks as the new faith.

Problems With Selection and Perfection

Whether the punctuated equilibria theory is accepted or not, evolution still demands that the transition from one species to the next be in graduated steps—a great number of steps in the case of the neo-Darwinian explanation and a lesser number for the new theory. This being so, there is still a major problem with the transition creatures who are really neither one species or another. Changing from reptile to bird, for example, would involve untold generations of reptiles with imperfectly formed scales in process of transition to birds with imperfectly formed feathers, and, in either case, the creatures would be vulnerable and certainly not the fittest to survive. Darwin's own natural selection would then be working against rather than for such imperfections ever evolving to become another, more perfect, kind of creature. In spite of this evident drawback, general textbook descriptions usually lead the reader to believe that a reptile's scales somehow got ragged at the edges, and, after many generations, became feathers.

This same kind of argument, generally known as the argument from perfection, was well known to Darwin, who recognized that an organ was not only useless but an outright handicap if it was not close to being perfect. However, he wrote confidently in the *Origin*: "If it could be demonstrated that any complex organ existed which could not possibly have been formed by numerous successive slight modifications my theory would absolutely break down" (Darwin 1859, 189). Shortly after he wrote this, he confided in a letter to the American botanist Asa Gray, "I remember well [the] time when the thought of the eye made me cold all over" (F. Darwin 1887, 2:296).[14] Evidently, complex and specialized organs such as the eye had earlier given Darwin cause for a struggle, but by sheer force of intellect he had overcome the problem, at least to his own satisfaction. Again, he gives his rationale in the *Origin*. First, he acknowledged the problem that complex organs such as the eye have to be perfect to be of any use. But somehow by his acknowledgment of the problem, the problem not only disappears, but the reader is left with the opinion that succeeding statements made by an author of such seeming forthright honesty are quite beyond dispute. The reader may see for himself in this lengthy quote how Darwin not only circumvented the difficulty but left convinced that the matter had been solved.

> To suppose that the eye...could have been formed by natural selection, seems, I freely confess, absurd in the highest possible degree. Yet reason tells me, that if numerous gradations from a perfect and complex eye to one very imperfect and simple, each grade being useful to its possessor, can be shown to exist; if further, the eye does vary ever so slightly, and the variations be inherited, which is certainly the case;...then the difficulty of believing that a perfect and complex eye could be formed by natural selection, though insuperable by our imagination, can hardly be considered real (Darwin 1859, 186).

What Darwin has actually done in this statement is to use natural selection to justify natural selection and dismiss the difficulty as not being real. Weismann, a self-confessed adherent to the theory of natural selection, questions Darwin's circular reasoning and then remarks: "It is not upon demonstrative evidence that we rely when we champion the doctrine of selection as a scientific truth; we base our argument on quite other grounds" (Seward 1909, 25). Those "other grounds" are clearly faith since, by definition, faith is being sure of what we hope for and certain of what we do not see; in short, it is the same stuff that makes religion. When we recall that not one transitional form leading to near perfect organs had been discovered at the time Darwin made these statements, we can appreciate that he had the kind of raw faith in his theory that would move mountains.

Trilobite Eyes

Without wishing to stress the complexity of the human eye and the seeming impossibility of its all coming together by accident, there is one other example of an eye even more remarkable, one that was unknown to Darwin. Long before the vertebrates, the reptiles, or even the fishes had been thought of, there was a very primitive creature that scuttled about on the floor of the Cambrian seas known as the trilobite; it came in various shapes and in all sizes up to about twenty inches, and it had large compound eyes. Recently, Clarkson and Levi-Setti (1975) of the University of Chicago have done some spectacular work on the optics of the trilobite eye lenses. It turns out that each lens is a doublet, that is, made up of two lenses, while the shape of the boundary between the two lenses is unlike any now in use—either by animals or humans

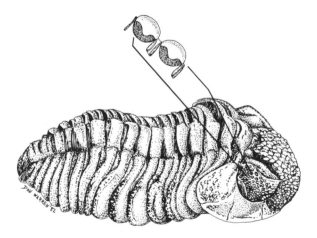

The trilobite had compound eyes and each of these had thick doublet lenses of oriented calcite to eliminate spherical aberration. The insert shows two such eyes in section. (Drawn by Dan Warren after Shawver 1974)

(Shawver 1974). However, the lens shape and the interface curvature is nearly identical to designs published independently by Descartes and Huygens in the seventeenth century. Their design had the purpose of avoiding spherical aberration and were known as aplanatic lenses. Levi-Setti pointed out that the second lens in the doublet of the trilobite eye was necessary in order that the lens system could work under water where the trilobites lived. Thus, these creatures living at the earliest stages of life used an optimal lens design that would require very sophisticated optical engineering procedures to develop today. If Darwin turned cold at the thought of the human eye at the end of the evolutionary cycle, what, one wonders, would he have thought of the trilobite eye near the beginning?

Survival of the Fittest

The terms natural selection and survival of the fittest are often used interchangeably in scientific literature. If there is any confusion in the mind of the reader, he will find some small consolation in knowing that Darwin himself was confused at first. The phrase "survival of the fittest" was actually coined by the armchair philosopher and eccentric Herbert Spencer (1865, 1:164)[15] and although Darwin took a personal dislike to the man, he nevertheless adopted the phrase as his own. In the first edition of the *Origin*, he regarded natural selection and survival of the fittest as different ideas, but by the time he had got to the sixth edition in 1872, he came to realize that they were one and the same thing, and he explained that survival of the fittest was a "more accurate" expression of what he had previously called natural selection (Darwin 1872, 49).[16] Among biological circles the term "survival of the fittest" is anathema and has not been used for years, although it seems that this message has yet to be carried through to the popular press. One of the early reasons for its unpopularity was the stigma of "eat or be eaten" and the savage and often brutal competition of the laissez-faire economists. But this was not all. Some detected circular reasoning when it was seen that a species survives because it is the fittest, and it is the fittest because it survives.

And there was more. The great wastefulness of nature had often been remarked upon by scientists, who cited the millions of eggs laid by the insects, fish, and frogs and noted that only a few ever survive to mature adults—all the others being eaten by predators. However, when this is said to demonstrate the "survival of the fittest" principle, it raises the question, How do we know that the eggs that were eaten were those of the least fit individuals? With "survival of the fittest" in disrepute, at some time within the biological ranks the equation changed to "differential survival", which meant that the fitter individuals will, on the average, leave more offspring. However, this is again a tautology since what is being said is that on an average, more offspring will survive from those parents who leave more offspring. In simple words this sounds ridiculous, but when couched in the jargon of science it becomes convincing, so convincing in fact that the authors are taken in by their own statements. Darwin fell into a similar trap when he explained away the evolution of the eye.

Finally we find that even "differential survival" is recognized as not being very explicit, and the term "adaptation" appears when it is argued that species die out because they lose the ability to adapt to a changing environment. However, even this has a problem: that is, the danger of reversing the statement and saying that certain creatures have lost adaptation because they have died out. An example would be: "The primitive ameba has remained adapted and therefore has survived while the dinosaur failed to adapt and therefore died out." It sounds very reasonable but is actually a tautology of exactly the same type as the "survival of the fittest". The words can even be substituted: a species survives because it remains adaptive and it remains adaptive because it survives. In short, this explains nothing.

The author is indebted to the legal mind of Macbeth (1971, 40) for this insight into these tautologies. A lawyer by training, Macbeth has seen clearly the deficiencies in the basic principles of the theory of evolution that less disciplined minds may only suspect but may not be able to express. One of the severest limitations of the human psyche becomes evident when it is confronted with a tautological argument; some will see it, others will not, while those with a commitment to the evolutionary viewpoint will usually be quite unable to see any problem at all.

The previously mentioned Wistar Institute symposium, held in Philadelphia in 1966 and entitled "Mathematical Challenges to the Neo-Darwinian Interpretation of Evolution", was a classic example of tautological blindness on the part of prominent biologists committed to their belief system. A number of mathematicians, whose discipline requires no particular commitment to the theory of evolution, were invited speakers. These men were quite familiar with the biological problems and plainly said that the basic statements of neo-Darwinism specifically relating to fitness and adaptation were tautologous and, as such, should be regarded as vacuous (Eden 1967, 5, 12, 13). The biologists were defensive from the beginning, and there was a good deal of exchange of definitions that really changed nothing except to make the same statements in different words. Although absolutely sincere in their beliefs, the biologists were seemingly quite unable to see through the deficiencies of their own arguments.

Industrial Melanism

Melanism means a darkening in color, and it is caused by an increase in a specific pigment. The human species has the pigment melanin in the skin; Negro people have a lot of melanin, Caucasians have relatively little. This is simply a variation within the species. Many animals have a similar type of variation—black-and-white mice come to mind, but the peppered moth, *Biston betularia*, is particularly important, because this species is believed to exhibit evolution in action and is given as the textbook example.

The peppered moth is usually a light gray color with speckled markings, but in 1848 an almost black form of this moth was observed near Manchester, England. This was extremely rare at the time, and it was given the subspecies classification *Biston betularia carbonaria*. Following that date, the dark form became more and more common and the light form correspondingly less common, until a century later, more than 90 percent of the peppered moths in the Manchester area were the dark form. In recent years, the light form has been increasing and the dark form decreasing in proportion. An explanation has been put forth that the peppered moth flies at night and rests by day on the trunks and branches of trees. With the rise of heavy industry about the Manchester area in the 1800s, the toxic gases and soot killed the light-colored lichen on the trees, and the trunks and branches displayed their natural dark color. The light-colored moth, which was previously camouflaged against the light-colored lichen, now stood out in stark contrast and was easily seen and eaten by the birds. Their numbers dwindled. The odd dark moth, however, was now protected and began to flourish. In recent years, the greater concern for clean air has reduced industrial pollution and the lichen is growing back on the trees allowing the dark moth to be seen, and it is now diminishing in proportion. The term industrial melanism describes this whole process, and it is seen to be a perfect demonstration of neo-Darwinian evolution: a change of environment has caused a mutant form (the dark moth) to become the dominant form (Bishop and Cook 1975).

Kettlewell (1959) is the acknowledged authority on these moths. It is always important to understand a person's intellctual approach, and Kettlewell is a perfect case of commitment to an idea. We shall see throughout these chapters that evolutionary ideas invariably arise from those who have made a commitment to the idea beforehand. Giving up a fifteen-year medical practice to study the peppered moth, in the belief that industrial melanism was proof of the neo-Darwinian theory, would make it very difficult not to approach the evidence with the answer in hand. Kettlewell's basic assumption is that the dark form is caused by a mutation of a single gene and that this has been brought about by a change in the environment. The argument then continues that for a number of reasons black is better, and so, by natural selection, the superior creature is allowed to develop.

Despite all the careful work and years of effort by Kettlewell, it has to be said that there are many difficulties with his arguments. When all is said and done, no new species has developed—the dark moths still remain moths, *Biston betularia*. The difference between two species of moth involve many hundreds of gene changes rather than just one, while there is always the open question that the peppered moth gene pool may have always contained the genes to produce the dark-colored individuals, in which case no mutations were ever involved. Kettlewell himself cites a number of problem areas, including those cases where melanese or dark moths develop where there is no protective dark-colored trees or cases where only the females of the species are melanic. The entire scenario of the birds picking off or selecting out those moths less well adapted is put in some doubt by Kettlewell's own reference to the eleven-volume work on British moths by C.G. Barrett, which states that there are many examples of white moths deliberately seeking out dark backgrounds and dark moths seeking out light backgrounds. This apparent vulnerability would appear to negate Kettlewell's entire work, but he dismisses this by saying it is only true of a minority of moths (Kettlewell 1973, 220).

The general public is not in a position to make these judgments, and all that can truthfully be said in the case of industrial melanism is that what is seen is a shift in population frequency in response to a changing environment. Consider, as an analogous case, a battalion of soldiers, some black, some white. When attacked by an enemy at night, the white soldiers are more readily seen and suffer greater casualties. Like the moths, this is natural selection, but it cannot be said to be proof of evolution.

Survival and Extinction

It has been pointed out that there is, within each individual, the potential to produce the full range of variation possible within the species; Darwin found that all the fancy types of pigeon, for example, could be produced after several generations by breeding from the common rock pigeon. When the environmental circumstances are unfavorable to one particular type of variation, it may decline almost to

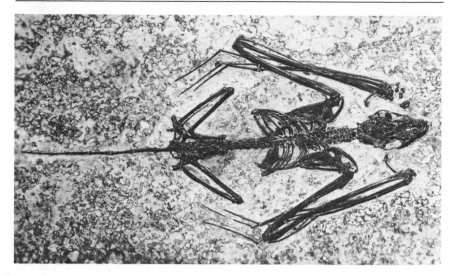

Fossil bat, *Icaronycteris index*, preserved in the Eocene rock stratum and thus supposedly fifty million years old, looks essentially identical to bats of today. Can the bat's environment have remained unchanged for this length of time? (Museum of Natural History, Princeton University)

the point of extinction. Yet all the time that other variants of the same species survive, there is the potential for that variant to reemerge when the environment changes. This is most likely the case with the light- and dark-colored peppered moths in England. Should the entire species, including all the variants, decline in numbers for some reason, there would come a point of no return, and eventually that species dies out, never to be seen alive again. This has happened to many species throughout history but particularly within the past century, while it seems as if the elephant and certain whale species are the latest victims as they fast approach the critical minimum number. Despite the sad fact that many animal species have become extinct at the hand of man, we are told that, according to the fossil record, for every species now in existence roughly ninety-nine have become extinct. The actual ratio varies according to the authority. Recognizing the fact that it is not possible to conduct breeding experiments with fossils to determine which creature belongs to what species, it is probably sufficient to say that in the long, distant past, there was a time when a great many creatures died never to appear on earth again. The dinosaurs were among this massive extinction, but to this day the theory of evolution has given no rational explanation for this extinction phenomenon. The word rational is used judiciously for two reasons: First, textbook explanations for extinction fall back on the old tautology once more. Mayr, a well-respected biologist, is typical in making the following statement: "Ultimately their extinction is due to an inability of their genotype to respond to new selection pressures" (Mayr 1963, 620). This may sound like science but actually resolves to "became extinct because they were unable to adapt", and Macbeth points out by analogy that this is like the coroner saying, "He died because he stopped breathing" (Macbeth 1971, 119). These may be correct statements, but they are not explanations.

The second reason for questioning the usual evolutionary explanations for extinction in the fossil record is really twofold and asks, Why did many creatures die out when it seems that they had remained perfectly adapted over long periods? Conversely, why have many creatures remained and are still with us today when, to all outward appearances, they should not have survived at all? One of the early explanations proposed for the extinction of the Irish elk or the woolly mammoth, for example, was that the antlers of the elk and the tusks of the mammoth became too large. This caused the creatures to become maladapted, even though the environment may not have changed. This explanation, however, does violence to the principle that natural selection selects the fittest, the best adapted, or whatever, and even suggests that natural selection bears within its bosom a malevolent extinction principle. The notion of an extinction principle runs counter to the theory of evolution and fosters the idea that some hidden overseer, such as Paley's Watchmaker, is calling the shots.

Finally, there are all those creatures that common sense would say should never have survived at all in the allegedly savage adapt or be eaten world of living things. The stupid chicken hasn't always been domesticated, but can its predecessors have been any more intelligent in the wild and survived for millions of years? Sheep are not much brighter, and there are still undomesticated sheep today, certain varieties of which, when attacked by a predator, make no attempt to run for safety or even fight but stand motionless and await their fate. We think of the animals and insects as being protected by their coloring in their natural habitat, yet this armchair explanation doesn't hold when, for example, the grasshopper chirrups to advertise its whereabouts. Wallace, exploring the Malay jungles, reported on the birds of paradise resplendent in the most fantastic colors, not at all camouflaged in their natural surroundings (Everett 1978).[17] They had decorated the private jungle paradise for centuries until they caught the eye of man and were then slaughtered by the million for women's hats. This commercial exploitation was finally banned by international agreement in 1924.

Examples of creatures that would appear to be poorly adapted to their surroundings could be multiplied, while the "living fossils" must

Wilson's Bird of Paradise. These brilliantly colored birds survived in spite of not being "best fitted" to their jungle environment. (Lydekker, reprint 1901)

be added to this list. Bats today are exactly the same as their fossilized counterpart, but in recent years less common living animals such as the peccary, the Okapi (formerly known as *Paleotragus*), the *Coelacanth*, and perhaps even the *Plesiosaur* have been discovered to be living unchanged for as much as 100 million years. It is no wonder that many of these discoveries cause controversy since their very existence challenges the faith in a theory that is based upon the assumption of enormous lengths of time.

Clearly, the problem of survival of some and not others, the extinction of many but not all, is a matter that has baffled evolution scientists ever since Darwin's day, and there has yet to be a satisfactory explanation. Of course, the Bible story about the Flood, which describes one massive and worldwide extinction of life except for the few that survived on the ark, would seem to provide a solution to most of the unanswered questions. But then to believe this, one would have to violate Darwin's most vital and cherished assumption, that divine intervention did not occur.

It is hoped that throughout this chapter some light has been shed on what, for many, is a mystique surrounding the species question. The wide variation possible within a species which can bring variants to the point of becoming reproductively isolated, has been called by some micro-evolution, but the only new species which has been created has been on paper by the term of the definition. The situation closely parallels that of the geologic column described in Chapter Four. As the fossils are ranked, so the living species are ranked and used to demonstrate evolution, but in either case, the actual evidence exists only on paper. The facts show that the tendency is for species to remain stable (stasis), and there is no evidence that extreme variants can continue to depart from the main type indefinitely (macro-evolution). Yet this is what the theory of evolution supposes.

The bottom line is that, after more than a century of sustained effort by literally thousands of workers, nature still provides us with a faith choice. That choice is to believe that, while living forms can vary about an average, they always remain fixed within the limits of this variation. Alternatively, we may believe that it is possible for the variation to become so extreme that reversion back within the normal limits becomes impossible and a new life form has thus evolved.

7

The First Missing Link

If we do not accept the hypothesis of spontaneous
generation [of life from non-living matter], then
at this one point of the history of development
[evolution] we must have recourse to the miracle
of a supernatural creation.
ERNST HAECKEL
(1876, 1:348)

T he idea that life on earth originated from a single-celled organism and then progressed onwards and upwards in ever-increasing complexity to culminate in man himself is what the theory of evolution is all about. The stages in progression from one life form to another are today depicted in what are known as phylogenetic diagrams, which tend to become minor works of art as they grow in detail and, necessarily, in physical size. They often finish as rather impressive additions to the wall of the biology classroom. Although these diagrams tend to differ in detail, they presuppose that all living things are related and represent the "family tree" of life; in fact, the first diagram of this sort published by Haeckel, in 1874, was drawn as an actual tree (Haeckel 1879, 2:189).[1] Ernst Haeckel was Germany's imaginative popularizer of Darwin's theory in the nineteenth century, and by use of the family-tree analogy, he effectively riveted the idea of the relationship of all living things into the common mind.

The previous chapter mentioned Darwin's problem of the apparent absence of creatures in the fossil record that were transitions between the major groups of animals. The absence of creatures showing the evolution of the backbone has been mentioned, but there are other major gaps within the family tree, such as that between the fish and the amphibian or between the amphibian and the reptiles. It would be expected that over the several million years required by the theory of evolution for the transition from, for example, the fish to the first amphibian, literally thousands of fossil creatures at every stage show-

177

Man's family tree according to
Ernst Haeckel (1874). A century
later, Gould (1977b) and others are
finally beginning to admit there is
not a shred of evidence for the
trunk or main branches. (Thomas
Fisher Rare Book Library, University of Toronto)

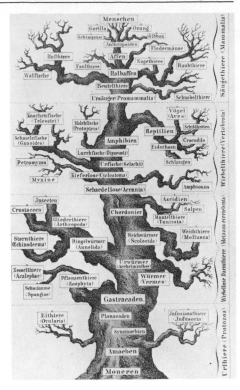

ing the gradual progression from fin to leg would be found. So far, not one has shown up.

According to the theory, flight evolved as four separate events: the winged reptiles such as the *Pterosaur*, all of which are now extinct; the winged mammals, such as the bat, the winged insects, and, of course, the birds. With the exception of the birds, not a single transition type of any of the other winged creatures has been found to prove that they evolved. The *Archaeopteryx* has for years held pride of place as the proof of transition from reptile to bird, but since Jensen's discovery in 1977 of a fossil of a true bird in the same geological stratum and, therefore, of the same age as the *Archaeopteryx*, its claim to be a transition is now in doubt (Jensen 1977).[2] Interestingly, it has been entirely rejected as a transition by respected paleontologists Gould and Eldredge (1977, 3:147) of Harvard University.[3] Eldredge also questions the familiar horse series and points out that there are no fossil forms between the different types of fossil horse. After more than a century of searching the fossil record, the actual evidence now in hand is seen to be discouragingly small and inconclusive, while there are a great many gaps for which not a single fossil has been found. In short, most of the "branches" and "twigs" of the family tree are missing. It begins to look as if the facts can be better explained by the idea of Special Creation.

Perhaps of even greater importance are the two major gaps that have occupied the minds of scientists since Darwin's day. The first is at the root of the tree and concerns the transition from non-life to life in its first stages, and the second is at the top of the tree and of more popular interest, concerned as it is with the transitions between apes and man. This chapter is about the first transition—the origin of life.

Did Life Begin Spontaneously?

The French wines produced in the year 1864 have never been surpassed, or so the connoisseurs claim, yet ironically the wine industry had been plagued for several years prior to this with a mysterious "wine disease". Wine production was and still is one of France's major industries, sanctioned and protected by government, and the slightest threat to production quickly reaches the attention of those in authority. In the 1860s the problem was related to the fermentation process and came to the attention of the Emperor Louis Napoleon III, grand-nephew to the first Napoleon, who immediately ordered one of the most competent scientists of the day to find a solution; the scientist's name was Louis Pasteur (Dubos 1976).

Louis Pasteur, 1822-95. Showed that life could only arise from existing life and set a major hurdle for Darwinian faith, which requires that life began spontaneously. (Lithograph by Albert Rosenthal, Academy of Medicine, Toronto)

In those days, just three or four generations ago, there was a running argument between men of science concerning the origin of life. Earlier chapters have shown that throughout history men have been divided in their views: some can accept the idea of supernatural creation whereas others prefer to stay with a naturalistic explanation. Creation of the stars and planets never seem to have been a great issue, but the creation of life and, ultimately our own origins, have always been a source of contention. Until comparatively recently in history, most people believed that life had begun by divine creation, and that since then every living thing had derived from a similar living thing before it. It was said that life begets life, and today we have a term for this, "biogenesis". In the other camp of belief, there were those who subscribed to the Aristotelian view, only half believing in a Creator but fully committed to the belief that life could be spontaneously generated from nonliving things without the necessity for divine intervention. This view is called "abiogenesis". The contention between the two views has blown hot then cold throughout the centuries and today appears to be growing once more into a hot issue.

There was rather an odd situation towards the end of the eighteenth century in which each side of the argument was represented by a Roman Catholic priest. Abbé Lazzaro Spallanzani, an Italian priest, was the champion of the Special Creation viewpoint (biogenesis) and the English Jesuit John Needham argued for spontaneous generation (abiogenesis). Needham's view rested on a severely strained interpretation of the biblical account and undoubtedly derived from his friend the Compte de Buffon. According to Needham there were two accounts of Creation in Genesis. In the first, God commanded the waters to produce the living things (Genesis 1:20-21), and in the second, God formed every beast out of the ground (Genesis 2:19). Needham and his followers took the position that having been ordered to bring forth life, the ground and the waters were forever after free to continue doing so. Spallanzi claimed that creation of life from non-life had occurred only once and that all life had since derived from it.

For those who wished to believe it, there seemed to be plenty of examples of abiogenesis; it was thought by a die-hard minority until just over a century ago that maggots were spontaneously created in rotting meat. However, the Italian physician, Francesco Redi (1626-79), had shown by some very simple experiments as early as 1668 that the maggots were the result of eggs laid by flies (Redi 1668). When the flies were kept away, there was no sign of the maggots. Nevertheless, Redi's observations were opposed by those who preferred to believe their own preconceptions. It was, after all, easier to believe what was really a poor observation than it was to believe in divine creation, which could not be observed at all.

Today, we never find a maggot in an apple, but before the days of chemical spraying, it was normal to find one in practically every apple—or worse, to find half of one! So it was perfectly natural to assume that the maggot had been spontaneously generated within the sealed fruit, and the apple with its maggot then became the armchair naturalist's example of spontaneous generation.

In addition to this conflict of ideas, in Pasteur's day there had sprung up the "germ theory", which maintained that the air we breathe contained small germs of life that could multiply and grow under favorable conditions. There was much opposition to this theory also, especially as it was not possible to see these "germs" even with the most powerful microscopes of the day; eventually when more powerful microscopes became available, the theory was confirmed, and the germs were called bacteria.

It took Pasteur about two years, in which he employed a series of elegantly simple experiments, to solve the wine problem. Until this time it had generally been thought that wine fermentation was simply a matter of the grape sugar turning to alcohol and carbonic acid gas, and that these chemicals in turn produced the microbes that were seen in the fermentation vessels; this example implied abiogenesis. Pasteur showed that it was yeast, which is a microbe and type of fungus, that caused the fermentation to take place and was introduced to the fermentation vessels in an incidental manner as a living organism on the skin of the grape (it is seen as the white bloom on the skin). The microbes seen, therefore, originated from preexisting microbes and not by abiogenesis or spontaneous generation. By the use of glass flasks in which there was a sterile nutrient—it had been thoroughly boiled—Pasteur showed that, in the presence of air from which airborne bacteria had been excluded by filtration, no organic growth occurred in the vessels, and the solutions remained sterile. In the presence of normal unfiltered air, however, growth did take place as seen by a darkening of the nutrient solution, indicating that air normally contains minute living organisms. Pasteur examined the air filters microscopically and found the bacteria as conclusive evidence of the "germ theory". It was almost incidental to his main purpose, but Pasteur had dealt a severe blow to the idea of spontaneous generation. The fact that this long-held notion was so effectively shaken by Pasteur in 1861 (Pasteur 1861) and not by Redi a century earlier was due to a number of factors, not the least of which was that the French wine makers evidently enjoyed greater public esteem than the Italian butchers.

Pasteur was a devout Roman Catholic and had been opposed to the idea of spontaneous generation ever since he had first learned of it. It seemed to him that it was going beyond the biblical dictum that creation of life was a divine operation that had been confined to and completed in the first week of Creation. Then again, Pasteur lost no time in making this clear in writing and in speeches. For example, he wrote in 1864:

> To bring about spontaneous generation would be to create a germ. It would be creating life; it would be to solve the problem of its origin. It would mean to go from matter to life through conditions of environment and of matter [non-life]. God as author of life would then no longer be needed. Matter would replace Him. God would need to be invoked only as author of the motions of the universe (Dubos 1976, 395).

Elegantly simple, Pasteur's work won him the coveted French Academy of Science's prize. He well recognized, however, that he had not proven that spontaneous generation did not occur by every imagined means, but he had grandly exposed the fallacy of all previous claims. Nevertheless, the fact that this work was published just two years after Darwin's *Origin* was particularly damaging to the fledgling theory of evolution for which the spontaneous generation of life from

Pasteur, acknowledged as a truly great scientist, gives away the fact that he was a devoted family man in this formal Victorian pose with his granddaughter. (Engraving by Johnson from the painting by Bonnat; Metropolitan Toronto Reference Library Board)

nonlife was crucial. Old diehards committed to spontaneous generation and new converts to Darwin did not appreciate Pasteur's remarks,
and there is some evidence that someone tried to discredit his work with
a deliberate hoax. The story is worth repeating because the basic idea
behind it is still very current.

In 1864, only five weeks after Pasteur had delivered a particularly
spirited and widely reported defense of divine creation as the only
possible initiator of life, a meteorite fragment purportedly containing
evidence of life from outer space was reported to have fallen at Orgueil
in southwestern France. A French chemist analyzed the fragment
within days of its having fallen and showed that it contained "a
complex mixture of high molecular weight" (Mason 1963, 45), which
suggested that it had derived from once-living organisms. The story
was given currency by the highest authorities. In 1871 Sir William
Thomson, president of the British Association, told the assembly that
life had come to this planet from outer space, carried on "countless
seed-bearing meteoritic stones" (Ellegard 1958, 88). As recently as 1964,
the popular Life Science Library series in its book *The Cell* declared
that "cell-like fossils have been found in meteorites" and concluded
that this was a "startling indication that life might have been much
more prolific on other worlds" (Pfeiffer 1964, 88).[4]

The Orgueil meteorite is technically referred to as a carbonaceous
chondrite and is kept at the American Museum of Natural History. In
1961 it was subjected to mass spectroscopy. The spectral characteristics
of the hydrocarbons detected very closely matched those of butter![5]
Incredibly, however, the investigators then soberly concluded that
because of the quantity of hydrocarbons present, there could be no
doubt that the meteorite and its compounds were of extraterrestrial

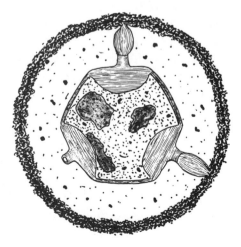

A drawing similar to this and
prepared from a photomicrograph
at x 3000 during the 1961
examination of the Orgueil
meteorite, was used in the popular
Life Science Library series to
illustrate the claim that "cell-like
fossils...40 million to the cubic
inch have been found in
meteorites." Unknown to the
public was the controversy among
scientists; some said the particles
were merely hexagonal crystals of
troilite or ferrous sulphide.

origin! (Mason 1963, 45). A more rational conclusion would surely have been to say that it was a hoax, and there was much controversy in the scientific press; some believed it to be genuine and others didn't.[6] The symptoms of commitment to an idea no matter what the facts seemed to be manifesting themselves again.

Another chondrite fell in Australia in 1969, and this time the investigators were more cautious, reporting twenty-three aromatic hydrocarbons but concluding that they were of abiotic origin—in other words, that they did not originate from anything living (Lawless et al. 1972). There the matter has rested. Yet, the life-on-other-worlds scenario is actually a vital part of evolution, cannot be abandoned and, as we shall see, is still very much with us.

Did Life Originate at the Bottom of the Sea?

Following our little inquiry into history, we find that notwithstanding Pasteur's blow to the followers of Darwin in the early 1860s, the idea of spontaneous generation again raised its head even before the closing of that decade, this time in Germany.

Professor Ernst Haeckel is largely unknown outside his own country, but in Germany he is a sort of national hero and regarded by many as one of the greatest scientists of the nineteenth century. That was not a universal opinion, however, and Rudolph Virchow, the father of pathology, was at least one who knew Haeckel from his graduate days and later branded him a fool (Ottaway 1973, 106). The least that can be said is that he was controversial—he was known as "Der Ketzer von Jena" (the gadfly of Jena)—and naturally he acquired enemies as well as admirers (Bölsche 1906; Klemm 1968).[7]

Ernst Heinrich Philipp August Haeckel was born in 1834, in Potsdam, into a Christian family whose head was a moderately successful lawyer. He was interested in natural science, but medicine was about the closest thing to natural science offered in the German universities of his day, and after studying at Wurzburg and Berlin he graduated as a physician in 1857 at the age of twenty-three. With a passion for the poet Goethe and a reasonable talent at painting, he spent the next few years traveling, painting, and studying "all the grandeur of godless nature" (Werner 1930, 28). As he explained in a letter to his mistress, written in his waning years, he began as a Christian but when he started to practice medicine and penetrate the mysteries of life and its evolution, he became, after the most desperate spiritual conflict, a free-thinker and pantheist (Haeckel 1911; Werner 1930, 28).[8] It was during this somewhat restless postgraduate period that he read Darwin's *Origin of Species*, which had been translated into the German language in 1860.

Impressed by Darwin, he began to study zoology and completed a dissertation in 1861. An academic by inclination, he took a teaching position at Jena University where the intellectual atmosphere was more receptive to Darwin and remained there as professor of zoology for forty-four years, retiring at seventy-five years of age in 1909. He died in 1919, having received many international honors in an extremely active life.

Ernst Haeckel, 1834-1919. Photograph taken in 1880. His student days long behind him, his reputation established, he had become internationally known as the "gad-fly of Jena". (Science and Medicine Library, University of Toronto)

Haeckel was a man of boundless energy, talent, and imagination, hailed (by some) as reformer of zoology, master of biology, and evolutionary prophet. He became Darwin's chief European apostle proclaiming the gospel of evolution with evangelistic fervor, not only to the university intelligentsia but to the common man by popular books and to the working classes by lectures in rented halls. A photograph has survived showing the properties used for one of his popular lectures on the evolution of man, and one cannot but be impressed by the sheer magnitude of effort in producing what has been described as a sort of Darwinian passion play (Gasman 1971, 8).[9] Thomas Huxley's similar efforts in England were gallant but never on this grand a scale, while the efforts by Dana and others in the United States by comparison pale into insignificance. In many ways Haeckel's personal life has more elements of human interest than other scientists, such as Darwin.

For example, beginning in his sixty-fourth year, when his wife, though younger than he, was an aging invalid and many of his friends

Photograph of a Berlin theater rented by Haeckel for a public lecture on evolution about 1905. The enormous backdrop shows embryos, skeletons, etc., relating man with the ape. (Reproduced from Peter Klemm, *Der Ketzer von Jena*, Leipzig: Urania, 1968)

had passed away (Thomas Huxley died three years previously), he had an ardent love affair, lasting five years with a woman thirty-four years his junior, while at the same time he was still teaching, writing, and giving public lectures. The intimate correspondence between himself and Frida von Uslar-Gleichen during this period has been published by Werner (1930), though regrettably in an expurgated edition.[10] Two things come to mind when one reads these quite literary works. First, notable from the dates on the letters is the promptness with which the postal service of a century ago made delivery! Second, one wonders how the man, with all his other activities, possibly found time for almost daily liaison? However, lest this digression begin to appeal to the reader's more prurient interests, we must return to pursue the origin of life at the bottom of the sea.

Haeckel was extremely systematic in his work. As has been mentioned, he devised the concept of the family tree, or phylogenetic relationship, between all living things. Having an orderly mind is usually an asset, but in Haeckel's case his orderly system became an end in itself rather than simply a means of explaining a supposed set of relationships. He imaginatively made up the names of organisms that he thought should exist and was not beyond cheating just a little if the

facts of nature did not fit his theories. Recognizing that there was a gap
at the base of the family tree, a vital transition missing between the
inorganic non-living matter and the first sign of organic life, Haeckel
invented a series of minute organisms he called the *Monera* to fill it
(Haeckel 1866, 1:135). He published details of the various kinds of
Monera, with drawings of these shapeless blobs of protoplasm without
nuclei that he said reproduced by a process of fission (Haeckel 1868).[11]
At the time he was writing, in 1868, not even a hint of the *Monera* had
been found, but, coincidentally, later that same year Thomas Huxley,
working in England, reported finding some microscopic organisms in
mud samples dredged up from the depths of the North Atlantic. These
small organisms appeared to be a very primitive form of organized life,
although the samples had been preserved in strong alcohol so that they
were not alive. Huxley recognized these organisms as Haeckel's *Monera* and proposed to call the particular species he had discovered
Bathybius haeckelii in honour of the professor at the University of Jena
(Huxley 1868, 210).[12]

Nothing better could happen to a natural scientist than to have his
name latinized and appended to some creature, no matter how lowly.
His fame spread, aided perhaps by the prophetic qualities that were
flatteringly ascribed to his many other talents. Throughout the 1870s
HMS Challenger continued to dredge up samples of mud containing
B. haeckelii, thus confirming Haeckel's prediction and Huxley's obser-

Frida von Ulsar-Gleichen,   *Ernst Haeckel at sixty-two*
1868-1903   *in 1896*

Haeckel actually outlived his mistress by sixteen years; she died of a heart
condition at the age of thirty-five. (Reproduced from Peter Klemm, *Der Ketzer
von Jena,* Leipzig: Urania 1968)

HMS Challenger during her voyage of exploration 1873-76. (Thomas Fisher Rare Book Library, University of Toronto)

vation. Meanwhile, great publicity was made of this since it implied abiogenesis and was urgently needed to prop up Darwin's theory. Many, perhaps wavering in their faith in divine creation, at last capitulated to science when confronted with *B. haeckelii* (Haeckel 1876, 2:53).[13] From the HMS Challenger work, Huxley confidently said that the *Bathybius*, this life in the making, "probably forms one continuous scum of living matter...on the sea bed...girding the whole surface of the earth" (Huxley 1871, 38).

It was customary practice at that time for living samples to be preserved for later examination by dropping them into a specimen jar of strong alcohol. This was done in a routine manner to the mud samples on board the HMS Challenger, but a chemist on the expedition, who seems to have been more committed to his chemistry than to biology, pointed out that the protoplasmic matter recognized as *B. haeckelii* was nothing more than an amorphous precipitate of sulphate of lime (gypsum) which forms when seawater is added to alcohol! (Murray 1875, 24:530; Buchanan 1875, 24:604).[14-15] The date was 1875 and that should have been the end of *B. haeckelii*, then and there, but it was vitally important that science, and particularly those promoting the theory of evolution, not lose the public confidence by exposure of this fiasco. Scientists were defending their authority as the Roman Church leaders had their authority in the face of Galileo's discoveries.

The matter was reported somewhat obscurely in the *Quarterly Journal of the Microscopical Science* and at the Royal Society of London the following year, but no public comment was made on the significance of this discovery (Thomson 1875, 390). The author is indebted to Rupke for scanning all the English and European journals of the day to find only one article, and that in French, which critically discusses the way the public had been misled over the question of the *Monera* (Rupke 1971, 178).[16]

One may well wonder how such a grand cover-up was possible. It is not difficult to surmise how when something of the conspiratorial nature of nineteenth century British science, with T.H. Huxley as the grand master, is understood. It has been exposed by Irving (1955) and more recently by Bibby (1972). The latter describes how the X Club—the members could never agree on a name—was formed by Huxley in 1864 and consisted of nine members who, with one exception, were all presidents and secretaries of learned societies; the one exception was Herbert Spencer, whom we shall meet in the final chapter. These nine were men at the top of their profession, handpicked for their views, and holding personal influence on almost every famous scientist in the world, as well as on many distinguished radicals.[17]

Neither Darwin nor Lyell were members, but their views were held in the very highest esteem. The members met for dinner always immediately before each meeting of the Royal Society, at which time strategy was plotted. By this means, British science was literally "governed", from 1864 until 1884, by Huxley and his disciples, and, with their combined influence over the scientific press it was little wonder that the 1876 report of the demise of Huxley's *B. haeckelii* was never made public. Perhaps even worse was the fact that the public continued to be

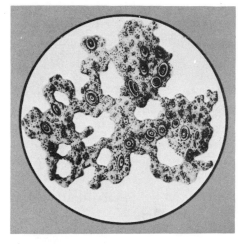

Bathybius haeckelii, 1868-76. Viewed under the microscope the small discoids are the exoskeletons of tiny sea creatures, while the jelly within which these are suspended is the gelatinous gypsum precipitate.

duped for at least another fifty years by the reprints of Haeckel's widely circulated and ever popular *History of Creation*—all completely unabridged and unrevised.[18] So far as Haeckel (1877) was concerned, he refused to believe that the *Monera* were nonexistent and went to his grave still convinced that a new *Bathybius* was out there on the seabed waiting to be discovered.

Did Life Originate Extraterrestrially?

With the collapse of the *Monera* affair, yet another blow had been struck to the idea of abiogenesis, and therefore indirectly to Darwin's theory. Haeckel had put his finger on the real need for spontaneous generation when he said, "This hypothesis is indispensable for the consistent completion of the non-miraculous history of creation" (Haeckel 1876, 1:348), and this is as true today as it was in 1876. Sure enough, the very next year an event occurred that turned the attention of science to the skies for the source of life. The need to provide a non-miraculous explanation for life's origin on earth had to be fulfilled. Relegating that origin to some cosmic outpost gave a measure of intellectual satisfaction since no amount of negative evidence could lessen the possibility of its being true; in other words, it was for the forseeable future beyond the reach of man's inquiry and could neither be proved nor refuted. There was always hope, of course, that there may be discovery of life, and better yet a living intelligence, and in the decades bracketing the turn of the present century, it was widely believed that just such a discovery had been made.

Percival Lowell was born in Boston, in 1855, into two of America's great and wealthy families. Educated in Europe and then at Harvard, he was able to enjoy the privileged life of the financially independent intellectual, traveling and keeping company with New England's affluent industrial aristocracy, who were generally keen practitioners of social Darwinism. Later in life, the psychologist William James and Ernst Haeckel in Germany became his personal friends (Hoyt 1976, 338).[19] Darwin's influence reached into the very wellsprings of Lowell's thoughts, and the latter applied the idea of evolution broadly in both science and society, as may be seen throughout his many writings (Hoyt 1976, 25-6). Several times a world traveler, he had a peculiar fascination with the Far East and spent some time in Japan where he learned the language with some proficiency. He penned his impressions of the Eastern peoples in one of his early books, entitled *The Soul of the Far East*. The influence of Darwin can be seen to dominate the whole theme, in passages such as the following:

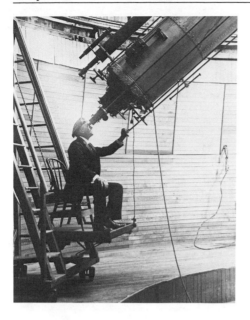

Percival Lowell, 1855-1916. His faith in the idea of intelligent life on Mars led him to dedicate the last twenty years of his life to find proof by the study of the "canals". The proof never came but he died convinced and was buried next to his telescope. (Lowell Observatory Photograph)

Dissimilarity of Western and Eastern attitude of mind shows that individuality bears the same relation to the development of mind that the differentiation of species does to the evolution of organic life (Lowell 1911, 194).

As a young man he was not only brought up amid the intellectual swirl of the Darwinian controversy, but his imagination was fired by a report, in 1877, of the Italian astronomer Schiaparelli who said he had seen "canali" on the planet Mars (Pickering 1896, 113; Serviss 1901, 93).[20-21] Schiaparelli's observations were actually within months of the formal demise of the *Monera* fallacy. It was a very cautious report, and the "canali" were simply meant as straight lines. A later report from Schiaparelli indicated that these were double lines, and in English "canali" became canals. Popular imagination took this to mean a sign of intelligent life, and there followed a public controversy almost as sharp as that which followed the publication of Darwin's *Origin*. The objections came from the theologians who saw the proposal of extraterrestrial life as threat to the doctrine of Special Creation. Their argument held that God had created life only on earth and nowhere else. Man, so the logic ran, was the only reasoning creature, uniquely favored among all of God's creations and the center of his attention (Hoyt 1976, 213).

Lowell made his last trip to Japan in 1892 with fellow Boston scientist George Agassiz—the son of the great naturalist Louis

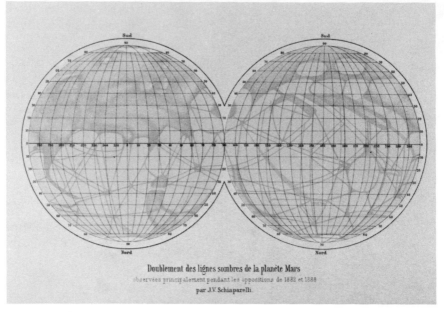

Schiaparelli's drawings of the planet Mars in 1882 and 1888 from Flammarion's French translation, where "canali" have become "doublement des lignes". Unfortunately for believers in the intelligent life notion, the double lines would form differing patterns from year to year. (Planetarium, Royal Ontario Museum)

Agassiz—with the purpose of investigating the mysteries of Shinto occultism (Lowell 1894), and it was during this visit that he learned Schiaparelli had been forced to abandon his work on the planets because of failing eyesight. Then and there, Lowell was impressed to pick up the Italian master's mantle and press on with the Martian investigation (Hoyt 1976, 26). Lowell returned to Boston in 1893, setting to work with incredible energy and at his own expense, to build, equip, and staff a major new astronomical observatory in the best possible location for the exclusive study of the planet Mars. Time was short, because Mars would be once more in a favorable viewing position in October 1894.

With amazing speed, a revolving dome observatory and eighteen-inch refractor telescope (later, he had a twenty-four-inch refractor) were built and installed on top of a hill overlooking the small town of Flagstaff, Arizona, where the air was particularly clear and viewing conditions exceptionally good. Lowell began on time in 1894 and continued unceasingly to observe and write about his Martian life theory for the next twenty-two years, until the day he died in 1916. He was buried next to his telescope, and there on his tomb is an epitaph extracted from his last book, *The Evolution of the Worlds* (1909).

Mars, as it appeared in Lowell's telescope under the best viewing conditions, is quite a small disc, and observation of detail is just about at the limit of resolution of the human eye. But over the years the number of canals reported and named by Lowell rose to more than seven hundred (Hoyt 1976, 64). He mapped and measured, published and proclaimed, continually fanning the flames of public interest. The life-on-Mars thesis caught the attention of England's science fiction writer of the day H.G. Wells, who wrote *War of the Worlds* in 1898, a classic to this day. Interest was revived a generation later when a radio drama based on Wells's book was broadcast in New York in 1938 and caused a minor panic among the listeners (Wells 1898).[22]

Herbert G. Wells, 1866-1946. Photograph taken in the 1890s at about the time he was inspired by Lowell's ideas and wrote his successful *War of the Worlds*. (Metropolitan Toronto Reference Library Board)

For the next sixty years after Lowell's death, no one could really refute the idea that there was life on Mars. If it were true, it would greatly support the theory of evolution, for it was argued that if life could evolve from nonlife on earth, then it was also possible to have evolved under similar circumstances anywhere else throughout the universe. More important, however, was the possibility that life could have evolved on a distant planet first and subsequently been brought to earth. Moreover, each of the millions of stars in the visible universe was a potential sun to a planetary system like our own, and by sheer weight of numbers it was reasoned, principally by Lowell, that there must be many with conditions suitable for life (Sagan et al. 1972).[23] Actually, to this day there is no direct evidence of a single planet beyond our own solar system.[24]

In July and September of 1976, the Viking space vehicles landed on Mars with equipment to carry out three life-test experiments. Even after they had completed reconnaissance of the planet four years beforehand, it was evident that there were no canals, no sign of intelligent life, and Lowell's theory promptly died—and so, it seems, did public interest (Masursky et al. 1972). The life-test experiments were also somewhat inconclusive, and there was a sense of reluctance in having finally to report that Mars is barren and totally devoid of organic life (Horowitz 1977).

It is fair to ask, Why was Lowell so misguided? Certainly not because he was a crank. An astute businessman, proficient in a number of languages, a degree in mathematics from Harvard, socially accepted among both the scientific and business communities, he had credibility almost beyond measure. And yet he was so obviously wrong. There is little question but that he was committed to an idea. In turn his idea committed him to a fairly sizable financial investment for the observatory, which still functions to this day although not for the exclusive study of Mars. The idea and the investment then became master of his life and he spent his remaining twenty-two years totally given to the study of Mars. Interestingly, it seems that it was just this intensity of commitment that enabled him to see what he believed in even though the object of his belief did not actually exist. This is a psychophysiological phenomenon related to human vision and has itself been the object of study by psychologists for a number of years, although it seems that the results of these studies have not been applied very well to astronomers (Young 1971).

Scientific observations must always be confirmed by other observers. There was much discussion in the professional journals of the day, because some observers could see the canals and others could not. At the time this was ascribed to different viewing conditions in various geographic locations, but in retrospect it would seem that, once again, it was the individual commitment to the idea that was playing a significant part in prompting the perceptions. Photographic records at the turn of the century were not of much help for a number of technical reasons, not the least of which is that even with the largest telescope of today, the red planet is still not very big and has ephemeral features.

The lesson to be learned from Lowell's folly is that presuppositions can not only make us see what does not exist but can also prevent us from seeing what does. Although every effort is made by scientists to remove the human element, there are still two vital areas in which human reason must be involved. The first concerns setting up the experimental conditions, and the second the interpretation of results; in either case, presupposition, consciously or unconsciously, tends to produce bias, a problem that is still very much with us today (Broad 1981; St. James-Roberts 1976; Wade and Broad 1983). The American space exploration program contains within it the presupposition that life of some kind may have evolved extraterrestrially, and to this end the multi-million dollar lunar receiving laboratory was built and the life-detection experiments carried out (Morrison et al. 1979). In the absence of any positive results, there has, in recent years, been a blending of real science with science fiction as, one by one, authorities have proposed that our planet has been "seeded" by intelligent extraterrestrial life.

Dr. Francis Crick, who received the Nobel prize for discovering the complex double-helix structure of DNA—the life "blue-print" contained within each cell—is probably more aware than any other man of the extraordinary complexity of the living cell. Crick and his associate, Leslie Orgel, at California's Salk Institute, are quite committed to the theory of evolution, yet they cannot accept the usual explanation that the first self-replicating cell came together spontaneously by chance. They concede that statistically it would just never happen. In 1973 Crick and Orgel seriously proposed that life initially appeared on earth as a direct act of "seeding" by intelligent life from another planet, and they call their theory directed panspermia.[25] As far out as this may be, and it is distinctly Lowellian Darwinism, the proposal is based on two observations: First, life as we know it depends on traces of the rare element molybdenum, and it is argued that it would more likely have evolved on a planet in which that element is more abundant. Second, there is but a single genetic code to all life, and, if it had developed by chance in "some primordial ocean", then with multiple chance begin-

Svente Arrhenius, 1859-1927. This Swedish physicist proposed that life arrived on earth from outer space in 1908—seventy years later the idea was being promoted by every form of the media. (Academy of Medicine, Toronto)

nings, more than one genetic code would be expected. The idea that life could have arrived by meteorite is rejected, because of the radiation damage during its long space journey. The field of possibility, therefore, has been narrowed to the choice between miraculous supernatural creation and life having been deliberately brought to earth by intelligent extraterrestrial beings in the remote past. Crick has placed his bet on the unprovable idea that somewhere in time and space there existed conditions on another planet more conducive to the spontaneous generation of life on our own planet under any possible conditions.

Back to the Sea

The excitement and speculation about intelligent life on Mars diminished significantly after Lowell died in 1916, although, of course, there was a world war that, in any case, moved all else to the newspaper back pages. The *Monera* notion for the beginning of life on earth had been effectively squelched in 1876, but Haeckel was still active with what eventually came to be seen as a rather crude and mechanistic model; he rejected completely the hypothesis of life from outer space. Haeckel died in 1919, and the *Monera* theory finally went with him, yet he had left a legacy in an idea that would be inherited just a year or so later by a Russian biochemist, A.I. Oparin (1953).

In the meantime, there seemed to be an impasse, for while the idea of life's origin being in outer space might have satisfied some, it was really removing the problem rather than providing a solution. It was almost taboo to speak of spontaneous generation occurring on earth, and yet philosophically it raised the awful specter that if life didn't arise spontaneously, then it must have been purposefully created. There was no third alternative. In the meantime, continuing research showed that elemental life was more and more complicated. Was there no way out of this dilemma? Gallant attempts were made, for instance, by invoking the radioactive powers of radium on mixtures of inorganic salts, and so on, but all to no avail (Oparin 1953, 57). Even the smallest particles of life known then, the viruses, could not be produced from nonliving molecules in the laboratory.

Haeckel had argued that although spontaneous generation is not observable under the present conditions on earth, it did take place in the earth's early history, when conditions were very different—he thus preserved his beloved *Monera* theory by assigning to it a past event. The idea did not take root and grow in Haeckel's time, possibly because it seemed so contrary to Lyell's doctrine of uniformity. Like the later panspermia theory, it relegated the origin of life to the nonobservable, in this case the past, and, thus, seemingly beyond man's inquiry. Yet there was something attractive about the idea, and it appealed to A.I. Oparin in Russia and, almost simultaneously, to J.B.S. Haldane in England; the idea was known for many years as the Oparin-Haldane theory. Both men were committed to the theory of evolution and independently promoted their idea, Oparin through his Communist influence in Russia and Haldane as an active Marxist and regular contributor to London's *Daily Worker* (Clark 1968, 144, 283).[26]

During the 1920s Oparin marshaled together a number of facts, among which were the advances then being made to produce organic compounds in the laboratory. The very name organic means that it is something derived from a living organism, such as sugar from grapes or carbon dioxide gas from burning wood, coal, or oil. At this time, however, chemists were becoming quite successful at synthesizing organic compounds in the laboratory from simple inorganic (from nonliving matter) chemicals. This suggested the possibility that what could happen in the laboratory could have happened by chance in the lifeless seas of the early earth; life was thus only a matter of chemistry, admittedly complicated, but nevertheless a Creator and his miracles were at last totally obviated. Earth's early atmosphere was believed likely to contain carbon, hydrogen, and nitrogen as simple gases such as methane, ammonia, acetylene, and cyanogen, but Oparin carefully excluded oxygen from this otherwise lethal list. The absence of oxygen was a vital part of the theory (Oparin 1953, 96). Astronomers reported finding what they thought was methane and ammonia on the planet Jupiter, while volcanoes were known to spew out metallic carbides on occasion that react with the water in the air to produce acetylene gas. These observations seemed to confirm the theory. The early seas were thought to be not too salty, and while textbooks speak of "a primordial soup", it should be thought of in terms of consommé rather than French onion. With volcanoes discharging and lightning flashing, Oparin suggested that organic molecules could be formed in the waters and, given enough time, that chance would bring some of these together to form amino acids which, it was known, form one of the building blocks of life. With more time the sea would become a liquid medium for amino acids. Still thinking in terms of consommé, chance processes would bring twenty-five or more together to form the first units of protein molecule, most of which consists of hundreds and even thousands of such units in a long chain. The fact that there were no enzymes to facilitate these complex chemical building processes was explained away by there being enough time for it to happen by chance.

Time and chance again, in this view, would then allow protein molecules to join in the right combination to form the first primal organism. Oparin made an ingenious suggestion that Darwin's process of natural selection even begins to operate at the molecular level (Oparin 1953, 191). He undoubtedly based his thinking on the observation that, for example, sodium and chlorine ions in solution all fit themselves together neatly and in an orderly fashion in little cubes when they crystallize as common salt. Chemical reactions are always reversible, and in the synthesis of living organisms, there is unfortunately a greater tendency to dissolve than to grow.

To provide the chemical energy to drive the reaction towards growth, Oparin suggested fermentation by breakdown, that is, sacrifice of some of the first primal organisms in order to allow others to grow to form more complex organisms. Fortunately, Pasteur had earlier discovered bacteria that could live without oxygen. This appeared to confirm the possibility of fermentation under these conditions. The important point, however, was that the fermentation itself generated carbon dioxide gas, which was essential for the higher organisms millions of years in the future. Since carbon dioxide is known to be a product of decomposed life, such as rotting humus, for example, it could not be included in Oparin's primal lifeless atmosphere. Moreover, the exclusion of oxygen from this atmosphere was vital, since this allowed the first primitive organisms to survive rather than perish by oxidation and to concentrate, ready for the next stage of the process.

Fermentation could not continue indefinitely because the organisms were feeding on themselves, but now another more efficient process began. Some organisms developed the photosynthesis mechanism whereby the energy from the sun could be captured for the molecular building process. Oxygen is a product of photosynthesis and at this point was added to the earth's atmosphere for the first time. With accumulation of oxygen and depletion of the initial hydrocarbon gases, the more advanced organisms developed a more efficient process of acquiring their energy needs. The cellular respiratory mechanism evolved all by time and chance, and so it was that the first self-reproducing living cells came into being.

Oparin first published his ideas in 1923, but after garnering more information, he finally published more widely in what became, in 1936, his well-known book, *The Origin of Life*. The theory he proposed, given only in outline here, is the explanation offered today in every biology textbook, sometimes in more detail, though often in less, in which case the whole scenario is dismissed in one or two paragraphs. For example, Bronowski's (1973) popular book *The Ascent of Man*, based on the equally popular BBC television series, introduces the subject of the origin of life with the words, "To talk sensibly about the

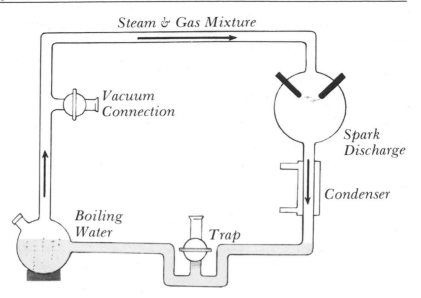

Steam & Gas Mixture

The Stanley Miller experiment, 1953. Upon boiling, the steam and gases passed through the electrical discharge and then were immediately cooled in the condenser to sweep any products away from the electric spark. The trap at the bottom caught and isolated the lighter products while the remaining solution passed back into the boiling vessel for recirculation. (Author)

origin of life we have to be very realistic" (Bronowski 1973, 314). Bronowski then describes Oparin's theory in four paragraphs, not mentioning one difficulty and leaving the reader with the impression that it is all ludicrously simple. This is by no means a balanced presentation and places the admonition to be realistic in serious question.

Work carried out in 1953 by Stanley Miller, a graduate biochemistry student, is invariably given to be undeniable evidence in support of Oparin's theory of spontaneous generation of life in the past. Miller attempted to simulate early conditions on earth in the laboratory by boiling a mixture of water, methane, ammonia, and hydrogen gases together under the influence of an electric spark discharge representing lightning over the primeval sea. There was a trap in the apparatus specifically to prevent any soluble organic products from being broken down by the electrical discharge, and, after a week, some amino acids were observed in the trap. This was acknowledged to be very far from having produced life, but it was encouragement to the believers. Of course, under any early earth conditions imagined there could not possibly be a trap, so that the simulated conditions were somewhat contrived. Nevertheless, the appeal to time and chance were once again believed to offer the solution.

The important point about this theory is that while it acknowledges that spontaneous generation does not occur today, it states that it did occur in the past under conditions that were *assumed* to be quite different. In fact, Oparin pointed out that life, having once started under these alien conditions, then changed the entire ecosphere so that such a spontaneous beginning could never occur again.

Since Oparin's time, great advances have been made in man's understanding of what was once thought to be the "simple" cell. It now turns out to be an extremely complex and efficient little assembly, constructed and operating at the molecular level, and although the theory is still taught and defended, the ranks of the faithful are being somewhat depleted by defectors of no mean caliber, such as the already mentioned Crick and Orgel.

The difficulties with the theory are acknowledged to be many, but perhaps the most serious are those organic units that are only effective when working in cooperation with one another. The process is called symbiosis, and examples can be found throughout nature from the molecular level, through the cells, to insects, plants, fishes, birds, and mammals, and perhaps we should even include man in a marriage partnership. Photosynthesis, in the Oparin theory, was said to have evolved, but there are three very complex components that must have arrived at the same point in time and space (within the primordial sea) in order for the process of photosynthesis to work. Chlorophyll, chloroplast, and cytoplasm are each very complex components containing thousands of atoms all in the correct order and arrangement and to have all three arriving at the same time diminishes the chances immensely. It has been discovered more recently, principally by Crick, that the DNA spiral-helix molecules found within the nucleus of every cell are the "blueprints" for cell building, but these molecules work in a symbiotic relationship with the RNA molecules, which transfer the information from within the nucleus to various parts of the cell. Only by this relationship can molecules derived from food be directed to where they are needed for cell building. In this case the theory requires that we believe that the two extremely complicated molecules, DNA and RNA, which must fit together perfectly, have each evolved separately and then appeared at the same time and in the same place in order to work together. Evidently, this was seen to be an appeal to the miraculous and went beyond Crick's credulity.

Throughout Oparin's theory for the spontaneous generation of life in the past, there is a repeated appeal for time, billions of years in fact, for chance processes to operate. Often, convincing arguments are put forward to show from probability theory that no matter how remote the chance may be, given a sufficient number of trials and time for these to occur, the expected event will have to take place. Mathematically, this is true, but somehow the false notion that figures, especially statistics, cannot lie has become sacrosanct, and the argument is accepted. Mathematics is only a tool which, when used intelligently, may tell us many things, but the results do not necessarily relate to reality. Take this example as an illustration of this point. Suppose a hare can run twice as fast as a tortoise, and the race begins with the tortoise one mile ahead. It can be shown that when the hare has run one mile to where the tortoise began, the tortoise has moved ahead half a mile and so on. At each increment of distance, the tortoise is always ahead and, according to this logic, the hare can never pass the tortoise.

This is, of course, a paradox pointed out long ago by the Greek Zeno, and in reality the hare would certainly pass the tortoise. Something of a paradox also occurs with the law of probability when it is shown that, mathematically, a certain event is probable. As the chance for that event becomes more remote, however, reality takes over and extremely remote possibilities become impossibilities (Borel 1962, 28).[27] At that point logic is taken beyond mathematical proof and into the realm of the unprovable, acceptable only by faith, and opinion is the expression of that faith. Where Oparin proposes that the impossible happened, many see this as clearly proposing a miracle, and they argue that there is no place for this kind of thing in science (Yockey 1977, 377).[28] These opinions are being voiced today in no uncertain terms by some weighty authorities.

Beginning perhaps in this present generation with the mathematicians attending the Wistar Institute Symposium, held at Philadelphia in 1966, we note that Murray Eden, of the Massachusetts Institute of Technology, pointed out that there must have been some restriction on the random variation for life to have begun spontaneously. Random variation is a basic pillar of Darwinism, essential to natural selection from the atomic level to the highest organisms, and his proposal to reduce randomness means to introduce order. Eden and others were convinced that randomness as a cause of evolution must be relegated "to a minor and non-crucial role" (Eden 1967, 110). They did not, of course, come out and say it, but the only alternative left is a design and a Designer (Eden 1967, 9).[29]

Sir Bernard Lovell, the British astronomer, makes the following statement in his book *In the Centre of Immensities* (1979):

The operation of pure chance would mean that within half a billion year period the organic molecules in the primeval seas might have to undergo 10^{50} (one followed by fifty zeroes) trial assemblies in order to hit upon the correct sequence. The possibility of such a *chance* occurrence leading to the formation of one of the smallest protein molecules is unimaginably small. Within the boundary conditions of time and space we are considering it is effectively zero. (Lovell 1979, 63; emphasis in original)

More recently, Sir Fred Hoyle (1981) has put the matter in more mundane terms:

Anyone with even a nodding acquaintance with the Rubik cube will concede the near impossibility of a solution being obtained by a blind person moving the cube faces at random. Now imagine 10^{50} blind persons (standing shoulder to shoulder, these would more than fill our entire planetary system) each with a scrambled Rubik cube and try to conceive of the chance of them all simultaneously arriving at the solved form. You then have the chance of arriving by random shuffling (random variation) of just one of the many biopolymers on which life depends. The notion that not only the biopolymers but the operating program of a living cell could be arrived at by chance in a primordial soup here on Earth is evidently nonsense of a high order. Life must plainly be a cosmic phenomenon (Hoyle 1981, 527).

Back to Extraterrestrial Origins

Although the idea of spontaneous generation may conjure up images of mice appearing from dirty clothes, it is of course visualized today to have happened at the molecular level. However, the entire scenario of life appearing from nonlife in some warm little pond is in serious question and we are witnessing at this time of writing a swing back to theories of a cosmic origin for life (Salisbury 1969).[30] The meteorites as carriers of life have come under suspicion because of terrestrial contamination, both incidental and intentional, but one slim hope remains— the comets. Halley's comet revisited our solar system in 1986 and there was great hope that a close fly-by of a space craft might detect organic matter or even obtain an uncontaminated sample (McNaughton and Pillinger 1980). However, had anything been found this would have been fanfared as conclusive evidence that life was "seeded" on Earth by comets; there has been no such news.

The stark reality of mathematical probability, however, dashes even this slim hope, because it is, after all, the origin of life and not the intergalactic carrier that is crucial. Two of England's leading scientists, Hoyle and Wickramasinghe (1981), working independently of each other came to the conclusion that the chance of life appearing spontaneously from nonlife anywhere in the universe was effectively zero. Surprisingly, these authors, respectively an agnostic and a Buddhist, concluded that the origin of life demands the existence of God to have created it. The London *Daily Express* (14 August 1981) headlined their conclusion: "Two skeptical scientists put their heads together and reach an amazing conclusion: There must be a God." As far as the dedicated humanist is concerned, this answer to life's riddle is totally unacceptable, but eventually some alternative explanation must be given to replace the long outdated Oparin theory. Only time will tell, but it is just conceivable that in the near future, textbook explanations for life on earth will appeal to that now-you-see-it, now-you-don't phenomenon, the UFO.

8

From Mammal to Man

*When preconception is so clearly defined, so
easily reproduced, so enthusiastically welcomed
and so long accommodated as in the case of
Piltdown Man, science reveals a disturbing
predisposition towards belief before investigation.*

JOHN READER
(1981, 81)

I n the previous chapter we saw that there were two intractable gaps
in the evolutionary family tree, one at the base where life began and
the other at the top between mammal and man; the chapter concluded with the views on the origin of life vacillating between two
inaccessible extremes: ancient seas and outer space. In this chapter the
evidence for the transition from mammal to man will be given a little
more than the usual exposure to help the reader draw his own conclusions concerning man's early ancestry. First, however, some philosophical background concerned with the "fall" of man in order to set the
stage for the ensuing review of the fossil men.

Ever since the dawn of history, by which we mean the earliest records
left to us of man's activities and thoughts, two antagonistic views have
existed regarding the life of the human race upon earth. The first of
these is the belief that man was created "in the image of God", as a
perfect being endowed with the highest moral and intellectual powers.
But there came a "fall" and, as its result, the entrance of disease, misery,
war, and death into the world. The effects of the Fall were seen to
extend into the inanimate world and account for the general downhill
decay, where each material thing that man has labored to win from the
earth—the metals, the minerals, the brick, and the stone—all eventually return to the earth. For more than a century now, scientists have
recognized this general tendency and have formulated it as one of the
universal laws of nature—it is known as the second law of
thermodynamics.

Pandora sculpted by Harry Bates,
late 1880s. Is Pandora of Greek
mythology the Eve of Genesis?
(Metropolitan Toronto Reference
Library Board)

In Greek mythology, as early as the eighth century B.C., Hesiod
wrote of a primeval period of innocence and perfection. He called it the
Golden Age, a time in which man had access to the Creator of himself
and the Paradise in which he lived. Then man rebelled and became a
"fallen" being, and there followed successively the Silver, Bronze,
Heroic, and Iron ages. Hesiod explained that disease and subsequent
misery were the result of the curiosity of the first created woman. Her
name was Pandora (Hesiod 1948; West 1978).[1-2] The names and some
of the details have changed and myths have been added, but the account
is very similar to the Hebrew version in the opening chapters of
Genesis, which suggests that there could have been a common earlier
version known to the ancient world (Plato 1933 ed., 23-24).[3]

The Roman poet Ovid, born just before the time of Christ, retains in
his long poem *Metamorphoses* the essential elements of the Golden
Age theme (Watts 1980). Since Latin was the *lingua franca* of the
Roman Empire, and this subsequently passed into the Roman Church,
the idea of the Golden Age was maintained in the collective consciousness throughout the next two millenia, Ovid being required reading
for those taking Latin at school. Latin only ceased to be a requirement
for entrance to Cambridge University, England, in 1965, and thus the
idea of a "fall" from a Golden Age was carried forward into modern
times. In addition to Latin, the theme was also perpetuated in the

English of King James by the poet John Milton in his *Paradise Lost*, which was required reading in schools well into the turn of this century (Eberhart 1969).[4] Finally, the account of the Fall of Man has been taught continuously throughout history, at first within the confines of the Jewish community and later throughout the Judeo-Christian world; it is still being taught in church and synagogue, though since Darwin's time the teaching has been carried out with varying degrees of conviction (See Genesis 3).

The second view of the progress of the human race began by saying that "nature" was working her purpose out, progressing from the imperfect to the perfect. The theme was that of evolution. Man was seen as the ultimate product, arising at the start from some mutant ape, gradually gaining in intelligence, leaving his low and brutal beginnings to form social groups, while his moral and ethical codes of behavior developed along the way. Thus, in contrast to the former view where man was "made in the image of God", the evolutionary view now saw man "made in the image of the ape", and it was little wonder that the sensibilities of not a few Victorians were upset. The modern evolutionary view claims that rather than a hierarchy of perfection, each living form is perfect for its particular niche in the environment. In this respect, the evolutionary view has almost come full circle to the biblical position, which claims that each living form was perfectly designed for its habitat.

One of the odd and seemingly inexplicable human traits that has been recorded throughout history is the child prodigy. To give a contemporary example, Myron Romano began learning the piano at the age of six. Five years later he was concert soloist with the Boston Pops Orchestra! Examples could be produced of men who have mastered twenty languages before their twentieth birthday, and so on, but as yet science has no explanation for this phenomenon.

If, by evolutionary reasoning, such genius is a foretaste of what mankind might aspire to, then teleology has to be admitted—that is, "blind nature" knows in advance the ultimate destiny of each species. Darwin could not accept this and thus could not speak of the "ascent of man". On the other hand, if such genius is a throwback to what mankind once was (some may see this as a revelation), then the "fall" of man has to be admitted and the theory of evolution dismissed. Either view is uncomfortable for the committed Darwinist.

As was shown in Chapter One, the progress of nature theme began among the Greek philosophers wanting to rid themselves of the idea of a supernatural dimension and certainly any idea of divine intervention. Democritas, in the fifth century B.C., and Epicurus, in the third, taught the materialist philosophy and influenced later writers, such as the Roman poets Lucretius and Horace. Thus, the alternate philosophy of the "ascent" of man posed by these Latin authors was impressed on the intellect of the medieval schoolboy, who was already contending with authors such as Ovid and Hesiod, who spoke of the "fall" of man. Nevertheless, the belief in the "fall" was universal in the common mind until very recently in history, while the opposing idea of the "ascent" of man lay dormant, like a planted seed kept alive by the few in readiness for the appropriate time of germination and growth. Growth began in the seventeenth century, when murmurings of opposition to the "fall" were heard from men such as Descartes and Voltaire, but it wasn't until the nineteenth century that the opposition became more intense, reaching its zenith shortly after the publication of Darwin's *Origin*. By 1871, when Darwin published his *Descent of Man*—a title contrary to the book's evolutionary message—a great deal of the steam had gone out of the opposition by the church. Darwin felt bold enough in his *Descent* to spell out in print what he had only implied earlier in his *Origin*, and this is where he flatly stated that man was related to the monkey:

> The Simiadae then branched off into two great stems, the New World [North and South America] and the Old World [Africa and India] Monkeys; from the latter, at a remote period, Man, the wonder and glory of the universe, proceeded (Darwin 1871, 1:204).

Some see only the similarities between ape and man, while others see only the differences.

Archaeology began as a discipline when the hunt for fossils in the early 1800s began to turn up human artifacts. One of the earliest organized efforts began with a scientific commission, created by the Danish government, to study ancient refuse heaps. As a result of this educated garbage picking, extensive collections were assembled at the Royal Museum in Copenhagen, and these were studied with respect to their appearance within the various strata. It was observed that there was a general tendency for crude stone tools to occur in the lowest levels, followed by stone tools of better workmanship, then copper and bronze tools, and finaly bronze and iron tools in successively higher layers. Christian Thomsen, the director of the museum proposed in 1837 a chronology of human culture divided into the Stone Age, the Bronze Age, and the Iron Age (Dunbar 1960, 440). Reminiscent of the progression of ages spoken of in Greek mythology and confirmed year by year by new evidence, this has now become part of the textbook creed and is seemingly irrefragable proof of the rise of man from brutal beginnings. Yet there were plenty of men, in both sacred and secular professions, still faithful to the original belief who contended that the overall evidence permitted an original high civilization wiped out by a worldwide catastrophe except for a handful of survivors. Most of these survivors, having the knowledge but not the means, became impoverished and degenerate; it was pointed out that the archaeological evidence could equally well indicate a recovery of lost arts rather than pristine discovery of new technologies. The high and early civilizations of the Egyptians and the Sumerians were pointed to as evidence that some of these early survivors had the knowledge and the means to rebuild quickly what they had formerly known. Nevertheless, the churchmen gave in, little by little, as the nineteenth century drew to a close and as each new piece of evidence came to light.

Perhaps there was no more convincing evidence than the fossil remains of what experts were certain were the transitional creatures between ape and man. The prognathous jaw, the low and brutal features of the reconstructed fleshy anatomy, and the glass eyes staring back vacantly at the museum visitor—who could fail to be convinced that indeed man had risen and not fallen from his beginnings in the dim and distant past?

The Fossil Men

Preconceived notions have always played an essential role in the study of fossil man; in fact, the entire subject of anthropology has been based on finding evidence to support a preconceived theory rather than based on evidence from which a theory is drawn. Further, as we have seen in previous chapters, the interpretation of evidence has been intimately associated with the personality and persuasive ability of the individual proposing the interpretation. It is remarkable how often the initial intrepretation of new evidence has confirmed the preconceptions of those responsible for the discovery. The discipline has thus tended to be dominated by ambitious men and, here again, the principle operates that the more fragmentary the evidence, the greater the degree of speculation—a principle often augmented by sheer force of argument.

The overwhelming problem in the study of fossil man is that the actual fossil remains are extremely rare, and when they are found, the pieces are so broken, distorted, and incomplete that entirely different interpretations are possible. The field is thus wide open for speculation which, indeed, has been carried out with abandon, particularly in the case of flesh reconstructions, which become the interface between the knowledge of the scientist and the view offered to the lay public. After almost a century of imaginative productions of the most grotesque images purporting to be our ancestors, it has finally been conceded that most of these are misrepresentations, and they are now quietly fading from textbooks and museum displays. This section of the chapter presents, very briefly and in chronological sequence, the salient features of those fossil remains that have been claimed were the missing links between mammal and man. One technical matter should be mentioned. Modern evolutionary theory maintains that both apes and man sprang from a common ancestor; it is technically incorrect, therefore, to speak of transitions between the ape and man or even of "ape-man". However, since there seems to be no clearcut agreement on the nature of this ancestor and since all the comparative work currently being reported is in terms of the ape, the traditional view of ape-to-man transition will be used throughout this chapter and the next.

Neanderthal Man

High up on a limestone cliff overlooking the river Dussel, Germany, quarrymen discovered a cave and, buried in the cave floor, a skeleton. Only the skullcap and some limb bones survived the quarrying operations, but here, in the Neander Valley near the city of Düsseldorf, was discovered a set of bones whose resting place would give the popular name to the first of a series of famous missing links. The date was 1857 (Huxley 1901, 7:168; Lyell 1914, 58). Just over a year previously, Professor Richard Owen, England's great anatomist, had addressed the Royal Institution of Great Britain on the comparative anatomies of man and the ape and pointed out the significant differences which, he claimed precluded man's link with the ape. At this time very few in the halls of

Richard Owen, 1804-92. Brilliant anatomist and creator and first director of the British Natural History Museum who opposed Darwin on scientific grounds. The Darwin memorial statue was installed shortly after Owen's death in 1892. (Engraved by D.J. Pound from a photograph by Watkins; Library of Congress, Washington)

science had openly said that man was related to the ape, although this was tacitly implied in Lyell's geology, and Owen had clearly seen where this reasoning might lead and had opposed Lyell's theory as he later had opposed Darwin's. In his address, Owen (1855) cited the great ape's prominent supra orbital torus, or eyebrow ridge, as a major featural difference; it was thus an extraordinary coincidence that within a few months the Neander Valley would disclose a skullcap, otherwise human, except for an enormous eyebrow ridge.

It was not until after the publication of Darwin's *Origin*, in 1859, that controversy over the Neanderthal remains really began. The Darwinists were looking for evidence to support the theory of evolution, and what better and more convincing evidence than a transition between ape and man? This more than any other thing would catch public attention and promote the cause.

In the opposing camp were those who maintained that it was nothing more than the remains of a human being with a gross pathological deformity. Several medical authorities had expressed this opinion, but in 1872, Rudolf Virchow, the greatest pathologist of the day, was given the opportunity to examine the Neanderthal bones. His diagnosis was that they were from a middle-aged individual who differed in appearance from normal *Homo sapiens* only because of "pathological changes" brought about by deforming diseases such as rickets and arthritis. Virchow had noted that the femur, or thighbone, was curved, a condition associated with rickets (Ottaway 1973). This evidence

Rudolf Virchow, 1821-1902.
Acknowledged as one of Germany's
truly great scientists, he laid the
foundation for modern pathology.
(Metropolitan Toronto Reference
Library Board)

strengthens the view held then, and by some today, that Neanderthal
man was capable of an impressive degree of social organization; without this the crippled owner of the skull could not easily have survived
into middle age (Ellegard 1958, 303; Vallois 1962, 214).[5]

Over the next few decades portions of the skeletons of more than
sixty individuals were found, mostly in Europe, though some were in
Africa and Asia, and these were all very similar with massive eyebrow
ridge, low forehead, strong lower jaw, but no chin, and curved but
heavily built leg bones. Virchow's diagnosis fell into disrepute. One
pathological deformity might be acceptable as an explanation but not
sixty!

The scientific fraternity had given credence and human status to the
Neanderthal remains by classifying them as *Homo antiquus* at first,
later changing the name to *Homo neanderthalensis*. However, the
popular press of the day called the remains Neanderthal man, and this
name has become fixed in the public mind ever since.

In 1908 a Neanderthal skeleton was discovered at La Chapelle-aux-
Saints in France, and Professor Marcellin Boule of the l'Institut de
Palaeontologie Humaine, Paris, described what Neanderthal man
would have looked like in life, based on his examination of these bones
(Boule and Vallois 1957).[6] Boule was a convinced Darwinist, and his
interpretation was biased towards seeing the bones as evidence of the
transition between ape and man. With this preconception, he described
an imagined creature, half ape, half man, head thrust forward, knees

slightly bent, while the numerous reconstructions that were subsequently modeled, drawn, and painted depicted this creature naked and hairy in a cave setting. It should be borne in mind that only bones had been found; all the rest of the reconstruction was speculation based on preconception; for all we know, Neanderthal man may have worn clothes and lived in houses.

Unlike the first Neanderthal, of whom only the skullcap was found, the La Chapelle-aux-Saints skull was almost complete, and Boule's measure of the volume gave a surprisingly high figure of 1,600 cubic centimeters, significantly more than the average person today. This aspect was all but ignored at the time because it did not fit into the preconceived view of early man, but as more Neanderthal-type skulls were discovered, it was found that on average all were slightly larger than that of man today. This raised the awkward question that if skull capacity was in fact a measure of intelligence, then possibly the old idea of the "fall" of man from some highly intelligent beginning had a ring of truth to it. Such a thought, however, was heretical to the new philosophy, which was at this time becoming nicely established, and a more rational explanation had to be found. To this day, the best explanation put forward for a race of ancient men having larger heads than modern man is that it is brain quality that counts rather than quantity—though, of course, with only skeletal remains, this is acknowledged to be an unproved assumption.

And so a preconception in the minds of only a handful of men, for the most part quiet, self-effacing, professional men, was carried forward and powerfully placed in the minds of the general public. If one picture was worth a thousand words, how much more valuable was a lifesize reconstruction? One of the best-known examples is Blaschke's lifesize cave scene showing a Neanderthal family, all based on Boule's interpretation. This became a permanent display in the most popular exhibition hall of the Field Museum of Natural History, Chicago, in the 1920s. For those not able to visit the Chicago museum, representations of the same cave denizens appeared in countless textbooks and encyclopedias over the next half century. Similar reconstructions appeared in virtually every major museum.

Almost fifty years after the discovery of the La Chapelle-aux-Saints Neanderthal specimen, anatomists Straus of Johns Hopkins University and Cave of St. Bartholomew's Hospital Medical College reexamined these bones and in 1957 challenged Boule's earlier description (Straus and Cave 1957). Boule had been incorrect in claiming that the big toe was prehensile, which is a characteristic of the apes, and the pelvis also was not at all ape-like as had been claimed. Moreover, the

This rare photograph by J.C. Schaarwachter shows Rudolf Virchow aged about eighty. After a highly successful career in the medical field where he seems to have been proved correct about the Neanderthal remains, he unsuccessfully ventured into the social sciences. (Academy of Medicine, Toronto)

individual *had* suffered from severe arthritis that affected the vertebrae and the jaw. It began to look as if Virchow had been right after all, and in the 1960s a new view of Neanderthal man began to emerge as it was realized that he was true man and walked as upright as any man today (Brace 1979, 21).[7] Gradually, new reconstructions were made, and one of these, by Krstolich, appeared in a lifesize diorama at Chicago's Field Museum. Oddly enough, however, this was confined to the basement while the original misinterpretation remained in place in the main exhibition hall, without a word of explanation, and was still there a quarter of a century later at the time this chapter was being written.

It might be asked that if Neanderthal man was truly human, why did they all have pathological deformities similar to these described by Virchow? Ivanhoe (1970), a medical specialist, concludes after examining many of these skeletons that the individuals had all suffered from vitamin D deficiency and that this was not restricted to adults but included children. This deficiency is known to cause osteomalacia and rickets producing a subtle face change by increasing the size of the orbit (eye cavity), especially in the vertical direction. It is commonly believed that the widespread lack of vitamin D was due to insufficient sunlight, and this is one reason Neanderthal man is always associated with the ice age. The point is seldom made however, that to have survived at all, especially the children, indicates that they had a highly developed sense of moral duty and a degree of social organization. Wright (1971), another medical specialist, acknowledges the work of Ivanhoe and proposes that congenital syphilis could also have caused the kind of bone deformities found in the Neanderthal specimens. Finally, on the question of the characteristically odd shape of the skull of the Neanderthals, some interesting observations by Israel (1973) show that certain living individuals today begin to develop Neanderthaloid features— the heavy eyebrow ridges, elongated cranial vault, and so on—with extreme age. Early man has always been assumed to have had a short life span, but this may be the first indication that their life span was as long as, or even longer, than ours today.

It is considered journalese these days to use the term "ape-man" in referring to the alleged transition between man's animal ancestor and modern man (*Homo sapiens*). Meanwhile, the anthropological fraternity hesitates to say where one species ends and another begins. They have resolved the difficulty somewhat, however, by introducing the concept of subspecies. Bearing in mind that breeding experiments are not possible with fossils, the classification is thus seen to be based on semantics. Neanderthal man is now officially called *Homo sapiens neanderthalensis*. Thus, a given fossil can be either true man or true Neanderthal, according to the particular school of thought held by the user of the term. One noted anthropologist has said that there was great variation in the bone structure of the Neanderthals just as there is in modern man, and they should be considered as simply a variant of *Homo sapiens* (Buettner-Janusch 1973, 253, 259).[8] It would appear then that Neanderthal man was true man, and, certainly, he is known

A Munda woman from the Chota Nappur Hills, India. The heavy supra orbital torus (eyebrow ridges) common to Neanderthal skulls does not necessarily mean that they all looked ugly or "primitive". (From Coon 1965; The Estate of Carlton S. Coon)

to have buried his dead with religious ritual, a positive indication of being truly human.

Neanderthal man is said to have lived between 35,000 and 70,000 years ago, but this varies widely from one authority to another and is based largely on the necessity to fit him into the overall theory for the evolution of man (Ivanhoe 1970). As we shall see, the subject has always been highly debatable, made even more so by discoveries of controversial fossils such as the Galley Hill man, found in 1894, and others such as Swanscombe in 1935, Fontechevade in 1947, and Vertesszöllos in 1965. These fossils are considered Neanderthal, but in each case consist only of a part of a skull. A difficult situation is made worse by the discovery in Poland of a tomb in which was buried a suit of chain armour containing a typical Neanderthal skeleton (Neanderthal in armour, 1908).[9] Finally, what would seem to be the ultimate difficulty was a living specimen of a Neanderthal, complete with the massive lower jaw, receding chin, heavy eyebrow ridges, small muscular frame, and short femur, found in the Philippine Islands and reported earlier in this century (Living Neanderthal man, 1910).[10]

In spite of all the imaginative pictures of Neanderthal man as a brutish cave dweller that have appeared in the Time-Life books, the evidence shows that these were truly human beings, displaying moral and social sensibilities and perhaps living under impoverished conditions, widely afflicted with rickets and osteomalacia; they may also have been given to promiscuity, resulting in widespread syphilis. With this newly emerging picture, it becomes more possible to reconcile the facts with the Genesis account of early man being brought under divine judgment.

The Lady From Guadeloupe

Before proceeding further with the more familiar Cro-Magnon man, it is appropriate at this point to introduce the lady from Guadeloupe, since this was a well-authenticated discovery, widely reported in the scientific journals of the day, and on display at the British Museum for more than half a century (Konig 1814). The discovery was made in 1812 on the coast of the French Caribbean island of Guadeloupe and consisted of a skeleton, fully human in every respect and complete except for the feet and the head; it was identified as that of a healthy woman about five feet two inches tall. Of importance was the fact that although many of the bones were twisted and joints dislocated, the skeleton was fully articulate—every bone was in its proper position. This vitally important feature is undoubtedly the reason for the specimen not now being on display at the museum or even mentioned in textbooks today.

The lady from Guadaloupe, discovered in Miocene limestone, was fully reported by Konig and illustrated by this engraving in the prestigious *Philosophical Transactions of the Royal Society*, London, 1814. (Science and Medicine Library, University of Toronto)

The limestone in which the skeleton was embedded was extremely hard and part of a formation more than a kilometer in length, while, according to modern geological dating, it is 28 million years old. This presents a very difficult problem for evolutionary theory to explain, for here is undeniable evidence of a perfectly modern human being on

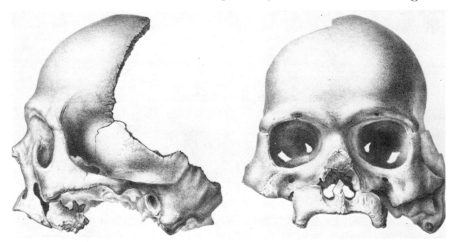

The Calaveras Skull. Calaveras in Mexican-Spanish means skulls. The associated stone bowls and other human artifacts are in the museum of the University of California (Voy collection) but have never yet been on display to the public. (Lithograph by P. Roetter; Science and Medicine Library, University of Toronto)

earth apparently 25 million years before man was believed to have swung out of the jungle trees (more will be said of this dating in the next few chapters). Not only that but, according to Darwin, man originated from the Old World monkeys in Africa, and modern-looking man was only supposed to have migrated to the Americas some twenty thousand years ago. Interestingly, two Neanderthal-like skulls were found near Santa Barbara, California, and reported in 1923, but because the great age attributed to Neanderthals does not fit the theory of recent migration to America, these skulls were dismissed as being from modern Indians having Neanderthaloid features (Ancient skulls, 1923).

Often when human remains are found in geological strata believed to have been formed millions of years before the advent of man, they are explained away as an "intrusive burial", brought about either by natural causes or by the deliberate hand of modern man. A classic example is that of the "Calaveras skull", discovered in 1866, 130 feet below ground in the gold-bearing gravels of the Sierra Nevada, California. The skull, which was almost completely mineralized, was authenticated by a physician as a modern type and by J.D. Whitney, chief of the California Geological Survey, as being found in the Pliocene stratum, that is, as living more than two million years ago. In his extensive report, Whitney (1880) lists literally dozens of stone mortars, bowls, and other quite evident signs of human workmanship that had been discovered over the years in the same gravels.[11] Whitney believed in evolution and was evidently not incompetent. Yet this evidence was an embarrassment to the theory of man's recent migration to America. Further, the skull's modern appearance did not reconcile with its supposed age or with its mineralized condition. As might be expected, there was controversy, but somewhat surprisingly it was the religious press that took the matter up and declared the "Calaveras skull" to be "a hoax". They argued that it had been washed out of a Local Digger Indian cemetery and then deliberately planted in the gravels to deceive and discredit Whitney who was "of an anti-Scriptural and geologic turn of mind" (Whitney 1880, 270). To this day this has remained the tidy explanation. It was even rehearsed as recently as 1977 by Keen.[12] While Whitney's report lies buried in library archives, never a word is mentioned about the stone mortars when the "Calaveras skull" is discussed. Where there can be no suspicion of intrusive burial by deliberate means, then a natural explanation is sometimes possible. It is argued, for example, that human remains in an upper strata may fall to a lower level and be reburied during a ground disturbance such as caused by an earthquake. Both of these explanations may be acceptable

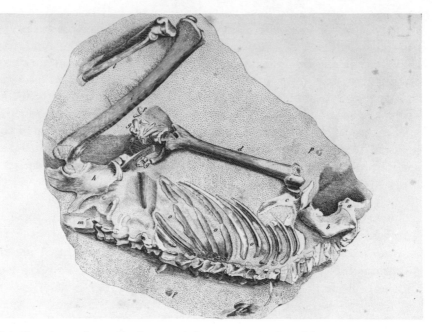

This French specimen of a human skeleton was also found in the Miocene
limestone of Guadaloupe at about the same time as the British specimen
(c. 1812). Cuvier included this fine engraving as Plate I together with descriptive
text in his *Recherches* of 1812. Again, it should be noted that although broken,
the bones are still articulated. (From Cuvier 1834; Science and Medicine Library,
University of Toronto)

for the isolated bone but certainly not for all the stone mortars, and least
of all for the Guadeloupe specimens, where every bone is in place and
an integral part of the Miocene limestone.

When the two-ton limestone block containing the skeleton was put
on display at the British Museum in Bloomsbury, in 1812, it was seen as
evidence of the great Genesis Flood and a reminder of past divine
judgment on men. Lyell and his demand for millions of years was
twenty years away, while Darwin and his theory would not appear for
more than half a century. When the British Natural History Museum
was opened in South Kensington, in 1881, the specimen was transferred, and it was undoubtedly at this time that it was considered in the
best interest of Darwinism to leave it in storage in the basement of the
new museum. Almost exactly a century later, it was discovered and
photographed by Bill Cooper, one of a new breed of archaeologists
untrammeled by the formal teachings of the discipline and free to
research data reported at a time when men had greater freedom to
publish their discoveries.

Cro-Magnon Man

The name Cro-Magnon comes from a cave discovered in 1868 at Les Eyzies, in the Dordogne area of France, and means, in the local dialect, literally "big hole". A number of these skeletons have been found, particularly in Europe, and many have been complete, but they have always been regarded as "cavemen" and never as ape-to-man transitions. The purpose of including them in this list of "missing links" is to help dispel the popular, but generally erroneous, image of man's early ancestor as being strictly a cave dweller steeped in misery and ignorance. The Time-Life books have contributed not a little to this popular image.

The Cro-Magnon were truly human, possibly of rather noble bearing, some being well over six feet tall and all having a cranial volume slightly larger than men of today; the heavy eyebrow ridges and curved limb bones were absent from these specimens. Remarkably, Cro-Magnon man appears in the fossil record abruptly, and in perfection. That is, he is truly human in the anatomical sense and evidently accomplished in at least several arts, among which are the now famous cave paintings discovered at Altamira, Spain, and at Lascaux in France. The discovery of these paintings indicates the degree to which men's view of their ancestors had turned from the idea of the "fall" of man to that of ascent. In 1879 Marcelino de Sautuolo discovered the cave at Altamira, but none of the authorities would at that time believe they were genuinely ancient, and he died in 1888 an object of ridicule (Schiller 1971). The Lascaux cave was discovered in 1940 and by then cave paintings were acknowledged to be genuine and the public allowed to view them. However, it took several decades of careful juggling with time estimates before the mind-set of science could accommodate the fact that intelligent and skillful man was evidently contemporaneous with prehistoric animals such as the woolly mam-

Cave paintings of mammoths, similar to those shown, have been discovered at Les Cambarelles, France. It is evident that intelligent man was contemporaneous with the mammoth. These paintings are one of the principal reasons the mammoth is assigned to a relatively recent era in the evolutionary time scale. (Kenneth St. Onge)

moth that appear beautifully painted on the cave walls. The photographs usually shown in the opening chapters of art history books cannot do justice to these incredible paintings because they are in fact three-dimensional. The artist has cleverly made use of the natural contours of the cave walls and ceilings to form the rounding of the belly or the depression for the eye of each one of the colored figures. In 1972 Marshack disclosed a mass of evidence showing that these Cro-Magnon people were not only proficient artists but had a very good grasp of the movements of the heavenly bodies and kept daily records of the position of the moon. This raises the question now seriously being posed: Were these Cro-Magnon people the originators if not the actual builders of the dozens of stone megaliths dotted across Europe of which Stonehenge in England and Carnac in France are probably the best-known examples? (Thom 1971).[13]

The fact that most of the Cro-Magnon artifacts have been found in caves does not necessarily mean that they all lived in caves, but rather that this is simply where their record has been preserved. There are indications that they did not necessarily dress in animal skins crudely draped about their bodies as usually depicted but had nicely cut clothes and even hairstyles. Surprisingly, a picture appeared in a Time-Life publication showing what appeared to be a mother and daughter wearing dresses and with their hair tied up (Prideaux 1973, 151).[14]

This is an exciting period for archaeohistory as many of the old preconceived notions of cavemen are giving way to a totally new

Woman and Child of Minateda, Spain. Discovered in a cave and authenticated by H. Breuil in 1920, even this featureless painting belies the conventional image of "primitive cave men". (After Breuil; Library of Congress, Washington)

picture in which it is recognized that these early ancestors were intelligent beings living in communities and in buildings, who quite possibly only used the caves for ritualistic purposes.

Java Man

This particular missing link is the product of the imagination of Eugene Dubois, and his is a classic case of a search for evidence to support a preconceived idea. Not only that, but once having found it, he spent the remainder of his life promoting the idea on the basis of the evidence, which was in fact, very questionable at the time and even less credible today.

Dubois was born into a Dutch Catholic family. In 1877, at the age of nineteen, he entered Jena University as a medical student. A considerable part of the next seven years before his graduation was spent under Professor Ernst Haeckel, whom we met in the previous chapter. At this particularly influential period of Dubois' life, exposed as he was to Haeckel's preaching, he became a convinced Darwinist. More specifically, his mind became set on discovery of the missing evidence between ape and man. In this crucial time for the Darwin followers, there was no actual fossil evidence of this or any other transition, and in the contest between academy and pulpit, this was acknowledged to be one of the great weaknesses of Darwin's theory. Claims were made for the Neanderthal remains, but these were too human-like to be convincing; however, the resourceful imagination of Haeckel supplied the missing evidence, in name and in pictorial form if not in fact. Haeckel considered that man and ape were so similar anatomically that the only real difference was that man could speak and the ape could not. This view was at complete variance with that of the outstanding anatomist of his day, Richard Owen, and of many scientists and the public in our day. Nevertheless, Haeckel called his missing link *Pithecanthropus alulus*, meaning speechless ape-man, and he had the artist Gabriel Max draw an impression of this imagined creature. The drawing, which was reproduced in many textbooks, shows a woman sitting cross-legged, suckling an infant, while her pot-bellied, beetle-browed mate stands half turned; both individuals have expressionless faces with not a glimmer of intelligence (Wendt 1972, 83). With Haeckel's infectious enthusiasm and his offering of details of where the remains of such a creature might be found, what young man could fail to be convinced? Certainly fame and possible fortune lay ahead for the committed treasure seeker.

Dubois graduated and obtained a good university position with prospects of a successful medical career, but he gave all this up in his

Ernst Haeckel, 1834-1919, poses
with a gibbon skeleton; Haeckel
fired the imagination of his
students with the prospect of
finding mankind's missing link
with the apes in the South China
Seas. (National Library of
Medicine, Bethesda)

commitment to find Haeckel's prophetic vision in the South China
seas. In 1887 he signed up for eight years to serve in the Dutch medical
corps stationed in the Dutch East Indies, with the express purpose of
using all his spare time to search for fossils in Sumatra and the other
islands. It wasn't long before he persuaded the authorities to let him
search on a full-time basis, and he was given army help, with at times
up to fifty men aiding him in searching and excavating. A great many
fossils were found; in fact, more than four hundred crates containing
thousands of fossil bones were shipped back to Holland, but all these
were of animals, and anything even remotely resembling human
remains was to prove to be extremely rare.

Beginning in Sumatra, he was soon encouraged to transfer his search
to Java, when he received from his friend, van Rietschoten, a human
skull found at Wadjak in the Javanese jungle. Arriving at Wadjak in
1889, Dubois found a second human skull in what he later reported
were tertiary rocks. Finally, he moved sixty miles away to Trinil,
located at a bend in the Solo River, where a number of animal bones
had been found. His laborers removed more than 10,000 cubic meters of
the river bank during the next three years, collecting a great many
animal bones, but the prize for all this labor was a tooth found in
September 1891, a skullcap found in October, a thigh bone the following August, and another tooth found in October. It seems that Dubois
was not actually present when these finds were made and their exact

Eugene Dubois, 1858-1940. The photograph taken in 1883 shows the young doctor with a medical career still before him. Driven by his obsession with finding Haeckel's ape-man, however, he wasted his medical talent and eventually his entire life. (Metropolitan Toronto Reference Library Board)

location with respect to each other varies from one report to another. There was a consensus that the skullcap was found about fifteen meters from the thigh bone, while the teeth were found three meters from the skullcap (Bowden 1977, 124).

Dubois easily recognized that the thigh bone came from a creature that walked upright. After some deliberation he convinced himself that these particular bones were all from the same individual and that indeed it was the long-sought-for missing link. He named it *Anthropopithecus erectus*, meaning upright, man-like ape. However, after some further thought in which he recognized that the evidence was scanty and the thigh bone perfectly human-looking, he finally called it *Pithecanthropus erectus*, meaning upright ape man; the transition was thus shifted slightly more towards true man. This was the proposal that he advanced in 1893, and in the absence of any more data, this idea became an article of faith dominating the rest of his life. Returning after his eight-year tour of duty, he went on a lecture circuit to show this now famous and eagerly sought piece of evidence to the scientific community. Paris, London, Dublin, Leiden, Berlin—on each occasion men were interested but generally uncertain of his interpretation of the evidence and particularly skeptical of his claim that the bones all came from the same individual. He had found an unwanted fame, largely rejected by science and wholly rejected by his church, while there had certainly been no fortune. He felt that he alone was in possession of a truth amid a sea of unbelievers, and the imagined persecution only served to reinforce his faith. Finally becoming irascible and secretive, he never returned to medicine or fossil hunting and would not let others see the precious bones. In 1898 he took a job as assistant professor of crystallography at the University of Amsterdam at a salary much less than he had earned ten years earlier just after graduation. This is rather a sad ending to what promised to be a successful career, but there is even more that illustrates the incredible lengths to which commitment to an idea will take a man.

In 1907 a group of scientists, under Professor Selenka from the Berlin Academy of Science, undertook a first-class expedition to Java to confirm the work of Dubois. Dubois offered them no cooperation, even refusing them permission to see his precious fossils. The Selenka expedition was carried out with exemplary German thoroughness, but after removing another 10,000 cubic meters of deposit and forty-three boxes of fossils from the same Trinil site, they declared the expedition fruitless; they had found nothing even resembling human remains that would confirm Dubois' work (Keith 1911).[15] Interestingly, they had excavated to the level previously reached by Dubois and observed that the main fossil-bearing stratum was the result of a large lava flow from a nearby volcano. This completely upsets the normal means of identifying the age by geological strata, and, although textbooks claim 500,000 years for Java man, the facts are that any age attributed to it is nothing more than inspired guesswork. The actual fossil remains discovered by Dubois are securely locked in a safe at the Leiden Natural History Museum in Holland and have never been subjected to a radiometric dating method, nor is this likely to be permitted. After all, even though radiometric methods are very questionable, as we shall see in later chapters, it is better to reside in fame, even if based on doubt, than to risk obscurity by raising further uncertainty.

Finally, what about those Wadjak skulls Dubois had acquired in the 1880s? In 1914 Dubois' Java man was becoming eclipsed by the attention given to the Talgai skull discovered in Australia some years before. *Pithecanthropus erectus* was by now becoming accepted as a transition, albeit with many reservations, and Dubois felt free to move back to center stage by revealing his Wadjak skulls, which he finally reported in 1920. Since their discovery thirty years earlier, he had not said a word about them, and in fact for most of this time they had remained hidden under the floorboards of his house. It seems that even men of science can have a skeleton or two in their cupboard! The Wadjak skulls were quite human, but since they had been discovered in geological strata similar to the Trinil discoveries, they represented damaging counterevidence to Dubois' claims for Java man as the missing link. In other words, since it was evident that true man was living at the same time according to the geological record, then Java man could not have been an earlier transitional form between ape and man.

When Dubois was over seventy, fresh discoveries were made in Sangiran, Java, by Ralph von Koenigswald. A dozen fine specimens were recovered, all very similar to Dubois' original Java man, but no limb bones were found. By this time, however, Dubois had become quite possessed by the whole thing, and in 1935 he published his claim that the skullcap he had discovered was actually that of a very large ape of gibbon-like appearance. This was an attempt to shift his claim further to the midpoint between ape and man, since the finding of either true ape or true man was of little significance compared with the finding of the true transition as long-sought proof for Darwin's theory.

Dubois died in 1940 and thus was saved from the final ignominy of seeing his beloved *Pithecanthropus erectus* reclassified and renamed in 1950 *Homo erectus* (Mayr 1950). In spite of its dubious history, it is now considered a hominid or transition. However, when dealing with fossils, there is no question of breeding experiments, so attribution of the dividing point between one species and the next among the alleged transitions becomes very subjective, and the experts do not agree among themselves. The "splitters" would make it a separate species, while the "lumpers" include it as an extreme variant of man. The issue is still undecided, but in any case it should not be forgotten that the entire case rests on the *assumption* that the ape-like skullcap and the human-like femur come from the same individual. Scientists in Dubois' day had grave doubts, while only a few decades ago Professor Thompson, when writing the introduction to the 1958 reprint of Darwin's *Origin*, was forthright enough to express surprise that a 1943 textbook, in the light of all that is known about Java man, would accept the diagnosis of the *Pithecanthropus* given by Dubois (Thompson 1958, xxi).[16] We may well concur and stand amazed as textbooks continue to include this specimen as bona fide evidence of man's ancestry.

Piltdown Man

Piltdown man was a diabolically clever hoax. Since it was exposed in 1953, a number of books have been written about this fraud, perhaps primarily because it makes such a wonderful "whodunit". So far, no one knows for sure who the culprit was. The investigations were necessarily limited to secondary sources, since at just about the time they were getting started, the last of the principal characters involved became no longer available for comment. Sir Arthur Keith and Teilhard de Chardin both died in 1955.

The Piltdown discovery was made at a most propitious time. Huxley, Darwin's promoter in England, had followed his mentor to the grave; fossil men, though not missing links, had been found all over Europe, while dubious claims were being made by a Dutchman for a missing link found in Java, of all places. In this vital area of prehistoric discovery, England was being left in a backwater and, worse, Darwin's position as England's great scientist had yet to be substantiated with proof for his theory. National pride was at stake. However, fate had not forgotten the cause, and another man was being prepared to take Huxley's place as a teacher and popularizer of evolution and, specifically, the evolution of man.

Arthur Keith, born in 1866, was a very capable physician and anatomist. His career has the unqualified ring of success enviable to any man moving in academic circles in England: a doctorate in medicine; Fellow of the Royal College of Surgeons; and Fellow of the Royal Society, serving variously as president of the Royal Anthropological Institute, the Anatomical Society, and the prestigious British Association for the Advancement of Science. Author of several classic works, he was, of course, a convinced Darwinist committed to the idea of establishing

Arthur Keith, 1866-1955. With impeccable scientific credentials and honors, Keith was nevertheless completely deceived by his own preconceptions. Status in the field of science is no guarantee of the truth. (Drawing by W. Rothenstein, 1928; National Portrait Gallery, London)

proof for the relationship between ape and man. When Keith was elected Hunterian Professor of Anatomy at the Royal College of Surgeons in 1908, his declared ambition was "to write the anthropological history of the British" (Keith 1950, 317).

The Piltdown remains were discovered during the period from 1908 to 1912 and only a few miles from Darwin's old home. Parts of a human skull, together with most of the jaw of an ape, had been stained to look aged and placed in the Piltdown gravels in the country just outside of London, which was known to interest an amateur fossil hunter, Charles Dawson. These remains had been brought to the attention of Arthur Smith Woodward, keeper of the department of geology at the British Natural History Museum and personal friend of the fossil hunter (Reader 1981).[17]

Woodward was a Darwinist and a paleontologist, widely regarded as the world's leading expert on fossil fish—he wrote more than six hundred papers on the subject during his lifetime. Arthur Keith, the anatomist, was called into the investigation. Soon the team was joined by Grafton Elliot Smith, a renowned brain specialist. The team consisted of some of the very best men of science; their collective credentials were not only impressive but impeccable.

The significance of these fossil finds lay not so much in the pieces that were found as in the pieces that were missing! The jaw was too big for a normal human skull but, significantly, the upper jaw and part of the lower jaw and face were missing and so were the important lower canine teeth. Also missing were the mating parts for the jaw hinge; the complementary nature of the parts, therefore, could neither be confirmed nor denied. Moreover, the skull was in several parts, and intermediate pieces were missing, so that the volume of the brain case could be made to fit any preconception. Indeed, paleontologist Woodward's first reconstruction came to 1,070 cubic centimeters, just midway between ape and man, whereas anatomist Keith's reconstruction came to 1,500 cubic centimeters, slightly larger than modern man but necessary, as Keith explained, in order to accommodate the huge jaw. Just as the disagreement appeared to be leading to acrimony, Father Teilhard de Chardin, from a local Jesuit seminary, found one of the missing canine teeth on the same site, and this quickly settled the argument. A new reconstruction was made having a capacity of 1,200 cubic centimeters and this seemed to accommodate nicely everyone's views on the subject.

When Piltdown man was formally announced at the Geological Society in 1912, it was warmly welcomed by the press as the sensational missing link. It was also accepted by many, though by no means all, members of scientific circles. There were some who argued that the jaw and the skull parts did not belong to the same individual and that it was just fortuitous that they were found together. Nevertheless, this being just the evidence Darwin's followers so badly needed, objections were given little or no publicity. The actual remains were locked away for safe keeping, but plaster casts were circulated to the major museums. The now familiar plaster reconstruction in brown and white took a prominent place in the British Museum of Natural History, while for the next forty-one years it sat in its vitrine sanctuary with toothy grin as literally hundreds of thousands of visitors filed past paying homage to their alleged ancestor. Needless to say, objections to man's ape ancestry made in the pulpit were effectively silenced. A whole generation grew up with Piltdown man in their textbooks and home encyclopedias; who in their right mind would question the veracity of the *Encyclopaedia Britannica?*

The principals in the discovery were immortalized in oils. A huge painting by John Cook, RA (Royal Academy), commissioned shortly after the discovery, hangs today over the main staircase of the Geological Society in London. Charles Dawson, the amateur fossil hunter, had received his glory when the Piltdown remains were given formal scientific recognition by being classified as *Eoanthropus dawsoni* (Dawson's Dawn man). Dawson died in 1916, and after a seemingly decent interval of time and in recognition of their contribution to king and country, Keith was knighted in 1921, Woodward in 1924, and Grafton Elliot Smith a few years later.

In 1953, Joseph Weiner and Kenneth Oakley conducted a recently developed fluorine test on the original Piltdown material and discovered that the bones were in fact relatively recent. The suspected hoax was finally exposed. There was something of a national scandal, and the integrity of the trustees of the British Museum was questioned. Eventually it all settled down to become an embarrassing moment in the history of science. But just who was the hoaxer? As with the authorship of Shakespeare's plays, this may forever remain the butt of speculation, but today suspicion is cast on either of two men. Both lived near the Piltdown site, both had the opportunity to acquire the fossil parts, particularly the jaw, since the ape was not native to the British Isles, and, more significantly, both had the special anatomical knowledge. The Jesuit Pierre Teilhard de Chardin is one popular suspect (Gould 1979)[18] and, rather surprisingly, Arthur Conan Doyle is the other (Winslow and Meyer 1983).

The Piltdown affair raises many moral questions and shows clearly that the belief system of a whole generation can be turned around by a

Pierre Teilhard de Chardin, 1881-
1955. Taken at Hastings in 1911,
the thirty-year-old Jesuit is on a
day out from the seminary. Exiled
from France a few years earlier, the
order had established new quarters
quite near Piltdown. (Archiv
Fondation Teilhard de Chardin,
Paris)

handful of intelligent men deceived by their own preconceptions.
Their preconception had totally blinded them. For example, le Gros
Clark, one of the principals at the British Museum, remarked on the file
marks on the teeth at the time the hoax was exposed: "The evidence of
artificial abrasion immediately sprang to the eye. Indeed so obvious did
they seem it may well be asked How was it they had escaped notice
before?" (Millar 1974, 204). A dental anatomist had been given the
opportunity to examine the original Piltdown material in 1916. Presumably, he came without preconceived notions, for the filed teeth
were evident to him. He reported this at the time, but the higher
authorities, that is, Keith and Woodward, chose to disregard these
details (Lyne 1916).

In any of the sciences, and particularly the discipline of anthropology, we might well ask that if men the caliber of Sir Arthur Keith, Sir
Arthur Smith Woodward, and Sir Grafton Elliot Smith could have
been deceived by their own preconceptions, how can we be sure that
men of science today are not also being deceived, not necessarily by
hoax, but by their own expectations? After all, those same preconceptions are still very much in the minds of the Leakeys, Johansons, and
others involved in the great African fossil hunt today.

Rhodesian Man

Sometimes called "Broken Hill man", this finding has always been an
enigma to the anthropological fraternity and is frequently not mentioned at all either in textbooks or popular books. It is not claimed to be

a missing link today, but its brief mention in these pages is to illustrate another example of preconception.

Accidentally discovered, in 1921, by zinc miners at Broken Hill, Zambia, formerly British Northern Rhodesia, this skull was almost complete and had the appearance of being ancient. That is, it had massive eyebrow ridges and a receding forehead. This skull and a number of other bones of three or four individuals were found in a cave at the end of a blocked passageway, but the miners were not aware of the necessity for careful documentation of their finding. It was unfortunate, therefore, that when the British Museum eventually received these remains, there was no way of knowing whether their burial was accidental or ceremonial. The hill containing the passageway and the cave all quickly disappeared under the miners' shovels. The capacity of the skull was found to be between 1,280 and 1,325 cubic centimeters, which is slightly less than the modern average man, while from the muscle attachment areas it was evident that the individual was very powerfully built.

When Arthur Smith Woodward of the Piltdown affair began to arrange for reconstruction of the fossil bones at the British Museum, his preconception with missing links was that this ancient-looking skull belonged to a creature that walked with an ape-like stoop. W.J. Pycraft did the actual reconstruction, and with this preconception before him, he reassambled the pelvic girdle, which had been found in fragments, and finished up with what they were pleased to call *Cyphanthropus* or Stooping man. Neither Woodward nor Pycraft were anatomists, but fortunately, the mistake they had made in their reconstruction was spotted by a competent anatomist. With a corrected and erect posture, *Cyphanthropus* was recognized as true man and renamed *Homo rhodesiensis* (British Museum 1928).[19]

There are two peculiar features about *Homo rhodesiensis*. First, although the bone is heavily mineralized and therefore presumed to be very old, the individual had suffered from Rigg's disease and dental

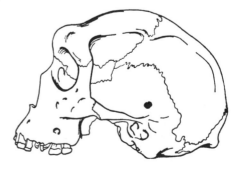

The skull of *Homo rhodensiensis* showing the pencil-sized hole in the left temporal bone—near the ear. (Author)

caries, which are gum and tooth disorders believed to be an affliction of civilization and not of ancient man (Brace et al. 1979, 88). Second, there are two holes, one on either side of the skull. The hole in the left temporal bone is perfectly round and slightly larger on the inside of the bone than on the outside. The hole on the opposite side of the skull is three or four inches in diameter with fractured edges, typical of spalling by ballistic impact. In the view of Professor Mair of Berlin, they looked like the entry and exit holes of a modern bullet (Wendt 1972, 155). It is not being suggested here that ancient man had firearms, but a crossbow at short range would be just as effective. Even so, the idea of man possessing the crossbow more than a hundred thousand years ago, according to Klein's (1973) estimate for *Homo rhodesiensis*,[20] does not conform to today's image of man just emerging from the brute at this point in our evolutionary history. One school of thought suggests that the small hole was caused by secondary infection from the tooth decay, while a second points out that there is no sign of disease and suggests that it was caused by a benign tumor (cholesteatoma) occurring in childhood (Price and Molleson 1974). No one seems to comment on the larger hole on the opposite side of the skull. More often than not, when the skull is illustrated, textbooks show the left temporal side since it is most complete, but make no mention of the small hole, which actually appears as a rather marked feature. A case in point is Pilbeam's book, which presents two colored photographs of the skull but makes no comment on the controversial hole (Pilbeam 1970a, 184). However, even worse is the popular work of Father Teilhard de Chardin entitled *The Appearance of Man*. In this, he gives a one-page description of Rhodesian man and two drawings occupying half a page. Not only is there no mention of the hole, but also the hole is entirely omitted from the drawing! (Teilhard de Chardin 1965, 114). We have met the good priest before, and he will appear again in these pages, but throughout, when closely inspected, we find that his scientific integrity is not quite up to the standards expected.

Nebraska Man

This infamous missing link is forgotten by most today. It has been included here as a reminder of the deceit that can be foisted upon the public mind by men in high places with preconceived ideas. This is not to say that the deceit was deliberate. This affair, however, resulted in the most farfetched case of misrepresentation, and as it will be seen, the timing of its discovery was rather significant.

In 1922 a single molar tooth was found in a Pliocene deposit in

Hesperopithecus harold cooki: the ape-man of the Western world, as it was
introduced to the public imagination in a double-page spread of the popular
Illustrated London News of 24 June 1922.

Nebraska. Professor Henry Fairfield Osborn, head of the American
Museum of Natural History, described it as belonging to an early type
of *Pithecanthropoid*, which he named *Hesperopithecus harold cooki*,
thus honoring Harold Cook, the geologist who discovered it (Osborn
1918).[21] At the same time Grafton Elliot Smith, who had been involved
with the Piltdown man affair a few years before, persuaded the prestigious *Illustrated London News* to publish an artist's conception of the
male *Hesperopithecus* and his mate. The tooth was all the evidence
there was, so the artist was instructed to draw something between the
ape and man. The magazine had a worldwide distribution, and
Nebraska man was hailed as another missing link; the date of the
publication that contained the picture across two entire pages was 24
June 1922 (Smith 1922).

The world's most famous court trial took place in Dayton, Tennessee, in July 1925. This was the trial in which John Thomas Scopes was
alleged to have taught evolution in a state school, which was contrary
to the law at that time (Scopes 1967). The trial was instigated by the
American Civil Liberties Union, and although they lost their defense,
they eventually won the battle. The trial had given good publicity to
the evolution issue and efforts were made to sustain the publicity in a
high court appeal. The law forbidding the teaching of evolution in the
state of Tennessee was eventually repealed in 1965. We see today that
the tables have turned completely to allow the teaching of evolution to

the exclusion of any other view (Davidheiser 1971).[22]

At the time of the trial, the image of Nebraska man was firmly fixed in the American public's mind, since it was, after all, America's only claim to a part in man's ancestry. Shortly after the trial, in 1928, it was discovered that a mistake had been made and that the tooth was not that of an early human at all but of an extinct peccary or pig believed to have become extinct at the end of the Pleistocene era! This embarrassment was compounded in 1972 by the discovery in the Chaco of Paraguay of living herds of the same species of peccary (Wetzel et al. 1975).[23]

Scientists can, of course, make mistakes, but when this mistake was discovered, it was not considered newsworthy. *Hesperopithecus* quietly disappeared from textbooks and encyclopedias. In the fourteenth edition of the *Encyclopaedia Britannica* (1929, 14:767) it was explained that *Hesperopithecus* had been found to be "a being of another order". To have told the whole truth, presumably, would have resulted in a loss of credibility for some individuals. As it was, Grafton Elliot Smith got his knighthood in 1935, approximately a decade after the two Arthurs and just two years before he died.

So far in this chapter only the earliest missing links and fossil remains have been described, and these were included for three reasons. First, it was felt necessary to state which of the famous "ape-men" have been regarded as missing links or transitions and which have not, in order to clear up any confusion. Second, it was important to remind ourselves of these follies of science and ask how it was that intelligent men were themselves deceived and how many others they in turn deceived. This leads to the obvious third point: Is it possible that science can be deceived by a hoax or present the public with a misrepresentation again? One hopes that those who are reminded of their history will not repeat it, and with lessons such as Piltdown before them, scientists today are a great deal more cautious. Not only that, but physicochemical methods of examination have advanced so far since those early days that it would be virtually impossible for a hoax to get by all the tests without detection. However, misrepresentations are still possible because of incorrect interpretation of the data. The days of full-scale reconstructions based on evidence as slim as a single tooth are hopefully now history. Lest we forget, however, we are reminded of yet another example in the next chapter.

9

More Fossil Men

No one is more strongly convinced than I am of
. the vastness of the gulf between civilized man and
the brutes, or is more certain that, whether from
them or not, he is assuredly not of them.
THOMAS H. HUXLEY, 1863
(Huxley 1901, 7:153)[1]

A Hong Kong drugstore would not seem to be the most likely place to hunt for the fossil remains of man's ancestor, yet this is precisely what an internationally recognized anthropologist did in 1935. The Chinese pharmacopoeia is not a bit like our Western potpourri of pills and potents. Among the dried herbs and lizards will be found "dragon's bones" and "dragon's teeth" that turn out to be fossils and may include an occasional human tooth. Ralph von Koenigswald was aware of this and, after sorting through a drawer of "dragon's teeth", found a large one that he believed had human characteristics (Koenigswald 1956, 63).[2] He named it *Gigantopithecus blacki* and, in spite of the fiasco over the *Hesperopithecus* affair only seven years earlier, claimed this as part of an early ancestor of man. Other similar teeth were subsequently purchased to support the claim, but it was not until 1970 that these were reexamined and shown not to have any human characteristics at all (Pilbeam 1970b). *Gigantropithecus blacki* quietly faded from its place as an ape-to-man transition and became simply another extinct ape having played a small though vital part in the overall grand delusion.

Peking Man

The story of Peking man, whose replicate plaster skull is found today in every major museum as man's link with the beast, begins in a Peking drugstore in the early 1920s.

Discreet inquiry by visiting Westerners had revealed the source of the fossil bones to be a hill twenty-five miles outside Peking, known as

Chou K'ou Tien, meaning, logically enough, "dragon-bone hill". In 1921 a Swede, Otto Zdansky, began excavations. Among the many animal bones he recovered the next year were two human-like teeth; he was very cautious in drawing conclusions, but the find caused excitement among others eager to fill the gap between ape and man. Zdansky returned to Sweden, and we hear no more about him, but one detail may be of interest. Zdansky's little foray was funded by the Swede Ivar Kruegar, who was internationally known in the 1920s as the multimillionaire "Match King" who eventually was discovered to be a swindler. He shot himself in 1932. Kruegar had financed the publication *Paleontologia Sinica*, which was the official newsarm specifically aimed at reporting anything relating to human origins found in China; there was evidently high expectation that such evidence would be found.

Two other characters now emerge to lead the search for man's early origins in China for the next decade. The first of these was a Canadian physician, Davidson Black, who had been greatly influenced by a book called *Climate & Evolution* by William Matthew (Hood 1964, 33).[3] With his imagination fired by the prospects of finding the elusive missing link, Black went in 1914 to England to study under Grafton Elliot Smith. Smith, it will be recalled, had been involved with the Piltdown man and was already receiving international recognition. Davidson accepted a position at the Peking Union Medical College, with the express purpose of exploring the area for human remains. He and his wife arrived in Peking in 1919, and up to this point his story reads very much like that of Eugene Debois a generation earlier.

The second character was the Jesuit priest Teilhard de Chardin, whom we met as a young seminarian of twenty-seven in the early stages of the Piltdown affair (Lukas 1977). Teilhard had since studied under Professor Marcellin Boule, who was responsible for the false impression of Neanderthal man. He, in turn, became professor of geology at the University of Paris. However, Teilhard was effectively banished to China in 1923 by his superiors in Rome because of his philosophical views on evolution and Christianity. He was forbidden to lecture or publish any theological works expressing these views although, interestingly, what are basically the same evolutionary views are being taught in many Catholic institutions today. (More will be said of this in Chapter Fourteen.)

In 1927, just as finances were running out, a tooth was discovered at Chou K'ou Tien, and Davidson Black considered that it had characteristics intermediate between ape and man. He announced the discovery of *Sinanthropus pekinensis*. The Peking Union Medical College had been opened in 1914 by the Rockefeller Foundation and was continuously funded by that organization, except for the years during World War II, until 1950. Black had expected to find his missing link in China, and the single tooth not only provided for his expectations but, along with his resulting enthusiasm, convinced the Rockefeller Foundation, and they forwarded eighty thousand dollars in American funds to set up a Cenozoic Research Laboratory, specifically for the study of human fossils. This was a large sum of money in those days—in China one dollar would hire a laborer for four days. At times up to one hundred laborers were employed at the Chou K'ou Tien site, a further sign of the deep commitment to finding fossil man. In 1929, after two years of digging and again just as funds were running out, an almost complete brain case was discovered fossilized and embedded in rock; there was no face, jaw, or base. Black fervently believed that this was indeed the skull of *Sinanthropus pekinensis*, the name he had previously coined on the basis of the single tooth found earlier. When the fossil was freed from the rock, Black estimated the brain capacity to be just under 1,000 cubic centimeters, which happens to be midway between ape and man. However, the other experts, Teilhard de Chardin, Grafton Elliot Smith, Marcellin Boule, and later von Koenigswald, who were all as anxious as Black to find the missing link, were sure, once they had seen the actual fossil, that Black's estimate for the brain capacity was too high. Their first impression was that it was more ape-like than human, and in a number of respects it was said to be very similar to the skullcap found by Dubois in Java; both of these skulls have since been reclassified as *Homo erectus* (Koenigswald and Weidenreich 1939; Teilhard de Chardin 1965, 65).[4]

This first skull, even though only represented by the top part, was one of the best in a series of fourteen that were discovered during the 1930s and reported in 1943. It should be added, however, that more than half of them consisted of merely a portion of cranium (Weidenreich 1943).[5] There were eleven jawbones, portions of seven thighbones, two upper arm bones, a wristbone, and 147 teeth, but many hundreds of tons of rock had been blasted to recover these trophies (Day 1977, 316; Teilhard de Chardin 1965, 88).[6] Oddly, although thousands of animal bones were found, including those of elephant and deer, no other bones of *Sinanthropus* were discovered. Moreover, the skull parts were mixed with the animal bones, and there was no evidence of any "progression" from ape towards man from the bottom to the top of the excavation, which amounted to 150 feet in the side of the hill.

In 1934, Black died of a heart attack at the age of forty-nine, after having received a great many international honors following his discovery and publication of *Sinanthropus pekinensis*. His place was taken by Franz Weidenreich, who subsequently reconstructed Peking man's skull from all the bits and pieces that had been found. Plaster models of Weidenreich's composite reconstruction are what we see today in museums, while photographs of this, labeled "Peking man", appear in textbooks. The brain capacity averages 1,000 cubic centimeters, and it is said to be half a million years old. It is held to be a hominid, which is a more respectable way of saying "missing link", on the basis of its brain capacity, its having teeth similar but not identical to human teeth, and its being found near signs of fire and crude toolmaking, indications of true man. More will be said of this later. Soon after the last of the fathers of *Sinanthropus pekinensis* had passed away (Weidenreich died in 1948 and Teilhard in 1955), the succeeding generation renamed it, first to *Pithecanthropus pekinensis*, then finally to *Homo erectus pekinensis*, thus lumping it together with Dubois' Java man, classified as a man-like ape.

Every one of the fourteen fossil "skulls" and all the remaining fossil pieces listed by Weidenreich in 1943 disappeared during the confusion of World War II. The only tangible evidence today of all this work are the photographs and the models of the plaster reconstruction (Janus and Brashler 1975; Shapiro 1971). The circumstances surrounding the disappearance are certainly mysterious, leaving us open to question if, in fact, the reconstruction by the actual fossil parts was carried out in a genuinely unbiased way. For instance, the picture of the Weidenreich reconstruction of Peking man, which may be found in every textbook on the subject, not only looks fully human but this impression is reinforced by the small size not being evident to the viewer without a normal human skull for comparison in the same picture. It might then be asked, Why did the early investigators who saw the actual fossil consider it to be so ape-like? One suspects that the only evolution that has occurred in the case of Peking man has been in the imagination of those making the reconstruction.

Since 1950 the Chinese Communists have continued to work on the site and have found two fragments of bone, one of a tibia (leg bone) and one a humerus (arm bone), and in 1966, parts of another skullcap. Further discoveries of this nature, though nothing momentous, continued to be made during the 1970s (Rukang and Shenglong 1983).[7]

The finding of only skulls, and these in a battered condition, has always been a puzzle. A number of suggestions have been put forward. Dunbar's popular textbook on geology is fairly typical of the kind of reporting received by students and in this case makes rather interesting reading. Quoting from the 1960 edition:

About forty individuals were recovered—men, women and children. These remains are nearly all skulls and lower jaws though a few limb bones were found. The base of each skull had its base broken away in a definite manner suggesting that the individuals had been decapitated and the brains eaten. Professor A.C. Blanc of the University of Rome advanced this interpretation based on some earlier work of Wirz on the Marind Anim tribe of New Guinea. This tribe opens the base of the skull in exactly the same manner to extract the brain which is then baked in a pie with sago and eaten as part of a ceremonial rite concerned with the naming of a child (Dunbar 1960, 447).[8]

It has to be conceded that this is the kind of reporting that is likely to impress itself on the Western mind. In the virtual absence of limb bones, many authorities today agree that the skulls of Peking man were probably of decapitated individuals having had their brains deliberately removed, suggestive of cannibalism.

But who was the hunter and who were the hunted? By assigning the classification *Homo erectus* to these skulls, it can only mean cannibalism, and using the words "men, women and children" leaves the indelible impression that they were human, although primitive. However, there are reasons to doubt that they were human, just as the early investigators doubted that they were human. Teilhard said at first that it was a large ape, and, interestingly, Dubois (1935) in his last days confessed that Java man was a large ape (Weidenreich 1938).[9]

However, there is more evidence that has been virtually suppressed since the earliest days. Professor Henri Breuil of the College of France and l'Institut de Palaeontologie Humaine, a world-renowned expert on the Old Stone Age, spent nineteen days at the Chou K'ou Tien site, in 1931, at the invitation of Teilhard de Chardin. Breuil found abundant evidence there of a large-scale human operation. A great number of antler bones had been worked, stone tools imported to the site from more than a mile away. Chippings eighteen inches deep in places indicated some kind of stone "industry". There was also evidence of a furnace operation of some kind. Breuil (1932) described this as an ash heap seven meters (twenty-three feet) deep that had evidently been kept going continuously for some time because the minerals in the surrounding soil had fused together with the heat.[10] However, the picture that is conveyed to the world outside did not derive from Breuil's report of 1932 but rather from the report issued the following year by the Cenozoic laboratory members, that is, principally, Davidson Black and Teilhard de Chardin (Black and Teilhard de Chardin 1933). They

Homo erectus pekinensis, more popularly known as Peking man, as presented to the public by the British Museum. Depicting early man quite naked is based entirely on the supposition that man evolved from the naked ape. (Courtesy of the Trustees of the British Museum, Natural History)

describe this furnace operation as "traces of artificial fire" and dismiss the matter in a few lines. Bowden (1977, 93)[11] shows that efforts were made to suppress Breuil's report, and virtually every textbook and popular book on ancient man since has used the expression "traces of fire" to describe the furnace operation (Boule and Vallois 1957, 144).[12] This conveys the impression intended, that this was man in his earliest stages having just learned to use fire. For example, Pilbeam, in his book *The Evolution of Man,* says, "From Chou K'ou Tien too came signs of the first use of fire" (Pilbeam 1970a, 176). To emphasize the point further, in 1950 the British Museum commissioned Maurice Wilson to paint a cave scene showing Peking man. The resulting picture shows a naked individual chipping away at some stones and squatted before a small fire consisting of three or four sticks. This is not representative of the facts, and even Teilhard admitted in his 1934 report that "traces of fire...have accumulated to the depth of several meters" (Teilhard de Chardin 1965, 72). In their 1983 paper, Rukang and Shenglong finally admit the ash heap is six meters deep (p. 93).

Breuil also collected a number of bone and stone items that bore the evident signs of human workmanship and left them on display at the local museum. These subsequently disappeared, however (Bowden 1977, 99). Were it not for Breuil's 1932 report, which has survived, it is certain that the only evidence available would be that which supports the view that Peking man was a hominid. As it was, more damaging counterevidence came to light in 1934 by the discovery of the parts of six truly human skeletons, including three complete skulls that were found in what was described as the "upper-cave". The word "upper" implies that these individuals were found in a higher stratum and were, therefore, more recent, but this is by no means clear from the description (Teilhard 1965, 75). In fact, even Weidenreich, who was in charge of the operation after Black's death, refers to the location as "the so-called 'Upper-cave' of Chou K'ou Tien" (Weidenreich 1965, 86). Evidently, the human remains caused difficulties for the imagined scenario especially as evidence for links between the two sites began to appear. It took Weidenreich (1939) five years to finally break the news of the discovery of the true humans, and at that it was confined to the relative obscurity of the *Peking Natural History Bulletin*. Even so, the popular books and most textbooks today never mention the appearance of true human beings at the site of Peking man.

Another notable to visit Chou K'ou Tien, at the invitation of Teilhard de Chardin, was his old professor from Paris, Marcellin Boule; however, when he actually saw *Sinanthropus pekinensis*, he was angry at having traveled halfway around the world to see a battered monkey skull. He pointed out that all the evidence indicated that true man was in charge of some sort of "industry" and that the skulls found were merely those of monkeys. It was further suggested at the time that the absence of the rest of the skeleton and the battered condition of the skulls were the result of the monkey brains having been eaten by the human workers, as indeed, this is still practiced as a delicacy in Southeast Asia to this day. Boule concluded with the comment: "We may therefore ask ourselves whether or not it is over-bold to consider *Sinanthropus* [now called *Homo erectus pekinensis*] the monarch of Chou K'ou Tien when he appears in its deposit only in the guise of a mere hunter's prey, on a par with the animals by which he is accompanied" (Boule and Vallois 1957, 145).

This question is still valid today. As one reads the original reports, and most are available in English, there is great inconsistency from one author to another. The number of *Sinanthropus* skulls varies from fourteen to forty for the same period of time; the number of limb-bone pieces varies from three to eleven; the location of the pieces varies from "upper cave" to "lower cave"; and the signs of human habitation are played down by most and seemingly honestly reported by others. And then authorities, such as Teilhard de Chardin, shift their position from saying quite positively at first that the skull was like that of a large ape to saying that it is a true hominid or primitive man. In the light of this tangled web of contradiction and the fact that the original fossils are no longer available, one is left with an impression that the whole exercise was carried out in a most subjective manner by fitting appropriate facts to a preconception. The reader is left to draw his own conclusions from this more complete story of Peking man, which is claimed to be a true missing link.

The African Fossil Men

Ever since the great fossil hunt began for conclusive evidence of the relationship between ape and man, those committed to the task have anticipated academic honor rather than financial gain as the principal reward. This appeal to human pride is a great motivator, and in some cases numerous honors have been heaped upon those blessed by fortune to find, for example, a tooth or even parts of a skull. The African story is no different, except that much greater publicity is afforded to the discovery while the discovery itself assures funding for another season. The assurance of financial backing has thereby become another great motivator and surely plays a significant part in the unconscious as interpretations are made on ambiguous evidence. Finally, in more recent years, competition has become a factor in the scramble for funding if not honor, and the interpretation of data will tend to be influenced by what the "competition" has found, since the most coveted prize is not just an ape with some human characteristics or a human with some apish traits, but some creature exactly in between.

Born in Australia in 1893, Raymond Dart studied brain anatomy under Grafton Elliot Smith in England, in the early 1920s, while the good professor was at that time still busy with the Piltdown man and Nebraska man. Needless to say, Dart became a convinced evolutionist. His particular interest was in the evolution of the human brain and nervous system. Upon completing his postgraduate training, he went to South Africa to become professor of anatomy at the medical school of the Witwatersrand University, Johannesburg. In 1924 a chain of circumstances led him to a fossilized front face and lower jaw of a young ape found in a cave in the Taung limestone quarry. Dart had been sufficiently indoctrinated by his training to come to expect ape-to-man transitions to be found, and he accepted this Taung skull as a missing link. He rushed to report this to the scientific press, and with some rather extravagant speculations on very little evidence named it

Australopithecus africanus, meaning man-ape of South Africa. Thus began the great African fossil hunt.

From the moment Dart (1925) announced his missing link, it generated controversy. Most of the authorities in the field rejected it as a young ape and scathingly referred to it as "Dart's child". It divided camps: Grafton Elliot Smith accepted his protégé's opinion; Arthur Keith rejected it (Keith 1925a; Keith, Smith, et al. 1925).[13] Even the popular press was divided; most met the announcement with outright derision, but a few of the 1925 headlines proclaimed that the missing link had been found in Africa, and, of course, this stayed on in the public mind (Reader 1981, 89).[14] Everyone seemed to have had his own personal reasons for accepting or rejecting what was really ambiguous evidence for man's link with the ape, and an interesting example of this at the time was General Jan Christiaan Smuts. Smuts was being snubbed politically, losing his position as prime minister of South Africa. Not having a government to run, he was indulging himself in writing a book called *Holism and Evolution.* Published in 1926, this has become something of a bible to the fringe medicine set of today, but Dart's discovery served nicely to support Smut's evolutionary thesis, while it was hoped that the ensuing publicity for man's origins in South Africa would further the political aims of himself as it supporter. As it happened, the publicity, good or bad, had no effect, and Smuts had to wait another decade to be reelected prime minister of South Africa.

Today, many authorities dismiss the Taung skull as that of a young ape sharing some interesting but irrelevant features with man, while Dart's name has passed into some of the mustier pages of history. More recently, Sir Wilfred le Gros Clark of the British Museum has remarked, "The extraordinary repetitious coincidence between Dart's discovery and that of Dubois in Java...seemed almost too much of a good thing" (Clark 1967, 26). The coincidence is even more striking when Davidson Black's name is added to that of Dubois and Dart, since all were physicians with a special interest in the evolution of man. All three studied under well-known evolutionists, and went to remote parts of the world. Within a year or two of arrival, each had discovered a missing link. Like Lowell and the Martian canals and Haeckel and the *Bathybius haeckelii,* all these men (and there have been many since) were committed to a theory and each was easily convinced the evidence had been found to support it.

A whole series of discoveries then began to be made in different parts of Africa as the trophy seekers moved in, and a plethora of jaw-breaking names was coined, each claiming a unique position among man's supposed lineage with the ape. Robert Broom, another physician dedicated to discovering the missing link, discovered, using very questionable methods, some fossil hominids at Sterkfontein, South Africa, in 1936 and then discovered more fossil hominids at the nearby site of Makapansgat Limeworks in 1938. Eventually, the anthropological fraternity sensed that the situation, with all the names and claims, was getting out of hand. They called a moratorium, renaming most of the discoveries under the general classification *Australopithecines* if the cranial volume was less than 750 cubic centimeters and *Pithecanthropines* if the volume was greater than 750 cubic centimeters. (More will be said of this later.) In the meantime the African search has continued into this present day with the Leakeys and Donald Johanson as the leading contenders.

Nutcracker Man

Louis Leakey, son of a missionary, was born in Africa. In 1959 he and his wife, Mary, working in the great Olduvai Gorge in East Africa, uncovered a skull. They called it *Zinjanthropus boisei*, meaning Boise's East Africa man; Charles Boise, the American who funded the expedition, thus became immortalized in the annals of science (Leakey 1959). However, the news media dubbed *Zinjanthropus* "Nutcracker Man" because of the huge jaw relative to the size of the skull (Leakey 1960a).

Olduvai Gorge is about one hundred miles west of Mount Kilimanjaro and consists of the three-hundred-foot-deep gorge that has cut through five main strata. These strata are horizontal beds that were numbered one to five upwards, and the *Zinjanthropus* skull was found in the lowest layer, Bed I, together with many stone tools of rather crude workmanship. On the basis of this very ape-like skull and the associated tools, Leakey claimed that the creature walked upright, thus giving it rudimentary human attributes and announcing it as the world's earliest man at 600,000 years (Reader 1981, 157).[15] This placed human beginnings much earlier than had been expected, and the whole thing was presented to the public in glorious Kodachrome in the pages of *National Geographic* (Leakey 1960b). Although the age had been a guess and was, in any case, not believed by many, the discovery was most timely since the Boise funding had run out and a new sponsor was urgently needed; the National Geographic Society responded generously and have funded the Leakeys ever since.

The *Zinjanthropus* skull was later (1961) dated at the University of California by applying the potassium-argon radiometric method to the mineral rock in which the fossil was found and declared to be 1.75

million years old (Leakey et al. 1961).[16] This was by far the oldest claim made for any hominoid fossil and caused much controversy but, nevertheless, the resulting publicity nicely served to further establish in the public mind man's evolutionary heritage from the ape. More will be said of radiometric dating methods in Chapters Eleven and Twelve. In 1968 further radiometric tests using the carbon 14 technique were applied to actual fossil mammalian bones found in the same location, Olduvai Gorge, but from the uppermost stratum, Bed V (Leakey et al. 1968).[17] Although normally on top, Bed V occasionally runs beneath Bed I, where the *Zinjanthropus* was found. The age of these fossil bones was reported as 10,100 years, a far cry from 1.75 million years and not paricularly newsworthy. But had this been discovered a few years earlier, Leakey's claim to have found the most ancient ancestor of man would have been doubted even more strenuously.

There was other, more serious, counterevidence. In 1913 a German anthropologist, Hans Reck, had discovered in Bed II a complete human skeleton together with many fossils of extinct animals, just above the bed where *Zinjanthropus* was discovered (Bowden 1977, 173). Reck (1914) took great care to ensure that the human remains were not intrusive—that is, that they had not been deliberately buried or had not

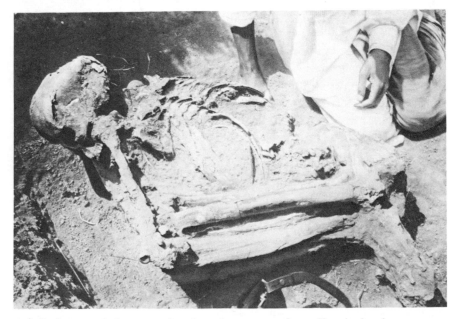

A fully human skeleton, modern in appearance and not disarticulated, was discovered by Hans Reck in 1913 in Bed II of Olduvai Gorge, in the stratum immediately above Leakey's *Zinjanthropus*. In order to conserve the theory, the facts have now largely disappeared. (Photograph by Hans Reck)

slipped down in a crevice from a higher stratum.[18] During the 1930s there was much discussion of these remains, and Louis Leakey (1928) was party to this, having personally examined the remains in Germany. When Leakey announced *Zinjanthropus* to the press in 1959, he said nothing of the perfectly human remains found immediately above it forty-six years earlier. Had he done so, this would be seen as damaging counterevidence. However, suspicions had been raised within the scientific fraternity, and in 1974 Protsch attempted to carry out some carbon 14 tests on Reck's human skeleton, kept in Munich, but only the skull could be found; all the rest of the skeleton had disappeared. The result obtained was 16,920 years and, although the actual test conditions left a fairly large margin for error, it was far removed from the 1.75 million years claimed for *Zinjanthropus* (Protsch 1974; Straus and Hunt 1962).[19]

Louis Leakey had made extravagant claims for *Zinjanthropus*, allowing his preconceptions to get the better of good science. Later he had to retract his claim that *Zinjanthropus* resembled modern man more closely than the *Australopithecines* that had been found in various parts of Africa up to that time. Eventually he conceded that *Zinjanthropus* was not unique at all but simply another *Australopithecine* and, thus, in the same category as Dart's Taung child. These creatures are believed by many to be what Keith (1925a) said they were —extinct apes—but the popular articles in *National Geographic*, declaring *Zinjanthropus* to be man's ancestor, remain fixed in the public mind.[20]

Louis Leakey's concession was made easier by the fact that a lucky discovery in 1964, only a few hundred yards from the Olduvai Gorge, revealed another creature, far more human looking than *Zinjanthropus* and found at the same stratigraphic level. Dating by the same potassium-argon method showed 1.75 million years (Leakey et al. 1968).[21] It seemed more reasonable that this creature was responsible for all the stone tools that were found at this low level. With the discovery of other scattered parts of the skeleton, including human-looking hand and feet on what was evidently an occupation floor, Leakey announced it as *Homo habilis*, meaning handyman (Leakey et al. 1964).[22] In Leakey's opinion, *Zinjanthropus* and the *Australopithecines* thereby represented aberrant offshoots that eventually died out, but *Homo habilis* was now claimed as the genuine link in the lineage between mammal and man. Again, this caused much controversy in the scientific press while all the public knew, through the pages of the National Geographic Society magazine and the popular press, was that yet another missing link had been found (Payne 1965).[23]

Olduvai Gorge is a rich fossil source for all kinds of animals, and it had been very carefully excavated by the Leakeys, but authorities opposed to their claim for *Homo habilis* pointed out that using the association of the tool-making evidence is hardly justified since the same evidence had previously been used for the *Zinjanthropus* and this claim had been shown to be incorrect. The case for *Homo habilis* was not strengthened by the facts that one of the hand bones was later found to be a vertebral fragment, two may have belonged to an arboreal monkey, and six came from some unspecified non-hominid (Reader 1981, 189). Many authorities at the time believed that *Homo habilis* was an *Australopithecine*. Since Louis Leakey's death in 1972, this has come to be the general, though not universal, opinion.

Finally, Bed I, the lowest stratum at the Olduvai Gorge and the layer in which *Zinjanthropus* was found, is described as an occupation floor where hundreds of fossil animal bones and stone tools were found (Leakey 1961).[24] The painstaking efforts of Mary Leakey in recording the exact location of each stone have led to the conclusion that this lowest occupation level dated at 1.9 million years contains evidence of a circular stone shelter. This evidence is completely inconsistent with the evolutionary origin of man, since it is held that man originally lived in caves and only began to build shelters for himself in the last few thousand years. Naturally, this is another item that is not widely reported, although interestingly, John Reader, in his excellent book *Missing Links*, not only describes this feature as "the earliest known evidence of a man-made structure" but even includes a full-page diagram of the site (Reader 1981, 173).

The "1470" Man

Richard Leakey is Louis Leakey's son. Although he holds no academic credentials, he is a very able administrator and fund raiser and has become something of a public figure, with frequent articles in magazines and books, and appearances on television. The success of African fossil hunting is directly tied to fund raising—more fossils, especially if hominid, mean more funds, and, conversely, more funds, more fossils.

The Leakey fossil preserve is not confined to Olduvai Gorge but extends for hundreds of square kilometers. During part of a systematic search in 1972, the famous 1470 skull was discovered at Lake Rudolf (Leakey 1973). It was fractured into a great many small pieces but when painstakingly reassembled looked very human indeed. The specimen was quite unusual; it consisted of a virtually complete skull except for the lower jaw, but opinions regarding its position in the lineage of man were sharply divided. Leakey maintained that it should be classified as

Homo, but others considered it to be another *Australopithecine.* Leakey's implications were enormous, because the age, according to potassium-argon dating, was 2.6 million years. This could be claimed to be virtually true man appearing in the fossil record long before any of the missing links, whether alleged, hoax, or misrepresentation (Fitch and Miller 1970).[25]

Such is the subjective nature of paleoanthropology that the 1470 skull was judged by others to be *Australopithecine* rather than have the whole of human evolution upset by one maverick fossil. However, the 1470 case was weakened somewhat by the discovery that the potassium-argon dating method tended to give uncertain results. The first sample of KBS tuff, the rock in which the 1470 fossil was embedded, gave an average age of 221 million years (Fitch and Miller 1976). This was about one hundred times greater than expected, so another sample was sent to the laboratory, and an age of 2.6 million, plus or minus 260,000 years, was produced and found acceptable. It could truly be said, with all the weight of laboratory proof and with tolerance values to substantiate impartiality, that 1470 was the world's oldest man. This is exactly how the headlines were printed, and once again the public was led to believe something that was extremely questionable, to say the least. Further tests on the same KBS tuff by the same method later gave results ranging from a minimum of 290,000 years to a maximum of 19.5 million (Reader 1981, 206).

The only conceivable reason for persisting with the potassium-argon method must surely be because it sometimes provides results that happen to fit the preconceived ideas of the paleoanthropologist. Any other discipline would certainly have rejected it long ago. (More will be said of this method of dating in Chapter Eleven.) After much controversy between geologists, paleontologists, and anatomists, the age of 1470 was quietly reduced to 1.8 million years, the same as *Homo habilis* (Curtis et al. 1975). Richard Leakey's belief remains firm that *Homo habilis* is the true ancestor of man whereas the *Australopithecines* were aberrant apes that became extinct (Leakey 1971).[26]

Since the original Charles Boise funding, Leakey's quest for man's ancestors have cost more than $800,000 in grants (Reader 1981, 197). All this had to be raised on the basis of a theory introduced a century ago by Charles Darwin, which says a lot for the power of persuasion by those genuinely committed to this belief!

Lucy

Donald Johanson, an American of Swedish parents, had set his mind upon the search for early man as his ultimate ambition. Diligent postgraduate work in anthropology and a measure of good luck brought him to Africa and to the great Rift Valley in southern Ethiopia, where the Omo River cuts through the sedimentary rocks to expose great numbers of animal bones. In the right kind of location, fossil bones from animals always seem to be plentiful enough, and fossil hunters collect and catalogue them by the thousand. Hominid remains, however, are extremely rare and when found are usually only represented by a fragment of bone or even a solitary tooth. In spite of all the claims that have been made for the number of missing links, it has been pointed out that the entire hominid fossil collection found in Africa, from Dart's Taung child to Leakey's 1470 skull, would barely cover a billiard table. In view of this, Johanson's delight at discovering a hominid skeleton about 40 percent complete can perhaps be appreciated. More than that, he was fortunate enough to collect in the same area 197 hominid bones, representing, it is believed, thirteen individuals. These bones represent young and old of both sexes and have given rise to the media's talk of a "family" (Johanson 1976). No skulls were found, which is strangely reminiscent of the Chou K'ou Tien situations, where, however, only skulls, and no bodies, were found.

The hominid skeleton was of a small creature about 100-120 centimeters tall, and except for the lower jaw there was no head, hands, or feet; other hands and feet were subsequently found. It was discovered about Christmas day in 1974 and was believed to be female; Johanson and his workers affectionately named their prize "Lucy" after the Beatles record that was popular at the time. The jaw more closely resembled the chimpanzee than man while without the skull there could be no estimate of brain capacity. Potassium-argon dating had given results from which the range 3.1 to 5.3 million years were selected as the benchmark of belief for the age of "Lucy".[27] However, more vital than the technicalities were the politics. The offering to the world of this long-awaited transition from ape to man could not be done in any haphazard manner. Announcement and publicity had to be carefully orchestrated for maximum effect; after all, research grants were at stake.

Lucy was kept a close secret for nearly four years until the most propitious moment, when *Australopithecus afarensis*, alias Lucy, was formally presented at the Nobel Symposium on Early Man in 1978 (Johanson 1979). The scientific establishment was not overly impressed. As usual, there was controversy, especially since there were no skulls. The principal contention seems to be between Johanson's claim for Lucy's being a missing link in the direct line from the common ancestor of ape and man to man himself and Leakey's claim that *Homo habilis* is the missing link. Each considers the other's claim to be an aberrant offshoot on the way to man. The popular treatment of Lucy was more favorable, and a book, television apperances, and numerous articles appeared to keep the latest missing link in the common consciousness (Johanson and Edey 1981). We can expect discoveries of this sort to be made every few years, as has happened throughout this century, and with increasing frequency. At this very moment, who knows how many discoveries have been made but are *in utero*, awaiting their moment for public birth?

Are Hominids Really Missing Links?

In the previous chapter and in our present discussion, a necessarily brief review of all the major missing links has been made and many little known details included to provide a more balanced picture of what has actually been discovered. For those who prefer their information input neatly pigeonholed, what has been said is concisely summarized in Table 1. Some words of explanation are necessary, however.

In the first place, the word "hominid" in the title embraces all the missing links and includes true man; this is in contrast to the related word "hominoid", which has a much broader meaning and includes all the apes and monkeys. As an aside, it might be added that the branch from the common ancestor of ape and man to man is said to have occurred about thirty million years ago, whereas the earliest *Australopithecines* are dated about three million years. There is, then, a huge gap of about thirty million years between this common ancestor and man, using round figures, abounding with speculation but precious little evidence. *Ramapithecus punjabicus*, consisting of two fragments of upper and lower jaw, falls into this category and hit the headlines as a missing link some years ago. It left an impression in the public mind then quietly faded away as controversy continued within the ranks of the enlightened (Pilbeam 1970b).[28]

Secondly, the use of the figure 750 cubic centimeters as the boundary between the *Australopithecines* and the *Pithecanthropines* is not entirely arbitrary and was proposed by Arthur Keith on the basis that it is the size of the brain that is the principal distinguishing feature between ape and man (Keith 1948, 206). The largest known brain size for the apes is the gorilla at 650 cubic centimeters (almost three kitchen cups), while the smallest size recorded for man—actually it was a woman—was 855 cubic centimeters. Thus 750 cubic centimeters falls nicely between these two limits. Anything greater than 750 is reckoned to be man and is classified as the genus *Homo*; Java man, with a capacity estimated to be 850 cubic centimeters, and Peking man, with an alleged average capacity of 1,000 cubic centimeters, are assigned as

TABLE 1. SUMMARY OF THE MAJOR HOMINID DISCOVERIES

AUSTRALOPITHECINES Ape-like man about 3 million years Cranial volume less than 750 cc Range 500-700 cc		PITHECANTHROPINES or HOMO ERECTUS Near man about half a million years Cranial volume more than 750 cc Range 900-1,225 cc		TRUE HOMO SAPIENS Any time in the last half-million years Average volume today 1,450 cc Range 850-1,700 cc	
	No.		No.		No.
S. Africa		*S. Africa*		*Germany*	
Taung		Swartkrans		Neanderthal	1
(*Australopithecus africanus*) ..	1	(*Telanthropus capensis*)	8	*France*	
Makapansgat	30	Broken Hill		La Chapelle-aux-Saints	1
Sterkfontein	40	(Rhodesian man)	1	La Ferrassie	6
Swartkrans	60			Cro-Magnon	5
		N. Africa			
E. Africa		Ternifine	4	*Italy*	
Olduvai Gorge				Grimaldi Grotto	2
(*Zinjanthropus boisie*)		*China*			
(Nutcracker man)	9	Chou Kou Tien		*Czechoslovakia*	
(*Homo habilis*)		(*Sinanthropus pekinensis*)		Predmost	20
(Handy man)	2-4	(Peking man)	40		
Lake Rudolf				*Yugoslavia*	
(1470 man)	30	*Java*		Krapina	13
		Trinil and Sangiran			
Ethiopia		(*Pithecanthropus erectus*)		*Israel*	
Omo		(Java man)	6	Mount Carmel	12
(*Australopithecus afarensis*)		Ngangdong	10	Jebel Qafza	6
(Lucy)	13				
				Iraq	
				Shanidar	7
				Morocco	
				Taforalt	180
				Algeria	
				Mechta-el-arbi	32

NOTE: Numbers refer to individual fossil pieces found.

Homo erectus, or near man, while the Neanderthals have a capacity of about 1,500 cubic centimeters, slightly greater than humans today, and are assigned as *Homo sapiens*. Anything less than 750 cubic centimeters is regarded as an extinct ape on the way to becoming man. It should be mentioned in passing that the *Australopithecines* seem to fall into two types assigned as gracile and robustus. The former is a daintier version of the robustus, which is massive in all respects except, of course, cranial capacity. Richard Leakey believes these are the female and male versions, repectively, of the same species of extinct ape (Walker and Leakey 1978, 63); this opinion, however, is not shared by all.

From what has been said of these fossil discoveries, it will be evident that very often the skulls are not only incomplete but, in some cases, entirely absent. Cranial capacity, therefore, cannot be used as a means of classification. Dentition, or teeth, then becomes a key item. Many times the fossil representing the "individual" is a jawbone or even a single tooth—in one case merely the crown of a tooth rates as an "individual", though better science has by now cautioned against an entire flesh reconstruction of the creature on such a basis!

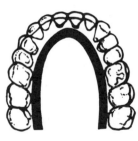

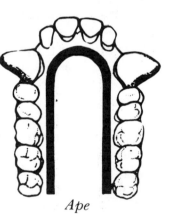

Man   *Ape*

The ideal ape-to-man transition would have a dental arcade midway between the parabola of true man and the U-shape of the ape.

Apes generally have a U-shaped dental arcade with large canine teeth—the fangs—and a corresponding gap, or diastema, in the opposite jaw to enable the animal to close its mouth. Man, on the other hand, has a parabolic, or curved, dental arcade and rather small canines with no diastema. Any fossil jaw found that has intermediate characteristics is thus considered an immediate candidate for an ape-to-man transition. *Ramapithecus punjabicus* fell into this category, and since no one has any idea what the rest of the animal looked like, it has to be conceded that using such evidence to substantiate a theory that man evolved from the ape is really only speculation in the guise of science. Indeed, the already controversial case of *Ramapithecus* was considerably weakened when it was discovered that a baboon living today, *Theropithecus galada*, has human-like dental characteristics very much like those of the fossil *Ramapithecus* (Pilbeam 1970b).

The geological strata is the third consideration and is the oldest and most established method, which, in spite of being based on circular reasoning and assumptions pointed out in Chapter Four, has now become sacrosanct and placed beyond question. The method relies on the index fossils found associated with the hominid remains and provides the appropriate period in geological history. When there is doubt or a lack of index fossils, paleoanthropology falls back on the solid reliability of physics and applies the potassium-argon method of dating not to the fossil but to the associated rock.

Heads, teeth, and geological strata then become the three major parameters that determine a candidate hominid's position in the lineage to man. It might be recalled that all three are based on the evolutionary assumptions that the brain became larger, that the teeth become smaller and more rounded, and that the degree of progression is consistent with what would be expected in the past two or three million years. In a nutshell, this is the reasoning underlying classification. For example, if a piece of thighbone is found and it is felt to be *Australopithecine*, then as many potassium-argon dating trials as can be afforded are made, until a result of about two million years is obtained. This value is accepted together with the tolerance figures and becomes proof for formal classification. Of course, it becomes very awkward in those cases, such as Java man and Peking man, now classified as *Australopithecines*, which were dated prior to the introduction of the potassium-argon method (about 1950) at only half a million years. Little wonder there is controversy and as many ape-to-man (including extinct ape-to-man) ancestral trees as there are specialists working in the field of paleoanthropology. With all due respect to Richard Leakey, his *Homo habilis* has been listed under *Australopithecines* in Table 1 simply because most authorities think that is where it should be, in spite of Leakey's claim that it belongs to the Genus *Homo*.

The numbers in the table refer to the number of "individuals" found, but these vary from one authority to another. As previously mentioned, it must be kept in mind that an "individual" is usually represented by only a part of a bone or, at most, a handful of bones. Some of the smaller discoveries have been omitted for the sake of clarity, so that, for example, Great Britain is not included since the only claim to date is of a small part of a cranium found in 1935, known as the Swanscombe skull and classified as *Homo sapiens*. The Americas are notable by their absence, but not because hominid fossils have not been found on the western side of the Atlantic—the Calaveras skull and the Guadeloupe skeleton mentioned in the previous chapter and the Laguna skeleton from California, described by Ceram (1971b), come to mind[29]—but because there is a general reluctance to admit the evidence. The reasoning is not difficult to perceive: having man evolve from the ape on one continent is improbable enough, but having man evolve simultaneously and independently on two continents presumably lies beyond the bounds of credulity of even the most hardened Darwinist, and the prejudiced mind naturally rejects the evidence.

Before deciding to accept or reject the evidence surveyed so far as transitional forms between ape and man, two more aspects should be considered. Until now all that has been described has been based on subjective analysis. In other words, the fossil hunter looking for human origins will, when confronted with a piece of jawbone, look at it and compare it visually with a corresponding bone from a true ape and another from a true man. From the details of shape and size, he will make a judgment on whether the fossil is from true ape, true man, or something unknown but lying in between.

Human judgment, however, is notoriously fallible and is especially susceptible to preconceived ideas (not to mention driven by the necessity for research grants); good science tries hard to remove the human element from the judgment of results. The classical way to do this is by statistical analysis. Fortunately, today there are computer facilities that take the drudgery out of this work. What in the past would be inconceivable in terms of man-hours of calculation is now routine. The bones of a pygmy and those of a heavyweight wrestler will be quite different in size and, in some respects, in shape also, yet this is the variation possible within true man. A similar argument applies to chimpanzees, gorillas, and the orangutans; today there are a great deal of data available on the variations in body bones and especially teeth possible for these creatures. Finally, to make a statistical and objective evaluation, a number of fossil bones of the same type are required to compare the variation possible in the hominid candidate with the variation known in a similar bone in true ape and true man. This has now become possible with the recovery of "families" of some hominids, where a number of bones of the same type have been found.

Charles Oxnard of the University of Chicago has carried out a multivariate statistical analysis of a series of *Australopithecus* bones, including pelvis, ankle, foot, elbow, and hand, and compared these with corresponding true ape and true man·bones. According to Oxnard (1975) the analysis shows that *Australopithecus* was not intermediate between man and ape but was uniquely different. *Australopithecus* was, in fact, as different from both man and the apes as each is from the other.

Another well-respected worker in this area of objective analysis by statistical computer techniques is Sir Solly Zuckerman. He compared forty-eight dental parameters of the Swartkrans *Australopithecines* with those of eighty chimpanzees, ninety gorillas, and fifty orangutans, and these results showed that these fossils were more like apes than like man (Ashton and Zuckerman 1950).

This leads us, finally, to the studies of real apes and real men, since so far in these two chapters all the claims for intermediate forms have been based on fossil bones. It has been pointed out in Chapter Six that we can tell nothing of blood grouping or chromosomal pattern from a fossil, and these are vital areas to determine phylogenetic relationships. Apes do look and act like humans, while the chimps' tea party at the zoo enhances this impression. Then again, there are some humans who, at first sight, seem to have swung out of the jungle trees just a generation or so ago. But of course these are just impressions, and those who study anatomy will tell us that there are far more differences than similarities between ape and man (Coon 1965; Huxley 1901, 7:77).[30-31]

The ape has forty-eight chromosomes and man has forty-six. This raises the questions of at what point in the transition from ape to man the two chromosomes became lost, and how they produced fertile offspring when this loss occurred randomly to some and not others. To take another example, the ape has a bacculum or *os penis* (a bone in the penis) and man does not. It might be asked, therefore, at what point in the line of transition the bone was replaced by the fluid mechanism, bearing in mind that it had to work flawlessly the first time in order to propagate the race (Metchnikoff 1907, 81).

The most important area of difference between man and the animal kingdom is the ability to communicate thoughts and abstract ideas to his fellow man through speech. It is commonly assumed that our spoken words developed from the grunts and howls of man's social ape ancestors, while great efforts have been made to confirm this notion by teaching apes to communicate with humans. But in spite of all the effort, and not a little controversy, Terrace (1979) has shown that the entire exercise is nothing more than the animals' response, causing the researchers to be self-deluded.[32] The question might then well be asked,

Just who is making a monkey out of whom? Although scholars debate the pronunciation of words in ancient languages, when all is said and done our record of the spoken language only extends to the beginning of mechanical recording—barely a century. The arguments, it is safe to say, are based on opinions. In contrast, the written language extends back approximately five thousand years, and here the study of human communication shows an interesting, though little publicized, pattern. Kluckhohn notes, "In contrast to the general course of cultural evolution, languages move from the complex to the simple" (Kluckhohn 1949, 149). A second linguistic expert, Elgin, is more specific and says, "The most ancient languages for which we have written texts ...Sanskrit, for example...are often more intricate and complicated in their grammatical forms than many contemporary languages" (Elgin 1973, 44). This same trend is acknowledged, for instance, by Shakespeare's being included in the high-school English class as an illustration of the English language at its best. The decline is even apparent when one compares the writers of today with those of just a century ago. The significance of this observation is that, for the period over which we have written records, the data substantiates the traditional view that man has fallen rather than ascended. But then five thousand years is a mere drop in the bucket compared with two million years, if indeed we can believe the radiometric dating methods.

*   *   *

When all is considered in this matter of missing links, the lives and lifestyles of the handful of individuals making the claims are believed to be important, because it is such a highly subjective discipline, heavily dependent upon what the seeker wants to find. Academic credentials are no guarantee, as we have seen in the case of the Piltdown affair, while it seems that absence of credentials is no guarantee either, as in Richard Leakey's case. What it ultimately boils down to is the individual's commitment to a belief system. We have seen in this brief overview that details of the claims for discovery of some likely-looking fossil continually shift as the claimants jockey for the prized position exactly between true ape and true man. Failure to report all the facts often results in less than honest and open discussion, and controversy abounds. Sir Solly Zuckerman is a champion of the evolutionary position yet makes the following statement regarding the fossil discoveries: "No scientist could logically dispute the proposition that man, without having been involved in any act of divine creation, evolved from some ape-like creature in a very short space of time—speaking in geological terms—without leaving any fossil traces of the steps of the transformation" (Zuckerman 1971, 64). Here, an authority in the field

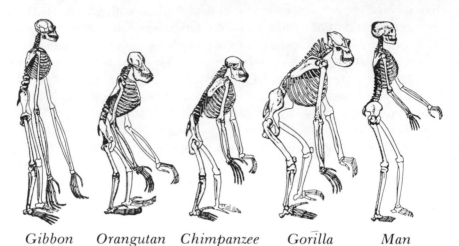

Gibbon   *Orangutan*   *Chimpanzee*   *Gorilla*   *Man*

Following the maxim that a good picture is worth a thousand words, Thomas Huxley had this drawing prepared from specimens in the museum of the Royal College of Surgeons for his essay *On the Relations of Man to the Lower Animals* in 1863. It has been repeated endlessly in various forms since that date. The gibbon was mistakenly reproduced at twice scale. (Author's collection)

of anthropology admits that there is no fossil evidence to link the higher mammals with man and hints at some sort of miraculous conversion. As we saw in Chapter Six, Gould has unwittingly implied this very thing with his theory of punctuated equilibria. The reader should weigh the evidence for himself and decide whether to believe the claim that proof has been found for man's relationship to the ape or to consider the alternate possibility, that all the *Australopithecines* and *Pithecanthropines* are nothing more than true, but extinct, apes.

10

Heads, Organs, and Embryos

*False facts are highly injurious to the progress of
science, for they often endure long; but false
views, if supported by some evidence, do little
harm, for everyone takes a salutary pleasure in
proving their falseness: and when this is done,
one path towards error is closed and the road to
truth is often at the same time opened.*
CHARLES DARWIN
(1871, 2:368)

T
he two previous chapters outlined the major features of man's
search among the fossils for evidence of his relationship to the
higher animals, yet there are biological features among living
things which are claimed as evidence for a continuous phylogenetic
relationship, from the lowest order of creature to man. Some of these
features are the so-called vestigial organs found, it is claimed, in both
animals and man and believed to be the remains of organs once useful
in a prior evolutionary stage. Another biological feature is the embryo,
or fetal stage, of higher organisms including man, which, it is said,
reproduces in itself several earlier stages of its long evolutionary history. Before taking a more detailed look at these textbook favorites,
however, this might be an appropriate place to say something about
heads, since the last two chapters were somewhat concerned with this
part of our anatomy. This subject will also serve as a foundation for the
final chapter.

Heads

It would be quite unusual these days to hear of an eminent man
making a posthumous donation of his head to science. In the nineteenth century, however, this was quite a respectable thing to do. Many
well-known writers, scientists, and notables in England and Europe
willingly acceded to this service to science by allowing their heads to be

removed as soon as decently possible after death, in order that the brain could be taken out, weighed, and studied. The idea that man's mind—that is, the seat of his emotions, his intellect, and will—is situated in the skull and, therefore, identified with the brain, does not have a long history and began in the seventeenth century with René Descartes. The first serious consideration was being given at this time to the study of man's soul, or psyche; since then the disciplines of psychology and psychiatry have been very much oriented towards the brain and considerable success has, in fact, been achieved in identifying, for example, various kinds of emotions with specific areas of the brain. In those early days, however, there was the unquestioned belief that every living person had a soul and that the soul left the body after physical death; attempts were made to prove this by weight-loss experiments after death, but without success. Although it is like looking in the stable for the horse after it has bolted, autopsy examination came up with the pineal gland, located in the front of the brain, as the seat of the soul, or the place where the soul had been during life. More will be said of the pineal gland later in this chapter.

Attention was then focused on the intellect as the more obvious manifestation of the soul, and there were two observations—both faulty. The first, announced in 1859 by Paul Broca, professor of clinical surgery in the Faculty of Medicine, University of Paris, stated that intelligence was directly related to brain size and, consequently, to the

Ivan Turgenev, 1818-83
2,000 grams

Anatole France, 1844-1924
1,017 grams

The cranial capacity of *Homo sapiens*, in the range of 1,000-2,000 cubic centimeters (or grams), clearly bears no relationship to intelligence. (Turgenev: after the painting by Kharlamov c. 1880; France: photograph c. 1900; Metropolitan Toronto Reference Library Board)

size of the head. The facts were then, as they still are today, that men of exceptional intelligence tend to rise to prominent positions in society, and some of these individuals do have larger than average heads. Jonathan Swift (1667-1745), author of *Gulliver's Travels* among many other writings, was one such well-known individual, with a cranial capacity reckoned at an astonishing 2,000 cubic centimeters, although this was never actually measured since he died before it became fashionable to contribute exceptional heads to science. Cases such as Swift nicely substantiated the theory, and later there were many others in which weights of the actual brain were recorded rather than the volume of the empty container, the latter being, of course, the only recourse in the case of those long dead. For all practical purposes, in the case of brain tissue, it makes no difference whether we speak of cubic centimeters or grams: the units are interchangeable, and the figures can be directly compared. The French paleontologist Georges Cuvier, with the most prodigious memory, had a brain that weighed in at 1,830 grams, while Russian novelist Ivan Turgenev's brain made the all-time record in excess of 2,000 grams. It might be recalled that the average adult brain today is about 1,450 grams, or approximately the same number of cubic centimeters.

It was a great temptation for craniologists of the nineteenth century to select such facts as these to fit the theory, and, eventually, they became so self-convinced as to be totally blinded to those cases of ignorant men with larger than average heads. These men usually did not catch the attention of society, and it was easy to overlook or explain away this kind of data. However, what was not so easy to ignore or explain away were those cases of brilliant men with smaller than average heads. In 1855 the brain of the great German mathematician Karl Gauss (1777-1855) weighed in at a disappointing 1,492 grams; then, as their days expired, there were other brilliant men with smaller than average brains, and finally, in 1924, when the brain in the rather peculiar head of the French novelist and satirist Anatole France joined others pickled for perpetuity, it was found to be a mere 1,017 grams. Data of this kind could not be ignored, and the theory fell into disrepute, but it had been widely believed and promulgated for almost a century and still lurks in the collective unconscious today (Gould 1981b, 73).

The second great fallacy that arose from faulty observation was related to, and a direct outcome of, Lamarck's evolutionary thinking, which argued that the mechanism responsible for one species becoming another was that of the inheritance of acquired characteristics. The giraffe's long neck, acquired by generations of parents reaching for the higher leaves of trees, is the classic example. This notion was applied to man's brain—the more he exercised it, the larger it became. The increase in size was said to be passed on to the next generation, which thereby had the immediate advantage over its normal neighbors by having a larger initial capacity for intellect. Darwin himself entertained Lamarckian reasoning, as we shall see in the next section, but the idea was not shown to be incorrect until the early 1900s, when the work of Gregor Mendel's genetics was understood and accepted. The Lamarck/Broca notion, that brain size increases with intellect and that this acquired increase is passed on to the next generation, is quite faulty reasoning, even though examples can always be found that appear to support the argument, and it has led to the most outrageous exercises in racial discrimination ever perpetrated in modern times (Haller 1971).[1] We will not pursue this fascinating horror story at this juncture but simply point out that these two related ideas were condemned to die in the Western Hemisphere shortly after the turn of this century. In Russia, Lamarckian thinking continued under Trofim Lysenko and was only abandoned in favor of Darwinian thinking with the death of Joseph Stalin, in 1953. However, in spite of all this well-known history, these ideas relating brain size to intelligence are still very much alive in the thinking of many today who really should know better but persist in perpetuating the myth (Tobias 1970).

The explanations put forward to account for one particular ape becoming man vacillate from the ape's purported ability to walk upright (bipedalism), to his discovered use of fire, to his ability to speak, and, most popularly, to the use of his brain. The use of the brain and consequent increase in size is the central preconception of those committed to find the elusive missing link. There has to be real dichotomy in thinking in order to be convinced that some extinct ape developed a larger brain, which enabled the creature to outwit and outsurvive others competing in the same arena of life. In making this claim, it has, at the same time, to be acknowledged that from all the work in the nineteenth century with living people and heads rather than fossils, the size of the brain, at least within the limits of 1,000-2,000 cubic centimeters, bears no relationship to intelligence. There can be no logical reason for claiming that brain size suddenly becomes significant in the range, for example, from 500-1,000 cubic centimeters, that is, from ape to man, except that this is a necessary *a priori* assumption in order to provide a framework for evidence to close that vital gap between ape and man.

This preconception can be seen to influence in a very tangible way the practical matter of the reconstruction of fossil skulls, particularly when the fossil is found in many pieces, some of which may be missing. If nature had supplied us with a perfectly spherical head, it would be a simple matter to determine the original skull size and, hence, the volume, from the curvature of only one small piece. But, of course, heads are not like this but consist of a multitude of curves, most of which would be known in only a general way beforehand. Reconstruction is thereby a complex problem and very much subject to the preconceptions of those doing the reconstruction. It may perhaps be realized that a small difference in any gap left in the fitting of the pieces to form a surface makes a large difference to the volume of the finished reconstruction. If, for example, the fossil pieces were discovered in strata believed to be half a million years old, the reconstructor might expect to be dealing with a *Pithecanthropine*, and the skull volume, accordingly, would be greater than 750 cubic centimeters. Unconscious bias, particularly in the hands of a skilled anatomist, would tend to fit the pieces together tightly or loosely to finish up with the expected volume. We saw that the reconstruction of the Piltdown skull gave volumes of 1,070 and 1,500 cubic centimeters in the hands of two experts with different preconceptions. We may then ask what assurance there is of the validity of Weidenreich's (1943) reconstruction of Peking man, which has exactly the expected skull capacity, when all the original fossil pieces have so conveniently disappeared.[2]

America's Golgotha

Even with complete skulls and accurate determinations of their volume, other factors, such as the height of the individual, are directly

Samuel George Morton, 1799-1851. Amassed one of the world's largest collections of human skulls and set the pattern for scientific racism for almost a century. (Library, Academy of Natural Science of Philadelphia)

related and have to be taken into account. However, superimposed on all consideration is the preconception of the investigator, since it is this factor alone that has the greatest influence on the interpretation of the physical data.

The classic example of preconception is that of Samuel Morton, who had more than a thousand complete and intact skulls to work with rather than a few fragments. But first, a look at the social background of his times.

In the early part of the nineteenth century when the Negro population of the southern United States was still in slavery, the white man became very divided on the question of racial superiority, which eventually led to the American Civil War in 1861. At that time the Bible was recognized as the standard by which to arbitrate all moral and ethical judgments, but those with a vested interest in the slave population found biblical arguments to support their own position. The ninth chapter of Genesis relates how the black races were descendants of Ham's son Canaan, who was cursed by Noah, and seems to indicate that they were forever destined to be the white man's servant. The South African policy of apartheid today began with this same biblical interpretation. A less popular school of argument (the polygenists) abandoned the Bible altogether and maintained that the races were separate biological species. Darwin cites one enthusiast who claimed that there were sixty-three species of man (Darwin 1871, 218). Even though interfertility between the races had been well demonstrated, attempts were made to expand the definition of "species" in order to accommodate the theory.

Whether arguing from biblical injunction or biological inferiority, the result was a no-win situation for the black slave. Moreover, whatever else was said, all were agreed that the Negro was of inferior intellect. And, of course, without educational opportunities for Negroes this reasoning was handsomely confirmed. The circularity of this argument was detected by some of the more enlightened, among whom was a fashionable Philadelphia physician of the polygenist school, Samuel Morton. Morton's single purpose of mind was dedicated to clear the air of this emotional issue and provide hard objective data showing the intelligence of Negro, white man and, for good measure, the North American Indian. Naturally, intelligence would be measured by skull capacity, and so it was that in the 1820s Samuel Morton began amassing one of the world's largest human skull collections, which may be found today in the department of physical anthropology at the museum of the University of Philadelphia.

At great personal risk, friends of Morton dug up Indian graves and cemeteries, and contributed assorted heads. All were carefully identified as to racial origin. Morton personally measured the capacity of each, using lead shot, and proceeded to carry out an elementary statistical analysis on the results, which were eventually published in the beautifully illustrated volumes *Crania Americana*, in 1839, and *Crania Aegyptiaca*, for Egyptian skulls, in 1844. There was a summary volume in 1849.

Morton died an early death in 1851 and was regarded as a well-respected scientist of his time who had provided the world with the definitive work on racial intelligence. The figures confirmed what everyone "knew": the white man was the most intelligent, the Indian next, and the Negro least of all. In his most charitable and Christian way, the white man was seen to be offering protection and security to his child-like black brother by employing him as a slave—wonderful justification, for no one could refute the hard facts of science!

It wasn't until the late 1970s that Gould (1978) reanalyzed Morton's original data and discovered that there was no statistical difference between the white, red, or black population figures. In other words, there was absolutely no basis for claiming that one race was any more intelligent than another. The statistical reworking had clearly shown that, though Morton was an honest man in that he had published his original data, he was biased in his thinking and had unconsciously selected his data to fit his three incorrect preconceptions: a) The Negro race was biologically inferior to the white races; b) as a result of biological inferiority, the Negro race was less intelligent; and c) intelligence could be measured by brain size or skull capacity.

Fortunately, in spite of all the hard "evidence", slavery was abolished in North America in 1865, but we may never know just how much these efforts were retarded by Morton's definitive data. Morton's story has been included here as a classic example of prejudice that unconsciously influenced the interpretation of data, with the result that untrue and dangerous statements masqueraded under the impartial banner of science for more than a century.

One final word on this subject of heads, or more specifically, the stuff that occupies them. Among a number of commonly quoted and well-known items of intelligence, whose authority and source no one seems to know or question, is the idea that man only uses about 10 percent of his brain capacity. Apart from wondering how this is measured, we may pose the question, If this statement is true, and regardless of what percentage figures are attached to it, how is it possible that natural selection (or any other evolutionary mechanism) has provided us with a brain capacity far exceeding our use of it? From the evolutionary standpoint, this leads to the uncomfortable conclusion that "nature" knows ahead of time what our future requirements will be. This is known as a teleological process and replaces the chance mechanism of evolution by an intelligence. Men such as Darwin have been struggling against just this concept since Aristotle proposed it and it is clearly unacceptable. But at the same time, this lack of full use of our brain leads to an alternative dilemma that long ago man used his entire brain capacity and has since allowed it to fall into disuse. The example of the child prodigy can better be explained on the basis of unusual retention of ancestral brain capacity rather than prolepsis of an evolutionary aspiration.

Vestigial Organs

Among the favorite pieces of "evidence for evolution", which is found in virtually every biology textbook, are what are claimed to be vestigial organs present in both plant, animal, and man. These are organs that are believed to have once been useful during a previous stage of evolutionary development but in continuing evolution are in the process of being selected out by modification. In other words, a changed habit or environment has rendered an organ redundant, and in disuse it has shrunk away until only a vestige remains. In chapter thirteen of the *Origin*, Darwin describes what he calls rudimentary, atrophied, or aborted organs, and he gives a number of examples from nature.[3] He includes the rudimentary pistil of some male flowers; rudimentary teeth in embryonic birds and whales; atrophied tails, ears, and eyes in certain animals; and atrophied wings in flightless insects and birds. He speaks of aborted organs, and notes certain features that are present in some varieties and absent in others of the same species—for example, the absence of the oil gland in the fan tail pigeon (Darwin 1859, 22). Some years later when he wrote *The Descent of Man*, Darwin went on to list a number of human organs that he claimed were rudimentary and included the muscles of the ear, wisdom teeth, the appendix, the coccyx or "tailbone", body hair, and the semilunar fold in the corner of the eye (Darwin 1871, 1:19-31).

Having laid the groundwork principles, Darwin left it for others to explore the field in detail. In Germany the anatomist Robert Wiedersheim, a Darwinian enthusiast, fulfilling all the expectations of his country's reputation for thoroughness, produced a masterwork, in 1895, entitled *The Structure of Man*. In this work he listed eighty-six human organs that he claimed were mere vestiges, no longer having any useful function (Wiedersheim 1895, 200). In addition, he had a shorter list of organs, which he claimed were retrogressive—that is, they were in the early stages of being atrophied. Wiedersheim's vestigial list included the pineal gland; the pituitary body; the lachrymal glands, which produce tears; the tonsils; the thymus; the thyroid; certain valves of the veins; bones in the third, fourth, and fifth toes; parts of the embryo; and certain counterparts of the reproductive structures of the opposite sex such as the clitoris. Of course, the list also included all those features mentioned by Darwin, such as the appendix and the coccyx.

Altogether this awesome list stood as landmark evidence of evolution in action, and, coming as it did from such a world authority in the field of comparative anatomy, it has been quoted and requoted in biology textbooks ever since. For example, the seventh edition of Villee's *Biology* claims there are more than one hundred vestigial human organs, but, in fact, the author mentions only six (Villee 1977, 773).[4] Other textbook authors, more conscious of the advances in medical knowledge during the past century, do not say how many vestigial organs there are but simply point to the appendix, or perhaps the coccyx, as examples.

At first sight Darwin's argument for vestigial organs as evidence for the theory of evolution may seem rational; the textbook authors claim it to be evidence, and this often causes the idea to be accepted without question. Darwin was very uncertain in his thinking as to why a vestigial organ should be evidence of evolution, yet, as usual, he comes away from his discourse fully convinced. However, a little thought and some insight show that the victory of his argument comes rather from the defeat of the case for Special Creation than from direct support for his own theory.

Nineteenth century writers of natural history advocated the idea of Creation and commented on the evidence of the Creator as the master Designer from design found in nature: each plant, animal, and man being perfectly designed for its particular environment. However, there were a few embarrassments, as there appeared to be some redundant organs, most noticeably, perhaps, nipples on the human male. Rather than cast doubts on the skill of the Designer, these apparent anomalies were explained as being created "for the sake of symmetry" or in order "to complete the scheme of nature". Darwin rightly pointed out that this was no explanation but merely a restatement of the fact (Darwin 1859, 453). On the other hand, his proposal that redundant organs were actually rudimentary, having been useful in a previous evolutionary stage, appealed to reason rather than sentimentality and was accepted by many. The critics, however, could see weaknesses in Darwin's explanation: for example, if the male nipples were a redundancy, this could only lead to the conclusion that in the past the young were fed at the male breast! (Darwin 1871, 1:31).[5] Nevertheless, for those seeking pure rationality, this detail was overshadowed by the redundancy claimed for all the other human organs and in doing so demolished the weak "symmetry" explanation used by the advocates of Creation.

The scientific aspects of the reasoning used to claim vestigial organs as evidence for evolution turn out to be rather hollow. To begin with, the notion is based on homologies: that is, all animals are claimed to possess some organs or structures that have no function, and these organs are homologous to organs that are functional in other related animals. The familiar example is the horse's ability to move its ears back and forth quickly, a very useful function for that animal. Man's ears are equipped with a similar set of muscles homologous to those of the horse, but of course, not nearly so well developed; the movement is thus much more limited. These muscles of the human ear were seen by Darwin and his followers to be vestigial, or mere rudiments of once fully functional muscles, capable of swirling the ears about when man was at a much earlier evolutionary stage (Darwin 1871, 1:19). To most biologists today, the presence of small organs, such as the human ear muscles, that seem to have no function in themselves but correspond to functional organs possessed by other animals, indicates inheritance from common ancestry.[6] Darwin (1871, 1:32) actually said this and it has been repeated, seemingly without the realization that the entire reasoning is Lamarckian (Darwin 1859, 457).[7] It will be recalled that Lamarck's mechanism for evolution of the species was by the inheritance of acquired characteristics. The long neck of the giraffe was acquired by the successive inheritance of slightly longer necks, produced by each generation stretching for the topmost leaves of the trees. The vestigial organ argument is exactly the same in principle, since it says that the rudimentary organs are acquired by successive inheritance of slightly smaller organs produced by disuse. Weismann's rather crude experiment, in which the tails of mice were cut off for nineteen successive generations (Weismann 1891, 1:444) convinced scientists at the turn of this century that Lamarck's ideas were invalid, and later when the inheritance of characteristics was found to depend on the DNA genetic coding and not habits, the reason why Lamarckism could not work was understood.

That Darwin's reasoning concerning vestigial organs is Lamarckian can be seen from two directions: from those examples that he and others claimed were vestigial and those cases that should have qualified as vestigial but were not so claimed. In the first place, Darwin's list of human organs, later expanded to more than one hundred by Wiedersheim, has now shrunk to two or three very questionable claims, due to advances made in medical knowledge, and leaves only one certainty, the male nipples, and, notably, most textbooks no longer include this item. Villee (1977, 773) makes an incredible exception! The medical advances made since Darwin's day have shown that virtually all of these vestigial organs do, in fact, have functions, many of which are very necessary at an early stage of our physical development. It would be a tedious exercise to list them all with their function, but a few familiar examples will help make the point that the former claims for functionless organs were made in ignorance, and it would be reasonable to say that any doubts that still remain will be dispelled as medical science advances. Scadding, writing in 1981, was forthright enough to admit that vestigial organs provide no evidence for evolution.

The thyroid gland. Once claimed to be useless, this is now known to be a vital gland for normal body growth, and oversupply or undersupply of this gland's hormone, thyroxine, will result in overactivity or underactivity of all body organs. Deficiency of this organ at birth causes a hideous deformity known as cretinism.

The pituitary gland. Another organ once claimed to be vestigial, this is now known to ensure proper growth of the skeleton and proper functioning of the thyroid, adrenal, and sex glands. Improper functioning of the pituitary gland can lead to Cushing's syndrome (gigantism).

The tonsils and appendix. The thymus gland, the tonsils, and the appendix are each a type of lymphatic tissue that helps to prevent disease germs from entering the system and operates principally in the first few months or years of human life (Maisel 1966). The human alimentary canal can be regarded as a pipe extending from mouth to anus, while just within the entry and exit ports are glands, the tonsils at one end and the appendix at the other. These glands provide protection against invasion of the body by pathogenic organisms. Once the child, during the first few months of life, has built up sufficient resistance to the usual disease germs, the importance of the appendix diminishes, while that of the tonsils diminishes after the first few years. For this reason, should these organs become infected, they can be removed from sufficiently mature patients without apparent loss.

The importance of these organs has been known among the medical profession for more than half a century. For example, Sir Arthur Keith, head of the Royal College of Surgeons, London, writing in the widely read journal *Nature*, in 1925, on the subject of imperfect organs, said, "The tonsils, the thymus, lymphatic glands, and Payer's patches have similar life histories, but no one would describe them as vestiges or rudiments" (Keith 1925b, 867). In the same article Keith says of the appendix, "An organ which increases in length until the twentieth year, or even until the fiftieth, does not merit the name vestigial" (Keith 1925b, 867). Nevertheless, writers of biology textbooks still regard the appendix as a vestigial organ and as evidence of evolution.

Oddly, although the appendix appears in what are said to be man's closest relatives, the apes, it does not appear in his more remote relatives, the monkeys, but appears again, further down the evolutionary scale, in the rabbit, wombat, and opossum (Mivart 1873, 161). In light of these facts, the view that the human appendix is a vestige of an organ useful at an earlier evolutionary stage is difficult to explain (Gray and Goss 1973, 1242).

The coccyx. Sometimes referred to as the "tailbone", this now is acknowledged to have the important function as a point of insertion for several muscles and ligaments, including the gluteus maximus, which is the big muscle that runs down the back of the thigh and allows us to walk upright. More will be said of the coccyx in the next section (Gray and Goss 1973, 118).

The semilunar fold of the eye. Some animals, and birds particularly, have a third eyelid known as the nictitating membrane, and it has been claimed, first by Darwin, that man has a vestige of this membrane at the

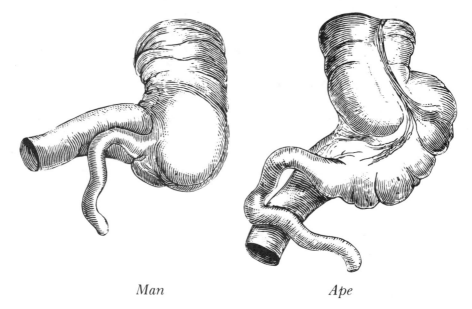

Man   *Ape*

The appendix in man and in the ape appear very similar and no doubt have the same function; some would see this as evidence for evolution, others recognize this simply as a common design. (Thomas Fisher Rare Book Library, University of Toronto)

inner corner of the eye. Contemporary books on anatomy describe this semilunar fold simply as that portion of the conjunctiva that aids in the cleansing and lubrication of the eyeball, making no reference to its being vestigial (Gray and Goss 1973, 1065).

The pineal gland. Once thought to be the seat of the soul and later claimed to be a vestige of a third eye, presumably by some student of Greek mythology, this gland is one of the remaining few for which the function is still not entirely known. It is known, however, that tumors of the pineal gland cause abnormal sexual functions, and in view of all the other discoveries made, it would be foolish to claim that this organ was functionless.

Returning to those organs that Darwin and others did not claim were vestigial yet which should have qualified according to the proposed definition, there are several interesting examples. The three-thousand-year-old Jewish practice of circumcision was mentioned previously but is still a valid example against the vestigial organ argument. Removal

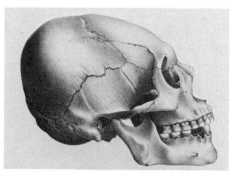

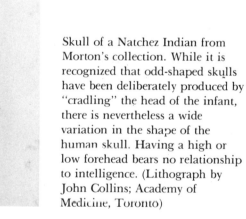

Skull of a Natchez Indian from Morton's collection. While it is recognized that odd-shaped skulls have been deliberately produced by "cradling" the head of the infant, there is nevertheless a wide variation in the shape of the human skull. Having a high or low forehead bears no relationship to intelligence. (Lithograph by John Collins; Academy of Medicine, Toronto)

Skull of Klatstoni Indian from Morton's collection and of relatively recent date. The forehead is virtually absent, yet this specimen has never been considered as an ape-to-man transition. (Lithograph by John Collins; Academy of Medicine, Toronto)

of the unwanted "organ" for more than one hundred generations has not made a fraction of an inch of difference, and Jewish male babies continue to be born "fully equipped". However, a more striking example was pointed out by Metchnikoff, a dedicated Darwinist, whom we shall meet later in this chapter. This enthusiast would have dispensed with half the organs of the human body, including the female hymen, which he carefully avoided calling vestigial or nascent but described simply as "useless and dangerous" (Metchnikoff 1907, 85); since it is absent in the anthropoid apes, he strangely considered it "new" to humanity (Metchnikoff 1907, 81). Metchnikoff said of the hymen that the only purpose it served was "the overthrow of the dogma of the inheritance-acquired characters" (Metchnikoff 1907, 85), and from this aspect it is fairly evident that, even though married three times, Lamarck was not overly familiar with this portion of the female anatomy.

Another example concerns the Chinese practice of binding the feet of girls. Having small feet was a mark of social distinction, and this practice was continued for several thousand years and only abandoned at the turn of this century. After generations of bound and virtually atrophied feet, the preferred small feet were never inherited, and Chinese babies continued to be born then, as they are today, with perfectly normal feet. The Flathead Indians of America provide another example; they bound or clamped the infant's head as quickly as possible after birth, while the skull bones were still supple, to produce the most peculiar-shaped heads. Presumably, this practice was of some importance to them, and a few examples may be found in Samuel Morton's classic *Crania Americana* (Morton 1839, plates 20 and 44)—we can only imagine what odd-looking individuals these must have been in life. In any event, after hundreds of years of this practice, the Indian babies continued to be born with normal heads. The conclusion from all these observations is that neither mutilation, deformity, excessive development (of muscles), nor atrophy through disuse has ever been inherited over even a hundred generations.

With today's understanding of the role of DNA in the transmission of genetic characteristics, we would not expect these uses or abuses to have the slightest effect over any number of generations. The same reasoning would also apply to any of the vestigial organs claimed in the animal or plant kingdoms. Perhaps the most notable examples are the vestigial "hind legs" of the whale and the "hind legs" of the boa constrictor, but few authors claim these organs as vestiges today, since their function is now beginning to be understood (Carpenter et al. 1978).[8] Darwin recognized that variation within a species does occur,

UPPER: An early display of a whale skeleton at the British Natural History Museum. Rather oversized vestigial "hind legs" can be seen suspended near the tail.
LOWER: A photograph taken of the same exhibit gives a more truthful impression of the "legs". There is no sign of a pelvis or any attachment of these two small bones to the vertebrae. (Author)

even to the point where an organ may entirely disappear. The absence of the oil gland in the fantail pigeon has been mentioned, but the creature still remains a pigeon; continued breeding will cause a reversion back to the common rock pigeon, complete with oil gland, so that it is evident that the genetic coding still retains this information in the fantail pigeon, even though it is not expressed. No one really expects the whale or the boa constrictor suddenly to "express" hind legs, although this is precisely the argument Darwin implied from his example of the pigeons.

To be as charitable as possible, it may be argued that Darwin simply had a theory about rudimentary organs that has since been shown to be incorrect, and that no harm has been done. He could be excused on the grounds of medical ignorance of his day, although there is no excuse for today's textbook authors (Biological Sciences Curriculum Study 1980).[9] It would not be true to say, however, that the theory has passed through history without causing harm. It has, in fact, been directly responsible for needless suffering at the hands of the medical profession for thousands who can only be described as victims of a delusion.

From the late nineteenth century, when the notion of man's emergence from the ape and the "evidence" of the vestigial organs began to appear in biology textbooks, medical students were required to subscribe to these ideas, and these students became the surgeons of the succeeding generation.

The French physician Frantz Glénard (1899) proposed the concept of visceroptosis—a prolapse, or falling, of the intestines and other abdominal organs—caused, he said, by man's erect posture. Very clearly this idea was based on man's supposed evolution from some lower animal. He wrote some thirty papers about this problem, and by 1900 the condition came to be called Glénard's disease. Patients complaining of abdominal pains, irregularity, and so on were advised to submit to ceco-colon fixation and/or gastropexy, each of which was a major operation intended to correct nature's fault by anchoring the colon and fixation of the stomach, respectively. Their original symptoms may or may not have been alleviated, but most of the victims were left with problems worse than those with which they began.

In England, Sir William Arbuthnot Lane was one of the most famous, skillful, original, and indefatigable surgeons of his time. Because of his personality and unusual powers of observation, it was said that he was the inspiration for Conan Doyle's Sherlock Holmes. Lane had conceived the theory of autointoxication, or self-poisoning, and claimed that, under certain circumstances, putrefaction of the intestinal contents occurred; toxins were formed and absorbed, leading to chronic poisoning of the body. By 1903 both the concepts of visceroptosis and of autointoxication were combined and given support by the Russian Nobel prizewinner Élie Metchnikoff (1907), who was a convinced evolutionist and presumed that man's alimentary system, which served in an anthropoid phase of human evolution, must be ill-adapted to deal with the dietary requirements of civilized man (Metchnikoff 1907, 69ff).[10] Convinced by Metchnikoff, Lane at first performed a short-circuiting operation (ileosigmoidostomy) to connect the lower end of the small intestine to the far end of the large intestine.

With further encouragement from the fearless Metchnikoff, who,

Élie Metchnikoff, 1845-1916. Member of the prestigious Pasteur Institute, Paris. The famous scientist for whom the institute was named would have turned in his grave had he known what nonsense Metchnikoff was preaching in the name of science. (Author's collection)

incidentally, was a zoologist and not a physician, Lane then performed a colectomy, or removal of the entire colon. In his enthusiasm Lane believed that this surgery was also of value in the treatment of duodenal ulcers, bladder disease, rheumatoid arthritis, tuberculosis, schizophrenia, high blood pressure, and a host of other ailments (Metchnikoff 1907, 248).[11] Lane alone performed more than a thousand colectomies, while dozens of other surgeons across Europe and the United States were stripping out the colon vestiges and leaving untold numbers of victims, few of whom were benefited more than temporarily. Many were made worse; some died (Layton 1956; Tanner 1946).[12]

The appendix was, of course, fair game in this drive to eradicate the troublesome vestiges, and it was not until the 1930s that these theories of visceroptosis and autointoxication began to be condemned in the medical textbooks, but the practices really only stopped with the demise of the practitioners and lingered on into the 1950s. The condemnation came about by the gathered evidence of such items as the wide diversity of bowel habits where, for example, it was discovered that it is not abnormal for some healthy individuals to go several weeks without a movement (Lambert 1978, 21).

All this needless suffering, we are reminded, resulted from Darwin's notion of vestigial organs, which he required as evidence for his theory of evolution. This theory is still central to biological thinking, and we may only surmise what other medical practices are being carried out today based on this premise and also having little or no good effect.

Embryos

There are probably few readers who have never been exposed to the idea that during the first few months in the womb each of us, as an embryo, passes through various stages in which we have gills like fish and a tail like a monkey. We do not have to look very far to recall where we were first introduced to this impression: it was, of course, in the biology classroom where we met the Biogenetic Law, also known as the recapitulation theory, one that was presented as cardinal evidence for evolution. Ernst Haeckel's Biogenetic Law, postulated in 1866, is now discredited, but it has only been in very recent years that it quietly disappeared from biology textbooks, although it still finds its way into popular science books. Richard Leakey's *Illustrated Origin of Species*, published in 1979, contains Haeckel's nineteenth century diagram (Leakey 1971, 213), which, as we shall see, was shown to be fraudulent more than a century earlier. Interestingly, the diagram has been altered by a modern hand, while Leakey's text with the picture makes no reference to this but advances as truth what is acknowledged by science to be a discredited theory. Even the fifteenth edition of the *Encyclopaedia Britannica* admits the discredited status, though obscurely, in the words, "The theory [of recapitulation] was influential and much popularized but has been of little significance in understanding either evolution or embryonic growth" (*Encyclopaedia Britannica Micropedia* 1974, 2:27).

Sir Gavin de Beer of the British Natural History Museum was more forthright. In 1958 he was quoted as saying, "Seldom has an assertion like that of Haeckel's 'theory of recapitulation', facile tidy, and plausible, widely accepted without critical examination, done so much harm to science" (Beer 1958, 159). Nevertheless, in 1958 and for almost two decades later, every biology textbook still presented the theory as factual, with the status of scientific law.

Just what was being said in the Biogenetic Law is important, because a fraud was involved that deceived laymen and scientists alike for more than a century; we should be aware that if it happened once, such a thing may well have happened on other occasions. Several recent cases have, in fact, been documented by Joyce (1981) and Ravetz (1971).

Historically, naturalists before Darwin had observed that higher animals tend to repeat, or recapitulate, in their early development the adult stages of various lower animals. The resemblance of the tadpole of the frog to the fish is the classic example, and, in this case, the frog is regarded as being higher in the evolutionary scale than the fish—shades of circularity can perhaps be detected in this reasoning. In the thirteenth chapter of his *Origin*, Darwin presented this notion as a principle by saying, "The community in the embryonic structure reveals community of descent" (Darwin 1859, 449). By this he was emphasizing the importance of the embryological evidence as support for his theory of the inheritance of slight modifications by descent. The widespread dissemination of this seed-thought in the *Origin* was bound to find some fertile ground, which, in fact, turned out to be the mind of Darwin's chief apostle, T.H. Huxley. Well aware that a good picture is worth a thousand words, Huxley included a pair of reasonably accurate drawings of the embryos of dog and man to show their similarities in his essay *On the Relations of Man to the Lower Animals*, in 1863 (in Huxley 1901, 7:77, fig. 3). Darwin used these same compelling drawings in his *Descent of Man*, in 1871 (Fig. 1). Haeckel, in Germany, seized upon Darwin's notion of recapitulation together with the idea of Huxley's illustration, and announced his *Biogenetic Law*, which he summed up in the dictum "ontogeny recapitulates phylogeny"—that is, the development of the individual repeats the development of his race (Gould 1977c).[13] Darwin had said nothing about man being included in the evolutionary order in the first edition of his *Origin*, but Haeckel had no scruples and published his ideas, in

Ernst Haeckel's series of embryos showing three stages of development in the pig, the bull, the rabbit, and man. Initially, all the embryos look alike, but as growth proceeds they take on their individual forms. In Haeckel's view this is convincing evidence for evolution. In fact, the embryos show greater differences than appear in his diagram. (From Haeckel's *Anthropogenie*, 1874; Thomas Fisher Rare Book Library, University of Toronto)

1866, in a two-volume work entitled *Generelle Morphologie der Organismen*. By his own admission this was not a popular work because of his attempted scholarliness in trying to emulate the style of his idol, the poet Goethe. The idea and his own fraudulent illustrations were then presented in a more successful attempt two years later in his *Natürliche Schöpfungsgeschichte* (the English translation was published under the title, *The History of Creation*, Haeckel 1876).[14] Haeckel's energy and persuasiveness in promoting his ideas resulted in yet another volume, in 1874, generally referred to simply as Haeckel's *Anthropogenie*, which included a number of illustrations of various embryos. These pictures appeared in textbook after textbook for the next century;[15] they are the same pictures found in Richard Leakey's *Illustrated Origin* (textbook examples range from Romanes 1892 to Winchester 1971).[16]

Haeckel stated that the ova and embryos of different vertebrate animals and man are, at certain periods of their development, all perfectly alike, indicating their supposed common origin. Haeckel produced the well-known illustration showing embryos at several stages of development. In this he had to play fast and loose with the facts by altering several drawings in order to make them appear more alike and conform to the theory. Haeckel was a scientific draftsman of no mean talent and good optical equipment was available for his use. Yet the alterations were deliberate, because he began with accurate drawings that had been published several years before. Wilhelm His (1831-1904), a famous comparative embryologist and professor of anatomy at the University of Leipzig, pointed out the liberties Haeckel had taken with the illustrations to manufacture evidence for his law. In a catalogue of the errors, His (1874) showed that Haeckel had used two drawings of embryos, one taken from Bischoff (1845) and the other from Ecker (1851-59), and he had added 3-5 mm to the head of Bischoff's dog embryo, taken 2 mm off the head of Ecker's human embryo, reduced the size of the eye 5 mm, and doubled the length of the posterior. His concluded by saying that one who engages in such blatant fraud forfeits all respect, and he added that Haeckel had eliminated himself from the ranks of scientific research workers of any stature (His 1874, 163). His, whose work still stands as the foundation of our knowledge of embryological development, was not the first to point out the deficiencies of Haeckel's work, nor indeed was he the last, yet Haeckel's fraudulent drawings have continued to the present day to be reproduced throughout the biological literature. It is also notable that the exposure of Haeckel's fraud by His in 1874 has been confined to the German archives and has never appeared in the English evolutionary literature. (The author is

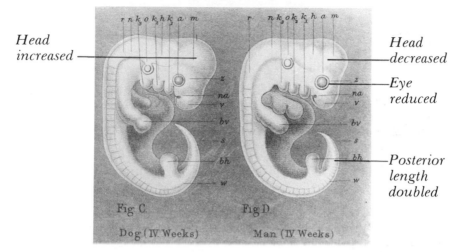

Head increased ——

Head decreased

—Eye reduced

—Posterior length doubled

Fig C.   Fig D.

Dog (IV. Weeks)   Man (IV. Weeks)

Haeckel's drawings made to show the resemblance of the dog and human embryos first appeared in the German edition of the popular *Natural History of Creation* in 1868. They were exposed as fraudulent by Wilhelm His in 1874. (Author's collection)

indebted to Wilbert Rusch (1969, 27) for his research and translation of the German texts.)

What then of the alleged gill slits and tail of the human embryo? In the first few weeks of development, the human embryo does have a series of creases having a superficial resemblance to those found in the fish embryo; however, the creases have no respiratory function and later develop into ear and jaw areas in the human, while those of the fish develop into the gills. The notion of recapitulation only existed in the minds of those such as Haeckel who wished to see this as evidence for the theory. The analogy might be of two modern assembly lines for automobiles: at the early stages both assembly lines appear very similar, but as development proceeds it becomes evident that very different-looking cars are being built. In no way could it be said that one car had evolved from the other, any more than similarity of embryos is evidence of man's evolution from the fish. A modern textbook on human embryology acknowledges the false impression given in earlier texts in the following statement:

> The pharyngeal arches and clefts [creases] are frequently referred to as branchial arches and branchial clefts in analogy with the lower vertebrates, [but] since the human embryo never has gills called 'branchia', the term pharyngeal arches and clefts has been adopted for this book. (Langman 1975, 262)

In the *Descent of Man* Darwin referred to the human *os coccyx* or

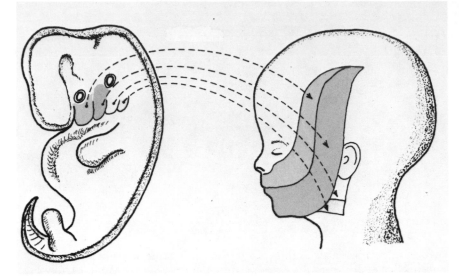

The alleged gill-slits in the human embryo become part of the face and are not connected in any way with our respiratory system. (Author)

'tailbone' as a tail, "though functionless" (Darwin 1871, 1:29). This became evidence for his theory, and from time to time ever since, when an infant is born with a "tail", it has merited national press coverage serving to keep the notion alive in the public consciousness. This very thing occurred as recently as 1982 and began with a case reported by Ledley in the respected *The New England Journal of Medicine* and captioned "Evolution and the Human Tail"; the press, and ultimately the public, could hardly fail to be convinced that some sort of evolutionary throwback was being reported. Of course, the human coccyx was listed as a vestigial organ for a century or so after Darwin, but in recent years even this has finally disappeared from the pages of biology textbooks.

There are several facts, well known to the medical profession, that explain the myth of the human tail. In the first place, the adult human has thirty-three vertebrae, and the human embryo has the same number, never any more. This constitutes the "back bone" and "tailbone", but in the early embryo stage the assembly does look like a long tail since the limbs begin only as "buds". The anal opening is always at the end of the "tail" so that it takes its normal place in the anatomy upon full development. Very exceptionally, there is an anatomical defect in the coccyx of the newly born, and this has to be surgically corrected, just as the harelip has to be corrected, but the coccyx is never removed because it is a vestigial tail. Biology textbooks as recently as

1965 made the erroneous claim that individuals were sometimes born with a tail that had to be surgically removed, but all that has ever been removed is a caudal appendage. The caudal appendage occurs quite rarely, contains no bones, and has a fibrous fatty core that is covered with skin. It is not located at the end of the backbone but sticks out on one side. It has never been regarded as a "tail" by the medical profession, yet the author of the 1982 article, in describing what was a caudal appendage, clearly identified it with an evolutionary tail and thus perpetuated the myth.

Now that the Biogenetic Law, or recapitulation theory of the embryo, has finally been discredited, it has been noted that biology texts, loathe to give up what has served well as evidence for the theory for more than a century, are now speaking about a "derived state" of the embryo. Toothlessness in birds and in anteaters is given as the example of a derived state, but a moment's thought will show that this is nothing more than the vestigial organ argument which, as we have previously seen, is based on the Lamarckian mechanism and is known to be invalid. In other words, the fact that some embryonic birds have teeth, whereas in the adult form they do not, does not necessarily mean that the teeth are vestiges, but that they undoubtedly do have some function just as the human appendix does at the fetal stage.

Why Erroneous Theories Persist After Being Discredited

Ever since the publication of Darwin's *Origin* in 1859, there has been a consistent trend, evident in these past five chapters, to interpret natural phenomena in a way that appears to provide evidence to support the theory of evolution. Some of these interpretations have turned out to be based on faulty observation, some on faulty reasoning, and some on blatant fraud, but the trend is always in the same direction. It might be asked why these unscientific illusions persist in spite of exposure within the scientific community, and why they have been maintained at the level of the general public, in some cases, for half a century. The underlying reason is not rooted in the plain facts of science but, rather, in unproved and unprovable philosophical beliefs and sociological views.

Darwin's theory of evolution has, in many minds, displaced the biblical Creation account of our origins, and to those who hold to this view it is vitally important to maintain whatever evidence there is, at least until sufficient better evidence can be found to replace it. To abandon discredited interpretations without replacement could place the theory of evolution in the perilous position of not being supported by any evidence whatsoever and incur the risk of having the creation account reintroduced. For this same reason, there is an extreme reluctance on the part of the scientific community to accept or even consider new evidence that does not support the current evolutionary dogma. Worse yet is the type of evidence that appears to give direct support to the book of Genesis, such as the fossilized human skull found in a coal bed and previously mentioned on page 102. Incidentally, this skull has recently been located in the Freiberg Coal Museum, East Germany.

Harding (1981) has concluded that the refusal to accept new information of this kind may be resolved into four attitudes:

1. *The rationalistic model,* which says that the only permissible approch is through reason and the established universal laws; no appeal can be made to the miraculous.

2. *The power model.* Though usually operating under a rationalistic model, this model is characterized by the scientist who dominates his field, seeking to maintain power, prestige, and pride of authorship. Often it is necessary to await retirement or even death of the individual before new ideas and better evidence can be introduced.

3. *The indeterminancy model.* Science has today become so specialized, with each discipline having its own technical language, that, unlike science in the nineteenth century, there is no spokesman knowledgeable in all fields. The communication of generalities from one specialty to another often results in unintentional overstatements and half-truths. Each specialist may question matters of evidence for evolution in his own field but remain confident in overall evolutionary theory, on the assumption that the other fields have all the really solid evidence.

4. *The dogmatic model.* This is characterized by an appeal to evolution as the "only *scientific* model for origins" and the statement that it is an "established scientific fact". That there are at least six mechanisms of evolution currently being proposed, with the experts divided among themselves, should alert the layman to the truth of the matter: nothing has been established.

The impression that scientists think rationally and fairly is a simplistic myth. The fact is they are subject to the same human failings as the rest of us. Looking inside the ivory towers we find the familiar power establishments, personality conflicts, and intellectual blind spots brought about by philosophical presuppositions. Several authors, such as Kuhn (1962) and Bereano (1969), have observed that science does not proceed in a smooth, orderly fashion but in fact remains virtually static under a dominant paradigm for long periods, before being overturned in a revolutionary manner. It may well be that science is on the brink of another revolution as voices within the ranks are raised against the theory of evolution. Rifkin (1983) has recently proclaimed this in print.[17] The only restraining influence would appear to be the united fear that, in the absence of anything else to replace it, some may be misguided enough to consider the creation alternative. In the next two chapters, we will see how the tricky subject of measuring time in the past has been handled by today's scientists, who, although competent, are still subject to the normal human failings.

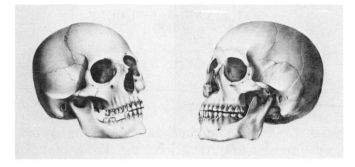

11

The Age of the Earth

The poor world is almost 6,000 years old.
WILLIAM SHAKESPEARE
(1599)[1]

I t seems that as long as mankind has been keeping records, there has
been a compulsion to keep track of time, the age of the individual,
of his social group, his country, his empire, and of civilization itself.
The records have been chiselled in stone and kept on paper and
papyrus, but it is only in the past two millennia that the Judeo-
Christian West has related its records to one historical event, a fact that
has greatly simplified the record keeping. Dates within the A.D. time
frame are, thus, fairly certain. The further one goes back in the B.C. era,
however, the dates become increasingly less certain until, eventually,
beyond about 2000 B.C., the dates given are actually a consensus of
opinions from the prevailing school of thought.

The archaeological dates depend on a continuum of evidence, such
as interrelated king lists with the years of reign, and as such, this is
primary data. Dating by the carbon 14 radiometric method, for example, is secondary data, because this method is first calibrated against
archaeologically dated material. More will be said of the carbon 14
method in the next chapter.

To go back further in time, estimates are made from the natural
processes, largely independent of each other and certainly independent
of the hand of man. More will be said of these in this chapter and the
next, but it may first be asked, Can we legitimately consider the ancient
written records? There are many of these of which the Bible is only one.
As in the case of the written testimony of our own birth, these records
are only as good as our trust in the authors. Although these sources
cannot be taken as proof of the beginning, we might consider their
coincidental record from widely different cultures to be circumstantial
evidence.

282

The Age of the Earth Before Lyell and Darwin

One concise and readily available source of nineteenth century information is Robert Young's concordance, and in the popular twenty-second edition, under "creation", will be found a list of thirty-seven computations of the date of creation from a possible list of more than one hundred and twenty. Of these thirty-seven, thirty are based on the Bible and seven are derived from other sources—Abyssinian, Arab, Babylonian, Chinese, Egyptian, Indian, and Persian. Not one of these ancient records puts the date of creation earlier than 7000 B.C. In all the hundreds of thousands of years over which hominid man is alleged to have evolved, it is surely more than coincidental that ancient civilizations, which were by no means ignorant of timekeeping by astronomical methods, should all begin their historical record at this arbitrary date. In addition, all the myths and legends, however bizarre, speak of instant creation just a few thousand years earlier.

In almost every system of historical chronology, either the creation of the world or the birth of Christ has been adopted as the reference point to which all other dates are subordinate. The dating system based on the birth of Christ will be familiar to most readers and is, in fact, used throughout the world today for business transactions. However, in non-Christian countries, and Israel specifically, the eras are referred to as: B.C.E., before the common era, and C.E., the common era. In religious communities dating is often from the creation of the world. For example, orthodox Jews begin their dating at 3760 B.C., while the Freemasons begin theirs at 4,000 B.C.

Before the rise of science, it was usual for the church hierarchy to set forth pronouncements and deliberations on such issues as the age of the earth. Until the time of Darwin, the Old Testament Scriptures were held to be the literal truth. While the Bible does not spell out the date of creation, it was believed that this could be derived from the somewhat complicated genealogies and ages of the patriarchs. A number of scholars in the past have attempted to deduce the date of creation by this means, and a few of the more popular estimates were: Playfair, 4008 B.C.; Ussher, 4004 B.C.; Kepler, 3993 B.C.; and Lightfoot, 3928 B.C. These scholars were each proficient in a number of ancient languages, yet the fact that their dates were close but not coincident means that it is not a simple matter to establish the beginning exactly from the biblical genealogies; to this day there are men still working on this problem. Nevertheless, the date 4004 B.C. has generally been thought to be the most likely beginning point, and this has been associated with Anglican Archbishop James Ussher, although several other workers arrived at this same figure in Ussher's day.

James Ussher, 1581-1656. A scholar
proficient in a number of ancient
languages, Ussher took the
Scriptures quite literally and
calculated the year of Creation to
be 4004 B.C. (After Sir Peter Lely;
National Portrait Gallery, London)

In 1701 the date 4004 B.C. for the year of creation was inserted as a
marginal commentary in the English edition of the Great Bible by
Bishop Lloyd and, by association, thus became incorporated into the
dogma of the Christian church. By the time the theory of evolution
came into open conflict with church dogma, almost every Bible published in the nineteenth century had Ussher's date appended to the first
page, followed by sequential dates throughout to the time of the birth
of Christ. As the church succumbed to the reasonings of science, these
dates were quietly dropped from the Bible's beginning around the turn
of this century.

There are few texts that, when discussing the age of the earth, fail to
mention Ussher's name and his date of 4004 B.C. Many of these texts
add a further detail ascribed to Ussher and pinpoint the time of creation
at 9 A.M. on 17 September or 9 A.M. on 23 October, depending on the
authority being quoted. The facts are that this specification of the
precise time of creation did not originate with Archbishop Ussher but
with his contemporary, John Lightfoot, who, except for a propensity
to indulge in some idle speculation, has been effectively used, particularly by geology and biology textbook writers, to discredit the Ussher
date. Characteristically, not only have the details been attributed to the
wrong author but careful reading shows, for example, that the 9 A.M.
statement was actually taken out of context in the first place (Lightfoot
1825, 2:335).[2]

So much for the time of creation and the consequent age of the earth
from the biblical perspective. If this record is to be taken at all seriously,
it may be appreciated that the minimum age of the earth at this point is

about six thousand years; while allowing for possible omissions in the genealogies, it might be a one thousand years or so older, but hardly more. The exact figure may never be known, but the point is that this is about a million times less than the current estimates of the age of the earth as given by science. Quite obviously, these two estimates are poles apart and provide the basis for diametrically opposed ideologies.

Time and Rationality in the Nineteenth Century

Historical time is unique; once passed, a moment can never be recaptured, and, without witnesses, can only be inferred from assumptions. It is no coincidence, then, that the theory of evolution, as formulated by Darwin and as we subsequently know it today, is founded on Lyell's geology. As we saw in Chapters Three and Four, Lyell's geology is, in turn, based on a device whereby traditional catastrophe became the quiet outworkings of natural processes observable today. That device was the philosophical stretching of time, from a few thousand years, implied by the biblical testimony and engraved on the nineteenth century mind, to an almost open-ended scale, reckoned today in thousands of millions of years. Lyell exploited the impossibility to recapture past events, and once having broken into this virgin ground, it then became a private preserve for his followers and had the convenience of having a sliding scale of time to fit the current theory.

Science was not very sophisticated in the early nineteenth century, and the only problem confronting the unproven assumption of the long ages proposed by Lyell was the mind-set of other scientists of the day and, of course, of the theologians, many of whom happened to be the same scientists! Nevertheless, the revolution in young earth to an ancient earth was the snowball starting the whole avalanche that eventually changed mankind's entire *weltanschauung*, or worldview.

Shortly after the time Lyell published his *Principles of Geology* (1830-33), men began to look for methods for determining the age of the earth that depended on natural processes rather than Archbishop Ussher's biblical interpretation. All these methods then, as today, depend on finding some chemical or physical process whose rate of activity can be measured. The product of the process is then found, and by simply dividing the product by the rate, the length of time the process has been in operation is derived. An example of this exercise was given in Chapter Four, which described the efforts in finding the age of Niagara Falls: the amount by which the falls retreats each year is the rate of activity, and the length of the gorge is the product of the process. On paper this is straightforward enough, but in practice assumptions have to be made that are subject to the preconceptions of those carrying out the work.

Lyell's preconception of long ages caused him to modify the figure he had been given for the rate of retreat of the falls, and he finished with an age that is now conceded to have been too great. It is important, then, that whatever rate is being measured be done so accurately and without bias; this is best carried out by taking an average of the values obtained by several observers over a number of years.

The most important decision that had to be faced when calculating the age of the earth was to agree that the measured rate of the physical process had always been the same. In nineteenth century investigations, as well as those today, the doctrine of uniformitarianism made it easy to assume that the rates of these processes, that is, cutting of gorges, settling of river sediments, etc., had been constant. In many cases this assumption was later concluded to have been quite wrong. But the ages that were derived at the time were held to be scientific fact, and, although this was unintended, actually served well to undermine the biblical catastrophists' beliefs of a few thousand years; these figures played a vital part in establishing the theory of evolution.

Some Former Facts of Science

It was recognized quite early that rivers carried a sediment that settled to the bottom when the water moved less rapidly, such as at points where the river entered the ocean or at times when the river was spread out in a flood plain. Many efforts were made to measure the sediment carried by river water each year and then measure the total quantity of sediment deposited at the river mouth. It was always assumed that the rate of deposition of sediment had been constant. While there were some uncertainties in measurement, in the 1850s there came a unique opportunity to measure both the rate of sedimentation and the total deposit at the same location and with some precision. Napoleon's popularization of the wonders of ancient Egypt brought the realization that the River Nile flooded the fertile valley every year and left a thin deposit of mud. The foundation of the colossal statue of Ramses II had been built on this deposit in the valley at Memphis and over the ensuing years had been covered by a further nine feet of river-laid sediment (Bonomi 1847; Lepsius 1849). When the hieroglyphics had been deciphered and the chronology worked out, it was established that the statue had stood for 3,200 years, so that with nine feet of deposit over this period, the deposition rate was three-and-a-half inches per century at this point (Dunbar 1960, 18).[3] Further excavations in the Nile valley showed that the sediment was as much as seventy-two-feet deep in some places, but

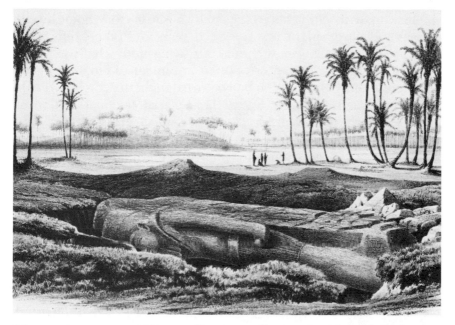

The seventy-ton statue of Ramses II as it was discovered at Memphis in the 1840s. The foundation lies buried in sediment under the feet of the statue. (Lepsius 1849; Thomas Fisher Rare Book Library, University of Toronto)

it was realized that the test hole now extended several feet *below* the level of the Mediterranean Sea, and further boring was discontinued (Lyell 1914, 29).[4] However, at the measured rate of three-and-a-half inches per century, this gave a maximum age of only 30,000 years, which was woefully short of the millions of years required for Lyell's geology. The borehole project, carried out between 1851 and 1858, became something of an embarrassment and was discontinued. However, there is an interesting observation that was passed over at the time and, so far as is known, has not been made since. The rates of sediment deposition at Memphis, or at any other location where it has been measured, can always have been greater but never very much less. At Memphis, in order to fit Lyell's geology of, for example, only one million years, the sediment deposited would be less than a thousandth of an inch per century. The most fastidious housewife knows that house dust accumulates at a greater rate than this! On the other hand, to fit Ussher's chronology, one or two large inundations of sediment prior to the erection of the statue would be all that was required. For instance, if catastrophes such as volcanic eruption with great quantities of ash are admitted, then any sedimentation rate in the past can have been very much greater and have had the effect of shortening the calculated life immensely.

The work with sediments was generally unsatisfactory. Some investigations indicated only a few thousand years and others only a few million, so that they were without consistency and, what was worse, were all too short. The most popular argument to circumvent this situation assumed that erosion had occurred in the dry eras between the times of immersion under water. This placed one assumption on another, and the argument became very strained. The situation, however, was nicely rescued in the early 1900s by the discovery of radiometric methods, which gave much longer lives. Today, little or no credence is attached to ages based upon sedimentation rates: not, we are reminded, because the rates of sedimentation were ever in question, but because the results were inconsistent and did not fit the preconceived ideas of Lyell and his followers.

Salt in the Sea

Another early attempt to measure the age of the earth was carried out by John Joly, in 1899, and was based on the amount of sodium chloride (common salt) in the oceans. Joly (1901, 247) assumed that the primitive ocean began as pure water and that the present rate of salt addition from the world's rivers had always been the same. Since the salinity of the world's oceans is nearly uniform and map measurements indicate the total volume of water, Joly, consequently, determined the number of tons of salt contained in the oceans. Measurements at the mouths of all the world's major rivers then showed how many tons of salt entered the oceans each year, and by a simple divison of the numbers, Joly arrived at 100 million years as the age for the earth. At that date, Darwin's followers reluctantly accepted this figure, and it became a scientific fact. But just in the nick of time, it seems, radiometric methods superseded all the other methods, and estimates of the age of the earth increased by leaps and bounds (Joly 1922).[5] For the next half century, a number of very vague reasons were advanced to explain away Joly's estimate based on the ocean's salt content, but the method was, in a sense, too good and allowed little room for argument. The original assumptions could not really be called into question, because to do so would only shorten the age. In fact, once it was admitted that the original ocean contained any salt at all, then it became anybody's guess, and the catastrophist could equally well claim that the ocean had been created salty in the first place, only a few thousand years ago.

At the time Joly was working on his salt method using the world's rivers and oceans, someone must surely have thought of the simpler approach based on the same principle but confining the work in terms of effort and certainty to Israel's Dead Sea.

Israel's Chronometer

Geologically, the Dead Sea Valley is part of a rift valley system that extends down through the Red Sea into the Afar region of northeastern Ethiopia. Textbook authorities maintain that the system was formed several million years go. For example, radiometric methods applied to the strata of the Afar region, where Donald Johanson discovered the now famous "Lucy", indicate that this geological formation was formed at least three million years ago (Johanson and Edey 1981, 187). At the other end of this rift valley in Israel is a water system consisting of the Sea of Galilee, the River Jordan and the Dead Sea, which are all below sea level and form a unique chronometer at the lowest point on earth. Fresh water from the Sea of Galilee flows continually into the Dead Sea via the River Jordan, while the only outlet for the Dead Sea is by evaporation; evaporated water contains no salt. Long ago the system came to equilibrium when the rate at which the water entered the Dead Sea exactly equaled the rate at which it left by evaporation, and the salts then began to concentrate.[6]

Fortunately for the armchair investigator, all the essential data concerning the rate at which salts concentrate in the Dead Sea have been published and conveniently may be found in the fourteenth edition of the *Encyclopaedia Britannica*:

The Dead Sea, which covers an area of 394 square miles, contains

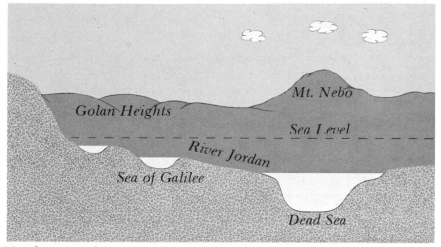

North to South Section through River Jordan Valley, Israel

Israel's chronometer. Located 1,200 feet below sea level, the water of the Dead Sea can only leave the basin by evaporation. The salts remain and concentrate. The parameters of this system are accurately known and indicate only a few thousand years for its existence. (Author)

approximately 11,600,000,000 tons of salt, and the river Jordan which contains only 35 parts of salt per 100,000 of water, adds each year 850,000 tons of salt to this total (*Encyclopaedia Britannica* 1973, 19:995).

By simply dividing the total quantity of salt by the annual rate of addition, the age of this geological feature is found to be a mere thirteen thousand years, which is a far cry from the three million years claimed for the other end of the rift valley. However, this is not all, since the same encyclopaedia (under "salt") also points out that there are salt water springs at the bottom of the Dead Sea and other streams that contribute salts, so that the overall effect is to reduce the age still further. It would be spurious to argue that the waters of the Jordan contained less salt in the past, because the enormous lengths of time demanded by geology would require a purity of Jordan water far greater than that of distilled water, and this is clearly not credible.

It is reasonable to suppose that others must have drawn these same conclusions on the Dead Sea years ago, when the waters were first analyzed, but by that time the orthodox geological dogma prevailed, and, so far as is known, this obvious conclusion has never been committed to print.

More Salts in the Sea

More recent work based on Joly's principle has been carried out by measuring uranium salts instead of sodium chloride in the rivers and oceans and was reported by Koczy (1954). These figures were, in turn, used by Cook to derive a statement commenting on the youthfulness of the earth and published by the respected British journal *Nature*. The statement was, however, not immediately obvious, couched as it was in the cryptic terms of the scientist. Cook (1957) concluded his article on radiogenic helium with the remark that his results were "in approximate agreement with the chronometry one obtains from the annual uranium flux in river water (10^{10}-10^{11} gm/yr) compared with the total uranium present in the oceans (about 10^{15} gm)" (Cook 1957, 213). Taking the figure of 10^{11} as the rate at which uranium enters the oceans and 10^{15} as the total product (the units may be neglected), the age is given simply by subtracting eleven from fifteen; that is, 10^4 or 10,000 years. Koczy pointed out in his paper that the deep sea sediments do not contain the enormous quantities of uranium that might be expected and leaves the reader with some vague assumptions to account for the "missing" uranium.[7]

All those who conducted the river water analysis, including the U.S.

A Greek myth tells us that the love goddess Aphrodite, otherwise known as
Venus or Cytherea, was born from the sea. Aphrodite means "foam-born". Does
this Greek wisdom hint that mankind too was born from the sea, as in the
textbook explanations we are given today? (Drawn by Mary Wardlaw)

geological survey, cannot have committed a million-fold error, and if
the 10,000 years is anywhere near correct, then it begins to look as if the
original ocean contained about as much sodium chloride as it does
today but contained no uranium salts. Boldly stated, this conclusion,
drawn from the published data, runs counter to the uniformitarian
dogma and would rarely be found within the pages of the professional
journals and never in the popular press.

Back to Discarded Myths

Before leaving the subject of salt in the oceans, it should be noted that it
was shortly after Joly had published his early work that A.B. Macallam,
in 1903, stated that there was a causal relationship between the salinity
of the sea and the salt content of blood plasma. This was said to be a
direct reflection of our ancient emergence from the sea, and until it was
refuted a few years later, this became another scientific fact supporting
the theory of evolution (Macallam 1903).[8]

Cooling of the Earth and Lord Kelvin

One final method, involving the measurement of rate and product,
concerned the cooling of the earth from an assumed hot liquid state.
This method is worth mentioning here, for some of the details will be

William Thomson, better known as Lord Kelvin, 1824-1907. A truly great scientist of the nineteenth century by whom we benefit today, his name has been overshadowed in the popular press by that of Darwin. Shown here with his compass. (Photograph by J. Annan, 1902; The Royal Photographic Society)

referred to in the following chapter. The Industrial Revolution had created a great need for coal to generate steam power. As coal mines were driven deeper, it was noticed that the temperature rose about 1°C for every thirty meters (one hundred feet), and it was realized that at this rate the earth must be white hot for the greater part of its core and only cool enough to support life on a thin outer shell. One of the nineteenth century theories for the origin of the earth was that given authority by the French mathematician Laplace, who proposed that our solar system began as a spinning blob of white-hot matter. Several small pieces then became detached, continuing to spin in the same direction and, under their own gravitational fields, formed spheroids orbiting the central mass. The spheroids cooled to become the planets, one of which was our earth. Although this entire scenario has been left in the mind of the general public even to this day, as we shall see, it was in fact refuted long ago.[9]

Shortly after Darwin published the *Origin*, William Thomson (1865), afterwards Lord Kelvin, began to calculate the age of the earth assuming it had originated as Laplace had described it. Kelvin took for his datum points the time at which the surface layer crusted over (freezing point of molten rock) and the rate of heat flow through the surface of the earth as found in the coal mines. In an elegantly simple two-page paper, he effectively demolished Lyell's uniformitarian assumptions and left Darwin's theory without a foundation (Thomson 1865). Kelvin showed that the age of the earth, based on the assumption that it had cooled, was a maximum of 400 million years, while an appeal to any greater length of time would leave the earth too cold today to support life. This upper limit was too short a time for Darwin, but Kelvin's scientific stature and mathematical demonstration could not be faulted (F. Darwin and Seward 1903, 2:163).[10] Ironically, this very argument was later misinterpreted by some of the clergy, who mistook Kelvin's defense of the Christian faith (by refutation of uniformitarianism) as an advocacy of an old earth. In this way some were weaned away from the Christian dogma of a young earth towards accepting an old-earth view and, eventually, the idea of evolution itself.

During the Kelvin-Darwinian debate over the age of the earth, nicely documented by Burchfield (1975), the Darwinians were set back by two astronomical discoveries, given relief by the death of Kelvin in 1907, finally taking the victory from the phenomenon of radioactivity that had been discovered a few years earlier. By observing the movement of sun spots, it was evident to astronomers that the sun was not spinning on its axis at the rate that would be expected from the Laplace theory; more devastating was the discovery that some planets revolved in a forward direction about their axis and others in a retrograde direction (see note 9). According to the theory, they should all revolve in the same direction. This effectively discredited the Laplace nebular hypothesis, although, after more than a century and without a better theory to offer, the modern theory is essentially the same except for the name.

The textbook explanation today for the origin of the solar system proposes that in a process called accretion, finely dispersed gases and dust were rotating and concentrating under gravitational forces. From the fiery ball of gas generated by this process, it is then said that a disc of gas was thrown off, condensing to form the planets and eventually cooling from liquid to solid. Darwin's theory was successfully rescued from the difficulties with Lord Kelvin and the astronomers by two brilliant assumptions based on Becquerel's accidental discovery of radioactivity in 1895.

First, it was observed that radioactive decay produced a small quantity of heat, and this fact was then called on to explain the sustained high temperature of the earth's core. Having broken through Kelvin's upper limit of 400 million years, an age of more than ten times this figure is today claimed for the earth; it should be remembered, however, that this is supported entirely on the assumption that an enormous and virtually inexhaustible source of heat resides in the radioactive elements within the earth. This assumption is seldom questioned, but

Ingersoll (1954) and his coworkers pointed out more than three decades ago that by reworking Kelvin's cooling data the age of the earth was shown to be 22 million years without radioactivity (Kelvin's minimum value based on Laplace's theory was 20 million years), but including the known radioactivity in the earth, the age could not exceed 45 million years (Ingersoll et al. 1954, 99). Clearly something is radically wrong, since this is but 1 percent of that required by today's biological evolution.

The second assumption was concerned with the rate of radioactive decay. An early discovered property of this decay process was that it appeared to be constant and seemingly unaffected by chemical changes, extreme heat, or pressure. The appearance of a constant decay rate was quickly assumed to be a fact, and radioactive decay was seen to be a unique and independent way to determine the age of the earth. Sir George Darwin, son of Charles Darwin, made this suggestion at the British Association meeting of 1905. By 1910 a method had been worked out and an age of 600-700 million years for a Precambrian rock mineral reported (Strutt 1910). This is modest by today's standard, but it did serve nicely as the second arm of attack on Kelvin's formidable 400-million-year barrier. Moreover, there was no likelihood of the figures being challenged since Kelvin had died three years earlier.

When these radiometric techniques were first introduced, many workers were skeptical, but as the expectation of geological ages seemed to be confirmed, the method became established and eventually swept aside all the earlier methods. It was at this point that the estimates of the age of the earth began to increase most dramatically. Engel, writing in 1969, showed that the textbook age of the earth has increased by a factor of almost one hundred since 1900, the accepted "age" then being 50 million years, while today it is claimed to be 4.6 billion, that is, 4.6 thousand, million years (see Appendix B).

The entire edifice of the old-earth model depends almost exclusively on the results given by the radiometric methods, while these, in turn, depend on the validity of certain assumptions. Textbooks tend to gloss over these assumptions, but an understanding of what is actually being assumed is essential in order to make an intelligent assessment of the method's credibility. For this reason, an attempt will be made in the remainder of this chapter and the first half of the next to patiently untie, rather than to cut, the radiometric Gordian knot.

Since these pages may appear as parched desert to the non-technical reader they may care to take the direct flight and continue from page 322. The essence of what will be said is that radioactive decay of certain elements, some of which are confined to the rocks while others form part of every living thing, is analogous to the old-fashioned hour-glass. The radioactive element is like the sand in the upper glass and as it decays to become the non-radioactive element, this material falls through into the lower glass. The method of finding when the hour-glass was started, that is the age, consists of determining the total amount of element in each half of the glass and measuring the rate at which it falls from the upper vessel to the lower. The smaller the quantity of radioactive material that remains relative to the non-radioactive material with which it is associated, the greater is the age of the sample.

Principles of Radiometric Measurement

The alchemists of the Middle Ages believed it was possible to transmute, or change, a heavy base metal, such as iron, into the heavier noble metal, gold, and thereby make a fortune. Modern science has shown that this is generally quite impossible, but there are naturally occurring processes in which transmutation takes place spontaneously in the reverse direction, whereby unstable elements change atom by atom to form lighter stable elements. This process is known as radioactive decay and, depending on the elements involved, may take the form of alpha decay, typically producing helium gas, or beta decay, where an electron is emitted, or decay by an electron capture mechanism. The characteristic that makes the radiometric methods so valuable is the decay process, which is believed to be constant, unaffected by temperature, pressure, or, indeed, the chemical form taken by the unstable element in its initial state.

The decay process is seen as a unique kind of clock which, having begun, has been running with unerring accuracy ever since. The underlying principle for all the radiometric methods is that once the rate of decay for the particular radioactive process is known, then the age of anything that contains within it such a process may be found simply by measuring the quantity of unstable element remaining and the associated quantity of stable element that has accumulated to this point. These elements are usually referred to as "parent" and "daughter" elements, respectively, and a simple calculation using this data then gives the time the decay process has been in operation.

The Radiometric Methods

The earliest radiometric method resulted from an observation made by Boltwood in 1907 that uranium and thorium minerals both decay radioactively to form lead and helium gas. The uranium/lead method, though limited to uranium-containing minerals, was used for many years and depends on the decay of uranium 238 to lead 206, through a complex process involving fourteen stages. Details of these stages are not essential to the present context and may be found in Appendix C. The numbers 238 and 206 refer to the atomic mass, or weight, and identify the specific isotope, or variety of the individual elements. Details of the uranium/lead method will be used to illustrate the next section.

Subsequently, other radioactive processes were found, such as the decay of potassium minerals into argon gas or rubidium minerals into strontium, and since rocks containing these elements as minerals are more abundant, these methods are now the most commonly used to date rock strata. In this way, absolute ages have been attached to the various parts of the geologic column and its associated fossil forms. The popular carbon 14 method, which depends on the radioactive decay of an unstable isotope of carbon, is somewhat different from the other radiometric methods and will be discussed in the next chapter.

Rate of Decay

Radioactive decay has always been assumed to be a constant process, occurring by random transmutation of the individual atoms of the unstable element. Some atoms will last only a few minutes before decay, while adjacent atoms will remain for thousands of years. No one can know when an individual atom will decay, and, for that matter, no one is sure why they decay. When a large number of atoms is involved, however, there is a certain statistical certainty that, at any given moment, a specific number of atoms will be in process of spontaneous change or decay. Details of these numbers give the vital rate of decay, but this is based on the assumption that it is a random process. During the past decade or so, statistical work carried out by Anderson and Spangler (1973)[11] has shown that, in fact, the decay process is not random; this means, however, that the decay rate cannot be known with certainty, putting all radiometric dating into serious question (Anderson 1972).[12] Not surprisingly, even though holding responsible scientific positions, these authors admitted to difficulty in getting their work published and since then have confessed that it has been "disregarded, discounted, disbelieved...by virtually the entire scientific community" (Anderson and Spangler 1974).[13]

Nevertheless, the rest of the scientific fraternity remain steadfast in their belief that the rates of atomic decay have been forever constant. Accordingly, once the rates of decay of the radioactive isotopes have been determined and published, redetermination from time to time is not warranted. Indeed, the very term "decay constant" would not encourage such a practice.

In the case of the uranium 238, the decay rate and corresponding constant was settled more than half a century ago. The method consisted of taking a small crystal of the uranium-containing mineral, either zircon or, less commonly, uraninite, and, by means of a Geiger counter counting the number of alpha particles given off over a measured period of time, usually two or three days. By simple arithmetic this is reduced to a rate of so many counts per milligram of sample per hour. The rate of decay is then expressed mathematically from this information as the decay constant, or as the more familiar half-life (these terms and their mathematical relationships are explained in note 14).[14] The half-life is a convenient way of expressing the life of a process that is, theoretically, never complete and states the time required for the quantity of the "parent" material, uranium 238, to decrease by half. The half-life of uranium 238 has been reckoned as 4.51 billion years, which means if a sample began with one hundred atoms of uranium then, after one half-life, only fifty atoms of uranium are left; after two half-lives, twenty-five atoms remain, and so on. After five half-lives, or 23 billion years, only three atoms are left—that is, the decay process is 97 percent complete. It is purely coincidental that the half-life of uranium 238 happens to be the current estimate for the age of the earth.

The number of alpha particles emitted per hour depends on the number of uranium atoms in process of decay, that is, upon the size of the sample, and for this reason the rate is expressed as "per milligram". However, the rate of emission will decrease slowly with time as the number of uranium atoms diminish but, of course, the time spans are so long that this has never been observed. In other words, the only measurements made have been in this century, while during the two-or three-day test period, the rate naturally appears uniform. The mathematical treatment of the rate to produce the decay constant, or the related half-life, removes the effect of the decreasing "parent" element. It is, then, assumed that the decay constant has, in fact, been constant throughout the entire age of the cluster of uranium atoms in the sample. This is the most important assumption and is based on the observation that the number of counts per milligram per hour appears constant, whether it was measured in the 1950s or the 1980s or from one sample to the next; moreover, neither heat nor pressure nor a number of other conditions imposed on radioactive materials seem to change this rate. It should be borne in mind that the assumption of constancy is a large step of faith, based on observations made over a few years and believed to apply to a process taking billions of years.

It was pointed out in the section on principles that as the "parent" material steadily decreases, the "daughter" product, lead 206, correspondingly increases. The greater the proportion of lead 206 to uranium 238, the greater the age of the sample. However, the age can appear to be much greater than is actually the case when the rock contained lead in its initial stages of formation. We will examine the problem of initial lead "contamination" in the next section.

The Initial Formation of the Mineral

In spite of the fact that the Laplace Nebular Theory was discredited many years ago, the modern accretion theory still holds to the assumption that the earth was at one time liquid and cooled slowly to produce a hard crust. Astronomy does not usually emphasize this aspect but it is quite essential for modern geology. Enormous lengths of time are then assumed, during which it is further assumed that erosion removed the top surface of all the original crustal material and redeposited it as the sedimentary (layered) rocks. In addition, there are some igneous rocks produced by hot liquid magma that has exuded to the surface from deep within the earth. It is usually only this latter type of rock, typified by the granites that have crystallized from the liquid, that is used for radiometric dating, while the age measured is from the moment the crystals were formed. This does not give the age of the earth directly because this is not the original crustal material, but this intrusive crystallized rock is useful to give the age of an associated sedimentary rock layer and, particularly, the fossils contained within it.

In cooling from the liquid to the solid state, there are definite rules that the rapidly moving mixture of atoms obey as they find their places in the crystal lattices of the solid material. In the mineral zircon, which is used for this method of radiometric dating, clusters of uranium atoms associate themselves with zircon atoms to become part of the crystal lattice. From the moment the lattice is formed, the uranium atoms continue to decay into lead atoms, but, in contrast to the liquid state, these now remain fixed within the lattice in association with the "parent" uranium. The proportion of lead 206 atoms produced *in situ* relative to the uranium 238 in the same lattice then gives a measure of the time since the crystal was formed. Now all this is straightforward enough, assuming that there has been no "contamination" of the crystal by the introduction of lead 206 at the time the crystal was being formed from the liquid. In fact, this very thing has often happened, which gives the impression that the crystal is much older than it really is. It may be appreciated, then, that it is important to know how much lead 206 was included in the lattice in the first place in order to find out how much lead 206 was produced later by the uranium 238 decay.

Complications by Lead 206 Contamination

It may be asked how it is possible to know what the original lead content was untold millions of years ago. Aston, in 1929, discovered that there are four isotopes, or virtually identical varieties, of lead. Of these four, one form is lead 204, which is not a product of radio decay, and another is lead 206, which is radiogenic and the ultimate "daughter" of uranium 238. The contaminating lead that found its way into the crystal as it was growing from the liquid is assumed to consist of a mixture of lead 204 and lead 206 in a certain proportion. By good fortune, the mineral zircon is often associated with the nonradioactive minerals feldspar and galena, which contain lead but not uranium, and the assumption is made that the proportion of lead 204 to lead 206 found in the feldspar is the same as the proportion that "contaminated" the zircon crystal. It is reasonably assumed that the two minerals were formed at the same time, while the quantity of lead 204 does not change in either. By finding this proportion of leads in the feldspar and knowing the total lead 204 and 206 in the zircon, it is a simple matter to find the initial quantity of lead 206 and subtract this from the total to leave that which was produced *in situ* by decay, and so find the age of the crystal (Nier 1939).

Having made this correction with its attendant assumptions for the initial lead "contamination", it is further assumed that since the decay process began, no "parent" and no "daughter" elements have been lost or added to the crystal lattice from outside sources. For this reason, precautions are taken to ensure that the crystal originates from deep within a rock mass so that ground water cannot have transported either uranium or lead atoms in or out of the crystal lattice since it was formed. The laboratory air, for example, must be lead free—that is, with no automotive fumes, which would cause sample contamination.

Finally, the analytical work is carried out on a selected small crystal of zircon or uraninite, while the proportions of uranium 238 and leads 204 and 206 are found by mass spectrometer techniques. The ages given by the uranium/lead method are very long running, from hundreds of millions to billions of years, but none so far approach the assumed age of the earth.[15]

One item of interest will be appropriate here concerning the current estimate for the age of the earth. In 1956 Holmes noted that the older the feldspar, according to the age given by the associated zircon, the less lead 206 there was in the mixture of leads 204 and 206. It was argued that the lead 204 had been associated with uranium, somewhere in the depths of the earth, before it was deposited at a later time in the zircon and feldspar crystals. By extrapolating backward in time, to the point where there was no radioactively produced lead 206 in the lead 204 mixture, Holmes (1956) obtained the time when he believed the earth first became crusted over. That time was 4.5 billion years ago.

The Potassium-Argon Method of Dating

One of the drawbacks of the uranium/lead method is that the uranium-containing minerals are not too common. Potassium is one of the most common elements found in rocks, and by 1948 Aldrich and Nier had worked out a method that depended on the radioactive decay of the isotope potassium 40 into the gas argon 40. The half-life of potassium 40 has been determined as 1,310 million years, which means that the age range capable of being dated by this method tends to be less than that of the uranium/lead method and varies between 200 million and 1,600 million years. The principles, assumptions, and many of the details involved in this method are virtually the same as those described for the uranium/lead method. Once the rate of decay of potassium 40 is known, it is only necessary to determine the proportions of "parent" potassium 40 to "daughter" argon 40 for the age to be found; the more argon 40 present, the greater is the age of the sample (further details of the method will be found in Dalrymple and Lanphere 1969).

The initial formation of the potassium-containing minerals by crystallization is similar, in principle, to the formation of zircon mineral. Once the radioactive potassium 40 becomes locked into the crystal lattice, it produces argon 40 *in situ*, but since this is a gas, there are always the questions of whether it leaks out indicating a younger age than is actually the case, or whether it can diffuse in either from adjacent rocks or from the atmosphere indicating a greater age. There is a further question relating to argon 40 trapped in the crystal as it was formed. If it is present and not taken into account, it would give the appearance of a much greater age. There is admitted to be some guesswork involved in determining the initial argon content, and it is generally assumed that because of argon's chemical inertness, no argon is incorporated into the crystal structure when cooling from, for example, a magma (molten rock). In answer to the first question, an unexpected discovery was made in 1956, when it was shown that the then popular potassium feldspars retain only about 75 percent of the argon 40 that is generated within them. Since that date, investigators have used the potassium-containing mineral, biotite, for the igneous rocks and glauconite for the sedimentary rocks; it is assumed that all the argon 40 is retained in these minerals (Knopf 1957, 232).

The second and third questions relate to the "contamination" problem. Routine corrections are made during analysis to eliminate the possible effects of initial argon contamination from the atmosphere. It turns out that the atmosphere contains about 1 percent argon, and of that, one part is the isotope argon 36, and 295.5 parts are argon 40. It is assumed that this ratio has always been the same, so that any argon 40 trapped from the atmosphere during crystallization can be found by measuring the argon 36 and multiplying by 295.5. This value for argon 40 by contamination is deducted from the total argon 40 to give that produced by radioactive decay. The fact that corrections are made indicates that recognition is given to contamination having taken place. However, the assumption that the ratio of 1:295.5 has been constant for all time is very questionable, because argon 36 is produced in the upper atmosphere by cosmic bombardment (Rosen 1968).[16] This means that the ratio was greater in the past and has been decreasing. Therefore, a greater correction would be necessary, resulting in the samples being much younger than they now appear.

Some of the reported ages for lava rocks from Hawaii, known to be less than 200 years old, have been given as 22 million years by the potassium/argon method; however, this is now known to be caused by initial argon 40 contamination during the crystal formation and can be corrected for by the method described above (Noble and Naughton 1968; Funkhouser and Naughton 1968).[17] It has also been found that submarine lavas contain an excess of argon 40. Interestingly, the greater the depth at which the lava was formed, the greater the amount of argon 40 contamination giving the false impression of a greater age (Dalrymple and Moore 1968). The pressure of sea water has seemingly "forced" more argon 40 into the molten rock during crystallization. Taking these facts together, an intriguing possibility presents itself: Accepting the Creation view of a worldwide flood only a few thousand years ago and when the argon 36 was absent or negligible, liquid magmas, crystallizing under a mile or two of sea water, would be expected to retain a rather high proportion of argon 40, quite indistinguishable from that subsequently produced by radioactive decay. Such material would appear to be of extremely great age, whereas it would, in fact, have been formed only a few thousand years ago.

Are the Radiometric Methods Reliable?

The two most popular radiometric methods have been described in these pages, but there are other methods, such as the rubidium/strontium, and thorium/lead, the lead 207/lead 206, and the uranium 235/lead 207, which are extensively used. These last three methods involving lead are directly related to the uranium 238/lead 206 method (see Appendix C) already described and are usually carried out at the same time. The hope is that the results from the various decay processes operating within the same sample will provide confirmation or concordance; usually there is 20-30 percent discordance in results, and a decision has to be made regarding which one to report. It is assumed that the discordance is caused by lead leakage from the mineral after it has crystallized; it may be observed that, of only two possibilities, selective lead leakage is more credible than selective lead addition. However, there is really no proof for either the one assumption or the other.

Concordance of another type is claimed from deep-sea drill cores. In this case the oxygen 18 isotope method is used, by which it is found that the absolute dates—at least those reported—are roughly the same from core to core and line up sequentially, with the most recent dates at the top and the most ancient at the bottom. However, occasionally a whole series of results will be discordant by 30 percent or more, which does not give great cause for alarm so long as the ages are thought to be in terms of millions of years (Emiliani 1958).[18]

The half-lives, or mathematically related decay constants of the various decay processes, vary enormously from fractions of a second to millions of years, as will be evident from the table of values for the uranium/lead system in Appendix C. They are all said to be generally repeatable in the laboratory with a reasonable degree of accuracy, though there is still disagreement over some values; the potassium 40 half-life, for example, is still within a few percentage points of agreement (Dalrymple and Lanphere 1969, 41).

Radiometric ages determined after about 1950 tend to be considered more reliable than earlier estimates for three reasons: first, the methods became more popular about that time, and with greater usage the equipment and techniques became more sophisticated. Second, partially concordant results began to be obtained from independent decay processes occurring simultaneously within the same sample. Third, as data accumulated and were published, researchers began to have expectations of results, and a tendency developed to report only those results that fit the expectations. This has become the normal practice, but the overall effect does tend to build up a false measure of confidence in the method.

When it is recalled that these radiometric methods are based on a series of similar assumptions, it is perhaps not too surprising that some concordance, or partial concordance, of results would occur. It will be useful at this point to see what has been said about these assumptions.

The Assumptions of Radiometric Dating

To recapitulate what has been said regarding the major assumptions on which the radiometric methods are based, we find:

1. It is *assumed* that the earth began as a spinning blob of hot liquid that cooled to form the original rock surface. It is further *assumed* that, because of the immense span of time during which erosion and rebuilding are believed to have taken place, none of the original crustal materials are now available for study.

2. It is *assumed* that the crystals that are selected for radiometric age determination have been formed either by growing from hot liquid, that is, igneous rock, or by metamorphosis. Metamorphosis is a process in which crystallization occurs in sedimentary rock and is believed to take place by sustained high pressure and possible high temperatures but without melting the rock.

3. Once the crystal has formed, it is *assumed* that it is a closed system, that is, no "parent" or "daughter" elements enter or leave the crystal lattice; the only change that takes place is *assumed* to be decay of the unstable "parent" with time and consequent increase of the stable "daughter" element.

4. When discordant results are obtained from processes operating within the same crystal, it is *assumed* that there has been loss or addition of the "daughter" product. That is, selective loss of either lead 206 or argon 40 is claimed when the sample appears too young and selective addition or contamination when it appears too old.

5. Contamination of the crystal during its formation by extraneous "daughter" elements has to be taken into account, and it is *assumed* that the various isotope ratios of the contaminating element were the same at the time of crystal formation as they are today.

6. It is *assumed* that the decay "constant", determined over a two-or three-day period and mathematically related to the rate of decay expressed as half-life, has remained unchanged throughout the entire age of the mineral sample.

Relevant to the first assumption, it is worth recalling that while Holmes (1956) has estimated the age of the earth to be 4.5 billion years, no terrestrial rocks of this age have ever been reported, since it is assumed that all the original crustal material had been eroded then redeposited as sedimentary rock. The oldest rocks on earth have a reported age of 3.8 billion years. However, it was realized that the moon would have crusted over at about the same time as the earth; since there is no wind or water to cause erosion, it was believed moon rocks would provide a direct radiometric age for the earth. Sure enough, after retrieval of the moon rock samples in the Apollo program, Holmes's estimation was claimed to be exactly confirmed, and the age of the earth confidently stated in the popular press[19] and textbooks[20] to be 4.5 billion years (Eldredge 1982, 104; Taylor 1975). However, the official reports and scientific journals, in which actual results of the radiometric determinations were given, showed that the ages of the moon-rock samples varied between 2 and 28 billion years (Whitcombe and DeYoung 1978).[21] Quite evidently, the data for public consumption had been selected to confirm the theory.

The last assumption (6) is, strictly speaking, an extrapolation of data on a huge scale, far beyond what is considered good practice under any other circumstance. We are reminded that the atomic decay is assumed to be at a constant rate, so that the data collected over a few days and checked infrequently during this century has been applied to billions of years. Some are beginning to question this whole line of thinking, and Professor Dudley, writing in 1975, has been particularly outspoken: "These equations resulted initially from studies done with crude instruments some 70 years ago. Bluntly they are incorrect, nonetheless appear in our latest textbooks to compound the errors of past generations. This in spite of more recent evidence" (Dudley 1975, 2).[22] At the root of this complaint is the constancy of the decay constant.

A Closer Look at the Universal Constants

The mechanics of radioactive decay are dealt with at length and in mathematical detail by specialist books on the subject, and it would not be appropriate to attempt to cover this topic here. Suffice it to say that radioactive decay depends on the probability of escape of certain particles from their orbit in the unstable atom. The decay rate is directly proportional to the speed of travel of the particles in their atomic orbit, and this speed is, in turn, directly proportional to the speed of light. It may seem odd that the speed of light is related to atomic phenomena, but it does turn up in a number of seemingly unlikely places as one of the universal constants. For instance, in the familiar expression $E=mc^2$, we find that the velocity of light, c, is related to the mass, m, and the energy, E.

There are other parameters with which physics is concerned and which are related to the speed, or velocity, of light. The permittivity of free space, for example, is one of the constants that relate electrical force to electrical charge, while there is another constant that relates electrical charge to the mass of the electron. However, the meaning of all these rather esoteric terms is not really important in this present context, and it need only be said that they are all interrelated as universal constants.

It was pointed out earlier in this chapter that it is a natural consequence of the uniformitarian mind-set to assume that the universal constants are, in fact, constant and have been throughout all time. Once again, we confront the unknowable and unprovable in dealing with events in the past, in this case dynamic relationships in natural processes.

The second law of thermodynamics points out that the universe is "running down", and, in familiar examples, we see the outworkings of this law in the death of living organisms and in the wear and decay of inanimate things, such as the family car. This is accepted today as a self-evident and universal law. But when it was first proposed by Kelvin and others in the last century, it met with great opposition from Darwin's followers. If accepted, they would be faced with the difficulty of showing how a chance process (natural selection) could build up the elements from the simple to the complex, that is, from nonlife to life. Nevertheless, the illogical has occurred and both the second law and the theory of evolution exist side by side today. From the universal nature of the second law, it might then be wondered if the universal constants are not also subject to the same law, bearing in mind that they were only assumed to be constants in the first place. In other words, it is legitimate to ask whether the speed of light could have been greater in the past, or the related question of whether the nuclear decay processes have been slowing down with time, so that the half-lives in the past were much shorter. There may never be proof either of constancy or change with time, but it is surely not in the true spirit of scientific inquiry to make the dogmatic assertion that the values have always been constant when no one measured these parameters in the remote past. In fact, there is some evidence to suggest that the universal constants have been changing with time and in the direction that might be expected from the second law of thermodynamics.

Is the Velocity of Light Constant?

The Danish astronomer Roemer made the first determination of the velocity of light in 1675 by observing the eclipses of Jupiter's moons (Velocity of Light 300 years ago; Hynek 1983).[23] Using the present-day values for the earth's orbital diameter about the sun, recalculation of Roemer's data shows that the velocity of light then would have been 301,300 kilometers per second (Goldstein et al. 1973).[24] Since that date, more than forty determinations have been made with increasing precision, and the accepted value today is 299,792.44 kilometers (185,871 miles) per second. However, there have been some unexpected disagreements, leading several workers to question if the velocity of light is actually a constant (Strong 1975; Tolles 1980).[25] Rush, writing in 1955, claims that it had increased by 16 kilometers per second during the previous decade. Setterfield, meanwhile, maintains that when the data for the entire 300-year period is subjected to analysis, there has been a definite decrease (Steidl 1982).[26] For those of sufficient curiosity, the values reported for the past three centuries are given in Appendix D.

The immediate reaction to an apparent violation of a universal constant is likely to be either outright disbelief or the cry that experimental techniques have improved and we now have more reliable values. The possibility of nonconstancy cannot be dismissed so readily, however, and for a number of good reasons. First, a universal law has not been violated; it is simply being proposed that the original assumptions were incorrect. Second, as more and better data accumulate, it is becoming evident that many parameters traditionally accepted as universal constants are changing; Wesson (1979, 115) and others have made this same observation (Catacosinos 1975; Dostal et al. 1977). Third, and most important, when taken all together, those universal constants for which there is sufficient data do show a definite change in both magnitude and direction, consistent with what would be expected from the second law of thermodynamics. The values of some of these related universal constants are listed in Appendices E to H, and in each case the gradual change of the "constant" with time may be clearly seen. The author is indebted to Barry Setterfield for these insights and painstaking gathering together of all the information (pers. com. 1983).

If, as it appears, these universal constants have changed with time, then the velocity of light and the nuclear decay constants will also have changed, since they are related. Moreover, from the direction of change indicated by the results, the velocity of light would have been greater in the past. This raises the possibility that the time taken for the light from the furthest star to reach earth may have been, for example, a few years rather than, as in current thinking, millenia of years. The distances may be great but the vast spans of time are based on an assumption. The subject has been questioned before; for example, astronomers Moon and Spencer (1953) have taken an entirely different approach and concluded that light from the most distant stars may have reached us in only fifteen years.[27] Even to countenance the possibility that the velocity of light has not been subject to the uniformitarian dogma requires a certain fortitude of character, because the whole of cosmology is dependent on this assumption, and it would mean, for example, that the age of the universe would require drastic revision—downwards.

Are Decay Constants Constant?

If all the other universal constants have changed with time, then the nuclear decay constants must also have changed, since they are related, and we would expect to find shorter half-lives in the past. Unfortunately, for a number of reasons there is very little direct evidence. First, the early measurements that were made more than seventy years ago were of rather low precision. In more recent years, the counting technique has greatly improved, with the result that there is now much greater precision; it is somewhat meaningless, therefore, to compare these results. Second, by calling the nuclear decay parameter a "constant", there is little expectation of a change once a value has been agreed on. Changes that may have occurred could, thereby, have easily been overlooked. From the published half-lives of some of the long-lived radioactive elements, it seems that there is a precision of about one part in a thousand, while there are two cases reported where the half-life is increasing with time. The half-life of protoactinium 231 has increased from 32,000 years in 1950 to 34,300 years in 1962, and the half-life of radium 223 has increased from 11.2 days to 11.68 days over the same period of time.

Although the proposal that nuclear decay has changed over thousands of years cannot be proven, neither can the assumption that it has been constant, and it would seem only fair to consider what a decreasing decay rate would mean. With an increasing rate into the past, this would mean that the half-lives would get progressively shorter further back in time, so that most of the decay would have taken place shortly after the beginning. This would explain why the naturally occurring radioactive elements all have relatively long half-lives today. At the same time it explains the absence of those elements with the shorter half-lives, since these would have long ago decayed past their ten half-life period and not now be detectable.

It was previously mentioned in this chapter that radioactive dates generally get older with increasing depth in the rock strata, and this is taken to be one of the prime pieces of evidence for evolution over vast periods of time. If the sediments were the result of a worldwide flood, however, then the lava flows that were intermixed with the sediments would have been deposited over a brief historical period—a year or so, for example. If this proposal is correct, then most of the radioactive decay took place in the first few days or weeks, and the record preserved in the rock immediately after it became solid. Lava beds that differed in age by weeks or months of each other would then appear to differ by millions of years.

Perhaps it is now possible to see how two observers could come to entirely different conclusions by approaching the same evidence with different preconceptions. The first observer, having been schooled to think in terms of Lyell's uniformitarianism, would assume that nuclear decay rates were constant throughout all time and from radiometric measurements determine that a certain fossil was, for example, 100 million years old. This value would be accepted by his peers if it conformed to the expected age for that particular fossil creature. The second observer might assume that nuclear decay had been subject to the second law of thermodynamics, by reason of changing permittivity, for example, and the decay rate itself had decreased with time. His mathematical interpretation of the same radiometric measurements for the same fossil would then yield a value of only a few thousand years, and this great difference in age, it will be recalled, came about by the initial assumption on the part of each observer.

*   *   *

This chapter has attempted to present, in sufficient detail, the assumptions underlying radiometric dating, in order that the reader may begin to judge for himself the claims for an old earth made on the basis of this method. The following chapter presents some further aspects related to radiometric dating that should be considered, together with a number of quite unrelated processes, all of which indicate a youthful earth.

12

Old Earth, Young Earth

*Biology takes her time from geology. The only
reason we have for believing in the slow rate of
the change in living forms is the fact that they
persist through a series of deposits which geology
informs us have taken a long while to make. If
the geological clock is wrong all the naturalist
will have to do is to modify his notions of the
rapidity of change accordingly.*

THOMAS H. HUXLEY
(1869, 25:xlviii)[1]

There is no question that technology has made tremendous
advances in the past few decades while, in contrast, science is
still laboring under the highly questionable Lyellian dogma
of uniformitarianism. More specifically, advances in technology have
enabled radiometric results to be obtained that, by uniformitarian
interpretation, appear to offer evidence supporting the evolutionary
requirements for an old earth. Textbook descriptions of these highly
technological methods are given in generalizations that leave the reader
convinced that the radiometric dating methods have long been perfected and now provide absolutely reliable results. For example, the
radiometric ages of fossil artifacts are often reported with plus or minus
tolerance values, which give an impression of integrity and precision.
What is often overlooked is that the tolerance figures apply only to the
technology of the method and have no bearing on the underlying
assumptions of science. These assumptions were listed in the previous
chapter together with some suggestion that the decay constants may
not have been as constant as it has been assumed. In this chapter,
further evidence is given that puts into serious question all the remaining assumptions related to the origin of the minerals on which radiometric determinations are conducted.

It was pointed out earlier, and it will be worthwhile to mention again, that in matters of time in the remote past, that is, prior to human records, there can be no absolute proof of the duration of time. Once datable human records begin to appear, roughly two thousand years ago, it then becomes possible to acquire independent confirmation of radiometric dates; in this case only the carbon 14 radiometric method qualifies, for reasons that will be made clear later in this chapter. For time periods believed to be hundreds of millions of years in the past, it is a matter of making assumptions rather than having faith in what is seen as solid evidence.

The radiometric methods appear to offer evidence for an old earth, but there are many phenomena that cannot be explained in terms of the evolutionary long ages; seldom are the implications or even the phenomena themselves mentioned in the published media. A few examples of evidence that indicates a young earth are given in the remainder of this chapter. It is only by considering a balanced sample of evidence that any meaningful judgment can be made to accept the validity of claims made for the age of the earth.

Enigma in the Basement Rocks

The principal assumptions associated with radiometric dating, which were listed earlier, began by presupposing that the earth originated from a spinning blob of hot liquid that cooled to form the crustal material. It is further supposed by current theory that the ravages of time preclude the survival of the original crustal material. All that is believed to remain today are the igneous rocks that have crystallized from hot liquid magma, long after the original cooling, together with the sedimentary rocks that have originated by erosion and redeposition. The igneous rocks are, essentially, the granites, and these form the basement material underlying all the layered sedimentary rocks. Often there are thousands of feet of sedimentary rock on top of the basement material, but, exceptionally, this basement rock is found at the surface, as it is over a large part of Canada, where it is known as the Canadian Shield.

Almost a century ago microscopic studies of this basement rock, taken from various parts of the world, revealed small concentric circles of discoloration associated with certain minerals (chiefly mica) within the rock matrix. These tiny, colored, circular rings are really the sections through spheres having a small inclusion at the center; they were at first called "pleochroic halos" but are now usually referred to as "radio-halos" (Joly 1917).[2] It was not until a few decades ago that the halos were recognized to be the "signatures" of the radioactive products of the uranium 238 decay series.

When an inclusion of uranium 238 in the mineral crystal lattice begins to decay, alpha particles (which finish up as helium atoms) or beta particles (electrons), depending on the stage of decay, are projected out in all directions at high speed and travel through the surrounding material. At each specific stage of decay, these particles all have the same energy, and all penetrate identical distances, leaving an abrupt edge to the sphere that appears as a circle when precisely sectioned. The circle diameter is, therefore, directly related to the particular energy of the projected particle, and since this is different for each stage in the decay series, the circle diameter becomes a "signature" of the individual decay process. The series of concentric circles is as sure as a fingerprint in identifying the decay process. There are actually fourteen stages in the decay of uranium 238 to lead 206, and these are given fully in Appendix C. However, one of the most common "signatures", found by the million throughout the basement rocks, is that of polonium 218 which occurs about midway through the overall uranium 238 decay process and has a half-life of only 3.05 minutes.

Robert Gentry (1974) is acknowledged to be the foremost expert in the field of radio-halos. By the use of the ion microprobe, he has been able to analyze the microscopic inclusions at the center of the concentric circles. This modern device was not available to early investigators and enables the identification of individual atoms, and also permits them to be counted in order to establish the relative abundance of each element present. Gentry's investigation of the commonly found polonium 218 halos by microprobe analysis has shown that the inclusion at the center consists mostly of the final product, lead 206. The startling thing is that there are no elements above polonium in the inclusion; in other words, the daughter elements are present but no parents (see Appendix C). When it is recalled that the half-life of the parent uranium 238 is said to be 4.5 billion years, then a little more than half the original quantity of uranium would be expected to be present. In fact, not one atom of uranium or thorium can be found, nor are there any traces of the characteristic halos for these elements.

There is no doubt that the halo "signatures" are genuinely those of part of the uranium 238 decay series. Even if the velocity of light and the related speed of particle emission had been radically different in the past, this would not, it has been pointed out by Setterfield, affect the halo diameters. This is because the electron rest mass was lower in the past (Appendix E), and the specific electron charge was higher (Appendix F); the differences thus cancel out and leave the penetration distance unchanged (Steidl 1982).

The simple evidence of the "daughter" elements without a trace of the "parent" leaves one little choice but to conclude that the decay process began with polonium 218. However, since the half-life of this element, even measured today, is only 3.05 minutes, it could not have begun in the liquid state. The reason for this is that all the alpha particles were emitted from the decaying polonium in the first hour or so and if emitted within a liquid medium, would leave no permanent record. This forces the conclusion that the polonium decay began in the solid state; we are faced here with evidence of the original Creation. If this is true, and no other rational explanation is yet forthcoming, then it means that all the basement rocks were supernaturally created in the solid form and never passed through the liquid to solid change by slow cooling. Gentry put the matter this way: "Is it conceivable that one of the oldest cosmological theories known to man [biblical Creation] is correct after all? Could the earth have been created by fiat?" (Gentry 1967, 78).[3]

The scientific community acknowledges that Gentry's work has been most thoroughly and carefully carried out, yet it is extremely reluctant to draw these conclusions from the evidence, because it would at once invalidate all the assumptions concerning the earth's origin and those basic to the radiometric methods.

The Appearance of Age

The evidence of the polonium radio-halos is, seemingly, evidence for *ex nihilo* creation—instant creation of something out of nothing. This is plainly a supernatural phenomenon and, to many minds, a major stumbling block. Yet what alternative explanation does the evolutionary scenario have to offer? In the introduction, Harlow Shapley was quoted as the representative of today's explanation for the origin of the universe, and his statement may be paraphrased, "...in the beginning hydrogen" (Shapley 1960, 3). However, when this is considered, it surely involves *ex nihilo* creation of hydrogen atoms from nothing and, as such, is no less supernatural than *ex nihilo* creation of solid rock containing polonium halos. So far as this author is aware, no other explanation has ever been proposed to explain the initial appearance of all things. *Ex nihilo* creation admittedly offers little intellectual satisfaction, in terms of today's scientific mind-set, but even to accept this as a theory would seem better than having no theory at all.

If the concept of a vast age for the universe is found to be based on assumptions and if there is good contrary evidence that indicates a young earth, then with a drastically shorter time frame, the initial appearance of matter could not have begun with hydrogen but must have begun with the universe, more or less the way it is today. The planet earth would have been created with the instant appearance of basement rocks, sand, topsoil, and all forms of life. This raises the question, If the initial life forms were created, how old did they appear to be at the first moment? It would be reasonable to say that the chicken appeared before the egg, and that being so, the chicken may have had the appearance of being, perhaps, one year old. The first man may have appeared to be, perhaps, thirty years old; hardwood trees, one hundred years old; and coral reefs large enough for fish to live in—perhaps several thousand years old. All this appearance of age is then a necessary part of *ex nihilo* creation, once this concept is accepted.

Carbon 14 Dating

One of the most spectacular sights to be seen in the night sky is the beautiful aurora borealis, known in the north as the northern lights and seen best in the extreme northern or southern latitudes. These appear as curtains or streamers of colored lights, very high in the atmosphere and stretching in an east-west direction, while slowly moving as a band across the sky towards the magnetic pole (Roble 1977). The lights are the result of the ionization of upper atmosphere atoms by cosmic rays and is the same type of effect as that produced by the applied voltage to neon gas in electric signs. Cosmic rays are extremely high energy particles that originate somewhere in outer space; their source is still uncertain (Rosen 1968). As the earth travels through space, it crosses the path of millions of these particles, which are similar to X rays and are known to cause genetic damage to reproductive cells and which, subsequently, result in birth defects. For this reason, there has always been concern about their effect on astronauts. Fortunately, for life on earth there are two protective barriers that prevent most of these harmful rays from reaching the earth's surface. The first is the earth's magnetic field, which extends into space and acts as a shield guiding any cosmic particles encountered towards the north and south poles. These potentially lethal areas are, in any case, inhospitable to life.

The second line of defense is the earth's atmosphere, filled with gaseous atoms, more than 70 percent of which are nitrogen, the remainder being mostly oxygen. A small residual percentage consists of helium and argon atoms, some molecules of water, carbon dioxide, ozone and, more recently, molecules that cause the acid rain problems. Bearing in mind that atoms and atom combinations (molecules) are mostly empty space, those high-speed cosmic particles that get past the magnetic barrier tend to pass right through many of the atmospheric atoms. When they eventually hit the nucleus of a gaseous atom, they release a neutron; the atom then becomes ionized. It is mostly nitrogen atoms that then capture the free neutrons, with the result that these stable nitrogen 14 atoms become unstable carbon 14 atoms. The number refers to the atomic weight or mass. Once formed, the radioactive C_{14} atoms begin to decay by emitting beta particles (electrons) and revert back to stable nitrogen 14 atoms once more.

The C_{14} atoms are comparatively rare since for every one of these there are 765 billion normal, stable C_{12} atoms. One of the important assumptions made is that this ratio of C_{14} to C_{12} (which has been determined in recent years) has been constant for at least the past fifty thousand years. This assumption is, in turn, based on the uniformitarian assumption that C_{14} production and decay has been going on for millions of years and long ago reached equilibrium; it is further assumed that perfect atmospheric mixing has been achieved, so that the ratio of C_{14} to C_{12} is the same everywhere. Immediately after formation in the atmosphere, the C_{14} atom is joined by two oxygen atoms to become a molecule of carbon dioxide, and together with all the other carbon-dioxide molecules containing the stable C_{12} atoms, becomes part of the great carbon cycle of life.

The carbon cycle is simply that process in which the carbon dioxide from the atmosphere is absorbed by the leaves of plants and, by the process of photosynthesis, is converted into sugars. The plants are part of the food chain for animal life, in which some carbon in the sugar is converted to carbonates for bone, etc. While most of the carbonates contain the stable C_{12} atom, some contain the unstable C_{14} atom; it is assumed that during life this ratio of C_{12} to C_{14} was the same as that in the atmosphere. In certain cases, however, this has since been found not to be true. When the food intake ceases upon the death of the organism, the ratio of C_{12} to C_{14} begins to change as the unstable C_{14} decays to nitrogen 14; the gaseous nitrogen escapes to the atmosphere. It is at this point that the C_{14} clock begins to measure time. The decay rate of C_{14} is assumed to have been constant throughout the ages, so that by finding this rate and the quantity of C_{14} remaining in the material being dated, it is, theoretically, possible to find its age.

Willard Libby, working at the University of California, developed the C_{14} dating method in 1947 and subsequently received the Nobel prize for his work. He found the nuclear decay constant and reported the mathematically related half-life for radioactive C_{14} as 5,550 years (1947 figure). The extremely small proportion of C_{14} to C_{12} in the atmosphere, and subsequently in the living organism, becomes even smaller as the C_{14} decreases with the length of time between death and analysis. For example, on the basis of Libby's original half-life, if the organism died containing, for example, one hundred C_{14} atoms, then after six half-lives, that is, 33,000 years, there would be less than two C_{14} atoms left. This presented an upper limit of about 50,000 years, beyond which the number of C_{14} atoms remaining would be too few to be detectable by the method. Even so, relatively large samples of one hundred grams (four ounces) were required and destroyed in the test (Libby 1955). Litherland (1980) describes a new high-energy method that has been developed enabling much smaller samples to be used and extending the time limitation somewhat beyond 50,000 years. The underlying assumptions for the C_{14} method, however, remain the same.

Carbon 14 Results

It was in the early fifties that archaeologists and geologists adopted the method as acceptable, even placing it above traditional methods of dating and sweeping aside physical evidence that showed the C_{14} results to be in error. Lee says that "radiocarbon swept the scientific world with all the fervor of religious fanaticism, as the new and 'absolute' chronology was established" (Lee 1981, 9). In those early days the method was applied to almost anything containing carbon, and the results were published in the newly formed *Radiocarbon Journal*, a kind of clearing house for C_{14} data from all the various laboratories. Hundreds of fossil bones of Neanderthals, Cro-magnons, mammoths, sabre-tooth tigers, and other extinct animals, as well as fossil trees, coal, oil, and natural gas, were all reported having ages, by the C_{14} method, of only several thousand years. The significant point is that every biological specimen tested contained C_{14}, and all appeared to lie within a 50,000-year time frame; a selection of some of these reported values is given in Appendix J. The great number of these results, indicating a young age for material in some cases believed to be millions of years old, had disturbing implications for the geological time scale; using the oxygen 18 method one outcome was that the long-accepted estimate of the time of the last ice age was cut down by half, to 11,000 years ago (Emiliani 1956; Knopf 1957, 233).[4]

These early workers were often physicists, and, perhaps somewhat naive to the prejudice of the establishment, many of them simply reported what they found. This is honest science carried out according to Baconian principles. In more recent years, C_{14} dates on such items as coal, oil, or dinosaur bones no longer appear in *Radiocarbon Journal*, because by now it has been impressed on research workers from their student years that the C_{14} method does not give results with materials "known" to be older than about 50,000 years; this is clearly untrue as shown by the early published results. The public, which ultimately pays for all this research, is generally quite unaware of the unbelievable circularity in the procedure for submitting samples to laboratories for C_{14} analysis. The investigator is first asked what date he will accept; then, when a figure is obtained that comes near this date, it is duly reported together with the tolerance value, and these figures become sacrosanct, reported in journal after journal, year after year. Ogden, the director of a radiocarbon laboratory, has made the remarkable confession: "It may come as a shock to some, but fewer than 50 percent of the radiocarbon dates from geological and archaeological samples in northeastern North America have been adopted as 'acceptable' by investigators" (Ogden 1977, 173). Clearly, the C_{14} method of dating, as with the other radiometric methods, is either reliable and useful or it is not.

In the last two decades some concern has been expressed for the usefulness of the C_{14} test method. Techniques have improved, but still there are uncertainties and absurd results, not with old material that appears young, for which there is no proof of age, but for recent material that appears old, for which there is proof. Living mollusk shells have been dated by the C_{14} method at up to 2,300 years, a freshly killed seal at 1,300 years,[5] and wood from a growing tree at 10,000 years (Dort 1971; Huber 1958; Keith and Anderson 1963). Whenever it can be justified, unexpected figures are adjusted up or down, according to the need, on the basis of a whole list of factors that are believed to have either added C_{14} atoms to the specimen if it appears too young or received too little C_{14} in the first place if it appears too old. For instance, the new high-energy mass spectrometry method, previously mentioned and involving a count of individual atoms, was delayed for some time because the ages of the samples consistently came out too young (Grootes 1980).[6] With the new technology, these were probably the true results, but they were found unacceptable because they did not reconcile with all the previous selected results and, ultimately, with Lyell's geology; the research workers were then forced to conclude that the young ages were due to an unknown source of C_{14} somewhere in the equipment! None of this is ever mentioned in popular magazines and textbooks, and the impression is left in the reader's mind that "absolute" chronology has been established by the radiocarbon method.

The Underlying Assumptions

The assumptions that were made when the C_{14} method was established in the early 1950s are summarized below; subsequent problems, however, have caused some of these assumptions to be modified, as will be explained later.

1. It is *assumed* that the rate of production of C_{14} from nitrogen has been the same in the past as it is today. This includes the *assumption* that the rate of cosmic ray bombardment and the magnetic and atmospheric barriers that provide protection have always been the same (Kulp 1952, 261).[7]

2. It is *assumed* that the C_{14} to C_{12} ratio reached equilibrium millions of years ago, and that during the course of this time there has been plenty of atmospheric mixing to give a uniform distribution. This may be recognized as a tautology, since what is really being implied is that, because the atmospheric system has been in existence millions of years, it must have reached equilibrium, and because it is in equilibrium, it must have been in existence for millions of years (Suess 1965, 5947).[8]

3. It is *assumed* (from assumption 2 above) that every living organism contained at death the same C_{14} to C_{12} ratio as is found in the atmosphere today.

4. It is *assumed* that the artifact being dated has been a closed system— that is, there has been no C_{14} loss other than by decay and no C_{14} addition during the period between death and analysis. However, this assumption can be overriden by making appeal to a wide range of causes *assumed* to have added or removed C_{14} after death in order to adjust the initial figures to those expected.

5. It is *assumed* that the measured specific rate of sixteen counts per gram per minute for C_{14} decay has been the same in the past. In other words, the related half-life of C_{14} is *assumed* to have always had the same value.

A Closer Look at Some of the Assumptions

Libby, in his original work in the late 1940s, found that the specific production rate of C_{14} in the upper atmosphere then was 18.8 atoms per gram per minute; details of how this measurement was made have been given by Libby (1955, 7) while the qualifying word "specific" relates to the units being expressed as "per gram" and simplifies the comparison of rates (these terms are explained in note 14 of Chapter Eleven). Libby then took samples of wood from Pharaoh's tomb and other carbon-containing samples of known age from many parts of the earth and found the specific decay rate of C_{14} very close to average 16 atoms per gram per minute. Now it may be seen that these figures for production and decay are not the same; in fact, there is almost a 20 percent difference, but Libby (1955) reconciled this by his statement: "The agreement seems to be sufficiently within the experimental errors involved so that we have reason for confidence in the theoretical picture" (Libby 1955, 7). The theoretical picture to which he refers is firmly rooted in the doctrines of uniformitarianism, which demands equilibrium between production and decay rates. To acknowledge any difference in the rates would allow the data to point to a beginning, which, in this case, would be relatively recent.

Now that the C_{14} dating method has been established, but essentially confined to the biosphere (samples of less than 50,000 years), statements are beginning to appear in textbooks that acknowledge that the C_{14} decay rate in living organisms is about 30 percent less than its production rate in the atmosphere.[9] Stansfield (1977, 83), in a recent textbook, even admits that from this difference in rates it can be argued that the age of the atmosphere is less than 20,000 years old. The evidence would seem to indicate that this is the case, while from the figures it may be appreciated that any increase in the difference between rates of production and decay will shorten the age of the atmosphere still further. Whatever the result may finally be, an age of thousands of years is far removed from the hundreds of millions required by Darwin. With this acknowledgment of a difference in rates, it is then reasonable to ask whether the production rate has increased while the decay rate remained constant, or whether both rates have changed. There is evidence that strongly suggests that both rates have changed with time, which not only indicates that the system must be relatively recent but also would shorten the ages found still further. First, however, we will see what has caused the C_{14} production rate to have increased throughout the centuries.

It was mentioned earlier that C_{14} atoms are produced in the upper atmosphere by the interaction of cosmic rays, and while the magnetic field of the earth provides a first line of defense against these powerful rays, it is known that the magnetic field has been decreasing at a rather alarming rate (Magsatdown 1980). With a greater field strength in the past, fewer cosmic particles would have entered the atmosphere, and fewer C_{14} atoms be produced. This would mean—under the reasonable assumption that the organisms that died in the past would retain the same C_{14} to C_{12} ratio as in the atmosphere at that time—less C_{14} to begin with at the time of death. After a further reduction in the C_{14} content by decay, the sample, when measured today, would thereby appear to be a great deal older than is actually the case.

The second line of defense against cosmic rays is the atmosphere itself; many, though notably Dillow (1981), suspect that in the past there was above our present atmosphere a water vapor canopy, or shell, several miles thick and enclosing the entire earth. Such a proposed canopy, quite transparent to sunlight but preventing radiant heat from escaping, would provide a "greenhouse" effect for the primeval earth and would account for the remains of tropical vegetation found in Siberia and Antarctica. The canopy would have contained a great deal of water, which would not only prevent cosmic rays from entering the atmosphere but would more than double the atmospheric pressure at the earth's surface (Dillow 1981, 146).[10] Absence of cosmic rays in the atmosphere would mean that no C_{14} was produced at this time. We have already seen from the difference in the rates of production and decay that C_{14} production appeared to begin about 20,000 years ago. However, as we shall see later, with some further downward correction for the changing decay "constant", the beginning of C_{14} production would be brought to roughly 5,000 years ago. Allowing that the vapor canopy collapsed at this time, possibly by dust nucleation from volcanic activity, the most unprecedented rainfall throughout the earth would have resulted, allowing C_{14} to begin to be produced and become part of the carbon cycle of life. The time of this proposed event, the resultant effects in terms of a worldwide flood, and the subsequent genetic damage by secondary radiation (C_{14} decay within living tissue) would seem to be confirmed by the worldwide Flood traditions and the Genesis account (Bjorksten 1963; Upton 1957).

One of the more interesting pieces of evidence for the previous existence of a vapor canopy is the pteranodon, an enormous flying reptile with wing spans of up to seven meters (twenty-three feet), whose remains are found in the Cretaceous sediments. Experts long debated whether the creature would have had sufficient muscular strength for powered flight. They concluded that it must have lived on cliffs and sailed on the updrafts above the sea in search of fish (Langston 1981). However, an even larger flying reptile, the pterosaur, with an estimated wing span of fifteen meters (fifty-one feet), was reported by Lawson in 1975.[11] This was particularly difficult to explain since it was found in a flat non-marine area in Texas; from these dimensions alone, there is seemingly no means by which it could have left the ground. However, if the atmospheric pressure—that is, the air density—was at that time twice as great, a whole set of calculations is changed, and it does appear that under these conditions the giant reptile could just have become air-borne (Bramwell and Whitfield 1976).

Finally, there is the question of the constancy of the nuclear decay constants for the radioactive elements, which was raised in the previous chapter. While published values of the half-lives of C_{14} do show an apparent increase from 5,568 years in 1955 to 5,770 in 1980, this has been brought about by an international agreement to make a correction for the manmade carbon dioxide and radiation introduced since 1850, and by the improved counting techniques (Stuiver and Suess 1966). However, the more complete counting of emitted particles would result in a shortening, rather than a lengthening, of the half-life, so that a real increase in the decay "constant" can be suspected.

Textbooks today recognize that correction factors are necessary to take into account the disequilibrium between C_{14} production and decay. Figures of 25 percent reduction in age for an uncorrected age of 10,000 years are quoted, while greater reductions would apply to material that appears older. Cook proposes even greater corrections of 20 percent for 1,000 years, 30 percent for 4,000 years, and so on, which would telescope all the long C_{14} ages to 12,500 years or less (Cook 1966, 8). If, in addition to this correction for disequilibrium between C_{14} production and decay, a further downward correction is made for a decrease in the decay constant, the radiocarbon method begins to produce ages all within a time frame of a few thousand years.

Whitelaw (1970) has subjected 15,000 published C_{14} dates to statistical analysis by ranking, and then has applied the correction factors using the acknowledged 30 percent difference in rates, and the entire data reduce to a remarkably sharp beginning point, about 5,000 years ago. This, again, is confirmation of the Genesis record for the time of the Flood and a good reason to question openly all the long ages given by the other radiometric methods, reckonings we have been assured are based on sound scientific principles.

What Can be Concluded About Radiometric Dating?

Very seldom is the word "calibration" mentioned in popular or even textbook explanations of radiometric dating, possibly because it is one of the weakest areas in the whole exercise. It is normal procedure in any analytical laboratory to calibrate the test method against a known standard before attempting analysis on the unknown sample. It is important that the age of the known standard, or primary calibration standard, has been determined by an entirely independent physical method; with the majority of radiometric tests this is, of course, quite impossible. Libby (1963) used archaeologically dated wood from Pharaoh's tomb for the early radiocarbon calibration, but since several ounces of sample were required and the test is destructive, calibrations of this type are, obviously, very limited (See Chapter Thirteen, note 9). Recognizing this limitation, attention was then given to the bristle-cone pine tree (Pinus aristata) and the giant redwood trees (Sequoia gigantea), which are among the oldest living things; Libby (1963, 279) thought they could be accurately dated by counting the rings. However, after a great deal of work it was discovered that these trees could add more than one ring a year, and this has evidently led to some inconsistencies (Glock and Agerter 1963; Jueneman 1972).[12] In any event, whether by using wood from Egypt or from the pine trees, this calibration material is only good for little more than three thousand years, but beyond this time there is still a real need for a good independent method of finding the age of carbon-containing material.

Lee, writing in the *Anthropological Journal of Canada,* makes the statement: "The necessity for calibration over the last 7000 years is well recognized and attended to, while the probable error in older dates receives no practical consideration at all. At a range of 20,000 to 30,000 years, it is true, one can only guess at the full extent of the problem. But one can be reasonably sure about its trend: *too young*" (Lee 1981, 25. Emphasis in original). This is a continuing problem among the radiocarbon fraternity, where there seems to be an ongoing search for reasons to increase the ages, while all the hard evidence keeps pointing in the opposite direction. Some investigators have become quite irritated, and Lee (1981, 27) sums up Stuckenrath:

> Radiocarbon method is still not capable of yielding accurate and reliable results. There are gross discrepancies, the chronology is *uneven* and *relative,* and the accepted dates are actually *selected* dates. "This whole blessed thing is nothing but 13th century alchemy, and it all depends upon which funny paper you read" (Stuckenrath 1977, 188).

This statement, by a worker in the field, sums up the truth of the matter—a far cry from the textbook claims of the "consistency of radiocarbon dates".

We may reasonably conclude that within the dating range of calibration standards, perhaps the past five thousand years, the carbon 14 method is probably a good indicator of true age, especially when carried out by the new high-energy technique. For material believed to be older than this, however, the results obtained are all subject to interpretation, according to the presuppositions of the investigator, and the exercise then passes from the area of true science into that of pseudoscience.

When it comes to the other radiometric methods, such as the potassium/argon, there are no independent test methods; thus there can be no primary calibration standards. The use of fossils to calibrate the radiometric method, meanwhile, is simply adding to an already circular situation. Any consistency found with various radiometric methods is simply consistency within test methods based on the radio-decay phenomenon and, as we have seen, these are all subject to the same assumptions. The acceptance of the extreme ages given by these radiometric methods is, therefore, not based on good science but rather on philosophical grounds, because they appear to give support to Lyell's geology.

Evidence That Demands a Verdict

The expanded time frame for the age of the earth is the central foundation stone for today's theory of evolution while the evidence for these long ages is provided, not by the C_{14} dating method, but by the other radiometric methods. The assumptions underlying these methods are crucial, and it is for this reason that some time has been spent bringing these into the light of day.

While it is quite unlikely that the exact age of the earth will ever be known, there is an impressive number of quite unrelated natural processes that indicate that the earth is less than one million years old; indeed, many of these indicate that it is less than 100,000 years old. In either event, these times are far too short for evolution to have taken place. The remainder of this chapter will present, quite briefly, some of these natural processes for which orthodox science has no satisfactory explanation but which can be readily explained by a young earth.

The Sun's Source of Energy

It has long been a cause for wonder how it is possible for the sun to keep pouring out enormous quantities of energy, of which the earth receives less than a billionth part, year in and year out, without any apparent signs of change. The problem is compounded by the fact that if the sun had been even slightly hotter or cooler in the past, then life on earth would not have been possible at all. The virtual constancy of heat output over the millions of years alleged for life to have evolved either has a rational explanation, or it is one of the miracles of evolution.

The German physicist Hermann von Helmholtz proposed a rational explanation, in 1856, and said that the sun was shrinking under its own gravitational force; it was the contraction that provided the constant source of energy (Helmholtz 1856, 506).[13] This explanation allowed a maximum possible age for the sun of about ten million years, which was all very well for the time prior to Darwin's *Origin* but began to fall badly short of all the time needed by Darwin and his followers. The theory of the shrinking sun was quietly abandoned, leaving no other

Hermann von Helmholtz, 1821-94. In a very readable little paper (1856), this German physicist showed that the sun's constant output of energy could most readily be explained by contraction under its own gravitational field. (Metropolitan Toronto Reference Library Board)

explanation. Then, in 1903, George Darwin, son of Charles, suggested that radioactivity, such as produced by radium, might be the source of the sun's heat, and within a week the idea was supported by others who could see this as an explanation for the greater age required by Darwinian evolution. As nuclear forces came to be understood in the 1920s, Sir Arthur Eddington (1926) then proposed that the sun's heat was produced by thermonuclear reactions, and, essentially, this has been the neatly pigeon-holed explanation to this day. The thermonuclear source of energy serves not only for our sun but for every star in the universe, but it is a theory held to more by faith than by fact.

Nuclear fusion processes, similar to that of the hydrogen bomb, produce subatomic particles called neutrinos. It was expected that the earth would be bathed in these particles as they continuously pour out of the sun's interior. After a number of elaborate experiments conducted by Bahcall (1969), however, the quantity of neutrinos detected was "less than a fifth of the predicted value and may be zero" (Yockey 1977; Bahcall and Davis 1976).[14] This leaves the theoreticians in a dilemma; indeed it has been admitted by two workers that the "situation has advanced in the past years from being merely difficult to understand to being impossible to live with" (Trimble and Reines 1973). The solar neutrino problem is not confined to our planetary system but has cosmological implications. If thermonuclear reactions do not provide the sun's energy and contraction is discounted because the process can only account for a few million years, then the whole of astronomical evolution faces a serious challenge (Sutton 1980).

Possibly because of the difficulty with the missing neutrinos, there

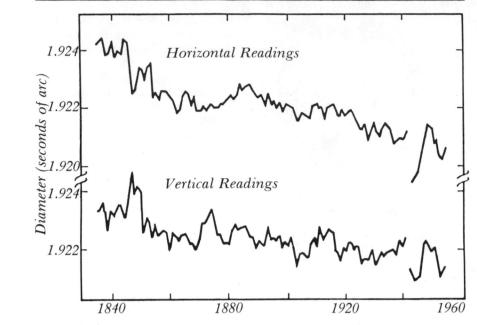

Contraction of the sun from Greenwich Observatory data. (After a diagram in *Physics Today*; author)

has been in recent years a renewal of interest in the solar contraction theory, and once again the camp has been divided between those who accept, and those who oppose the facts. Astrophysicist Eddy and mathematician Boornazian (1979) analyzed solar measurements made regularly from 1836 to 1953 at the Greenwich Observatory and found a statistically significant decrease in the sun's diameter that exceeded errors of observation and likely observer bias. The same effect had been noted by others (Wittmann 1980).[15] The rate of contraction amounted to about 0.1 percent per century, which is surprisingly high and greater than that proposed by Helmholtz in 1854. The objections to these findings came from two directions. Parkinson (1980) made out an apparently convincing case by arguing that there was bias among a series of observers, and he juggled the statistics to show random variation but no contraction.[16] Stephenson (1982), on the other hand, accepted the data as valid and the decrease as real, but then argued that the phenomenon is cyclical; that is, the observation is part of an ongoing cycle of contraction and expansion.[17] While there is not a shred of evidence or explanation for this proposal, the underlying purpose would seem to be to ensure leaving an open-ended time in the past. The central problem of modern theories that try to explain the source of the sun's energy and its necessarily constant nature is the assumption that the sun is billions of years old. Without this overriding presupposition, the evidence may be allowed to speak for itself, and while the observations on contraction are still being debated, they can easily be accommodated into the creation scenario and can readily explain the sun's source of energy.

Rotating Sun—Rotating Earth

When Galileo turned his telescope on the sun in 1610, he discovered dark spots on its luminous surface. From their movement he deduced that the sun rotated on its own axis once about every twenty-seven days. Since Galileo's time, many observations have shown that the spots at the higher latitudes rotate more slowly than those spots at the equator. Since the sun is gas and not a solid, these differences in rates of rotation are possible, although perhaps unexpected, and have given rise to speculations concerning the sun's interior, which, of course, is not directly visible. Some have argued for a rapidly rotating core, suggesting one turn a day, which has led to controversy, since it could be argued perhaps more cogently that the core was rotating more slowly than the envelope. The truth of the matter is that no one knows. But the awkward fact remains that different rotation rates exist. Howard has pointed out that the solar "wind", consisting of solar particles, constantly streaming away into space from the rotating surface, "exert a dragging effect that is strong enough to stop the rotation of the convective zone in only one million years" (Howard 1975, 112). In addition to this, the friction between the layers of hot gases within the sun's interior tend to reduce the differences in their rates of rotation and would shorten the overall rotation time still further. Howard confesses that "a million years is a short time...and we know the sun's surface layers cannot be decelerating [slowing down] that rapidly. If they were...only a few hundred million years ago the sun would have been rotating so fast that it would have thrown off an appreciable fraction of its mass by centrifugal force" (Howard 1975, 112). The central problem here is the assumption that millions of years are involved, while this, in turn, has led to the further assumption that the sun's surface is not "decelerating that rapidly". Without the biological and geological demands for billions of years required for evolution, the astronomical sciences would be free to push ahead with real scientific investigation of the cosmos. In the case of the sun's rotation, for example, the plain facts, without any appeal to miracle, would indicate that the age of the sun is certainly less than a million years.

Of course, the earth also rotates about its own axis once each day, and with the introduction of atomic clocks in the early 1960s it became possible to measure the length of the day to the nearest billionth of a second. A telescope was sighted onto one of the fixed stars and the interval timed when the same star returned to the cross hairs. It became evident that the earth was slowing down, and the small daily difference, when allowed to accumulate, amounted to 0.005 of a second per year each year; this is the earth's rate of deceleration (Thwaites and Awbrey 1982).[18] A remarkably stable system, really, but, nevertheless, this slowing of rotation in the vacuum of space is caused principally by the moon's gravitational pull on the oceans and the subsequent dissipation of this energy as tidal friction.

It is a fact that by international agreement a "leap second" has been added to the world's clocks every year since 1972 on 31 December (Fisher 1973). This second includes the 0.005 of a second due to deceleration, and the remainder of the second is a "velocity" adjustment to bring the atomic clocks in exact alignment with the rotation of the earth. So far this gives us no indication of a young earth; in fact, at the present rate of deceleration, it can be shown that 4.6 billion years ago, the "day" would have been a modest fourteen hours long (Thwaites and Awbrey 1982, 19). As tidal friction is slowing down the earth's spin, other processes tend to work in the opposite direction (Challinor 1971).[19] There is, for instance, undeniable historical evidence from eclipse data showing that this has happened; a change as simple as a one meter fall in sea level would decrease the rate of deceleration from its present value (Stephenson 1982, 183). However, these changes in the earth's rate of rotation are miniscule in comparison with an additional "leap second", which, *The Astronomical Almanac* (1983) records, has been added every year in July since 1981.[20] This now amounts to two seconds a year for correction instead of one, and only time will tell what future changes will be necessary. The sea levels certainly have not risen significantly, so that the earth's deceleration rate cannot be responsible for the extra second; the situation does cast a nagging doubt that perhaps the atomic clocks are not so constant after all.

Icy Visitors From Space

Every few decades our attention is drawn to the night sky to watch and wonder at the latest comet, although those within the living memory have turned out to be rather disappointing, in spite of the dire portents of doomsday prophets. Nevertheless, there is by now a lot of information about these icy and infrequent visitors which have been aptly described as "dirty snowballs", since they consist mostly of frozen water and dust. What we see as the comet head and long tail is really the sunlight scattered by the fine dust left behind as the ice ball evaporates in the vacuum of space; evaporation only occurs as the comet swings into orbit towards the sun. The comet, for us to see it with the naked eye, has to contribute about ten tons of dust every second to the inner solar system. This output of dust is represented by a much larger amount of frozen water, which comes off the ice ball as a fountain in all directions and dissociates into its component parts. A comet is, thus, in a process of rapid decay, which may last several months while in its orbit around the sun, all the while leaving behind a trail of gases and dust millions of miles long. Comets are believed to be as old as the solar system, and of the six hundred or so comets that are known, about one hundred move in orbits with periods of less than two hundred years. Probably the best known is Halley's comet. The painstaking records of the Chinese show that Halley's comet has appeared twenty-nine times at intervals of seventy-six and seventy-seven years; the first well-observed passage was 239 B.C. and the most recent was a disappointing appearance in 1986. It is estimated that the icy ball inside the head of this comet is some five miles in diameter, and conservative estimates are that the comet loses a fraction of 1 percent of its total substance on each return (Whipple 1974).

It should be evident from these figures that a comet must have a finite life of only a few thousand years—with possibly 10,000 years, but certainly not millions or billions of years, as the upper limit (Van Flandern 1977). It has been argued on this basis by J.H. Oort (1950), of the University of Leiden, that somewhere out there in the darkness of space beyond our solar system, there is a great cloud of comets, and that every so often one is disturbed and enters the solar system, thus replenishing those that are used up.[21] It is admitted that there is not the slightest piece of evidence for this fantasy (Brady 1970, 1064). Again, like Francis Crick's Panspermia theory for the origin of life, an appeal is being made here to realms beyond man's reach in order to safeguard the long ages required by the theory of evolution (Noerdlinger 1977).

Meteorites, Tektites, and Moon Dust

On a clear night one can usually see a "shooting star", which nearly always seems to appear in the corner of the eye as a momentary streak of light among the stars, there for a second and then gone. In its orbit through space, the earth's atmosphere encounters a great many solid particles, most of which are of pinhead size. Occasionally, however, there is a larger piece. Upon entering our atmosphere at forty kilometers per second, the particles are very effectively burned up—hence the streak of light—and the oxides left form a fine dust that eventually settles to the earth (Moulton 1956, 59; Singer 1954). On rare occasions a large meteorite manages to survive in its passage through the atmosphere and land on the earth, where it often receives newspaper attention. These meteorites, when found, generally finish up in museums and have been extensively studied; they consist mostly of iron but contain some cobalt and approximately 2.5 percent nickel. It will be recalled from Chapter Four that while fossilization is claimed to be a rare event, it is nevertheless argued that the great number of fossils found in the sedimentary rocks is a result of the enormous spans of geological time available. By this same argument, then, it might be thought that although meteoritic impact on the earth's surface is a relatively rare event, nevertheless, because of the great spans of time available, the sedimentary rocks, should contain large numbers. The facts are, however, that not a single true meteorite has ever been found in the sedimentary rock record (Hindley 1977; Mason 1962, 4; Tarr 1932). The mystery deepens when it is found that stoney meteorites that contain potassium compounds and, thus, allow dating by the potassium argon method, have reported ages of 4.6 billion years since solidification; that is, since they entered the earth's atmosphere. These stoney meteorites and tektites, which are small glassy beads of cosmic origin, are only found in recent deposits. Again, the tektites have been dated by the potassium/argon method and independently by the fission track method and have yielded ages ten times greater than expected by their position near the very top of the geologic column; this has given rise to a lot of controversy behind doors generally closed to the public (Gill 1970).[22] All this does not tell us the age of the earth but the absence of meteorites in the geologic column should lead us to question seriously the enormous spans of time claimed for the formation of all the sedimentary rocks. At the same time, the extreme ages claimed for the stoney meteorites and tektites lying within recent deposits should raise questions about the validity of the radiometric methods.

Returning now to the shooting stars and the meteoritic dust: Pettersson (1960), of the Swedish Oceanographic Institute, working on high mountain tops filtered measured quantities of air and analyzed the particles he found. Since the meteorites that have survived contain an average of 2.5 percent nickel, then the nickel content of the dust extracted represented that which came from meteors rather than from terrestrial sources. From a knowledge of the total volume of the earth's atmosphere, Pettersson reckoned that 14 million tons of meteoritic dust settled on the earth's surface each year; however, because of some variability in results, he concluded with a more conservative figure of five million tons (Pettersson 1960, 132). Isaac Asimov, the popular science writer, took the more liberal figure and concluded that at that rate, the dust piles up to about ten-millionths of an inch per year. This is certainly not much to get excited about. However, he then pointed out that over nearly five billion years, this would add up, if undisturbed, to a layer fifty-four feet deep over the entire surface of the earth (Asimov 1959, 35). Recalling that this dust is mostly iron and nickel oxides, it will be evident that no such layer or any trace of it is to be found; then, of course, it is argued that wind and water carried it all away and it is now in the ocean sediments.

Asimov, writing at about the time the Apollo moon landing was being planned, was reflecting a concern among scientists that in the absence of wind and rain a similar depth of dust would have accumulated on the moon's surface (Gold 1955; Lyttleton 1956).[23] There was before them the prospect that the Apollo lunar module would land only to disappear by slowly sinking into the moon dust! To avoid this very possibility, the lunar module was equipped with large pad feet. On 21 July 1969, more than 600 million people watched as television transmitted mankind's first footstep onto the moon's surface. Neil Armstrong's reply to CBS interviewer Walter Cronkite is worth quoting since the opening dialogue, reported by Wilford of *The New York Times* (21 July 1969:1), concerned the depth of the dust: "The surface is fine and powdery. I can pick it up loosely with my toe. It does adhere in fine layers like powdered charcoal to the sole and sides of my boots. I only go in a small fraction of an inch, maybe an eighth of an inch." As if to confirm this, astronauts Armstrong and Aldrin had great difficulty planting the American flag into the rocky and virtually dust-free ground, yet not one comment was made on the significance of the absence of the great depth of dust.

Pettersson (1950, 44) found meteorite spherules (microscopic spheres) in deep ocean sediments "millions of years old" so that they are recognized not to be a recent phenomenon; this leaves only two alternative explanations for the missing moon dust: either Pettersson and others were half a million times too high in their dust estimate, or there is something radically wrong with Asimov's five billion year assumption.

Before leaving the subject of the moon and the Apollo program, one of the experiments witnessed by television viewers during the moon walks was the installation of a small bank of mirrors facing the earth (Bender et al. 1973).[24] These were for the lunar laser-ranging experiments that have been carried out regularly since that time to measure the earth-moon distance to within a few centimeters. A large telescope on earth is aimed at the mirrors, a pulse of laser light sent out; the time interval between leaving and returning gives a measure of the distance.

The laser-ranging experiments showed that the distance is increasing by about four centimeters per year—nearly two inches (Stephenson 1982, 173). This is not only a remarkable testimony to the state of technological perfection achieved, but confirms and provides quantitative data for earlier theoretical work that predicted the separation as a result of the moon's gravitational pull on the oceans and the subsequent dissipation of energy as tidal friction; a further result of this same cause is a slowing of the rotation of the earth.

Jeffries, in 1929, recognized the possibility of calculating the age of the earth-moon system from theoretical considerations of the dynamics involved, but in the absence of real data it was necessary to make some assumptions. As more information accumulated, however, it became possible to get better estimates—but then, even before the lunar laser-ranging experiments were conducted, it was evident that serious difficulties were being encountered. Baldwin explained the situation this way:

> Jeffries' [1929] early studies of the effects of tidal friction yielded a rough age of the Moon of four billion years. Recently, however, Munk and MacDonald [1960] have interpreted the observations to indicate that tidal friction is a more important force than had realized and it would have taken not more than 1.78 billion years for tidal friction to drive the Moon outward to its present distance from any possible minimum distance. This period of time is so short, compared with the age of the earth, that serious doubts have been cast upon most proposed origins and histories of the moon (Baldwin 1965, 40).[25]

Hammond (1974), having the benefit of the laser-ranging data, concluded that the current rate of separation of the earth-moon system implies an initial separation of less than one billion years ago. Clearly, these times are too short for the demands of evolution, and the method, once thought to provide evidence for the long ages and earlier for George Darwin's fission theory for the moon's origin, is now not likely to be seen in textbooks. Nor are these same textbooks likely to make Baldwin's (1965, 42) candid admission that science is at a loss adequately to explain the moon's origin, but would, it seems, rather continue to promote outdated and thoroughly discredited theories. All this lack of complete honesty, it may be recalled, results from the most sacred of all precepts, bringing hasty excommunication to any who would question its veracity—namely, that the earth is 4.5 billion years old.

Earth's Decaying Magnetic Field

The earth is a magnet, and for a long time now navigation by compass has made use of knowledge of this fact. There are, of course, north and south poles, and just like the little bar magnets used for school instruction, it is commonly believed that the interior of the earth consists of iron or some mixture of iron and nickel. The core may be iron, but unlike the bar magnet this is not the source of the magnetic field. It has been noted earlier that the temperature increased 1°C every thirty meters (one hundred feet) down into the earth, and, at this rate, by twenty-five kilometers (sixteen miles) the temperature would be more than 750°C, which is a red heat, and would continue hotter towards the earth's center (Thomson 1865).[26] A mere eggshell thickness thus separates all life on earth from the terrible heat beneath. At temperatures above their Curie temperature, that is above 750°C, all magnetism in iron or magnetic iron ore is completely lost.[27] It is evident, then, that the earth's magnet cannot be of the permanent type, such as in a bar magnet, but must be the electromagnetic type and function by huge electric currents surging around in the core.

The source of this electric current is unknown. Runcorn (1955) is a latter-day proponent of the theory that a dynamo, or electric power generator, operated by hypothetical movements of fluid in the earth's core, provides the current. However, mathematical analysis of the facts shows the dynamo theory to be totally inadequate as an explanation for the earth's magnetism (Cowling 1934). Horace Lamb provided a unique solution to the problem in 1883. He proposed that the electric current circulating within the earth is freely decaying; that is, its cessation has been retarded by self-induced currents created by the decay of the magnetic field. This effect may be experienced on a small scale when a radio continues to play for a second or so after its power has been disconnected. Lamb left open the questions of where the electrical power came from in the first place and when it was turned off, but at least the free decay he proposed is now well supported by more than 150 years of real magnetic data. Lamb's theory has not found the acceptance of orthodox science, even though it is just as plausible as hypothetical dynamos. One may suspect that the reason lies in the fact that, inadequate though it is, the dynamo theory offers an open-ended past, whereas Lamb's theory points to something abhorrent to many scientists, a relatively recent beginning (Jacobs 1967).[28]

The earth's magnetic field varies slightly from place to place and can also vary slightly from day to day. In appreciation of this, Karl Gauss (1834) organized magnetic measuring stations around the world and a method to collect data that could be mathematically reduced to a single

Horace Lamb, 1849-1934. One of
England's great scientists in his
early fifties; his work on
geomagnetism refuted the Darwinian
demand for long ages and is
seldom mentioned today.
(Metropolitan Toronto Reference
Library Board)

figure representing the total strength of the earth's magnet.[29] This
value is the magnetic moment and was first recorded at the surprisingly
early date of 1835. Measurements have been made every few years since
then, and the published figures show a relatively rapid decay amount-
ing to about 5 percent per one hundred years (McDonald and Gunst
1967, 1).[30] The actual data from a U.S. government report is given in
Appendix K. This adequately confirms Lamb's theoretical work of a
century ago and raises the immediate question: When was the earth's
electrical power shut off, or when did magnetic decay begin?

Barnes (1971) has analyzed the published data from 1835 to 1965 and
concludes that the decay rate is exponential, with a half-life of only
1,400 years. An exponential decrease is normal for most natural processes and consists of an initial rapid decrease that becomes ever slower
as it progresses. Half-life is just a convenient way of expressing a decay
process that is theoretically never complete. More recent data from the
Magsat geophysical exploration satellite shows that the overall intensity of the earth's magnetic field is declining at twenty-six nanoteslars
per year, or has a half-life of a mere 830 years (Magsat down 1980).[31]
This means that the magnetic field, which provides protection against
cosmic radiation, is diminishing very rapidly and will be completely
ineffective in a few thousand years. It also means that the magnetic field
and the directly related electric currents must have been greater in the

FRONT: Karl Gauss, 1777-1855.
REAR: Wilhelm Weber, 1804-91.
Gauss the mathematician and
Weber the physicist collaborated
between 1831 and 1837 to organize
the Magnetische Verein, which
united a worldwide network of
magnetic observatories; Europe
alone had twenty-three stations.
(Metropolitan Toronto Reference
Library Board)

past, perhaps, double every 1,400 years, to use Barnes's estimate of
half-life. There is an upper limit, however, because the circulating
electric currents dissipate heat, and with double the current, the heat
generated would be more than twice as great.[32] After only 8,000-10,000
years in the past, the heat generated in the core at that time would have
been too great for life to have been possible on the surface. The most
straightforward conclusion that can be drawn from the hard data
(Appendix K) is that the decay of the magnetic field of the earth has an
exponential relationship, and that from the Joule heating effect mentioned, the decay is not likely to have begun more than about 10,000
years ago. Evidence from other natural processes would indicate that
this was coincidental with the earth's beginning. Suppose we acknowledge the fact that extrapolation of data is a hazardous business. Then
even if the beginning point on the decay curve is off by two orders of
magnitude—a virtual impossibility—the beginning is merely set back
to a million years. This is far too short a time for the guardians of
Lyell's uniformitarianism; it is not surprising that Barnes's analysis of
the data has been totally rejected, as has the earlier work of Lamb.
However, the facts remain, and an ingenious escape has been found,
similar in principle to the argument used to refute the evidence of the
shrinking sun.

When hot molten rocks (magma) containing iron oxides cool below the Curie temperature, they become magnetized by the earth's magnetic field, and, it is believed, so preserve within their mass the earth's magnetic intensity and pole direction at that time. Many of these rocks have been found, in which their north and south poles are reversed with respect to the earth's magnetic poles of today. From this it is argued that the reversed rocks are evidence that the magnetic field of the entire earth has reversed a number of times in the past. This pole-reversal theory allows the magnetic field to oscillate, that is, alternately increase and decrease an indefinite number of times and so leave an open-ended past. The data accumulated over the past 150 years is seen as merely being the most recent decreasing cycle. One might wonder why science would go to the trouble to set up measuring stations about the earth or go to the expense of the Magsat program if measurements of paleo-intensity and magnetic orientation were sufficiently reliable from the individual rocks. The answer becomes clear from rarely made admissions, such as those by Jacobs, that the reversal of polarity in rocks can occur by any one of four known physicochemical processes. In order to prove that the earth's magnetic field has caused the reversal in the rocks, it is necessary to show that reversal cannot have been made by one of these physicochemical processes. Jacobs admits that "this is a virtually impossible task" (Jacobs 1963, 106). Very clearly the discipline of paleomagnetism is an exercise in selecting data to fit the theory; it could well be argued that the physicochemical processes themselves, rather than the earth's magnetic field, were responsible for the pole reversal in the rocks in the first place. It also becomes clear that the very tenuous claims of reversing poles are the only recourse to refute a recent beginning in the face of the hard evidence for decay of the earth's magnetic field. The grounds have thus shifted from science to philosophy. In spite of all that is claimed for the pole reversal theory, the more responsible authors admit that no one knows the initial source of the earth's current, and even less can anyone guess what possible mechanism could be responsible for diminishing the current, reversing it, then increasing it again (Carrigan and Gubbins 1979).[33]

The Missing Radiogenic Helium

During the radioactive decay of uranium and thorium in the earth's crust, alpha particles are given off, and these become helium 4, the most abundant isotope of helium. A glance at Appendix C will show that a total of eight alpha particles are produced as each uranium 238 atom decays to lead 206. Estimates have been made of the total uranium and thorium in the earth's surface, and from this the rate of production of helium is reckoned to be 3×10^9 grams per year. In addition to this, about the same quantity of helium is generated each year in the upper atmosphere by the bombardment of cosmic rays. If helium 4 has been released into our atmosphere at this rate for some four billion years, then the total quantity of helium 4 present today should be about 10^{20} grams. In fact, the actual quantity found is a thousand times less than this figure, which would indicate that the earth is only a few million years old.[34] The immediate reaction is to suppose that since helium is a light gas, it has been lost from our atmosphere to outer space. This is not, however, necessarily so and it appears that our atmosphere has more likely gained helium from space. It turns out that atmospheric helium consists of a mixture of the isotopes helium 3 and helium 4 in a certain ratio, whereas the ratio of helium 3 to helium 4 in the earth's crust is ten times less. If helium was being lost to space, both isotopes would go at the same rate, and the ratio would have remained constant. The evidence of the difference indicates that the ratio must rather have been increasing from that in the rocks to that in the atmosphere by a factor of ten times to reach its present value. Taking the difference in the two ratios, Cook (1957), writing a cautiously worded letter to *Nature*, has concluded that helium 3 must have been added to our atmosphere. That being so, he then points out the process could have begun not more than ten thousand years ago.

Stalactites or Stalagmites?

Returning to *terra firma*, there are, in almost every country, limestone caverns with intriguing names, such as the Dragon Caves (Island of Majorca), that capture the tourists' attention. Carlsbad Caverns, New Mexico, are probably the best known in North America (Sutherland 1953).[35] Typically, the visitor receives for his entrance fee a printed tract and a guided tour, in which he is assured that the beautiful floodlit cave formations have taken millions of years to reach their present size. Stalactites, incidentally, are the ones that hang downwards. When water runs through limestone, it dissolves some of this mineral. As the mineral-laden water hangs as a drop from a crack in the cave roof, it is exposed to the air, where the water evaporates and leaves the mineral deposit. How long does all this take, drip by drip? In underground vaults and tunnels, stalactites, in their initial stages, can usually be found and are known as "dripstone". Dripstone can grow to appreciable lengths in just a few years if left undisturbed and may even be seen an inch or two long in underground railway stations that are in daily use. The photograph shows dripstone as minor stalactites more than sixty centimeters (twenty-four inches) long in a London tunnel, disused since its days as an air-raid shelter, 1941-45. They have grown this

When opened after thirty-three years of disuse, a tunnel bored through London
clay was found to contain stalactites or dripstone more than twenty-four inches
long. (*The Times*, London)

length in only thirty-three years, and little imagination is required to
picture their growth after just a hundred times this number of years.
Five thousand years is a more reasonable age for the limestone caverns,
but the little tracts ask us to believe it has taken a thousand times longer.

Very High Pressure Oil Wells

When drilling for oil and gas, the drill passes through solid rock for
thousands of feet, and well drillers have become accustomed to increasing pressure with depth at the rate of about a half pound per square
inch per foot depth, so that at 10,000 feet, the pressure is 5,000 per
square inch. Fairly massive equipment is required to handle these
pressures, but, occasionally, a zone is encountered where the pressure
more than doubles, causing difficulty and some danger in the drilling
operation. In these circumstances, the drill passes from a zone of high
pressure to an adjacent zone of exceptionally high pressure, and structural geologists have wondered how it is possible for such great pressure differences to have existed side by side for "scores of millions of
years" (Dickey et al. 1968).[36] The broader question might also be asked:
How can oil or gases remain under great pressure for millions of years
without dissipation and leaking through to the surface? From what has
already been said in this and the previous chapter, the millions of years
that are taken for granted should be the first area open to question.

After all, the reported ages of the oil and gas by the C_{14} method were only a few thousand years, yet these results are usually dismissed, not for actual technical reasons, but because they do not meet the expectations of a much greater length of time. The whole area of preconception and presumption in science is not merely of academic interest, since the assumed age and stability of rock units directly influence such issues as the storage of nuclear wastes. The high pressures in oil and gas wells are, rather, evidence for a youthful age, indicating, perhaps, thousands of years—rather than millions of years—for the rock units.

Population Explosion

Government policy makers are always on the horns of a dilemma when it comes to the question of human population. On the one hand, they warn against population increase in foreign countries because of the extra mouths to feed, but on the other hand, they like to encourage an increase in their own country because the babes of today become the taxpayers of tomorrow. By the time the problem gets to the United Nations, it becomes a very confused matter of wheat deals, family taxation or subsidy, and contraceptive devices. No one can be certain of the number of people in the world, and the figures, particularly from the underdeveloped countries, are largely estimates. Nevertheless, there is no doubt that, even though the reproduction rate per family is relatively low today, the overall number of people in the world is greater than it has ever been, and that it is continuing to grow. A generation ago, the writings of William Vogt (1948) stirred the imagination of Dixie-cup king Hugh Moore, who flooded America with alarmist and blatantly untruthful literature intended to curb the population increase. Moore died in 1972 and so, it seems, did the campaign, but the United Nations has continued to play its own low-key, but steady, part in bringing the world's population growth to zero.[37]

Demographers earn a living by juggling with the figures of population obtained in the national census. By the use of mathematical formulas, they can usefully predict, for example, when and where to build schools for tomorrow's students. There are a number of formulas, all of which tend to give roughly the same result but with various degrees of refinement (a rather simple one is given in Appendix L). Of particular interest, however, is the fact that these formulas can be used to find populations in the past as well as in the future (for examples see Appendix L).

If humanity is really 3.5 million years old, or whatever the latest Leakey/Johanson debate has decided, then today's world population can be predicted by use of the formula and selecting likely data. For example, with a modest estimate of 2.2 children per average family, an equally modest average generation life span of twenty years, and parents never living long enough to see their grandchildren, then the world population would have grown from a single family to 10^{2070} (one followed by 2,070 zeroes!) people alive at the same time at the end of the first million years. This number is so large that our entire universe could contain only a small fraction of them, stacked shoulder to shoulder!

The use of formulas gives the maximum figure possible from the variables that have been selected, and it is cogently argued that natural disasters have always played a hand in keeping human population in check; the long-term picture is thus seen to be one of population stability. History shows, for example, that the Justinian plague, A.D. 540-90, took 100 million lives; the Black Death, A.D. 1348-80, swept away 150 million from Europe alone; and even as late as 1918-19, the influenza epidemic took 25 million lives (Wallace 1969; Webster 1799). Four things need to be kept in mind (it might also help to practice with a computer or large calculator to get a "feel" for the way populations grow). First, so far as they go, historical records show that families did not stop at 2.2 children, but many, it seems, approached the biological maximum. About half survived, and there were consequently four or five left to reproduce in the next generation. Second, the picture of ancient man scratching a bare existence in caves is nineteenth century speculation. The very earliest remains of human habitation, as at Mohenjo-daro in India, for example, have been found with the lowest strata showing a more advanced city civilization in the fourth millenium B.C. than more recent occupation levels (Durant 1:395). Third, no matter how infrequent fossilization of human or animal remains may claim to be, the fossil record simply does not support the millions upon millions of creatures that would have existed over the vast ages required. And fourth, the awful figures for natural disasters are very quickly made up for by the subsequent rates of increase among the survivors (Langer 1964).[38] It is difficult to imagine how reproduction and disaster can have kept such a delicate balance for a million years or more among the human population. Zero population growth occurs when there is an average of 2.0 children per family, but even the slightest imbalance, for example, from 1.09 to 2.02 children per family, causes a tremendous difference over the evolutionary time scales proposed. When textbook authors, such as Stansfield (1977, 82), acknowledge the population problem at all, they explain it away by speaking of "population stability". However, what is really meant is "population oscillation near the zero growth level", and this, it may be recognized, is

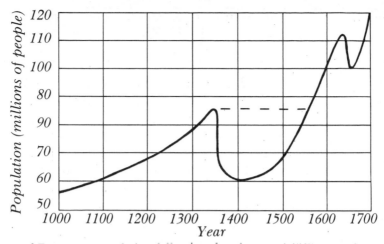

Recovery of European population following the plagues of 1347 was only two hundred years—an insignificant moment in the evolutionary time scale. (After Langer 1964; author)

the same strategem used to refute the shrinking sun and the decay of the earth's magnetic field.[39] On the other hand, if the young earth can be accepted, then the world's population today would be almost exactly what would be expected from the four couples surviving the Genesis Flood some five thousand years ago and would take into account all the natural disasters. Details are given in Appendix L.

*   *   *

These two chapters have dealt with the important issue of time and, specifically, the age of the earth. In summary, a number of examples have been given of natural processes that are well documented and for which science has no adequate explanation, in terms of an old earth. While some of these processes indicate an age of millions and others of thousands of years, no single process yet gives an exact age. When taken together, however, an age of less than 10,000 years fits all the facts most reasonably. There are many other natural processes, all of which indicate a young earth—that is, at least a thousand times less than the current estimate of 4.5 thousand million years. In contrast, the evidence for the old earth model hangs almost exclusively on the assumptions inherent within the radiometric methods. Even then, the C_{14} method must be excluded, since it supports the young earth model. There will probably never be proof for either model, and it becomes a matter of personal choice for each individual to adopt the model that best seems to fit all the facts. In the next chapter, some of the mental contortions to try to reconcile the young earth/old earth debate will be shown, together with a little insight into the characters responsible for these ideas being still very much with us.

13

From Revelation to Scientism

*Extinguished theologians lie about the cradle of
every science as the strangled snakes beside that of
Hercules; and history records that whenever
science and orthodoxy have been fairly opposed,
the latter has been forced to retire from the lists,
bleeding and crushed if not annihilated; scotched,
if not slain.*
T.H. HUXLEY
(1893, 52)

W hether we like to acknowledge it or not, man has a built-in propensity to worship some being greater than himself. Evidence from the most primitive tribes to the medieval cathedrals of Europe and the evangelical movement beginning in the 1960s and extending into the present day attest to this. Yet there will still be those who would question the relevancy of this activity for the twentieth century. Part of the problem here is the word "worship", which, for some, has connotations of a candle-carrying, incense-swinging ritual, mindlessly played out to the strains of some Gregorian chant; for others, it is simply stoic attendance at an approved assembly. However, a moment's thought will show that the worship principle has a much broader application. The Fascist salute of the followers of General Franco or Adolf Hitler was a sign of adulation copied from the raised hands of the Jewish and Islam worshipper. The portrait banners of Joseph Stalin and Mao Tse-tung in principle were no less than the Roman Catholic banners and the Eastern Catholic icons. And May Day parades are held to glorify nature in the same way as the pageant and procession of religious festivals glorify God. Certainly, the "Alleluias" sung to the glory of God had their counterfeit in the paeans of "Seig Heil", sung by the Nazi party to the glory of their fuhrer, while the crucifix and swastika may be seen to fulfil similar purposes in the minds of their followers. The Madonna has been copied in the Atheist Church of America; the latter's Madonna is its founder, Madalyn Murray O'Hair. These are all forms of worship and are distinguished by *who* is being worshipped.

The parallel would not be complete without the books used in the same way as the Christian Bible for final authority and instruction. Familiar examples are the *Book of Mormon*, Hitler's *Mein Kampf*, and the little red book of Chairman Mao. Finally, the root meaning of the word "worship", which has to do with reverence, adulation, and the devotion shown towards a person or principle, can be applied alike to the names of Christ, Mohammed, the bishop of Rome, Karl Marx, or even Charles Darwin.

Most thinking individuals, at some point in their life, are faced with having to make a choice of the particular philosophical system they wish to follow. For example, one focal point for that choice lies in the vote cast for a political candidate. The belief in any one particular system eventually leads to a confession of that belief before others, which then has the effect of establishing a commitment to that belief system. This confession is an essential part of all religious systems but is also carried out by those organized activities that valiantly try not to be regarded as religious. The "harmless little ritual" imposed on the initiates of transcendental meditation, the oath taken by the competitors of the Olympic games, the endless affirmation of the cause by the members of the Communist party, and a similar principle of confession inherent in these activities, may be recognized in the continual and outspoken reference to the belief in evolution by informal discussion, at the oral examination, and from the lecture platform.

We have seen throughout the preceding chapters that there is no actual proof for evolution; it has never been demonstrated by laboratory experiment, and when all is said and done, it turns out to be a belief system (Keith 1925c).[1] Repeated confession of belief in something for which there is no proof is a well-recognized and practiced religious device, used to build the faith of the believer. This applies whether that faith is in Special Creation, in evolution, or in the existence of intelligent life in outer space. The principle is no less true today than it was at the time of the Roman Empire. The emperor, Marcus Aurelius, observed: "Such are thy habitual thoughts, such also will be the character of thy mind; the soul is dyed by the thoughts" (Long 1869, 112).[2] It is well known that certain books, when read and reread, have changed the lives of individuals. Darwin was no exception. He confessed that the great merit of Lyell's *Principles* was that it "altered the whole tone of one's mind" (F. Darwin and Seward 1903, 2:117). More will be said of the religious aspects of evolution in the following chapter.

Another aspect of human nature, touched on in Chapter One, concerns the individual's ability to accept the supernatural or the miraculous. Taking an example from the Greeks, the Athenian people, in their long history, had always been proud of their intellectual and artistic achievements; they had, after all, produced some of the greatest philosophers, still acknowledged to be so by the Western world today. Paul of Tarsus, a man of no mean intellect, visited Athens almost two thousand years ago and noted that the Athenians worshipped many different gods. He was invited to tell them of the Christ, and they listened attentively until he mentioned the resurrection from the dead, at which point they burst forth in mockery and disbelief (Acts 17:31). All else up to this point had been perfectly rational and natural, but now he was asking them to believe in the miraculous. They felt their intelligence had been insulted.

The situation has not changed a bit since Paul's day, and many who, as did the Greeks, worship their particular gods find it difficult if not impossible to accept all the biblical miracles. For example, Westfall (1981) has pointed out that one of the greatest of English scientists, Isaac Newton (1642-1727), a deeply devout man, believing in Christ and the message of salvation, was racked with anxieties about the rationality of Christianity.[3] In fact, he actually committed himself to saving Christianity by rewriting the Bible and purging it of what he

Issac Newton, 1642-1727. Although Newton is upheld as a British national hero, some of the seamier aspects of his life are not generally known among English-speaking people. (Engraving by W.T. Fry after the painting by Kneller; Academy of Medicine, Toronto)

called the "corruptions", that is, the miraculous events (Cohen 1955, 72). He totally rejected the doctrine of the Trinity.[4] Newton's name is not alone, and a little digging into the writings of the famous reveals many who piously wrote of God's love and salvation but who, at heart, could not accept the miraculous. The Virgin birth and the Resurrection were too essential to the Christian creed to express open disbelief, but anything else, particularly events as remote as the Creation account and the Flood, eventually became fair game for skepticism.

Towards the end of the nineteenth century, when evolution was becoming respectable in some quarters, if not all, David Strauss (1846), a German biblical critic, admitted that Darwin's theory was irresistible to those who thirsted after "truth and freedom".[5] In his *The Old Faith and the New* (1873), he expressed the feelings of those not able to accept supernatural events, fairly typically as follows:

> Vainly did we philosophers and critical theologians over and over again decree the extermination of miracles; our ineffectual sentence died away, because we could neither dispense with miraculous agency, nor point to any natural force able to supply it, where it had hitherto seemed most indispensable. Darwin had demonstrated this force, this process of nature; he has opened the door by which a happier coming race will cast out miracles, never to return. Everyone who knows what miracles imply will praise him, in consequence, as one of the greatest benefactors of the human race (Strauss 1873, 205).

David Strauss, 1808-74. This German theologian openly expressed what many felt, that Darwin's naturalistic explanation had at last freed them from having to admit to the miraculous. (John P. Robarts Research Library, University of Toronto)

The recognition of "what miracles imply" is two great fears: the fear of the arbitrary interference of God in the affairs of men and the fear of accountability after death. Darwin and evolutionary materialism had emancipated man from the first, if not both, of these fears. Man could feel secure at last under the rigid and inviolable law of nature.

The Roman Catholic and Protestant churches had always believed in a supernatural dimension, while until the nineteenth century they had no difficulty with the biblical miracles, including the six-day Creation and the Genesis Flood. However, differences on the supernatural at the personal level, in terms of revelation, were what initially divided Protestant from Catholic. Beginning at about the time of the French Revolution, Christianity itself was challenged from three directions. In the first place, the philosophers, such as Descartes and Rousseau in France and later Hegel and Nietzsche in Germany, cast doubt on the Judeo-Christian lifestyle and proposed alternate worldviews. The second direction was from science, in the writings of Lyell and Darwin, and the third from history, in the guise of biblical criticism. This chapter and the next will attempt to show, very briefly, the church's response to this challenge, and how the church leaders capitulated, so that what some denounced from the pulpit as a damnable lie yesterday was preached from the same pulpit as an eternal truth only a few years later.

Preparation for the Challenge

The great evangelical revival in Protestant England during the latter half of the 1700s, led by a handful of men such as John and Charles Wesley, was briefly introduced in Chapter Three. One outcome of this revival was an outspoken rejection of the ungodly philosophies that originated in socialist France and which were being emulated by a few English sympathizers. Perhaps one of the most influential naturalist writers of this period was the theologian William Paley (1743-1805), who published his *Natural Theology* in 1802. In his book he gave innumerable examples from nature of the evidence of design pointing to a Designer, and by this he hoped to combat the humanist influence of the pro-French philosopher in England, David Hume. Even so, Paley was not of the evangelical school and tended to leave God "out there" remote from his creation.

The evangelical revival spread to the colonies in North America and continued on through into Victoria's reign in the 1800s. The evangelicals were found mainly within the Anglican Church and in the then recently formed Methodist Church. The essential difference between the evangelical Christian and the conventional Christian, often sitting in the same pew, did not hinge on belief in the Genesis account of Creation and the Noahic Flood, since virtually everyone at that time accepted this as a literal fact. Rather, the distinguishing feature was the evangelical's active concern to bring others to an experiential and personal relationship with the Deity. This compelling inner drive was an outcome of the rediscovery of what had been found by the early Protestants in the Roman Church. It was based on the recognition that while man's five senses and reason (Aristotle's path to wisdom) were untrustworthy, it was possible to acquire a sixth sense and receive a higher wisdom through revelation. Only a minority, in terms of the overall Christian population, could accept this personal contact with the supernatural. But this minority was nevertheless highly influential (Howse 1976). Statistics may be questionable even when available, but one English example reports that in 1820 one Anglican clergyman in twenty was evangelical, and by 1830 the ratio had risen to one in eight (Hennell 1977, 513). By this time there had been a moral revolution in England: cock-fighting and bull- and bear-baiting had died out through lack of support; bookstores selling "dirty books" had closed down for lack of customers; and many of the Bible societies, missionary societies, and religious tract societies had been started. The Lord's Day Observance Society was founded in 1831. In government, many members were evangelical, while both houses of Parliament were extremely "right-wing", in comparison with any named governing party today. There is little doubt that this position had been reinforced by the memory of the awful consequences of the "left-wing" uprising in France. "Democracy" had become something not even to be contemplated (Howse 1976, 45).

This, then, was the climate into which Charles Lyell entered history, in 1830, with his *Principles of Geology*. It was not well received by the church nor by many others who were aware of it, even though Lyell was cautious enough to present the case for uniformitarianism simply as a possible explanation. However, most "men of the cloth" could detect this as the thin edge of a very large wedge that would eventually undermine the Christian faith, and they condemned Lyell's heresy soundly from every pulpit. The more far-sighted may have recognized within it an unwitting attempt to introduce socialism through science, but all saw it as a flagrant violation of the Scriptures. In contrast to any individual today with unorthodox scientific views, Lyell was in a sense insulated from criticism, since he was independently wealthy and could take refuge in the company of like-minded Fellows behind the doors of the Royal Society. Just at this time, during the 1830s, when Lyell was struggling against evangelical orthodoxy, fate provided the means by which some would be won over to the new faith. It is a principle as old as Adam that the most effective way of introducing a new belief system is first to prepare the minds of would-be converts by creating doubt in the established creeds. This doubt came at precisely the right time and from a direction not unfamiliar to the evangelicals—ancient Egypt.

The Long Shadow of the Sphinx

In the wake of the French Revolution, there arose one of the world's most infamous despots. Napoleon Bonaparte's quest to rule the world had brought him to Egypt, and by 1798 he had conquered the Mamaluke army in the Battle of the Pyramids. The evident signs of a once mighty civilization intrigued Napoleon, and he ordered a small army of engineers, artists, and scholars to record and describe the ruins (French Government 1809).[6] By the turn of the century, artists' engravings of imaginative reconstructions of the Pharonic palaces and temple began to appear in popular magazines and to excite the imagination of the public (Denon 1803; Roberts 1846-49).[7] The questions foremost in most minds would certainly have been, Who were these monument builders and how long ago did they live? Unfortunately, at that time no one could read the Egyptian hieroglyphics. But it seems fate had raised up a man whose specific task was to decipher the mysterious picture language.

Napoleon Bonaparte (Napoleon I), 1769-1821. Emperor of the French socialists (1804-15) and megalomaniac, he adopted the Roman Caesar pose for this, one of many hundreds of portraits. (Engraving by C. Barth after the painting by Gerrard; Metropolitan Toronto Reference Library Board)

Jean François Champollion, 1790-1832. A child prodigy, he seems to have been destined for the single purpose of breaking the secret of the Egyptian hieroglyphics. (Engraving after the painting by Leon Cogniet, 1831; Metropolitan Toronto Reference Library Board)

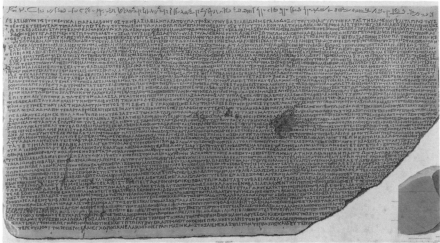

The Greek portion of the Rosetta Stone recorded before the days of photography as a copper-plate engraving. (From the French government volumes *Description de l'Egypt*, 1825; Thomas Fisher Rare Book Library, University of Toronto)

Jean François Champollion was born in France in 1790, under rather peculiar conditions (Ceram 1971a, 88).[8] It was said that while he was in his crippled mother's womb, she was miraculously healed by the local magician who prophesied that the boy-child she carried would achieve fame and be long remembered. Whatever the truth of the matter, it was evident by a very early age that he was a prodigy, and by the time he was sixteen, he had mastered half-a-dozen Oriental languages, as well as Latin and Greek; when he was seventeen he went to the University of Grenoble, not as a student but as a member of the faculty!

In 1799 a hard black tablet, about three feet square, containing three blocks of text in three languages—Greek, demotic Egyptian, and Egyptian hieroglyphic—was discovered by Napoleon's army in the village of Rosetta. This memorial stone commemorated a victory that took place in 196 B.C. A plaster copy of the stone eventually became available to Champollion when he was in his prime, having mastered by this time a dozen ancient languages including Coptic, the oldest Egyptian language known.

He soon brought his lifetime knowledge of languages to bear on the task, and by 1822 he had decoded the hieroglyphs. It seemed again that fate had put him on earth for this one purpose, because he then spent the next ten years preparing a grammar and dictionary of Egyptian hieroglyphics, and with this complete he died at the age of forty-two; the great work was published posthumously, between 1836 and 1841.

With the key to Egyptian history before them, scholars now began to prepare king lists and work out dates for the various dynasties, and by the late 1830s several things became very clear. In the first place, the Egyptian civilization was far older than the Greek, which at that time was thought to be the oldest. Further, it appeared that there had been a continuous and highly developed civilization long before 2300 B.C., while, according to every theologian's interpretation of Genesis, this was about the time of Noah's Flood, which was believed to be worldwide. But this was not all. Since the earliest civilization was evidently so advanced in terms of the written language and the use of mathematics, it seemed only reasonable that there must have been a long unrecorded time prior to this when men were developing from barbarism to organized civilization.

Worse was to come. Not once did the Egyptian records appear to mention the Israelites but according to the record in the book of Exodus, they had spent more than four centuries in Egypt and then made a most spectacular and memorable exit. This apparent absence of concordance with Jewish history cast doubt on Archbishop Ussher's chronology; for some in the higher echelons of the church, Lyell's interpretation of geology began to be viewed more favorably.

The new and popular science of archaeology in the nineteenth century brought to light much evidence from the traditional Bible lands, some of which appeared to refute, though much of it to confirm,

Napoleon's army expedition to Egypt explores the Sphinx and Pyramids of Giza. (Engraving from *Description de l'Egypt*, 1825; Thomas Fisher Rare Book Library, University of Toronto)

the Scriptures. The prejudices of the individual scholars translating and reporting these discoveries have, however, always played a significant part in tipping the scales of judgment in either one direction or the other. So far as the apparent absence in Egyptian records of reference to the Israelite nation is concerned, massive documentary evidence has, in recent years, been put forward to show that traditional Egyptian dating should be advanced by about six hundred years, which would then bring it into line with the dating of surrounding nations, including Israel. The Papyrus Ipuwer and the Tell El-Amarna tablets, discovered in Egypt, are cited as giving almost line-by-line correspondence to details given in the books of Exodus and Kings, respectively (Velikovsky 1952, 23, 223). More than two decades ago when Libby was calibrating his carbon 14 method with wood from the Pharaoh's tomb, he added a footnote from an eminent Egyptologist to say that Egyptian historical dating was "perhaps 5 centuries too old" (Libby 1963, 278).[9] To this day the public is generally unaware of this albeit begrudged confirmation of Egyptian and biblical concordance (Mure 1829).[10] The entire issue still remains bogged down in controversy and while the scholars try to forget Dr. Velikovsky, the sphinx, that symbol of ancient Egypt, will no doubt continue to remain just as inscrutable as when it was first seen by Napoleon in 1798.

Wavering Faith

Until the 1830s and the beginning of the controversy surrounding Lyell's geology, collecting fossils was a popular outdoor hobby in England as well as on the Continent; it was believed to be a tangible way of touching the Genesis record of the great Flood. However, the scathing execrations heaped on Lyell's *Principles* from almost every pulpit had, by association, given geology the reputation of a "dangerous science"; tampering with it would cause the faithful to "risk eternal damnation". Rock and fossil collecting began to lose its popular appeal and eventually a pall of gloom was cast over the whole exercise by the suicide of the author-geologist Hugh Miller, in 1856; more will be said of this later. The other popular pastimes of the nineteenth century included collecting beetles (the young Darwin was a particularly keen collector), collecting butterflies and ferns, and so on, but all with a sense of attaining a closer understanding of nature's master Designer. These activities were at first called natural theology. Later, what began as a hobby became for some a scientific profession, the word "theology" with its "religious" association was dropped, and the subject became known as natural philosophy; later, this was changed to natural history. Barber (1980) very attractively documents the relationship between the declining public interest in natural history and the coincident ascendancy of the theory of evolution.

Armed with what was believed to be unassailable Egyptian evidence for the mythological basis for the Bible, and with Lyell's interpretation of recent geological discoveries before them, a few leading lights of the church, who had always had difficulties with miracles, began to express their true feelings openly. They wrote their own interpretations in scholarly biblical commentaries. Impressed by their peers, some of the lesser lights began to waver in their faith.

At first, the authors of these commentaries felt compelled to reconcile Scripture with geology and cautiously suggested that the great Flood was merely a local affair. After a decade or so in print, this view was then surrendered to that of the entire account of the Flood being a myth, or at most, a spiritual analogy. The irony of this situation was that in the nearly thirty years between Lyell's *Principles of Geology* and Darwin's *Origin*, the most fruitful and practical work in geology was carried out by men such as Adam Sedgwick, William Buckland, William Conybeare, Roderick Murchison, Louis Agassiz, and others, most of whom in those early years were convinced of the historicity and universality of the Noachian Flood.[11]

It has been mentioned previously that in any organization, such as a

Nicholas Wiseman, 1802-65   *Henry Manning, 1808-92*

Within the Roman Church in England, Cardinal Wiseman abandoned the biblical account of Creation in favor of Lyell as early as 1836. Cardinal Manning, a conservative within the same church, took active steps in 1861 to defend the biblical account. (Author's collection)

government department or a church denomination, the views of the man at the top—the capstone—are reflected, for the most part, all the way down through the organizational pyramid. When an underling disagrees with these views and says so, it is heresy; when those in highest authority change the prevailing view, it is held to be genuine enlightenment. The dates at which these moments of enlightenment came to be made can be pinpointed. For example, Dr. Samuel Turner, professor of biblical literture at the general theological seminary of the Episcopal Church in New York City (equivalent to the Anglican Church in Canada and Great Britain and an important seminary), published his *Companion to the Book of Genesis* in 1841. In it he claimed that the Flood was a local affair (Turner 1841, 216). Naturally, his students had to use this as a textbook, and so, within a few short years, this message was promulgated across a hundred American pulpits to a thousand parishioners. In England, one of the pillars of the Roman Catholic Church, Cardinal Nicholas Wiseman, in a series of twelve lectures published in 1836, rather more quickly abandoned the accounts of the Scriptures for that of geological science. The Roman Catholic Church in Germany began to cast off the biblical Flood under the teachings of Professor Reusch (1886) at Bonn University, in 1862. It is still possible to see how the commonly held belief in the Mosaic Flood was turned to unbelief in the nineteenth century by the cautious wording employed in the 1884 edition of Smith's *Dictionary of the Bible*. This book is popularly reprinted today, and the item in question will be found under "Noah" (Smith 1967).[12] A dreary catalogue of further examples is perhaps unnecessary to underscore the way by which a belief, held unquestionably true for several thousand years, first by the Jews and Arabs and then by the Judeo-Christian world, was abandoned little by little beginning with a few leaders of the Christian Church, though by no means all. One notable exception was Roman Catholic Cardinal Manning (1865-74).[13]

While the shades of disbelief in the Bible and the Flood in particular were percolating downwards through the theological ranks, a series of archaeological discoveries were made in the Middle East by the Englishman Austen Henry Layard; his very exciting accounts were made popular during the 1850s. Until this time the names of Nineveh and Babylon found so often in the various books of the Bible had to be accepted on faith; there was in fact not a trace of these allegedly huge cities. Layard (1849) was an extremely capable and adventurous individual with a flair for languages and an ability to write; his popular accounts are well worth reading, even today.[14] He discovered the legendary city of Nineveh, excavated just a fraction of the palace and the library, and shipped a great many priceless and massive pieces back to the British Museum. A special department was built to house those treasures that were proudly exhibited to an enthusiastic public.

Reminiscent of Ezekiel's vision, statues of the strange creatures found in the palaces of Nineveh were removed by Layard and brought to the British Museum where they stand to this day. (From Layard 1849, Vol. 1; John P. Robarts Research Library, University of Toronto)

Layard's friend, Emile Botta (1846-50), working for the Louvre museum in Paris, had in the meantime discovered the fabled city of Babylon.

The Bible accounts of these cities had thus been vindicated, and those of wavering faith could feel assured that the ground had not shifted beneath their feet (Brackman 1978).[15] The evangelical movement received a considerable boost because of Layard's discoveries (Bradley 1975; Habershon 1909; Thompson and Hutchinson 1929).[16] Later on, some of the Bible critics turned this biblical confirmation to their own advantage, as we shall see in the next chapter, but in the meantime, the reassurance that began with Layard in 1849 continued for the next decade. Then came Darwin in 1859.

Loading the Dice

The ground had been prepared for Darwin over an entire generation in several ways and by no less than six editions of Lyell's *Principles* (Lyell made this boast to Haeckel; Lyell 1881, 2:436).[17] First, although Lyell never openly criticized the church or theological dogma of the day, his interpretation of the geological evidence that was then being gathered cast increasing doubt on the Bible's early chapters—particularly on the account of the Genesis Flood. To some, the concept of an earth millions of years old rather than thousands began to seem more rational. Second, Lyell absorbed much of the invective heaped on his work by the church and the press, so that the blows later dealt against Darwin had by his time been considerably softened. Finally, all the controversy over Lyell's geology had actually been good publicity and served well to prepare the minds of would-be converts to Darwin's evolution. The stratagem of well-publicized controversy may be recognized as a pattern that has earmarks of deliberate orchestration and followed such events as the publication of the *Origin*, the Bishop Colenso affair in 1860, and the famous Scopes "monkey" trial of 1925 in Tennessee; more will be said of these events in the following chapters.

One other item of importance that paved the way for Darwin was the anonymous publication in 1844 of the book called *Vestiges of Creation*. Based on Lyell's principle of uniformity, the author described the development (evolution) from lower to higher forms of life over very long times; however, no mechanism for this development process was suggested. What was particularly shocking to the Victorian mind was that the deity was reduced to virtual redundancy by allowing nature to operate through the natural laws.

All the public outcry against the *Vestiges* had thoroughly condemned it, yet the book had planted an idea. Understandably, the author was not made known until forty years after publication, by which time its purpose had been served and even the dust of Darwin's controversy had mostly settled. The author was Robert Chambers, a distinguished Scottish author and editor (among his publications, Chambers' dictionary), who had actually secluded himself for two years to prepare for this work (Chambers 1844).[18] Since he knew that what he was saying would be controversial and had to be published anonymously to protect his reputation and business interests, what was his motivation? After all, there was no assurance the book would be a financial success. It happened that it was very successful, and ten editions were produced in as many years—though, as every competent naturalist of the day knew, it was shot full of errors and flights of fancy. Darwin thought the book absurd but admitted "it had done excellent service... in calling attention to the subject, in removing prejudice, and in thus preparing the ground for the reception of analogous views" (Darwin 1872, xvii).

There is evidence to indicate that a cadre of keen and influential minds had been skillfully prepared to be apostles of the new faith for some time before the publication of Darwin's *Origin*. The first edition of the *Origin* was published in London on 24 November 1859, and contemporary accounts give rise to the oft-repeated statement that an eager public bought up the entire first issue of 1,250 copies on the first day. That the publisher, John Murray, sold the entire issue is not in

Philip Gosse, 1810-88. Experienced naturalist, author, and member of the Plymouth Brethren Church, he would not abandon the biblical fixity of species. (Thomas Fisher Rare Book Library, University of Toronto)

doubt, but the assertion that it was bought by an eager public has been seriously questioned by Freeman (1965, 21), since the book was not even advertised. What seems more probable is that most, if not all, the first issue was bought up at the dealer's auction by an agent of Lyell and Hooker a week or so before the official date of publication. These copies were then sent gratis to known sympathizers in positions of influence. This was not an uncommon practice, and two incidents strongly suggest that this is precisely how Darwin's theory of evolution was promoted.

The first incident is documented in the biography of Philip Gosse (1907), an experienced naturalist and member of the Royal Society who was also in the 1850s a very popular writer of natural history. The biography states that he was approached by Joseph Hooker, after one of the Royal Society meetings during the summer of 1857, as a possible candidate for enlightenment into the mysteries of natural selection. Evidently, it was Lyell's idea to quietly sound out and initiate a core of influential naturalists sympathetic to the idea of the mutability of the species—those, that is, who found difficulty with the supernatural creation and fixity of the species (Gosse 1907, 116).[19]

Gosse's biography shows that, after he was approached on this very issue by Hooker, Darwin then made the same overture, all of which took place more than two years before the *Origin* was published. As it happened, Gosse was a member of the Plymouth Brethren and a firm believer in the biblical fixity of species; he would have nothing to do with the heresy being hatched by Lyell and company. It is highly unlikely that Gosse was the recipient of one of the copies of the first issue of the *Origin*, since he had by this time made clear his views on the subject of origins in his *Omphalos*, a rather strange and totally unsuccessful attempt to reconcile geology with Genesis (Gosse 1907, 121).[20]

The second incident is found in the correspondence of amateur naturalist, author, and Anglican divine, Charles Kingsley. Kingsley had been approached, found to be, as suspected, a sympathizer, and did receive a copy of the *Origin*. Interestingly, Kingsley's letter of thanks to Darwin was dated 18 November 1859; he must have received it a full week before the official publication date (F. Darwin 1887, 2:287). Kingsley wrote, "I must give up much that I have believed and written." To underscore the victory, Darwin quotes from Kingsley's acknowledgment in the second edition of the *Origin*:

> A celebrated author and divine has written to me that "he has gradually learnt to see that it is just as noble a conception of the Deity to believe that He created a few original forms capable of self

development into other needful forms [evolution of one species from another], as to believe that He required a fresh act of creation to supply the voids caused by the actions of His laws" (Darwin 1860, 481).

Darwin had lost no time in quoting from Kingsley, since the second edition appeared only two months after the first (January 1860), while there is little doubt that this confession from a notable member of the clergy was extremely helpful in overcoming the major source of opposition to the theory.

Kingsley's expression "self development into other needful forms" soon found its outworkings in his book for small children written about two years later, in 1863, while on a fishing holiday. Entitled *The Water Babies*, this work is fairly typical of Victorian literature of its genre. Whereas most paid respect to Father God from evidence of design, however, Kingsley modified this to Mother Nature, with allusions to evolution (F. Kingsley 1904, 245).[21] The story has the child, Tom, approach Mother Carey (a synonym for Mother Nature), expecting to find her "making new beasts out of old". She explains to him that she has no need to go to that much trouble but simply has to sit and "make them make themselves" (C. Kingsley 1979, 232). It is a remarkable fact, when the outdated Victorian moralizing is considered as well as the quite dreadful illustrations, that Kingsley's little book is still in print; a reprinted edition appeared as recently as 1979.

Charles Kingsley may be taken as typical of many men of the clergy, not only of his own time but perhaps especially those today who feel

Charles Kingsley, 1819-75. Seduced from the orthodox faith by Charles Darwin, he quickly adopted the new faith and was rewarded for doing so by being made Canon of Westminster in 1873. (Metropolitan Toronto Reference Library Board)

somehow intimidated by the men of science. After he made his confession of belief to Darwin and shortly after the publication of *The Water Babies*, he was elected a Fellow of the Geological Society in 1863; he had been promoted by Lyell. Kingsley wrote in gratitude for belonging to the society: "I feel how little I know and how unworthy I am to mix with the really great men who belong to it" (F. Kingsley 1904, 249). Did he but know that some of the most cherished ideas of Darwin were shown to be "vacuous tautologies" by men of science almost a century later, he almost certainly would have turned in his grave, which is, incidentally, near Darwin's in Westminster Abbey.

Turning Point

The actual moment of truth in the confrontation between revelation and reason, between the mind-set of four millenia and Darwin's evolution, came on 30 June 1860 at the Oxford meeting of the British Association for the Advancement of Science. The first edition of the *Origin* had been judiciously placed in sympathetic hands high in church and state. The second edition had been assured of public success

The contenders of the Oxford debate of 1860 shown here in photographs taken at about that date. Huxley, then thirty-five, may have had some misgivings about taking on a man twenty years his senior and in his opponent's home territory. Wilberforce is wearing the academic dress of an Oxford don, but he also held the position of bishop in the Anglican Church, the title by which he is usually represented in popular accounts. (Metropolitan Toronto Reference Library Board)

by good fortune appointing Thomas Huxley to write the influential *London Times* (26 December 1859) book review of the previous month, and now all was ready for the contenders to enter the lists.

As usual Darwin was ill at the time and did not attend the Oxford meeting, but Huxley had arisen as a self-appointed bulldog, who was to prove to be Darwin's most able mouthpiece. The motivating force that drove Huxley was his feeling of animosity towards the clergy who, at that time, had far greater status than the scientist. Huxley found the hard facts of science to be an invincible weapon to use against the pompous rhetoric of some of the authority figures in the Church of England. Years later, as he looked back over the battle for Darwinism, he said, "My dear young man...you are not old enough to remember when men like Lyell and Murchison were not considered fit to lick the dust off the boots of a curate. I should like to get my heel into their mouths and scr-r-unch it round" (Ernle 1923). Although he did not agree with all that Darwin had said, the *Origin* gave him the opportunity he needed to do public battle with church authority.

The opposing contender and champion of the orthodox view was Anglican Archbishop Samuel Wilberforce, son of the famous politician William Wilberforce and well known for his debating skills. Although a theologian, Wilberforce was an extremely able naturalist and no ignoramus to science; he had acquired a first in mathematics in his graduate days at Oxford. The popular accounts of the debate invariably depict Wilberforce as the unreasoning bastion of prejudice who finished as a broken pillar of the church, but Lucas (1979) shows that the facts do not support this view.[22] In the first place, it may confidently be said that not one of the dozens of different accounts is correct, because there was no shorthand record of this famous debate, so that all that has been written is based on hearsay. Secondly, Hooker was there (Lyell was absent) but neither thought that the Archbishop had done badly, but said that it was rather Hooker himself who had made the case for Darwinism.[23] Finally, Wilberforce had written a review of the *Origin* shortly before the debate of 30 June 1860, and it was published the following month; it would seem likely, therefore, that his presentation would be based on this review. The review contained very carefully argued points showing that in view of the known stability of species, Darwin had not made out his case in supposing that one species could be transmuted into another (Wilberforce 1860). Darwin acknowledged the cogency of this critical review article as "uncommonly clever: it picks out with skill all the most conjectural parts, and brings forward well the difficulties" (F. Darwin 1887, 2:324).[24]

The outcome of the Oxford debate was that Darwin and evolution

Michael Faraday, 1791-1867. One of the true scientists of the nineteenth century whose electrical discoveries have benefitted mankind. He never accepted Darwin's theory.
(Engraving by Johnson Fry of Faraday holding a bar magnet; Academy of Medicine, Toronto)

were perceived to be the victors, while Wilberforce and the church retired to nurse their battered status, to retrench and perhaps find some compromise to restore the Bible's tarnished image. This was very largely true, although there was an intense but diminishing rearguard battle as, one by one, theologians capitulated to accept what was really at this time still only a minority view among scientists.

There is a tendency for accounts of nineteenth century science to focus on Darwin and neglect to mention such men as Michael Faraday, James Maxwell, and William Thomson, later Lord Kelvin, who at the time the *Origin* was introduced were the true giants of science. These men had great credibility among scientists of the day and never did accept Darwin's theory; neither were they hesitant to defend the biblical account of origins. Within a decade of the publication of the *Origin*, however, so many of the church leaders had found some sort of compromise between the Darwinian and scriptural versions of man's origins, there was little opposition—at least little that could be expressed openly in the national press. As each newspaper, magazine, and journal became committed to the evolutionary position, it grew increasingly difficult to publish articles with the opposite viewpoint. Consequently, those of the clergy who still objected to Darwin often found the press closed, and they had to resort to the use of tracts. The general argument of those who still defended the biblical position of origins was that once a part of the Scriptures was discredited and relegated to myth and legend, it would then be easy to discard any other part that happened to be difficult to believe—the Virgin birth and the Resurrection were seen as eventual candidates. They further pointed out that central to the Christian faith was the belief that Jesus Christ was the Son of God and that he acknowledged the writings of Moses and specifically mentioned Abel, the son of Adam, and the Flood of Noah.[25] If these accounts were not literally true, they argued, then Christ was either completely ignorant and not the Creator he claimed to be, or he was a liar; either way, there could never be certainty that anything else he said was true (Bozarth 1978).[26] This line of reasoning had been voiced since the controversy over Lyell's *Principles*, but now it was beginning to divide between liberal and conservative views within the church. As a result, various compromise solutions, some quite ingenious, were proposed.

Compromises—Day Age and Gap Theories

Nineteenth century people were avid readers and familiar with the controversy surrounding Lyell's geology. As new discoveries were made, particularly those that appeared to contradict the Genesis account of Creation and the Flood, there arose a need for some sort of reconciliation whereby both science and Scripture could be true. Unlike much of common thought today, most people of that era believed that the Bible was divinely inspired and without error. The multiple catastrophe-recreation theory of Cuvier (described in Chapter Three) had been a popular compromise in England for a short while but virtually collapsed in the face of Lyell's evidence of apparently so many catastrophes. More than that, however, reconciliation seemed impossible when geology demanded millions of years and Genesis would only allow a few thousand. Then an ingenious Scot appeared on the scene to popularize a solution.

Hugh Miller had been brought up with a Calvinist background and believed in the literal interpretation of the book of Genesis. An unusual man, he worked as a stonemason in the quarries, which gave him an intimate familiarity with the rocks and fossils, while at the same time he was highly literate, with a rare gift for writing. He wrote several books glorifying the rocks and their maker and in this way helped to dispel much of the negative aspects of Lyell's geology.

The working classes could easily identify with Miller, which made his books extremely popular. He was much opposed to the implications of Lyell's geology and, particularly, to Chambers's *Vestiges*. In

Hugh Miller, 1802-56. Stonemason, geologist, and author, this talented Scotsman shot himself in a fit of depression on Christmas Eve 1856. (Author's collection)

arguing against progressive development (evolution), he pointed out that geology revealed a regression of life as often as a progression. Working at the rock face for many years, Miller was certainly in a better position to make this statement than Lyell or the author of the *Vestiges*. Miller (1849) wrote *Footprints of the Creator* to refute the *Vestiges*, which had appeared five years earlier, and he made some insightful statements concerning what he held to be the monstrous development theory (evolution). He said that the logical outcome of this theory that argued that man was related to the beast was that man's soul cannot be immortal (otherwise it would have to be conceded that animals also have immortal souls and require salvation in the same way as man). "And thus," he concluded, "though the development theory be not atheistic, it is at least tantamount to atheism. For, if man be a dying creature [that is, has no immortal soul], restricted in his existence to the present scene of things, what does it really matter to him, for any one moral purpose, whether there be a God or no?" (Miller 1849, 14). This statement, made in 1849, echoed the sentiments of many of the clergy throughout the rest of the century, while its prophetic outworkings are painfully evident in our society today.

During the extensive geological work that accompanied the Lyell controversy, many new fossil species were found; the ark of Noah was becoming impossibly crowded, and Miller adopted and popularized the view then being considered by others, including Lyell, that the Flood was not universal but simply a local event. This was really a serious departure from the orthodox belief. Some, however, accepted it as a compromise, seemingly without considering that a local flood made it unnecessary to build an ark at all since Noah could simply have moved out of the area. The local flood idea had other problems, because at that time the fossils in the sedimentary rocks were held to be the result of the Genesis Flood, and sedimentary rocks were found throughout the world. This strained interpretation of the Genesis account was caused by the great number of species being claimed at that time by the naturalists, but, as it was pointed out in Chapter Six, some scholars are beginning to realize there may have been archetypes, which would reduce the overall number considerably.

Miller (1857) made one other important concession and interpreted the Mosaic "days" of Creation as epochs, with the final three days corresponding to the primary, secondary, and tertiary geological periods. Miller claimed that the days were twenty-four hours, but that they took place on top of Mount Sinai as a revelatory vision of Creation given to Moses and were not at Creation week (Miller 1857, 179). Others of his time had applied a similar sort of argument based on the biblical dictum, "One day is with the Lord as a thousand years, and a thousand years as one day." Thus, the Creation week could in this view be six thousand years (2 Peter 3:8). Miller and other geologists "knew" that six thousand years was a hopelessly inadequate time for sedimentary deposits to build up hundreds of feet deep; for this, millions of years were needed. However, the Scripture clearly said "thousand" and not "million", so this became another strained interpretation, generally referred to now as the Day-Age theory. Two very similar theories are popular in some circles today and are known as "progressive creationism" and "concordism". In deference to radiometric dating, both of these theories equate the days of Creation week with lengthy periods of geological time and are essentially Day-Age theories (Ramm 1954).[27]

Miller's version of the Day-Age theory was popularized in his *Testimony of the Rocks*, which was actually published posthumously, in 1857, since he shot himself in a fit of depression on Christmas Eve 1856. Those of the clergy still loyal to the literal interpretation lost no time in pointing to Miller's suicide as a consequence of bending Scripture to fit science, and so not only the credibility of his argument but geology as a hobby then quickly lost popular appeal.

An earlier attempt to reconcile geology and Scripture had been put forward by another Scotsman, Thomas Chalmers, an evangelical professor of divinity at Edinburgh University. He founded the Free

Church of Scotland, and because of his outreach to the poor and destitute he later became known as the "father of modern sociology". Traceable back to the rather obscure writings of the Dutchman Episcopius (1583-1643), Chalmers formed an idea, which became very popular and is first recorded from one of his lectures of 1814: "The detailed history of Creation in the first chapter of Genesis begins at the middle of the second verse" (Chalmers 1857, 5:146). Chalmers went on to explain that the first statement, "In the beginning God created the Heavens and the Earth and the Earth was without form and void and darkness was on the face of the deep," referred to a pre-Adamic age, about which Scriptures was essentially silent. Some great catastrophe had taken place, which left the earth "without form and void" or ruined, in which state it remained for as many years as the geologist required. Finally, approximately six thousand years ago, the Genesis account continues, "The Spirit of God moved upon the face of the waters." The remaining verses were then said to be the account of how this present age was restored and all living forms, including man, created.

This explanation, variously known as the Ruin-Restoration theory, or simply the Gap theory, allowed that all the fossils were evidence of the life that once existed in the pre-Adamic age, while it still permitted the Genesis "days" to be literal twenty-four-hour days. The theory was attractive and seemingly offered the perfect reconciliation between science and Scripture—provided neither was examined too closely. It was adopted, perhaps uncritically, by a number of writers in the

Thomas Chalmers, 1780-1847. The engraving shows the subject at forty-one, just a few years after reintroducing the idea of a gap of indeterminate length between Genesis 1:1 and 1:2. (Knox College Library, University of Toronto)

nineteenth century, but notably by Pember, with his *Earth's Earliest Ages and Their Connection With Modern Spiritism and Theosophy.* This was first published in 1884 and continued under a slightly different title on to the fifteenth edition, in 1942 (Pember 1884).[28] The theory eventually became canonized into the faith by being adopted into the footnotes to the popular Scofield reference Bible. First published in 1909 and republished regularly since then, the theory may be found in recent editions as the footnote to Isaiah 45. However, by no means did everyone subscribe to the Gap theory, since it involved so much special pleading for the interpretation of certain Hebrew words and because it could not be reconciled with several other important statements in Scripture. For example, one of the important doctrines stated in Scripture is that death, as evidenced by the fossils, came after Adam and not before (Romans 5:12).

Today, in the light of serious deficiencies now evident in Lyell's uniformitarian geology, very few who favor any sort of biblical view hold to the Gap theory (Custance 1970; Fields 1976).[29] Rather, they have found it more believable simply to accept the literal understanding of the first chapters of Genesis, without the complications of "gaps" or "days" meant to be "ages". Those who hold to this literal view of fiat creation, often referred to as "Creationists", are now a fast-growing minority and represent a full-circle return to the belief in the total inerrancy of the Bible, which was the common position before Darwin (Numbers 1982).[30]

These, then, were some of the more popular attempts to reconcile geology with Genesis, and many of these ideas still linger in the collective unconscious today. Each of these attempts mixes more or less science with more or less Scripture and produces a result more or less absurd. But many now believe there is a more elegant way of reconciliation and thus present Christianity more respectably before the altar of science. Basically the argument states that God used the method of evolution to bring all things into being. The next chapter will examine the origins of this popular notion in both the Protestant and Catholic churches and set the scene for the final chapter where science, church, and politics each gravitate to become universal.

14

The Road to Atheism

*Never in the history of man has so terrific a
calamity befallen the race as that which all who
look may now behold advancing as a deluge,
black with destruction, resistless in might,
uprooting our most cherished hopes, engulfing
our most precious creed, and burying our highest
life in mindless desolation.... The flood-gates of
infidelity are open, and Atheism overwhelming is
upon us.*

GEORGE ROMANES
(personal friend of Charles Darwin; 1878, 51)

Thomas Huxley, bulldog and champion of Darwin, had a high
regard for the Bible, although like Isaac Newton and others before and since, he could not accept the possibility that natural
laws had been violated by supernatural intervention. The Virgin Birth
and the Resurrection were usually held in a peculiar dichotomy of
mind, at the same time both believable and unbelievable, but such
items as *ex nihilo* Creation, the Fall of man, the Genesis Flood, and the
New Testament miracles were quite unacceptable. Upon the death of
his young son in 1860, Huxley described his religious views to Rev.
Charles Kingsley, and by the 1880s many others were prepared to admit
openly these same convictions which were, by then, termed "agnosticism". Huxley had said that he was prepared to follow his intellect as
far as it would go but stop short of accepting conclusions that were not
clearly demonstrable. For Huxley, agnosticism was an attitude of
healthy skepticism, a tool of the intellect, essential to the working
scientist. Moreover, as a newly coined term it had none of the stigma of
"unbeliever" or "atheist", and in Victorian society that was important
in order to be accepted socially.[1] In his later years, Darwin was
approached by Edward Aveling, Karl Marx's son-in-law, who extended

the hand of greeting to a fellow atheist, but Darwin corrected his inquirer by referring to himself as an agnostic.[2] Writing of this meeting some years later, Aveling consoled himself by pointing out that "Atheist is only Agnostic writ aggressive, and Agnostic is only Atheist writ respectable" (Aveling 1897, 1:323). In the final analysis, and from Huxley's definition, the existence of God and anything beyond material phenomena is not clearly demonstrable, so that the shades of difference between agnostic and atheist blend and can no longer be discerned.

Theistic Evolution

In the wide spectrum of beliefs, ranging from those accepting literal fiat Creation to the rank atheist for whom the only explanation for our origins is materialistic evolution, there is a school of belief that characterizes liberal Christianity and is known as theistic evolution. This school places belief in evolution first and by whatever the latest scenario demands: that is, orthodox Darwinism, neo-Darwinism, punctuated equilibria, etc. There is the concomitant belief in the Deity and the thought that he directed the process of evolution to bring about planet earth and all living things. The entire first eleven chapters of Genesis, including the creation of Adam and Eve, the Fall of man, the Genesis Flood, and the Tower of Babel, are denied and relegated to myth, allegory, or fable. Theistic evolution acknowledges intelligent design, but the Designer's involvement extends from virtually none at all in the Deist position, in which God is limited to initial creation of the universe only, to the full theistic position. At the full theistic end of the involvement spectrum, God is responsible for directing evolution of one species to another in a series of steps, while the last of these steps was the creation of humanoid characteristics in selected anthropoid bodies (Adam and Eve).

The subscriber to theistic evolution would seemingly welcome the latest theory of punctuated equilibria (see Chapter Six) as evidence of the Creator's intervention in the natural selection process, but then the theistic model begins to enter a philosophical minefield. Adopting the theory of punctuated equilibria to explain the gaps in the fossil record is safe enough, but when evolution is said to be an ongoing process today (the peppered moths are always cited), then the Creator's intervention is also brought into the present day, and for some this becomes an uncomfortable realization. The thought of being observed and accountable to an omnipresent Judge definitely interferes with lifestyle. For this reason theistic evolution usually stops at the Adam and Eve stage, while only the bold, willing to dispute the veracity of the

Asa Gray, 1810-88, a Harvard professor of botany, tried to reconcile Darwin's natural selection with Christianity's belief in supernatural intervention and finished by being true to neither. (Photogravure of the subject at fifty-seven; Metropolitan Toronto Reference Library Board)

Scriptures with the Deity himself, will concede to divine intervention in the affairs of nature and man into this present age.

Unitarian Origin of Theistic Evolution

One of the earliest and most active advocates of theistic evolution was Darwin's American correspondent, Asa Gray. A Harvard professor of botany, he was, to some extent, one of the founding fathers of the theory of evolution and from 1860 on became Darwin's promoter, ambassador, and apostle in the United States. Although a lifelong Congregationalist, Gray's faith was undoubtedly affected by his wife, Jane, who was a devoted Unitarian and attended the services at Harvard College Chapel (Dupree 1959, 182).[3]

Asa Gray's new gospel contributed not a little to Harvard University's stature as the American center of Unitarian thought. Gray was concerned about the absence of transition fossils to support Darwin's theory, while at the same time he was more positive than Darwin and saw in nature evidence of intelligent design. Darwin confessed to being in "an utterly hopeless muddle" over the question of design.[4] Conscious that literal belief in the Bible ran very high in America, Gray was concerned that, for this reason, Darwin's theory with its atheistic overtones would not be accepted by the majority of people. He wrote: "Since atheistic doctrines of evolution are prevailing and likely to prevail, more or less among scientific men [Gray was promoting the *Origin* at the time], I have thought it important and have taken considerable pain to show that they may be held theistically" (Dupree 1959, 359). Gray conceived the view that all these difficulties could be solved at one stroke. The hand of the Deity was, of course, responsible for design, but might also be invoked to explain the missing fossils and persuade the atheist away from his position. The Christian community would thus find Darwin's theory more palatable. Gray explained the position in a private letter:

> The important thing to do is to develop aright evolutionary teleology, and to present the argument for design from the exquisite adaptations in such a way as to make it tell on both sides; with Christian men, that they may be satisfied with, and perchance may learn to admire, Divine works effected step by step, if need be, in a system of nature; and the anti-theistic [atheistic] people, to show that without the implication of a superintending wisdom nothing is made out, and nothing credible (J.L. Gray 1893, 2:656).[5]

The "step by step" process is the supposed divine intervention in normal chance variation to purposefully direct one species to become another. John Dewey, the founder of the American liberal education movement, later referred to this as "design on the installment plan" (Dewey 1951, 12). Gray's noble intentions were nevertheless seen by some to be an attempt to smuggle Paley's watchmaker into Darwin's natural selection.

Gray (1861) exerted considerable influence by written articles,[6] and he tried to persuade Darwin to adopt his position of theistic evolution. Darwin quickly saw through the fallacy of Gray's argument, however, and rejected it outright. In a letter written to Lyell in 1861, he said, "The view that each variation has been providentially arranged seems to me to make Natural Selection entirely superfluous, and indeed takes the whole case of the appearance of new species out of the range of science".[7] Darwin later made his views very clear to Gray.

An interesting aside here is that Darwin attached an historical sketch to the fifth (1869) and sixth (1872) editions of his *Origins*, in which he quoted Aristotle as the classical forerunner of his own view that chance and chance alone was responsible for natural selection (p. xv). This was Darwin's only reference to the Greek philosophers, and in that he tripped up rather badly. He had taken the quote from Aristotle's *Physics*, where Aristotle (1961 ed., 36) set out Empedocles' argument for chance processes and then proceeds to show how impossible this must be.[8] Aristotle had always maintained that nature herself is the builder, proceeding according to an inner plan and idea (teleology) and always striving after the better. Whether we call that inner working nature, an intelligence, or plainly God, this is theistic evolution and was precisely the view that Darwin would not entertain, in spite of the fact that he had paid lip service to the Creator in the conclusion to the *Origin* (Darwin 1860, 488).[9] He had taken Aristotle out of context and turned him on his head to support his own theory of evolution based on chance.

Darwin publicly rejected Gray's argument when, on the last page of his *Variation of Animals and Plants Under Domestication*, published in 1868, he concluded, "However much we may wish, we can hardly follow Professor Asa Gray in his belief in lines of beneficent variation" (Darwin 1868, 2:428). Asa Gray's theistic evolution was not only rejected by Darwin, but also was never seriously considered by any of the other founding fathers of evolution.

Darwin had put his finger on the fundamental problem with theistic evolution, and it recalls the proposition made by the poet Lucretius more than two thousand years ago. Lucretius visualized primeval space to be occupied by free-falling atoms and said that only by the deviation of some atoms at some time from their straight course, a *moment mutatem*, could a creative process begin (Lucretius 1951, 66). The parallel here is that free-falling atoms and chance variation in nature are both dynamic processes under nature's rigid law. This is evolution and no teleological process is involved—that is, there is no final design, no end purpose, built into the species to determine what they will ultimately become. Once intelligent direction by some spiritual agency is admitted, however, then the free-falling atoms of Lucretius will deviate from their path, and chance variation will become purposeful change. With this modicum of control, no matter how slight, evolution based on pure chance eventually falls apart. The rigid law of nature is broken, experience becomes unrepeatable, future results unpredictable, and man eventually loses control in all empirical inquiry.

The dilemma then facing Gray, though he seems not to have recognized it, was that either he believed that God was in control, in which case he could not genuinely call himself a believer in evolution—Darwin himself made this clear—or he could believe in evolution and concede that God had no control in the process whatsoever. In short, nature's laws, universal in time and space, are either laws or they are not, and, ultimately, the proponents of punctuated equilibria will have to face this same question.

So much for the problem from the point of view of reason, but there were equally fundamental problems from the point of view of revelation, as the theologians of the day were quick to point out. Denying the first eleven chapters of Genesis, they said, was bad enough, but seven of the eight New Testament writers (all but James) referred affirmatively to these chapters, in a total of thirty-two verses.[11] Casting suspicion on these authors as either fools or liars then placed the whole of the New Testament in doubt, including all the words of Christ, since it was either spiritually inspired and the truth or it was not.

But worse than all this, the literalists thundered from their pulpits, was that denial of Adam meant that Christ himself was denied. Their argument ran that denials of the literal truth of the third chapter of Genesis entailed a denial of an actual man, Adam, of his disobedience, and of mankind's subsequent fall. This being so, there was no need for redemption or a Redeemer. This was plainly a rejection of the very core of the Christian faith (Bozarth 1978, 30).[12] Nevertheless, times have changed, and in these days of enlightenment, such railings against the doctrine of theistic evolution, which were loudly heard in the 1860s, are almost an anachronism. Should a lone apostle have the temerity to bring this same message to the liberal church today, it would be regarded as the outworkings of lunacy touched, perhaps, by the petulance expected from a dyspeptic eunuch.

Asa Gray's Followers

Asa Gray became necessarily coy when faced with admitting that, from his position, the ape was our Adam. This was, perhaps, not too surprising since he was employed by Harvard University, which had become the bastion of anti-Darwinism in America through its most famous scientist, Louis Agassiz. Agassiz was a committed Christian and vigorously opposed to Darwin, but conveniently he died in 1873

James Dana, 1813-95. Yale professor of geology and confessed Christian fearlessly proclaimed the new gospel of theistic evolution, claiming man's ancestry to the ape. (Engraving by A.H. Ritchie from a daguerrotype by Moulthiol; Yale University Library Archives)

and so left Gray (1880) a few unhindered years to promote the new gospel.[13] However, about a day's journey away, at Yale University, James Dana, professor of geology, found no such restrictions and fearlessly proclaimed man's ancestry to the ape. Like Darwin, Dana had been on a four-year voyage around the world, and then, for a further four years had traveled across America for the newly formed Smithsonian Institution, gathering geological information for the building of railways. Dana was a Christian and, at first, a follower of Cuvier, but after reading the *Origin* he did some soul searching and became a convinced Darwinist, holding to Gray's position of theistic evolution. Although he was no Huxley, Dana almost single-handedly converted Yale University from the orthodox Christian belief to evolution by using Gray's argument that evolution could be supported theistically. Dana's pride was that he had made Yale a stronghold of evolutionary science to "correct false dogma in the theological systems" (Wendt 1968, 259).

Little by little the American clergy began to bend to Dana's promulgation of Gray's theistic evolution. The silver tongue of the most popular American evangelist of the day, Henry Ward Beecher, argued convincingly that the theory of evolution was the key to many secrets of nature and a constant revelation to man of the works of God (Beecher 1885). The message lost some of its credibility, however, when Beecher was found to be having an affair with his friend's wife, Mrs. Tilton, an affair for which he was subsequently tried, found guilty, and drummed out of his church (Caskey 1978; Stowe 1934).

In this present century another notable American preacher to bring

Henry Ward Beecher, 1813-87. A full-time Christian evangelist and gifted speaker, he was impressed by the new gospel of professors Gray and Dana and promoted it vigorously. (Engraving made at about the time of his trial, 1871; Metropolitan Toronto Reference Library Board)

reconciliation between evolution and Christianity was Harry Emerson Fosdick of the Riverside Church in New York City. He was a liberal actively opposed to the fundamentalists for more than two decades. After causing several uproars by preaching against Special Creation, he was asked to resign from his first church in 1922.[14] With financing by John D. Rockefeller Jr., he had the inter-denominational Riverside Church built for his own use and for the next twenty years brought the modern gospel message to listeners every week on a nationwide radio program.

In the meantime, just a few blocks from the Riverside Church, a former Baptist turned Unitarian, Charles F. Potter, had taken the liberal gospel far beyond Fosdick's preaching. He finally went even beyond the tolerance of the Unitarian Church and in 1929 was asked to resign. Potter started an independent Humanist Church and boldly proclaimed the genesis of the new faith with a statue entitled "The Chrysalis". Displayed where one might expect to find a crucifix in a Roman Catholic Church, the statue consisted of a naked man emerging chrysalid-fashion from an ape-skin; it nicely summed up Potter's central belief (Potter 1951).

Theistic Evolution and the Roman Catholic Church

At about the time young Darwin was about to start on his five-year voyage and when Lyell was publishing his *Principles*, there were

John Henry Newman, 1801-90. Drummed out of the Anglican Church for his attempts to reintroduce Roman Catholic traditions and doctrines, he later became a cardinal in the Roman Church in England. (Engraving by T. Cole after the portrait by Ouless; Metropolitan Toronto Reference Library Board)

within the English evangelical Anglican Church some who urged fasting, celibacy, confession, and other Roman usages that had been dropped at the time of the Reformation. These stirrings began among the Oxford University academics and became known as the Oxford Movement. This was a drift towards Catholicism without actually becoming Roman Catholic. The leader of the movement was John Henry Newman, who argued that the thirty-nine articles of Anglican doctrine (which pointed out the basic differences between the Protestant and Roman Catholic beliefs) could be interpreted in a Catholic sense. He caused a great furore, particularly among evangelicals. Eventually he resigned from the Anglican Church (1843) and was received into the Roman Catholic Church in England in 1845. Various other originators of the Oxford Movement also defected to the Catholic Church, but the movement became dominant within the Anglican Church and continues today among the church hierarchy under the banner of Anglo-Catholicism.

Newman had anticipated the theological outworkings of Darwin's *Origin* by almost a decade in his proposition that the Christian doctrine had developed, i.e. evolved (Lash 1975).[15] In this he was several years ahead of his time, and the idea was carried with him into the Roman Church. After the publication of the *Origin*, the Vatican deliberated on its moves for fourteen years before Pope Pius IX issued the "Syllabus of Errors", condemning "progress, liberalism and modern civilization". This was generally understood to be in reference to Darwinism, although it did not actually say so; surprisingly, neither the *Origin* nor the *Descent* were placed on the Catholic Index.

Newman became cardinal in 1877, and his notions of the development of theology as man's mind developed paved the way for others in the church hierarchy to accept biological development. The works of Darwin thus began to take their place beside the very books they denied in the private libraries of bishops and prelates, and eventually these thoughts began to spill across the pulpit to the people. Catholicism has always placed a greater dependence on the authority of the church than on Scripture and, without specific condemnation of Darwin, Catholics were free to explore evolutionary lines of inquiry so long as they were from the theistic viewpoint. By 1950 Pope Pius XII was sufficiently concerned to issue the encyclical *Humani Generis*, which soundly condemned the evolutionary teaching, in the key passage stating the reason:

> Some imprudently and indiscreetly hold that evolution which has not been fully proved even in the domain of natural sciences

...and audaciously support monistic and pantheistic opinion that the world is in continual evolution. Communists gladly subscribe to this opinion so that, when the souls of men have been deprived of every idea of a personal God, they may the more efficaciously defend and propagate their dialectical materialism (Carlen 1981, 175).

However, the Jesuit left arm of the church was evidently not working in accord with the papal right, and, as we shall see, it is clear that the Jesuit view has prevailed.

The philosopher, paleontologist, and Jesuit, Pierre Teilhard de Chardin (1881-1955), produced one of the most esoteric versions of theistic evolution, combining within it elements of eastern mysticism. It will be recalled from Chapters Eight and Nine that the good priest was involved in the Piltdown man affair and the dubious circumstances surrounding Peking man, while his superiors never seemed to have attained to his degree of enlightenment—he was exiled twice, the first time to China and the second time to the Wenner-Gren Foundation in

Pierre Teilhard de Chardin, 1881-1955, shown on the right receiving the Mendel medal in Philadelphia, March 1937, from Fr. Edward V. Stanfort in recognition for his contribution to science. (New York *Herald Tribune*)

New York (Speaight 1967). As a student, Teilhard had been influenced by philosophy professor Henri Bergson's *L'Evolution Creatrice* (1907), and for the remainder of his life he had built on Bergson's principle of orthogenesis, that is, of an intelligent guiding principle in evolution rather than chance.[16]

The culmination of Teilhard's thinking on theistic evolution is contained in his *Phenomenon of Man* (1955), while a more explicit work entitled *Christianity and Evolution* was published posthumously in 1969.[17] Since then, and with the aid of several small but organized bands of followers,[18] Teilhardian evolution has diffused not only in England but throughout the Catholic West (Glick 1976). An interesting development soon took place. In 1957 the Holy Office ordered the works of Teilhard removed from the libraries of Catholic institutions and forbade their sale in Catholic bookstores. At this date the *Catholic Index of Forbidden Books* was no longer being kept. This was followed by a letter or *monitum*, in June 1962, advising the faithful of errors and ambiguities in Teilhard's writings (Masala 1962).[19] At the same time, however, the Jesuit arm of the Roman Catholic Church produced a stream of literature defending Teilhard's writings and actively promoted his works (Kopp 1964).[20] The effect has been that evolution has been considerably depolemicised in most intellectual and educational sectors of the Catholic world, while the *monitum* is now, clearly, a dead letter.

Theistic evolution, with a bias towards the Teilhardian view, has thus become firmly established within the Roman Catholic Church, and, in retrospect, this might be expected since the long and posthumous shadow of Aristotle is still cast over Rome. It will be recalled from earlier chapters that Aristotle's ideas, including his concept of teleology in nature, were carried forward by Thomas Aquinas and became integrated within the foundation of Catholic teaching. However, this must cause a mental schism in any who stop to think about what is actually being said. This "doublethink" situation will be apparent when it is recalled that theistic evolution of any kind does not accept the first eleven chapters of Genesis, but at the same time the original commandment to "be fruitful and multiply" (Genesis 1:28) in the first chapter is rigidly upheld by the prohibition of birth control. Examples could be multiplied.

If Teilhardian evolution is on poor ground theologically, it is revealing to read of opinions of his views in scientific circles. Sir Peter Medawar's now famous critique of Teilhard's *Phenomenon of Man* leaves prospective readers with an accurate picture of what to expect. Medawar begins:,

It is a book widely held to be one of the utmost profundity and significance...some reviewers hearabouts have called it the Book of the Year—one, the Book of the Century. Yet the greater part of it...is nonsense, tricked out by a variety of tedious metaphysical conceits, and its author can be excused of dishonesty only on the grounds that before deceiving others he has taken great pains to deceive himself...but consider first the style, because it is the style that creates the illusion of content (Medawar 1961, 99).

As in modern art Teilhard has become a cult figure to a circle of devotees who give the benefit of any doubt in his writings to profundity rather than confess to their total incomprehensibility. Indeed, incomprehensibility is the most marked characteristic of authors writing in support of theistic evolution. The reader can usually be sure that if what is being said is not absolutely clear on first reading but is couched in long and tortuous terms, then it is fairly certain that some version of theistic evolution is being promoted.

More serious than small groups of misguided intellectuals is the fact that the Communist party has recognized the usefulness of theistic evolution for its own purposes. Today, they are actively promoting Teilhard's work among Christian intellectual centers and particularly among Catholics in Europe and South America (Garaudy 1968; Kristof 1969; Lischer 1979).[21] The Marxist element in the Jesuit teaching order has recently been well documented by Martin (1978) and is the vehicle primarily responsible for bringing theistic evolution to today's generation. The founding father of communism, Karl Marx, recognized that "religion is the opium of the people" (Marx 1843).[22] He further recognized that religious beliefs stood in the way of the vision for a new world order, while heading that list of religions was Bible-based Christianity. Direct persecution has, since Roman days, proven ineffective, serving only to reinforce the faith of the survivors; the alternative strategy adopted today is deliberate erosion of belief from within the Christian organizations. Evolution now has the respectability of science, and for the Catholic Christian particularly, Teilhard's theistic evolution appears as the perfect compromise, with just enough science tempered with just the right amount of religious mystery. With the church's sanction and blessing, what more could the layperson ask? As we saw in the *Humani Generis* and as we shall see later, there is a very short step between theistic evolution and the outright atheism of the Communist party; the next generation should see some very interesting developments between the Communist governments and Roman Catholic Church.

Michelangelo's Sistine Chapel ceiling depiction of the creation of Adam, painted in 1508. This evolutionary interpretation has been repeated endlessly in recent years to advertise products from shoes to the movie E.T. (Drawing by Mary Wardlaw)

One intriguing and significant facet of today's Catholic teaching of theistic evolution is related to Michelangelo and the Sistine Chapel ceiling. Unlikely as this may seem, it is, nevertheless, a remarkable fact that when painted in 1508 Michelangelo took the bold step of departing from the biblical account of the creation of man to depict what is today seen to be a theistically evolved version. Prior to this time, artists had stuck to the Genesis description of a non-living being made from the dust of the ground becoming a "living soul" by the infusion of God's breath (Genesis 2:7). Michelangelo's now famous painting of the creation of Adam shows a human form quite evidently alive with a raised arm and in fingertip union with God. The question this painting raises is that since the creature is alive, what kind of pre-Adamic being does it represent? Enterprising Jesuit teachers have seized upon this as the historical vindication of the truth of theistic evolution, so that the creature depicted must then be some kind of advanced anthropoid. There can be absolute certainty that nothing could have been further from Michelangelo's mind, yet the Greek influence and tendency to rationalize revelation is represented symbolically throughout the entire painting, not only in style, but by the insertion of Greek sibyls between the Old Testament prophets.

Theistic Evolution in the Protestant Churches

Within the Protestant English church, Anglican Charles Kingsley was an early admirer of Darwin and, as we have noted earlier, confessed upon reading the *Origin*, that he had long "learnt to disbelieve the [biblical] dogma of the permanence of species".[23] As with many intellectuals of his own class, rather than adopt the then currently popular

Day-Age and Gap theories, he chose the position of theistic evolution as the rational alternative to Special Creation.

Another influential advocate of Darwin was the ordained Anglican Oxford professor, Baden Powell, father of the founder of the Boy Scout movement. Elected to the Royal Society while still a vicar in 1824, he was an admirer of Lyell's uniformitarianism and one of the first major theologians to adopt Chambers's *Vestiges* (1844). Miracles of any kind were inconceivable to Powell, and he considered the entire Old Testament to be irrelevant (Powell 1857).[24] Not surprisingly, he was opposed to the evangelicals and often involved in religious controversy. One of the great scandals was caused by Powell's review of the *Origin* when it first appeared. Powell took the theistic position and wrote a glowing review indicating how much greater God was from Darwin's evolutionary viewpoint than from questionable Jewish records. A few years earlier the church would have condemned Powell as a heretic, but in 1860, although it was controversial, his view was tolerated.

Interestingly, at the very same time there was another Anglican churchman who as less cavalier towards the Old Testament than Powell and yet who suffered greater censure by his church. John Colenso, educated at Cambridge, became Bishop of Natal and set about to translate the Bible into Zulu. It was during this time that he discovered what he considered to be discrepancies in the early books of the Old Testament and published a critical examination in *The Pentateuch and the Book of Joshua*. This caused so much controversy that in

John Colenso, 1814-83. Dispatched from England to become the Bishop of Natal, he was later denounced for expressing far less serious doubts than were being publicly expressed by more senior members of the church hierarchy. Was he being made a Anglican scapegoat? (Metropolitan Toronto Reference Library Board)

Frederick Temple, 1821-1902. Headmaster of Rugby School, Bishop of London, and finally Archbishop of Canterbury; one wonders if this highly successful advancement in power would have been achieved had he not been a follower of Darwin. (Metropolitan Toronto Reference Library Board)

1860 there was a public trial and the Bishop of Cape Town, as his Metropolitan, declared that he be deposed. Five years later, after the issue had settled down, an appeal was made to the Privy Council and the disposition declared void. Colenso kept his job. Why the fury of church authority was directed to Colenso and not Powell is not clear; perhaps a scape-goat had to be found. One thing is certain, however:

William Temple, 1881-1944. Son of Frederick Temple, he closely followed in his father's footsteps, becoming Archbishop of Canterbury in 1942. Author of the thoroughly Darwinian *Nature, Man and God* and contributor to several left-wing magazines, he master-minded the British Council of Churches and later the World Council of Churches. (Photograph by Bassano, Camera Press; Miller Services)

Colenso's trial brought tremendous newspaper publicity at precisely the time of the public outcry against the *Origin*. The most notable statement made by Colenso at his trial was: "The 'scandal' they complain of is not caused by me, but by those who maintain a state of things in the Church opposed to the plainest results of modern science" (Cox 1888, 1:236). This won many sympathizers, and the affair served extremely well from three aspects: it temporarily diverted attention from the criticism aimed at the *Origin*, it focused on the apparent unsoundness of the Bible, and it won many converts to Darwin. In sum, the publicity could not have come at a better time to aid the establishment of evolution.

One by one theologians gave in to Darwin's evolution through the theistic argument. It all seemed so rational, and it removed the necessity to have to confess to those embarrassing miracles. The most effective converts were those near the top of the ecclesiastical pyramid, since by their influence they controlled the dogma of the incoming generation of theologians. Frederick Temple was headmaster of Rugby School when he compromised his faith with Darwin in 1860.[25] He steadily rose through the ecclesiastical ranks to become Archbishop of Canterbury in 1896, the highest position in the Anglican Church (Temple 1860). The theistic version of Darwin's evolution thus began to filter down as acceptable dogma among the hierarchy before the turn of the century. In fact, by the time Darwin died in 1882 and despite all the outcry there had been a quarter of a century earlier over his *Origin*, the church now insisted that he be given a hero's funeral and state burial at Westminster Abbey. Yesterday's heresy had become today's divine truth.

It will never be known how many defections from the church were caused by this reversal of stand, but it did cause many of the bitter disputes within the church, the conservatives holding to the literal truth of the Genesis record of Creation pitted against the Liberals holding to theistic evolution. These same tensions still exist today, not only within the Christian church but also in the orthodox Judeo and Islamic worlds, while the point at issue is still revelation versus reason.

From Evolution to Atheism

At first Darwin's *Origin* was primarily accepted not on any scientific merit but rather because it offered an apparently rational alternative to the miraculous; the early followers were, therefore, not the scientists of the day but rather theologians who found themselves in the profession for any number of personal reasons, the least of which was they had been "called" to that vocation. There was no doubt much truth in the Victorian quip that the fool of the family was either sent into the army or the church, and Charles Darwin's father may have considered these alternatives when he sent young Darwin to Cambridge for clerical training. Darwin's followers each had their particular motive: some, like Huxley, because the theory was anticlerical and others simply because it was antiestablishment. Perhaps the most notable was Karl Marx, at the time living in London and attending Huxley's public lectures on Darwinian evolution. Marx found the struggle-to-the-death principle in natural selection a perfect confirmation of his own view of man's class struggle and, in appreciation, sent Darwin a copy of his *Das Kapital*, in 1873—it had been published in 1867 (Padover 1979, 139).[26] Six years later, Marx wrote to Darwin requesting permission to dedicate his next volume to him; however, Darwin declined the offer explaining "that it would pain certain members of his family if he were associated with so atheistic a book" (Keith 1955, 234). Darwin would turn in his grave if he knew of the excesses his theory has been asked to justify in this twentieth century!

The Karl Marx incident is an appropriate point at which to introduce the German philosopher Georg Hegel, whose ideas not only greatly influenced Marx but also many German free-thinkers in the nineteenth century. In Hegel's philosophy, God did not exist over and above the world as in Christian orthodoxy, but was rather a world spirit found in the depths of all natural processes. All reality was simply a manifestation of this world spirit, referred to, in sum, as the Absolute Spirit, while religion was an imaginative and pictorial way of representing the truth of this philosophy.

Hegel visualized the Absolute Spirit to be directing an ongoing

Karl Marx, 1818-83. Born to Jewish parents, he became a Christian, studied philosophy, and turned his back on any kind of theism. He was expelled from Germany for his political views and found refuge in Victorian London. (Metropolitan Toronto Reference Library Board)

Georg Hegel, 1770-1831. Introduced the idea that God is a world-spirit present in all natural processes. The outcome of this thinking is pantheism or nature worship, while Jesus becomes merely an enlightened teacher. Engraving by Bollinger after Xeller. (John P. Robarts Research Library, University of Toronto)

developmental (evolutionary) process in nature, including humanity, while that process had taken an irregular course of continuing ascent. The upward path was seen to be one of a dialectical struggle between positive and negative entities, but the outcome was always to produce a balanced, harmonious synthesis—something better. Ultimately, perfection would be reached. Writing more than a century later, Teilhard de Chardin called this ultimate goal Point Omega. If all this sounds vaguely like Asa Gray's theistic evolution, it is, essentially, just that, although Hegel had reduced the Christian God almost beyond recognition to a mere impersonal intelligence directing the destiny of nature.

Hegel's ideas were developed before Lyell wrote his *Principles*, but they lay waiting for science to catch up to philosophy before they could come to full fruition. Once the development process (evolution) appeared to have support from science, Hegel's philosophy became popular in Germany. However, it was but a short step then to say that the Absolute Spirit directing nature was none other than Nature herself. Charles Kingsley's transition from Father God to Mother Nature may be recognized as an instance of this subtlety. Ludwig Feuerbach, a student of Hegel, made this transition more boldly and then explained away four millenia of man's relationship to God by saying that God was really only the projection of man himself. Theology, thereby, became anthropology. George Bernard Shaw expressed the concept, in his usual witty way, half a century later by saying that God was made in the image of man—a parody of Genesis 1:27. At this point God's function in the thinking of Hegel's followers was virtually redundant, and in 1882 Friedrich Nietzsche took it upon himself to take the final step and pronounce that God was dead (Nietzsche 1882, 3:108).[27] Coincidentally, this was the same year that Darwin died while, as if under a divine curse, Nietzsche lost his professorship and was eventually declared to be hopelessly insane. Nietzsche died a few years later. It had taken less than a generation from the time Hegel's philosophy had been given credibility by Darwin's *Origin* to the formal declaration of atheism. Only acceptable to the apostate extremists at first, the high road to atheism had been established, and now, through the new world order set out by Karl Marx (1850) in his *Communist Manifesto*, man was seen to be at last totally freed from the shackles of religion.[28]

It should be emphasized that Darwin's primary concern was for his theory. The fact that the theory provided some with a rational justification to reject God may have given him concern at first, but it seems to have passed with time and the acceptance of his theory by his peers. In the meantime, Haeckel was working hard in Germany and Huxley in England promoting the theory of evolution by presentation of evidence in books and public lectures for the working classes. As we have seen throughout these chapters, this ninteenth century evidence, used so convincingly to destroy the faith of those who would listen, has since been shown to be completely invalid. But there were still many who clung doggedly to their Bibles, totally unconvinced and unmoved by science; it was for such as these that there arose in Germany towards the end of the nineteenth century a handful of theologians who took it upon themselves to destroy credibility in most of the early books of the Bible.

Biblical Evolution

Julius Wellhausen (1844-1918) was a brilliant German theologian who, it is said, occupied a position in the field of Old Testament study analogous to that of Darwin in the area of biological science. As a student, Wellhausen's ideas had been conditioned by the evolutionary concepts of Hegel, who maintained that man had ascended from primitive beginnings. This was quite contrary to the biblical teaching of the Fall of Man, but the steady pressure of geological evidence by Lyell's interpretation, followed by the biological evidence by Darwin's interpretation, had by this time relegated the Genesis Flood to myth in the minds of many. The first five books of the Old Testament claim to have been written by Moses, and since these books contain the accounts of Creation, the Fall of man, and the great Flood, they now became suspect and the legitimate object of intellectual inquiry. Others, such as Graf, working before Wellhausen, had developed a scholarly approach for the analysis of the Hebrew texts in which the books of Moses were written, an approach that eventually became known as Higher Criticism.

Wellhausen's followers, well versed in this albeit useful type of analysis, adopted the assumption that because the more significant Mosaic laws and regulations were neglected for prolonged periods in the early history of the Israelite nation—that is, in the fourteenth to tenth centuries, B.C.—Moses could not have introduced these regulations prior to this time during the Exodus in the fifteenth century (Harrison 1970, 127). Although the actual time of the Exodus has still not been settled, Harrison, a respected Old Testament scholar, has made it clear that this assumption is "wholly fallacious" (Harrison 1969, 20).[30]

Wellhausen assumed that there had been a progressive development of religious practices by absorbing ideas from surrounding cultures until from polytheistic beginnings they had emerged as a monotheistic nation. At this point, it was argued, certain priestly editors, writing perhaps as late as two centuries B.C., ascribed all the regulations and monotheistic theology that had developed to the quasi-mythical patriarch, Moses. The Wellhausen school maintained that by diligent analysis of the Hebrew Scriptures, the characteristics of the individual editors could even be identified; these were referred to as J, E, D, and P. Enormous volumes of literature and Ph.D. theses have since been generated by this line of inquiry, which became known as the Graf-Wellhausen Developmental or Documentary Hypothesis. Graf was acknowledged as one of the early workers in this field. The hypothesis was based squarely on Hegelian evolutionism and commended itself to many who sought to solve problems by a single interpretive principle (Driver 1891).[31]

The Developmental Hypothesis seemingly gained support from archaeological findings of the day. It will be recalled that Layard discovered a whole "library" of clay tablets at Nineveh, and although no one could read the cuneiform inscription at the time, George Smith, an engraver working at the British Museum, eventually discovered the key, and by 1872 a most exciting discovery had been made. A Babylonian narrative, very closely resembling the Genesis account of Noah, the ark, and the great Flood, appeared recorded in the ancient tablets (Ceram 1971a, 276).[32] The conservative scholars said that this was a corrupt account of an earlier version that had been preserved in its pure form by the Hebrews. The liberal scholars of the Graf-Wellhausen school, on the other hand, claimed that the Hebrews had taken it from the earlier Babylonian version and that this was one of the most convincing pieces of evidence for the Developmental Hypothesis. Their argument was that the archaeologically dated earlier version ascribed the Flood to the caprice of one among many gods (polytheism), while the later Hebrew version ascribed it to judgment by one supreme God (monotheism), thus showing the evolution of the higher concept.

The liberal scholars of the late nineteenth century eventually gained the upper hand, filling all the key posts at the theological colleges, while conservative scholars were not promoted and assumed the lower positions (Lindsell 1976).[33] As one generation of students passed into the next, the teachings of Graf and Wellhausen became established dogma, and the result was a growing disbelief not only in the book of Genesis but in the entire Old Testament.

A particularly effective means of broadcasting the liberal interpretation of the Bible opened up, either fortuitously or by some manipulation, in the appointment of William Robertson Smith as joint editor and then chief editor of the prestigious *Encyclopaedia Britannica* in 1881. Smith was a brilliant theologian, Semitic scholar, philologist, physicist, and archaeologist, to whom the miraculous was totally unacceptable. He wholeheartedly adopted the Developmental Hypothesis and expressed this unorthodox interpretation in his article on the Bible in the ninth edition of the *Britannica* (known as the "Scholars edition"), published at that time in England over the period 1875-89. There were cries of outrage from the public who still retained the

Harry Emerson Fosdick, 1878-1969. Gifted speaker and tireless worker for the liberal church, he preached and broadcast the message of theistic evolution in America for more than twenty years. (Keystone Picture Agency)

orthodox view, but, nevertheless, the die had been cast, and the ninth edition would stand as the font of all truth and knowledge on countless library shelves in most English-speaking countries for at least another generation.

Smith's service to the cause completed, the controversy caused him to be expelled from his chair in the Free Church College at Aberdeen, Scotland, and he died at the early age of forty-seven. A second, very effective means of broadcasting the liberal gospel took advantage of the technology of this century to reach the listener rather than the reader. Harry Emerson Fosdick, mentioned earlier in this chapter, conducted a nationwide radio broadcast every week from 1926 to 1946. This served well to establish the view that the early books of the Bible were steeped in myth and legend, while most of the books of both the Old and New Testaments had been written, even edited, hundreds of years after the events they describe. This message became entrenched in the young minds of those who have since become today's leaders in many, if not most, of America's theological schools and seminaries where the Developmental Hypothesis is still taught.

Hypothesis Not Supported by the Facts

Ever since Darwin's *Origin* gave credence to the Hegelian notion that human culture had ascended from brutal beginnings, there has been a running controversy among archaeologists working in areas that provide the biblical background. The liberal element has tended to look for evidence to support the Developmental Hypothesis and ignore that which refutes it, whereas the more competent workers have not set out with the idea of proving one view or the other, but simply to draw objective conclusions from all the facts. Chief among these latter scholars was the towering figure of William Albright, a man with prodigious mental capacities and reputedly familiar with more than twenty-five languages. As a result of his work and influence on Palestinian archaeology from 1920 to 1940, Harrison (1969, 60) makes the statement that all books written about Old Testament history and archaeology before 1940 must be regarded as obsolete. This effectively casts aside all the archaeological evidence which, it was claimed, supported the Developmental Hypothesis. A vast amount of hard evidence has been acquired during the past half century that confirms the accuracy of the early books of the Old Testament, while even some of the early narratives of the book of Genesis have been clearly vindicated (Kitchen 1978, 26).[34] Radday (1982) has recently carried out a computer analysis of the Hebrew words of Genesis and has shown, beyond doubt, that the book had but a single author.[35] This confirms the conservative

traditionalist view while refuting the liberal view of multiple authorship and, naturally, has wrought further controversy within the scholarly ranks.

Harrison (1969, 61) pointed out several years ago in his now classic
work on the Old Testament that in spite of the overwhelming archaeological evidence supporting biblical accounts, there are still some who
exercise a studied disregard for the evidence and prefer subjective speculations such as the Developmental Hypothesis. Often, however, the
confirmatory evidence tends to remain in the relative obscurity of the
scholarly journals, while the outdated liberal view is the one conveyed
to the general public by the popular press (Magnusson 1977).[36] Among
numerous major discoveries, such as those at Mari, Nazu, Ugarit, the
Dead Sea scrolls at Qumran, and more recently those at Tell Mardikh
(Ebla), each has confirmed the biblical accounts and established the
traditional dating; the Mosaic laws were given to the Israelites *before*
they became an established nation and not centuries after, and the New
Testament record was written within the lifetime of eye witnesses and
not centuries later, as has been claimed. However, it is the evidence for
the Genesis account of a universal flood that is the most vital from the
point of view of Lyell's geology and, subsequently, Darwin's theory.
Naturally, this is a very sensitive area, and the evidence can only be
circumstantial, but, nevertheless, it should not be suppressed but
brought into the light of day, where the reader may judge for himself.

James Frazer and the Flood

The Genesis account of the great Flood is not a piece of folklore
confined to a small tribe of Israelites. Oral and written accounts are
found throughout the world. Before the days of the ubiquitous Coca-
Cola machine or even the radio, when some human cultures were still
untainted by Western ideas, anthropologists sought out remote tribes
and diligently recorded their oral traditions. They were careful to note
any evidence of borrowing from other cultures including any influence
of missionaries, who were then just beginning to fan out into places
such as "darkest Africa". All this work was carried out early in the
nineteenth century, and James Frazer, later Sir James Frazer, brought it
all together in his massive three-volume work *Folklore in the Old
Testament*, published in 1918.[37] This work includes 138 flood accounts
from the north, south, and central Americas, from all over the Pacific
islands, India, China, and from the less populous parts of Europe.
Each account has obvious elements of fantasy and local coloring, but
throughout, and almost without exception, there are four basic themes
common to them all and common to the Genesis account. First, there

was a moral cause for the flood, either because of the misconduct of
men or the misconduct of the gods. Second, all accounts agree that
either a god or an animal gave one man advance notice of the flood.
Third, without exception, all agree that the flood wiped out all of
mankind except those specifically warned and that these survivors are
the progenitors of the present world population. Fourth, the animals
played a significant part by giving warning of the flood or by indicating that the flood waters had abated and that dry land had appeared. In
addition to these four basic themes, a great many of the stories mention
or imply that eight people were saved while almost all say that some
kind of vessel was used to house the survivors (Custance 1979, 88).[38]

The conclusion to be drawn from the fact that all the accounts have
certain important features in common is inescapable. Since the stories
are worldwide and yet speak of a specific incident happening at the
time of a great catastrophe, this indicates not only a large element of
truth but a common geographical origin for mankind. The Genesis
account places this origin at the triple-point of eastern Turkey, southern Armenia, and northern Iran—probably one of the most politically
sensitive areas in the world today.

A notable postscript to the veracity of these flood legends lies, ironically, in the motives of their editor, Sir James Frazer, who is perhaps
better known for his great anthropological essay *The Golden Bough*,
published in 1890 and still available in reprinted editions today.[39] Sir
James Frazer was the dutiful and obedient son of staunch Presbyterian
parents who were strictly orthodox in the Calvinist tradition; his early
home life centered around daily worship and good reading. As a child
he never dreamed of questioning parental or religious authority. As a
man, however, he spent more than sixty years in the libraries of Trinity
College, Cambridge, undermining belief in a literal acceptance of the
Bible. His quiet and persistent rebellion, effected through scholarship,
produced such works as the collection of flood traditions, which in fact,
and in spite of Sir James, remain as a testimony to the authenticity of
the Genesis account (Kardiner and Preble 1961, 78).

It is appropriate to mention at this point that of all the numerous
stories, deathbed confessions, and even a sample of hand-tooled wood
and faked photographs that have resulted from the search for Noah's
ark on Mount Ararat over the past century. So far there is not one shred
of evidence, let alone proof, that an ancient vessel resides on the
mountain (Montgomery 1972).[40] As previously mentioned, this geographical area is a politically sensitive region, with a Russian missile
base on the Armenian side of Ararat; in addition to having to deal with
a whole snow-capped and treacherous mountain range rather than a

James Frazer, 1854-1941. A Scottish
anthropologist and academic who
spent more than sixty years in the
libraries of Cambridge University
undermining by scholarship the
literal interpretation of the Bible.
(Lafayette, London)

single mountain, exploration is also politically difficult. Nevertheless,
we may be sure that if the ark is ever discovered and unquestionable
proof furnished, this will create the greatest controversy ever heard,
because the whole of Lyell's geology and the evolution dogma will
then have to face their most serious challenge.

The Ebla Controversy

One of the greatest archaeological discoveries of this century began in
1964 at Tell Mardikh, located about one hundred and fifty miles north
of Beirut in northern Syria. Just when biblical scholars believed they
had everything finally in place for Israel's earliest period, that is, for the
time of Abraham, the discovery of a mighty Canaanite empire, with its
all but forgotten capital city of Ebla, made history books obsolete once
again. Until this discovery, the conventional thinking was of the
Egyptian kingdoms to the south and the Assyrian empire to the north
with nothing very much in between; but now the biblical land of
Canaan, part of which later became Israel, was found to be a major
empire competing in trade with others around it.

A team of Italian archaeologists, working in cooperation with the
Directorate General of Antiquities and Museums of Syria, made international news in 1975 when Ebla's royal archives were unearthed,
containing the greatest cache of inscribed tablets ever discovered (Pettinato 1976). There were more than 15,000 clay tablets and fragments,
which will take years to translate, but these have already revealed that
Ebla was a cultural and trade center of some quarter million people.
Ebla flourished at the time the Egyptians were building the earliest
pyramids at Gizeh, believed to be about 2500 B.C. The key member of

the Italian team, Dr. Giovanni Pettinato, had been superbly prepared, as one of the few scholars fluent enough in the key languages, to unlock the secrets of Ebla. He soon began to find names and statements from the cuneiform script that appeared to confirm the early biblical accounts. This kind of discovery was, naturally, of great interest to many people and caused the most bitter controversy between the conservative scholars, who were pleased to find confirmation of the early biblical accounts, and the liberals, who still subscribed to the Developmental Hypothesis. To make matters worse for the outside world, the Syrian government took exception to the tenor of these reports on political grounds and imposed a virtual news blackout on the work at Tell Mardikh in the late 1970s (Mikaya 1978).

Some of the dust surrounding the Ebla discoveries has since settled, and with the simultaneous publication of two books by the principal investigators, a fair notion of the truth 'of the matter can be discerned. Paolo Matthiae represents the liberal school and, in the preface to his *Ebla: An Empire Rediscovered*, cautions the reader:

> Polemics often harsh and always painful for the author have arisen from individual speculations about presumed connections between the Ebla texts and Biblical characters, stories and episodes. The interest aroused among the public by these unfounded inferences of a relationship between Ebla and the Bible is understandable, but it must clearly be said that documentary evidence of them is effectively non-existent (Matthiae 1981, 11).

Giovanni Pettinato (1981), on the other hand, represents the conservative view and, in his *Archives of Ebla*, quietly presents the sifted and incontrovertible evidence.

In the first place, the discovery of 114 bilingual dictionaries and the very sophisticated handling of trade and commerce leaves no doubt that the scribes were proficient in several languages and that the arts of writing and computing were highly developed (Pettinato 1981, 235). All this existed at least a thousand years before the time of Moses (circa 1500 B.C.), who, we are told, received the best of Egyptian education. This evidence alone should be sufficient to refute the Developmental Hypothesis, which claims that the art of writing was not sufficiently developed at the time of Moses and that the early books of the Bible ascribed to him were merely passed on by oral tradition.

Of more specific interest was the discovery of two copies of the Babylonian Gilgamesh epic, which is a pagan version of the biblical Flood, and three beautifully preserved copies of a creation account that bears close resemblance to the account in the first chapter of Genesis

(Pettinato 1981, 238). Pettinato provides the translation to this remarkable hymn of praise written, it will be recalled, a thousand years before the biblical text and thus completely refuting the notion of oral tradition:

> Lord of heaven and earth
> the earth was not, you created it
> the light of the day was not, you created it,
> the morning light you had not (yet) made exist.
> (Pettinato 1981, 244)

The Eblaite account of creation is also dramatically different from the later creation records, such as the Babylonian *Enuma Elish* and the *Epic of Atrahasis*, which date about 1600 B.C. and have grotesque absurdities such as gods fighting and cutting each other in half, making the earth from one half and heaven from the other. Clearly, the more elegant account is the most ancient and does not support the evolutionary notion of the ascent of man (Heidel 1963).[41]

Genesis in China

There is a final illustration of the fact that the Genesis accounts of Creation and the Flood were not confined to the oral tradition of an obscure tribe of Hebrews. This is to be found, of all places, in the old Chinese written characters. The Chinese can authentically boast of 4,500 years of unbroken civilization, and it is believed that they originally migrated from a site in Mesopotamia because of similarities to the later Babylo-Assyrian culture in arts, sciences, and government (Sayce 1893).[42] The approximate date of their origin, 2500 B.C., is coincidental with the beginnings of many other civilizations in the Middle East and India. The Chinese written language, which it is believed developed at about the same time, is based on pictographs, or stylized pictures representing things such as people, trees, houses, etc., while the more complex ideographs use combinations of pictographs to express ideas. Chinese rulership has always been extremely bureaucratic, laying down rules and regulations for every detail of life. This applied also to the thousands of written characters, which became standardized in the second century B.C., long before Christian missionaries. These characters remained virtually unchanged until the Chinese Communist reforms, which began about 1948.

When the Christian missionaries entered China and began to learn the written language in order to produce the Bible for the Chinese, it was discovered that the Chinese ideographs for many ideas specific to creation and the flood accounts already existed. Moreover, these ideo-

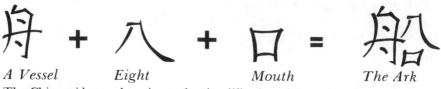

A Vessel   *Eight*   *Mouth*   *The Ark*

The Chinese ideographs prior to the simplification of the written language in 1948, showing how the symbols were combined to form the specific word "Ark" in the context of the Genesis Flood. (Kang and Nelson 1979)

graphs contained a recognizable "picture" of the Genesis meaning. For example, the ideograph for the word "ark", as in Noah's ark, consisted of a symbol for a boat plus symbols for eight mouths or people (Kang and Nelson 1979, 95). It is surely more than coincidental that in the Hebrew version eight people were saved in the ark. For the past two thousand years, China has nurtured three religions that have essentially become fused into one, all three often being found in the same temple. Confucianism, which is really a philosophy, entered China about 500 B.C., while Taoism and Buddhism (Buddhism admits of no Supreme Being) entered during the first century B.C. Prior to this time, the Chinese empire served only one God; they had no myths or idols and kept a strict moral code. They called their god Shang-Ti, meaning heavenly emperor (Tax and Callender 1960, 3:13).[43] Once more, the Developmental Hypothesis, which declares that man began in barbarous beginnings worshipping many gods (polytheism) and then ascended to higher cultures in which only one god was worshipped (monotheism), has been shown to be untrue. In China, they began with one god and degenerated to many gods with Taoism.

Evolution, a Basis for Religion

The point was made at the beginning of the previous chapter that man has an innate tendency to worship some being greater than himself. The narrow use of the word "worship" was then broadened and found to apply to many fields not normally considered to be religious. Each case involved affirmation of a position adopted without proof.

Evolution by its very comprehensiveness makes it impossible to prove or even test scientifically. Evolutionists Birch and Ehrlich have remarked:

> Our theory of evolution has become...one which cannot be refuted by any possible observations. Every conceivable observation can be fitted in to it...No one can think of ways in which to test it. Ideas, either without basis or based on a few laboratory experiments carried out in extremely simplified systems, have

attained currency far beyond their validity. They have become part of an evolutionary dogma accepted by most of us as part of our training (Birch and Ehrlich 1967, 352).

One of the most respected biological evolutionists of today, Ernst Mayr, has stated, "The basic theory (of evolution) is in many instances hardly more than a postulate and its application raises numerous questions in almost every concrete case" (Mayr 1963, 8). A postulate is a supposition assumed without proof; the truth of Mayr's statement may be evident from those pieces of evidence offered as "proof" in the past, such as *Bathybius haeckelii*, the vestigial organs, development of the embryo, and the numerous fossil men, each of which eventually turned out to be misrepresentation or even fraud. If the "proof" in the past was spurious, it might be asked if genuine proof has been offered more recently, but there is, as yet, no affirmative answer. Colin Patterson, senior paleontologist at the British Museum of Natural History, should be in a position to know, yet declared before his peers at a meeting in 1981 that evolution was "positively anti-knowledge", saying that "all my life I had been duped into taking evolution as revealed truth" (Patterson 1981, 2).

The attempt to provide proof by expanding the definition of the term "species" was evidently not acceptable to Erhlich, Mayr, or Patterson, and until concrete proof is provided, it has to be concluded at this point that evolution is a belief system held to by faith. Of course, the Creation account is similarly a belief system held to by faith, and the parallel may be recognized that neither explanation for origins has been observed, neither can be tested in the laboratory, and neither is refutable; that is, neither explanation can be proved or disproved.

A second parallel involves the appeal to the supernatural. There has never been any dispute about the role of the miracle in the literal interpretation of the Genesis account, first for Special Creation and then for the great Flood. The theory of evolution makes no less of an appeal to the miraculous, as may have become evident throughout the previous chapters. The odds against the right combination of elements joining together in the right order for the first living cell to appear from nonliving matter are so enormous that it can only be concluded to have been miraculous. Some, such as Nobel prize winner Francis Crick, are fully aware of these odds and, unable to accept the miraculous, have turned to extraterrestrial sources for the beginning of life. Many other examples run through these pages, such as the unvarying energy output by the sun for several billion years and the very finely balanced population growth over several hundred thousand generations—

clearly appealing to the miraculous. A prominent British biologist and Fellow of the Royal Society has also observed these parallels in his introduction to the 1971 reprint of Darwin's *Origin of Species*. Professor Harrison Matthews stated there that "belief in the theory of evolution" was "exactly parallel to belief in special creation", with evolution simply "a satisfactory faith on which to base our interpretation of nature" (Darwin 1971, x). The theory of evolution, then, cannot properly be included in the field of science, which deals with the physical universe, since it is a non-physical belief (Harper 1979).[44] Belief is a thing of the human mind and determines the way in which we interpret the physical things about us; some will see a fossil as the result of the Genesis Flood, others will see the same fossil as evidence of evolution.

Faith in a belief system takes us beyond science into the metaphysical and, thereby, into the realm of religion. Many writers are beginning to recognize this; for instance, historian and philosopher of science Grene says, "It is as a religion of science that Darwinism chiefly held, and holds, men's minds. The derivation of life, of man, of man's deepest hopes and highest achievements, from the external and indirect determination of small chance errors, appears as the keystone of the naturalistic universe" (Grene 1959, 48). Macbeth (1971, 124), a nonreligious critic, notes that Darwinism itself has all the attributes of a religious faith and lists five major points, one of which is that the true disciples manifest an outright contempt for Christianity. For example, those holding a belief in biblical Creation are today rooted out of teaching positions with the same righteous fervency as the heretics were at one time rooted out of the church. Thus the ongoing evolution-creation debate, which has been blowing hot and cold ever since Darwin's *Origin,* is clearly a matter of two diametrically opposed belief systems or religions: atheism on the one hand and theism on the other.

The central issue in this debate is the belief in the existence of a Supreme Being. Julian Huxley, grandson of Thomas Huxley and one of the foremost evolutionists of his day, was an unabashed atheist. He pointed out in 1959 that Darwin's real achievement was to "remove the whole idea of God as the Creator of organisms from the sphere of rational discussion" (Tax and Callender 1960, 3:45). The belief in a Supreme Being may at once be recognized as the one essential characteristic of a theistic religion. It is perhaps surprising, however, to find that the belief in the nonexistence of a Supreme Being is also considered to be a (nontheistic) religion. Thus, atheism was formally declared to be a religion by the United States Supreme Court in 1961, together with Buddhism, Ethical Culture, Secular Humanism, and others that do not teach a belief in the existence of God (Bird 1979).[45] The Atheist Church of America and the American Ethical Union, for example, are both bona fide tax-exempt religious organizations.

The fully committed Darwinian, such as Julian Huxley, forthright enough to confess his belief, is clearly in the atheist camp,[46] while those holding to the literal interpretation of the Genesis Creation account are in the theist camp. Many in the theist camp are committed Christians, but they are not alone, for it also embraces members of the orthodox Jewish and Islamic faiths. However, those holding to belief in *theistic evolution*, no matter how seemingly reasonable and popular, are not really true to either camp. In this position, the foundation for Christianity has been replaced by Darwin, while still retained is an illusion of a prayer-hearing God. The illusion becomes evident when it is conceded that divine intervention ceased after the creation of Adam and Eve. Theistic evolution is clearly only a stepping stone to ease the theist into a new faith whose foundation is evolution. That new faith is not necessarily outright atheism, since this is only for the very few, for the dedicated purist. It is tailor-made for those for whom there is still a need to satisfy the worship principle.

That spiritual aspect will more often than not be met by the would-be worshiper turning to occult practices. This was true in the case of the Nazi party members in Germany, is true today in the case of the Communist party members in Russia, and is a growing trend among members of the liberal church in the West.

We shall see in the next and final chapter that the new faith is secular humanism in which man replaces God and declares himself to be free at last to be master of his own destiny.

15

New World Order

*It is essential for evolution to become the central
core of any educational system, because it is
evolution, in the broad sense, that links inorganic
nature with life, and the stars with the earth, and
matter with mind, and animals with man.
Human history is a continuation of biological
evolution in a different form.*

SIR JULIAN HUXLEY, 1959
(Tax and Callender 1960, 3:42)

The previous chapters have spanned history from the Greek philosophers to Darwin, and have passed into this present day showing history to be a series of ever deepening confrontations between opposing ideologies. As pointed out in Chapter One, the first of these ideologies consists of the belief in the existence of a Supreme Being and the concomitant belief in the survival of human consciousness after physical death. While there is no proof for either, these are mankind's most basic and deep-rooted beliefs. Throughout history, and even to this present day, the majority of people have believed in an afterlife, no matter how hazy their concepts of this personal future, while there is among most the belief in a Supreme Being who created man, gave him rules to live by, and is interested in the management of human affairs. Over the past few generations, many of the details of this scenario have been lost or forgotten, but the essence of the idea still remains firmly entrenched in the human consciousness. The written source of these concepts in Western society is recognized to be the Bible which, it is believed, is God's revelation to man of those things that would otherwise be unknowable. The origins of the universe, planet earth, and life itself are among those mysteries unknowable except by revelation.

The opposing ideology, in its extreme, relies solely on what is demonstrable to the human senses. Thus it denies a conscious existence after physical death and the existence of a Supreme Being. It logically follows that there is no divine law-giver, no Judge, and no would-be master of human affairs. Naturally, there is a spectrum of beliefs between these two philosophical positions, while the typical view of many today was expressed by Albert Einstein, when asked about his views on God: "I believe in Spinoza's God who reveals himself in the orderly harmony of what exists, not in a God who concerns himself with the fates and actions of human beings" (Hoffman 1972, 95). This is not only Spinoza's God, but, it will be recalled, was also Aristotle's. When pursued to its ultimate conclusion, this common view places God as a disinterested party, leaving man without rules and thus without accountability, destined to manage the world in which he lives. In a nutshell, this is the view of the humanist today.

Humanists are a steadily increasing and influential minority, quite sincere in their dedication to bring about world unity and peace through intelligent human management. They argue, not without some justification, that, historically, theistic religions have been responsible for the dissension between nations, and that in today's crowded and complex world it is vital to eliminate this source of division. Ultimately, the humanist aim, as set forth by the second Humanist Manifesto, is to eliminate national sovereignty itself in order to achieve a new world order (Kurtz and Wilson 1973, 4).[1] One of the principal architects of world humanism in this century was Julian Huxley, biologist and grandson of Thomas Huxley. As first director

Julian Huxley, 1887-1975. Grandson of T.H. Huxley but without his forebear's mastery of rhetoric; he nevertheless carried the atheist banner further by quiet strokes of the pen than by debate. (Photograph by Godfrey Argent for the National Portrait Gallery, London; Miller Services)

general of the United Nations Educational, Scientific and Cultural Organization (UNESCO), which is the body that attempts to monitor, if not control, all that enters the human mind, Julian Huxley in his framework policy included the following aim:

> Thus the general philosophy of UNESCO should it seems, be a scientific world humanism, global in extent and evolutionary in background. Evolution in the broad sense denotes all the historical processes of change and development at work in the universe. It is divisible into three very different sectors: the inorganic or lifeless, the organic or biological, and the social or human (J. Huxley 1976, 16).[2]

We have seen in the previous chapters that Lyell provided what was seen to be evidence for inorganic evolution; Darwin provided the parallel evidence for biological evolution; and Herbert Spencer, their Victorian contemporary, laid the groundwork for the more subjective area of social evolution. This brings us now to the social sciences as the third leg of the evolutionary structure that supports the humanist worldview.

The social sciences are generally recognized to be the least rigorous of scientific disciplines and have certainly provided the seedbed for many of the most flagrant examples of prejudice in the name of science. Classic examples of the search for evidence of evolution of human intelligence were given in Chapter Ten, but further aspects of the social sciences need to be brought to light in order to evaluate this somewhat hollow third leg.

Latter-day Law-giver

Herbert Spencer was quite clearly eccentric. The lone survivor of nine offspring, from chronically alienated parents, he was the living example of his own maxim that evolutionary progress is made by "survival of the fittest". Spencer's "fitness" was, he believed, a superhuman intellect, which brought together, for the benefit of mankind, a perfectly axiomatized system of all knowledge, from the evolution of the galaxies to the evolution of human ethics, morals, and even emotions. He had rejected all ideas of the supernatural at an early age. From a mechanistic viewpoint he saw developmental (evolutionary) adaptation in every conceivable discipline (Spencer 1904, 1:151ff). He was even convinced that all previous philosophers had become "adapted" to their environment and claimed that their thinking was thus colored by the society in which they lived. Spencer chose to be different and deliberately kept himself apart from society. He never married, was

Herbert Spencer, 1820-1903.
Eccentric armchair philosopher
wrote prolifically and convinced
many Victorians of his evolutionary approach to the social sciences.
(Photograph by Lalonde; Library
of Congress, Washington)

most argumentative when in company, and, as is often the case with individuals of this type, could be observed absentmindedly talking aloud to himself in public (Spencer 1904, 1:174). This was the self-taught, self-confessed genius who between the years 1860-96 produced the *Synthetic Philosophy*, a mammoth dissertation on all human knowledge—in ten volumes. The tragedy was that for all this effort, and there were other works besides the *Synthetic Philosophy*, he had selected his facts to fit the theory and was seemingly totally blind to facts that did not fit (Irving 1955, 237).[3]

Spencer introduced the expression "survival of the fittest", in his *Principles of Biology* (1864). Although the *Biology* was generally out of favor with the true Darwinist because of Spencer's sympathy to Lamarck's ideas, Darwin himself was somewhat double faced in the matter. First, he was pleased to lift the expression "survival of the fittest" directly from Spencer's *Biology* and incorporate it into the fifth edition of the *Origin* (Darwin 1869, 92). Second, it seems that by 1868 Darwin had recognized that chance and chance alone—that is natural selection—was insufficient to account for the origin of new species. He could not accept teleology as a mechanism, since this bordered on the supernatural, and the only recourse left was an appeal to Lamarck's theory on the inheritance of acquired characteristics. But to accept any Lamarckian concept would severely reduce in stature his precious natural selection. Nevertheless, Darwin did just that, although this transgression of the father is seldom mentioned in commentaries by the faithful. Vorzimmer (1963) points out that, on reading the *Biology*, Darwin lifted Spencer's Lamarckian notion of "physiological units", called them "pangenes", and incorporated the idea as his own "Provisional Hypothesis of Pangenesis" in his *Variations of Animals and Plants Under Domestication* (Darwin 1868, 2:357).[4] Throughout Darwin's writings, particularly those of his later years, shades of Lamarck can be detected. A wonderful passage, deleted from his autobiography, written in 1876, will serve as an example not only of his Lamarckian leanings but as an insight into his irreligious nature:

> Nor must we overlook the probability of the constant inculcation in a belief in God on the minds of children producing so strong and perhaps an inherited effect on their brains not yet fully developed, that it would be as difficult for them to throw off their belief in God, as for a monkey to throw off its instinctive fear and hatred of a snake (Barlow 1958, 93).

It would seem that the psychologists are less cognizant or, perhaps less critical, of the long discredited Lamarckism, because Spencer's speculative *Principles of Psychology* (1870-72) elevated him to the title of forefather to the functionalist school of psychology (Zusne 1975, 124); in this work he claimed that man had evolved emotionally as well as physically, thus emphasizing the continuity from animal to man. Continuing in the same speculative vein, his final work on the *Principles of Ethics* (1893) maintained that man's laws evolved as societies became more complex. This is held to be true today, in spite of the fact that a system of jurisprudence given to desert tent dwellers in the fifteenth century B.C. is still the best system and has been maintained in Judeo-Christian countries thirty-five centuries later.

Spencer was never more than an accomplished amateur in the sciences and had little knowledge of history, with the result that specialists in the fields of history, science, and philosophy were not impressed with his efforts. The principal criticism was directed against his "deductive" method, where he inferred subtle laws from vague first principles and then selected material from the literature to illustrate these laws. Darwin strongly objected to Spencer's methods (Barlow 1958, 109). Nevertheless, Spencer evidently wrote what some wanted to read, and by the 1890s he was internationally famous, having had great influence on nineteenth century thinking. Ironically, in spite of his complete rejection of Christianity, it was the *Christian Spectator* in England that elevated him to almost supernatural status in writing: "Like Moses, when he came down from the Mount, this positive philosophy [evolution] comes with a veil over its face, that its too divine radiance may be hidden for a time. This is Science that has been conversing with God, and brings in her hand His law written on stone" (Kardiner and Preble 1961, 42).

As with many "great works" based on speculation, Spencer's contribution to the wisdom of mankind was destined to be short-lived. Nevertheless, the notion that morals and ethics have evolved imposed itself on the thinking of the day, for whether there is evidence to support it or not, if biological evolution is true, then there must have been a gradation from the amoral to the moral as animal became man. More than half a century of anthropological inquiry, often with questions unwittingly slanted to elicit the desired reply, has naturally given confirmation of that expectation. This being so, it is then argued that our highly civilized state today has come about by a continual and progressive change of mores, and it is incumbent on today's leaders to direct that continuing change in order to produce a more perfect global society tomorrow.[5] Examples of this very thing are numerous, and anyone with a memory span of a decade or more can recall, for example, that though lotteries were once considered immoral and were illegal, they are not so today. Then again, the death penalty for murder was abandoned in the belief that civilized man had evolved beyond having to impose this primitive sentence. Somehow the question was never raised about the evolved status of the murderer. While Spencer's legacy to mankind is evidently quite hollow, its conclusions had been given substance by Darwin, and we clearly see the outworkings today. However, there are other avenues of the "fuzzy" social sciences that also take their substance from Darwin and need to be brought into the light of day.

Franz Joseph Gall, 1758-1828. Viennese-born physician living in Paris believed the human brain was physically developed according to its use and began the fashionable (and lucrative) practice of phrenology—determination of an individual's potential by feeling bumps on the head. This pseudoscience later led to the idea that brain size is directly related to intelligence (Academy of Medicine, Toronto)

Nature or Nurture?

The perennial question on the new parent's mind is, Will little Willie take after his mother, his father, neither, or both? Only time can tell, it seems, yet there has been a divided opinion over this problem of the origin of human personality ever since thought was first given to it. Some would argue that the infant is born as a blank sheet on which the environment writes, and that it is therefore the quality of nurture that determines our ultimate personality. Others have argued with equal conviction that our personality is determined genetically through immediate parents and ancestors, and that it is therefore nature that is the controlling factor; environment, in this view, is thought to play little or no part.

Today, responsible scientists concede that both heredity and environment—nature and nurture—play important parts, but during the past century or so, the opposing schools of thought not only produced several intellectual scandals of major proportions but also were directly responsible for the extermination of millions in the Nazi gas chambers. The "nature" school, which maintains that heredity molds behavior, is known as biological determinism and began with Francis Galton.

Galton's Inheritance

Francis Galton was the younger cousin of Charles Darwin and an independently wealthy member of England's upper class (Cowan 1969). As a child prodigy, he had developed an obsession for quantifying every conceivable human act, and in 1859, the year of the publication of Darwin's theory of evolution and Broca's theory of brain size, Galton immediately became convinced of both. It will be recalled from Chapter Ten that French physician Paul Broca had maintained that human intelligence was directly related to brain size and, consequently, to the size of the head. This seemingly permitted intelligence to be measured directly with calipers and tape measure. Chapter Ten also pointed out that this notion was Lamarckian and had influenced Darwin's thinking on the question of mentality. Darwin (1868, 2:357) came to believe that inheritance took place by a blending mechanism, and Galton (1897) later developed this into a law.[6] Galton's law stated that an individual's total personality is the sum of all ancestors, consisting of a quarter from each parent, plus a sixteenth from each grandparent, and so on. Environment had no part in Galton's law. However, this entire mathematical edifice collapsed—or should have collapsed— with the "discovery" of Mendel's genetics in 1900 (his findings were actually first published in 1865). Nevertheless, in the 1860s Galton

Francis Galton, 1822-1911. The mechanistic world of Francis Galton would reduce every one of man's functions to a number that could then be treated statistically. He was fully convinced that nature's survival of the fittest principle applied to man and should be under the control of some elitist group. (Metropolitan Toronto Reference Library Board)

began his lifelong quest to quantify human nature. In this attempt he added somewhat to Broca's theory by expanding "intelligence" to mean a number of intangible behavioral qualities. For instance, a highly intelligent individual would also be highly moral and, conversely, those of low intelligence would be "wayward". Naturally, examples could always be found to support this simplistic notion, and Galton made great use of this device, steadfastly ignoring instances that did not fit the expected pattern.

The full title to Darwin's *Origin* reads *On the Origin of Species by Means of Natural Selection or the Preservation of Favoured Races in the Struggle for Life*. The word "races" in the subtitle led to many social inequities between the leaders and the led and between ethnic groups, causing much class distinction, all justified on the basis of the new-found biological science (Hoffstader 1944). Darwin had used the word "race" to mean variants within the species, but this eventually came to include man and raised the question, Whom did nature wish to preserve? White man or black? Christian or Jew? Protestant or Catholic? The possibilities for subdivision were limited only by man's actual prejudices. This was the basis for what became known as Social Darwinism, in which the class structure was assumed to be fixed by the laws of nature. It was thus biologically impossible, for example, for a laborer's son ever to aspire to any better station in life, and vestiges of this nineteenth century class distinction can still be seen today in the British Rail system.[7]

Francis Galton played no small part in all this, since he firmly believed that within the English nation there was a genetically superior stock, inheritable and manifested as the most eminent families. In 1869 Galton published *Heredity Genius*, a study of the variability of the human intellect through the biographies of great men—he included the Darwins. Other works followed in which he introduced the term "nature and nurture", allowing for the effects of environment, but throughout he remained a convinced hereditarian, emphasizing that all that we are is the result of inheritance. As time went by, however, it gradually became evident that acquired intellect cannot be passed on to the next generation, and by the turn of the century Mendel's laws made the reason clear: the genetic materal that we pass on to the next generation is determined at the time of our birth and cannot be influenced by subsequent events in adulthood. Accordingly, Galton then shifted the argument slightly, eliminating the need for "acquired characteristics". He was now left with the claim that certain races were inherently superior and that their superiority was fixed forever from the past as well as into the future. Although this raised the obvious and very awkward question concerning the interfertility of the races, purportedly originating from different sources, this issue never seems to have bothered Galton or his racist followers. The conclusion to Galton's argument then followed that, for the sake of mankind's future, pollution of the precious superior gene pool by interbreeding with inferior stock had to be stopped at all costs.

It was but a short step from this conclusion to suggest that measures should be taken to intelligently direct man's evolutionary progress rather than leaving such a vital matter to random chance. "Judicious marriages" of the superior stock of human beings over "several consecutive generations" would, Galton proposed, produce a "highly gifted race of men" (Galton 1869, 1). It was an obvious final step to propose active discouragement of breeding by the inferior stock and so raise the general level of intelligence and morality of a whole nation. Galton had utterly rejected the Christian doctrine and wrote openly about this; he had no qualms about speaking of controlled breeding of the human race in the same breath as breeding dogs and race horses (Galton 1869, 1; Russell 1951, 49).[8] Getting these racial notions accepted by the scientific community of the day was another challenge, especially since psychology at that time was held to be a philosophy rather than a science. However, by working in cooperation with the mathematician Karl Pearson, Galton applied a number of refined statistical techniques to his anthropomorphic measurements. With numbers and formulas to grace the pages of publications, psychology thus took upon itself the appearance of a scientific discipline, the diminished comprehensibility serving greatly to increase credibility. Exactly the same approach has been used more recently, and seemingly for the same purpose, by Harvard's sociobiologist Edward O. Wilson, working with physicist Charles Lumsden (Lumsden and Wilson 1981).[9]

Galton's next step to gaining acceptance by orthodox science was to coin the name "eugenics" from the Greek; the term means "well-born". Here was the science to produce the utopian dream of a super-race to control tomorrow's world. The dream began to be realized in 1901 with the founding of the Eugenics Education Society, based at the statistics department of University College, London. Galton lived to see the Eugenics Society eventually become a flourishing political movement, while the work on which it was all founded, the calipers and stopwatch (to measure reaction times) applied to the heads of idiots and criminals, was given scientific respectability in the professional journal *Biometrika*, founded and edited, of course, by Galton and Pearson.

Before Galton died in 1911, some of the scientific community had evidently become convinced. He received many honors, including the Darwin and Wallace medal, the Copley medal, the Huxley medal, and a knighthood. However, divine retribution forbade that he should live to fulfill his own eugenic obligation. Scion of two prominent English families, married to the daughter of a third, Sir Francis Galton had died without issue.

Galton's Legacy

The reader should not be misled and imagine that Darwinian honors and a knighthood were bestowed because there was any scientific merit to Galton's work. It was, we should remember, shown to be fundamentally unsound on several grounds (Cowan 1969, 9).[10] First, as pointed out in Chapter Ten, intelligence cannot be determined by the size of the head, and in Galton's day there were a mounting number of cases of ignorant men with large heads and brilliant men with small heads. Second, Mendel's work on genetics was beginning to be accepted in 1900 and showed that neither intelligence nor any other acquired characteristic can be passed on genetically. Finally, as early as 1892, Boas had demonstrated that lack of adequate nutrition and proper sanitation facilities not only retards physical growth of children, but also retards their mental faculties (Boas 1892).

The effect of nurture denied by Galton is thus crucial. This has been confirmed many times since; laziness, for example, was thought to be an inherited trait until real science located hookworm as a culprit (Williams 1969).[11] Given these facts and the general belief in the bibli-

cal description of mankind as originating from a single mating pair
(Galton's inherent racial superiority required multiple mating pairs),
it was incredible that the knighthood should have been awarded as late
as it was, in 1909. Only the previous year the Hardy-Weinberg law
concerned with population genetics had been introduced, which put
the final nail in Galton's eugenical coffin (Hardy 1959). The only
positive aspects of Galton's work were the development of statistical
techniques and his work on fingerprints, neither of which would seem
to justify all the approbation. Clearly, the honors were awarded for his
gallant though misguided attempt to usher in the brave new world
with calipers and ruler, not for any genuine contribution to science.

I.Q. and Sterilization

Craniometry, or the measurement of heads, was a serious scientific
occupation a century ago; seven million school children in Germany,
for example, submitted to this pseudoscience as part of Rudolph Virchow's quest to find a distinctly German racial type—the results
showed that there was no such thing (Ackerknecht 1953). In France
Alfred Binet measured the heads of many schoolchildren and criminals, but finally came to the honest conclusion that any craniometric
differences there may be between a group of intelligent children and a
group of normal children were too small to be significant.

What was just as important, however, was Binet's realization that the
measurements themselves were very much influenced by the expectations of those making the measurements. As we have seen in previous
chapters, preconception did produce an unconscious bias, which, in
this case, happened to be the most significant factor in the analysis.

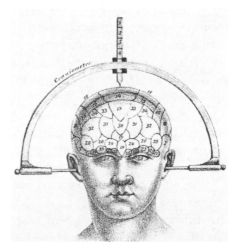

An illustration from Thomas
Sewall's 1837 lectures on
phrenology showing the use of the
craniometer. Originally intended
for the determination of personality,
its use was eventually confined to
the measurement of intelligence
and assessment of "racial
characteristics". (Academy of
Medicine, Toronto)

Binet then set out to develop an alternative approach to quantifying intelligence, not based on a Lamarckian concept, but based more rationally on the intellect itself. The method consisted of a series of test questions on a wide range of topics requiring only simple answers that could easily be reduced to a single number. Thus was born, in 1908, the concept of the Intelligence Quotient, familiarly known today as the I.Q. test (Binet and Simon 1973; Stern 1914).[12] Binet never claimed it to be anything more than a means of sorting out those who were not average, and this would apply to the very bright as well as to those with problems. There were enthusiasts, however, who took Binet's work as a means of grading society according to the I.Q. score, and since intelligence was still firmly held to be racially inherent, this meant that the overall intelligence of the nation could be improved by preventing those near the bottom of the scale from making a genetic contribution. This was surely a noble evolutionary aspiration, and the American psychologist Henry Goddard (1866-1957) was its principal advocate and crusader, while the Rockefeller foundation provided the funding.

Now while idiots and imbeciles are clearly not normal people—that is, even when afforded every opportunity these individuals are mentally incapable of mastering full speech or the written language—there will always be a complete spectrum of people in between, from the level of the imbecile to that approaching the level of the normal person. This group has traditionally been referred to as the "feeble-minded" and poses the problem of where to set the limit on who should and who should not be allowed to reproduce.

For the committed eugenicist, however, playing the role of God posed no problem, and Goddard's (1914) vigorous propaganda campaign convinced the American people that the nation was being threatened by the "menace of the feeble-minded" outbreeding the rest of normal society. Not only was this "human refuse" (Galton's phrase) said to be generating at an alarming rate within the nation's slums and backwoods, but, it was pointed out, they were actually being imported from Ireland and the Jewish ghettos of Europe. By the 1920s, extensive testing programs had been set up within the American school system to separate the feeble-minded children by means of a modified I.Q. test; this was merely substituting Galton's calipers and ruler with Binet's paper and pencil. Many, if not most, of these feeble-minded children, it must be remembered, were simply undernourished children of the unemployed. Institutions were built whereby the separated children could be made to feel comfortable among their own kind, but above all, the system was organized with the ultimate purpose of preventing the feeble-minded from breeding.

Between 1907 and 1938, sterilization laws were passed in thirty American states, and the surgical operation (tubal ligation for women and vasectomy, or even castration, for men) carried out on a volunteer basis at first, but "voluntary" tended to become "forced", especially for those regarded as degenerate, defective, or criminal. For example, it was a simple matter then, as it is today, to delay the welfare check to the unmarried mother until "voluntary" sterilization had been agreed to—cooperation was usually assured within a day or two. The dissemination of birth control information and devices among the poor and unemployed during the 1930s was promoted by female libertarian Margaret Sanger.[13] However, she was viewed with suspicion by the orthodox eugenicists, since they felt that the surgeon's knife was the only sure and permanent way of halting another generation of welfare dependents (Douglas 1970).

Half a century later the situation has changed little, except that it has become more liberal. The law now allows abortion to be included as a method of birth control, although, strictly speaking, it should be regarded as death control and be put in the same category as euthanasia. Finally, it must not be overlooked that the utopian ideals of the eugenicist have tended to become politically expedient, especially in a time of high unemployment. After all, the notion that feeble-mindedness is passed on genetically is still fostered in the attitude that says sterilization today is a small price to pay to minimize welfare payments tomorrow.

The Road From Darwin to Hitler

Galton had based his ideas of orderly upgrading of the human race squarely on Darwin's evolution. It was argued that, in obedience to nature's great principle of survival of the fittest, only the fittest human beings should be allowed to enter the world; with Galton's laws in hand, mankind was in a position to control human evolution and even produce a super race. On Galton's demise, the prophet's mantle was passed to America and shared among the disciples: Henry Goddard, Henry Fairfield Osborn, Harry Laughlin, and Madison Grant, to name a few. In England, the eugenical banner was being carried by such notables as Leonard Darwin (son of Charles Darwin), Winston Churchill, the Lord Chief Justice, and the Anglican Bishop of Oxford (Chase 1980, 136).[14] There was also a strong following in Germany, and Gasman (1971) has documented in fine detail[15] the steps from Darwin's chief apostle Ernst Haeckel to the German National Socialist Party (Phelps 1963).[16] For example, Haeckel in his *Wonders of Life* observes (incorrectly) that the newborn infant is deaf and without consciousness, from which he concludes that there is no human soul or spirit at this point. He then advocates "the destruction of abnormal new born infants" and argues that this "cannot rationally be classed as murder" (Haeckel 1904, 21). Haeckel's logic then carried him further, and he noted that "hundreds of thousands of incurables—lunatics, lepers, people with cancer, etc. are artificially kept alive...without the slightest profit to themselves or the general body" (Haeckel 1904, 118). He suggested that "the redemption from this evil should be accomplished by a dose of some painless and rapid poison...under the control of an authoritative commission" (Haeckel 1904, 119).

All this great wisdom from a Darwinian prophet will be recognized as the grist for Hitler's mill. Keith (1949, 230), himself a Darwinian, noted the strong connection between evolutionary theory and the German Fuhrer's objectives.[17] Further direct inspiration has been noted by a recent author, Werner Maser (1970, 77) who shows from his analysis of Hitler's *Mein Kampf* (1924) that Darwin was the general source for Hitler's notions of biology, worship, force, and struggle, and of his rejection of moral causality in history. More recently still, Kelly (1981) has traced the rise of Darwinism in Germany.

Adolf Hitler was dedicated to the idea of an Aryan super race for millennial rule of the world. He had been profoundly influenced by German translations of two American publications. *The Passing of the Great Race,* by eugenicist Madison Grant, first published in 1916 and with subsequent revisions, purporting to show how the American nation was being genetically polluted by those unfit to breed. Grant also provided the answer to German embarrassment at having lost the First World War, and Hitler was quick to include this in his *Mein Kampf* (Hitler 1941, 597). According to Grant, so many of the big, blonde fighting men indigenous to the German nation had been killed in the thirty year war (1618-48) that the German armies of 1914-18 had been insufficiently stocked with their superior blood! (Grant 1918, 184). Hitler's rational answer was, of course, to produce more of this Aryan super race—and quickly—for the coming world conquest by the Third Reich. Human stud farms were set up during the 1930s to breed from the select few thousand pure stock that remained; Galton's "judicious marriages" had thereby become reality.

The second publication was Harry Laughlin's unabashed creed written in the early 1920s and spelling out exactly who were the socially inadequate and subject to the sterilization laws. The list had grown well beyond Goddard's feeble-minded people and now included the insane, the criminal, the epileptic, the alcoholic, the blind, the deaf, the deformed, and the dependent, including orphans. Voluntary sterilization laws had been in effect in Germany since 1927, but when the National Socialists, or Nazi party, came to power in 1933, with Hitler as their elected chancellor, little time was lost in adopting not only Haeckel's recommendations for infanticide and euthanasia, but virtually the whole of Laughlin's list of race polluters; these individuals were destined for forced sterilization—it was no longer voluntary (Popenoe 1934). After the collapse of Hitler's thousand year Reich in 1945, the well-kept German records showed that between 1927 and 1933, about eighty-five people a year were voluntarily sterilized. Under the Nazis, at least two million human beings had been forcibly sterilized at a rate of about 450 per day (Chase 1980, 134). These operations were not carried out by steel-helmeted storm troopers but by civilian medical doctors, while the commission set up following Haeckel's recommendation to dispose of the "utterly useless" consisted of university professors, who stoically made their life-and-death decisions on the basis of a completed questionnaire. Haeckel's "dose of some painless and rapid poison" was the subject of research and development at the laboratories of Degesch chemical company. The most effective agent for dispatching thousands of "worthless race types" was found to be prussic acid gas, which the Leverkusen plant of the chemical giant I.G. Farben produced under the trade name of Zyklon B and sold to the Nazi concentration camps. The company had stockpiled enough of the lethal gas to kill more than 200 million people, more than thirty times the actual number destroyed. One can only wonder how many people would have been left to rule had Hitler's Third Reich actually conquered the world (Sutton 1976, 37).

When the German atrocities were exposed to a horrified world at the Nuremberg trials during the late 1940s, the pseudoscience eugenics took upon itself a very low profile, and lost much of the support it had had among the scientific community. It is still very much alive in the minds of a few enthusiasts, however; an attempt was made as recently as 1969, by Jensen, to revive the myth of innate physiological racial differences, said to be responsible for higher intelligence among white people as compared with blacks (Van Evrie 1868).[18] We should be reminded that the Nazi extermination of six million "racial undesirables" began with the quiet implementation of Galton's eugenics by the medical profession and within a decade had grown to become an "industry" of human destruction.

Before leaving this section, the committed Darwinist, loathe to see a lifetime's inspiration associated in any way with obvious political despots, is inclined to raise the objection that Darwinian social science cannot lead to socialism and certainly should not bear the stigma of

Marxism. Haeckel expressed this argument, typically, by pointing out, "The theory of selection teaches that in human life, as in animal and plant life everywhere, and at all times, only a small and chosen minority can exist and flourish, while the enormous majority starve and perish miserably and more or less prematurely" (Haeckel 1879b, 93).

In short, the political doctrine implied by natural selection is elitist, and the principle derived according to Haeckel is "aristocratic in the strictest sense of the word" (p. 93). Now this was precisely the Fascist ideal of the Nazi Socialist party, that is, rule by the elite. However, Fascism or Marxism, right wing or left—all these are only ideological roads that lead to Aldous Huxley's brave new world, while the foundation for each of these roads is Darwin's theory of evolution (Carmichael 1954, 373).[19] Fascism is aligned with biological determinism and tends to emphasize the unequal struggle by which only those inherently fittest shall rule. Marxism stresses social progress by stages of revolution, while at the same time it paradoxically emphasizes peace and equality (UNESCO 1972).[20] There should be no illusions; Hitler borrowed freely from Marx. The result is that both Fascism and Marxism finish at the same destiny—totalitarian rule by the elite.[21] Nolte (1966) has pointed out that Fascism and Marxism have this mutual bond,[22] and a moment's thought will show that the living conditions under General Franco of Spain or those in the Soviet Union during the same period were the same—permanent rule by the elite, with no free elections, representation, or trade unions, with censored media and, always, a fear of one's neighbor. The French socialist promise given in 1793 of liberty, equality, and fraternity could not have been a greater lie.

Cyril Burt—Eugenics' Death Knell

In some of his early work, Galton had included the study of twins separated at birth and brought up under different environments. This was a very obvious way of identifying the effects of nature and nurture since the twins would be genetically identical. However, Galton had used his trusty calipers to measure intelligence, and, sure enough, although the twins had received different kinds of nurture, their intelligence was seen to be identical. This confirmed Galton's fondest hopes, and intelligence was thereby held to be strictly an inherited entity. During the 1930s, the English psychologist Cyril Burt, a committed hereditarian and, thus, of the biological determinist school, began to repeat Galton's work with twins, although the discredited calipers were now replaced with modified Binet I.Q. tests. Burt eventually obtained a position with the London County Council and had access to birth records, in which he located a total of fifty-three sets of twins that had, for one reason or another, been separated at birth. His published work, over the years, showed that although their environmental backgrounds were quite different, the mental characteristics of each pair were the same. This was taken to confirm Galton's work. This was a signal victory for those on the nature side of the nature-nurture controversy and amply supported the eugenicist. Burt became the dominant voice in educational psychology in Great Britain, which eventually earned him a knighthood.

When Burt died in 1971, the nagging doubts some had felt regarding the authenticity of his work gradually became confirmed, and by the time Professor Hearnshaw, who began as an admirer of Burt, had finished the definitive biography, it was evident that science had a major scandal on its hands. Cyril Burt had fabricated research data and invented non-existent colleagues to write supportive articles in the *British Journal of Psychology*, of which Burt was the editor. He had also invented two nonexistent collaborators and attempted to steal the credit for C.E. Spearman's statistical work on factor analysis (Gould 1981, 234). For all this thoroughly unscientific effort, Hearnshaw graciously suggested that Burt suffered from paranoia (Hearnshaw 1979, 289). The affair discredited the biological determinist position, should have been the final blow to eugenics (although only time will tell), and was no doubt gleefully seen as a victory by the rival nurture school. It is the behavioral determinist "nurture" school that has the dominant position today (Mahoney 1976).[23]

Wilson's Sociobiology

A year or so before Burt's fraud was exposed, Edward Wilson of Harvard University produced his massive half million word study *Sociobiology: The New Synthesis* (1975). This was actually a synthesis of a number of other people's ideas, but finished as Wilson's theory, which stated that there is a biological basis for all social behavior in the animal kingdom. This view is firmly based on biological evolution. It proposes that whether insects, animals, or man are considered, there are specific genes that control behavior. Wilson is an acknowledged expert on insect behavior. He spent twenty-six chapters of his book rightfully in this area, but then, in the twenty-seventh, launched out and applied his findings to man. This controversial chapter and, subsequently, an entire book (*On Human Nature*, 1978), is primarily an extended speculation on the existence of genes for specific and variable traits in human behavior—including spite, aggression, xenophobia, conformity, homosexuality, and the characteristic differences between men and women.

Wilson began in this study with a question that severely troubled Darwin and concerned altruism among species. By the rules of natural selection, it is dog-eat-dog and only the fittest survive, but, in fact, many creatures cooperate and defend others even at the cost of their own lives. Wilson's proposal was that it was all in the genes. All very complicated, to be sure, but if there can be a gene for altruism, then there can be genes for other qualities, and so we find the list for human behavior. Presently, there is virtually no data to support this theory, but proponents will no doubt be found, evidence apparently supporting it reported, and contrary evidence suppressed. And by the familiar bootstrap technique, sociobiology will become a "respectable" science.

Unlike Galton, Wilson is not a eugenicist and does not suggest inherent eliteness, although he has been severely criticized by scientist and layman alike for providing opportunities for eugenicists and overt racists to use his findings to justify racial discrimination. The eugenicist has surely had his day, but a more serious consequence of this as yet unproven theory is likely to be in the area of ethics, since it destroys the concept of free will. It is perfectly evident from other scientific theories reviewed in these pages that Wilson's theory does not have to be proven in order to be accepted—all that is required is a nucleus of devotees with a will to believe. It should be possible, after a modicum of acceptance among the scientific community, for thieves, murderers, and homosexual offenders to be legally defended from "science" by arguing that the accused are simply acting out the dictates of their genes and, therefore, are not morally responsible for their actions. This may be recognized as Rousseau's dictum that man is inherently good, dressed in modern guise.

The Nurture Side of the Controversy

Franz Boas (1858-1942) was raised in a Jewish home in Germany by liberal "free-thinking" parents, and he was particularly influenced by his mother, who was something of a political activist in the abortive German socialist revolution of 1848 (Kardiner and Preble 1961, 134). Graduating with a doctorate in physics at the age of twenty-three, he turned to anthropometry, or the measurement of the human body, and received training under the great Rudolph Virchow. Now well qualified, he entered the United States in 1887 and rose to be America's foremost anthropologist. Boas was well aware of the wild racist claims made by the eugenicists, mentioned earlier, and was particularly sensitive to their claims that America was being polluted by "worthless races from Europe's ghettos".

Boas set about conducting a vast study of immigrant parents and children. The first study was carried out in 1891 and demonstrated what hundreds of subsequent public health studies continue to show today—that the children of poor parents grow and develop at rates far lower than those of more affluent families (Boas 1892). Boas had a running battle with the eugenicists, and this work should have shown that, contrary to their views, environment had a significant effect. With characteristic German thoroughness, Boas continued the research and, in 1912, published the results of a massive work in which he studied the variations in head forms of 17,821 subjects. Eugenicists had argued that the shape of the head was characteristic of "race", but Boas showed that significant differences occurred in head shape between American immigrants (Italians, Czechs, and Jews) and their American-born children, the differences varying directly with the length of time the parents had been in the United States. The changes were all in the direction of the Anglo-Saxon type dominant in that country (Boas 1912). In 1916 Boas pointed out that "the more far-reaching the environmental influences that act upon successive generations, the more readily will be a false impression of heredity be given" (Boas 1916, 472).

An example might be the biceps of the blacksmith, which appear to be transmitted from father to son when the son follows the father in the same occupation; however, diet and even geographical location are also known to have an influence during the growth stage of human development. It was not surprising, then, that beginning with a preconception, the committed eugenicist would be deceived by this kind of evidence, which appears to support the hereditarian notion. The better scientist, Boas, had dug deeper and discovered the truth, which was that the genetic characteristics contributed by each parent are not entirely fixed characters but rather potentialities dependent on the environment for the particular form they will eventually assume.

The nature-nurture controversy should have died with this classic work of Boas in 1916, but, in fact, a recent book by Eysenck and Kamin (1981) shows that the argument still has its protagonists.[24] Some of the prejudice-generated smoke can be cleared by considering peas in a pod rather than people and races (the author is indebted to Chase 1980, 637 for this analogy). All the peas in a single pod are phenotypes grown from a single genotype and, therefore, are related to each other in the same way as human twins. If the individual peas are planted in separate pots and placed in differing environments, some with proper sunlight and water and others in harsh, shady conditions without adequate nutrition, their growth rates and final appearance, as would be expected, will be quite different. Here, the inheritance has been the same, but nurture has caused radical differences in the final result; this is what Boas had shown with his immigrant studies. All is not quite so clear-cut as this example may suggest, however, because unlike the peas, people do not all arrive from the same pod. The other half of this experiment consists of planting different varieties of peas under identical conditions. Where these conditions are good, each resulting pea plant would reach its full potential; some plant varieties, for example, would be taller and some shorter. Where the conditions are poor, some varieties would respond better than others. This is where the eugenicist argues that in the dim and distant past some "peas" originated from an entirely different and superior kind of "plant". The argument is one from silence, but the eugenicist always lives in the hopes that each new fossil man discovery will break that silence.

Now it has to be agreed that there are racial differences, and color is perhaps the most obvious example. The cultural or behavioral determinist school of Boas would certainly have to admit that environment has had no effect on the color of the Negro since he left Africa for the cooler northern climate, six to ten generations ago, and, by the same token, the Dutch immigrants to South Africa have not changed color either. Common experience would also tell us that tall parents tend to have tall children, although, like the peas, if the child is nurtured under impoverished conditions, it will not reach its full potential height.

It should now be evident that both heredity and environment play an important role. When all is said and done, many parents having two or more children know that even though they have had a similar genetic makeup and have been raised in the same environment, there can still be great differences in appearance, intelligence, and temperament. So far as intelligence is concerned, below average parents can produce brilliant children and intellectually brilliant parents can have below average children. This is a common enough observation yet has evidently passed unnoticed by some of the world's scientific elite. Nobel prize-winner and life-long Marxist Herman J. Muller advocated human sperm-banks in 1946. California's Robert Graham has recently put this idea into practice. Five Nobel prize-winners have contributed to *The Herman J. Muller Repository for Germinal Choice* (William B. Shockley is one admitted donor), and when reported in 1980, three women were pregnant (Broad 1980). The very existence of a human sperm-bank with the object of perpetuating genius indicates that even those who occupy the most exalted halls of science are not immune from the type of irrationality practiced by the eugenicists and the extreme element in the biological determinist school. We will now look at one or two examples of the cultural or behavioral determinists who went to the opposite extreme.

Scientific Sanction for Free Love

Margaret Mead was a diminutive twenty-three-year-old graduate student, assigned by Professor Franz Boas of Columbia University to study the adolescent culture of the Samoan people. One of the priorities of this nine-month exercise in the South Sea Islands, begun in 1926, was to attack an idea then popular in Germany and originating from the rival "nature" school. This school argued that the turmoil of adolescence was a biological necessity and, therefore, universal.

Boas maintained that the turmoil evident among Western youth was more cultural than biological and ascribed its cause, among other things, to repression imposed by the Judeo-Christian ethic on the adolescent's discovery of sexuality (Kardiner and Preble 1961, 139).[25] The people of Samoa were removed, historically and geographically, from the influence of the Christian church, and even though there were a few missionaries and churches, it was felt that the native people were sufficiently unspoiled, and that the effect of indigenous culture could be separated out by judicious questioning. Mead studied only sixty-eight teenage girls and, by a great stroke of luck, discovered, to her satisfaction, and more significantly to her professor's satisfaction, that indeed there were no inhibitions against casual "love under the palm trees", and, in consequence, there were no guilt feelings, and adolescent turmoil was unknown (Mead 1973, 67, 72, 75). This was surely worth a doctorate, while, as a further accolade, Mead popularized her findings in *Coming of Age in Samoa*, which when first published in 1928 immediately became a highly controversial best-seller. It was still being reprinted forty-five years later.

Mead's future was assured, and she spent the next fifty years promoting the message that as a result of our code of ethics, which included prohibition of premarital sex and sex with only one life partner within the family unit, Westerners suffer guilt, stress, and adolescent turmoil. She hastened to point out that the scientific evidence shows that happy, graceful lives can be lived with casual family ties and easy sex without signs of guilt or neurosis. Mead became the darling of humanists such as Bertrand Russell (1929, 132) and Havelock Ellis, who cited her work often to promote their own ideas of sexual liberation. She was also the natural ally of those who promoted free education, relaxed sexual norms, and parental permissiveness. Between Mead and Benjamin Spock, the pattern of North American child rearing was radically changed, and the fruits of their labors are now becoming evident in today's divorce statistics. Mead's own modest contribution to these statistics consisted of having had three husbands, which would seem to refute the promise of a happy and graceful life she claimed science

Margaret Mead, 1901-78. The anthropologist being quizzed by students during
one of her visits to an American university in 1968. Her advocacy of greater
sexual freedom, legalized marijuana, and two-stage marriages made her a virtual
guru on campuses during the turbulent 1960s. (Bob Levin, Black Star)

showed to be possible with the liberated sexual lifestyle. Ironically, for
both science and the alleged happy life, Mead, one of America's leading
scientists and a purported Christian, died in 1978 in the arms of a
psychic faith healer.[26]

In 1983 anthropologist Derek Freeman produced his *Margaret Mead
and Somoa: The Making and Unmaking of an Anthropological Myth*,
in which he showed that Mead's work had been based on a lie. Mead
had reported:

> Romantic love as it occurs in our civilization inextricably bound
> up with ideas of monogamy, exclusiveness, jealousy and unde-
> viating fidelity does not occur in Samoa. Our attitude is a com-
> pound...of the institution of monogamy, of the ideas of the age of
> chivalry, of the ethics of Christianity (Mead 1973, 79).

Mead's happy picture of Samoan life, gleaned in only a few months,
was of a society in which there were only loose family ties, uninhibited
by paternal authority, and with mere lip service paid to bridal virginity;
she further hinted that forcible rape, when it occurred at all, was
unknown prior to the introduction of the moral trappings of white
civilization (Mead 1973, 70). Freeman had spent half his life studying

the Samoan culture and, in complete contrast, found the Samoans to have always had firm family ties, to be quite authoritarian, and to strongly maintain a cult of virginity that forbade premarital sex. Moreover, Freeman more diligently dug up the rape statistics and pointed out that Mead had evidently not read a local newspaper, such as the Samoan *Times*, which regularly reported rape cases during her stay in 1925-26.

Clearly, Mead's was hardly an objective and scientific exercise. Freeman charitably suggests that Mead was the unprepared innocent receiving compliant replies to questions unwittingly slanted to elicit her preconceived views. This type of bias was constantly to be guarded against and, in Mead's case, resulted in half-truths, if not pure fiction, presented as fact representative of the whole. Her doctorate gave the exercise scientific credence, swaying the minds of liberal educators and any others who had reasons for wanting to believe. Fifty years later it seems the truth can be told, but, unfortunately, two generations deluded by this pseudoscience have now set a pattern of behavior difficult to correct.

Behavioral Modification

Harvard's Burrhus F. Skinner is one of the most controversial advocates of the nurture school. From 1930 he carried out experimental work with rats and later with pigeons in what became known as the "Skinner box". The box enabled the environment to be controlled while the subject's behavior could be studied in terms of the conditioned reflex. By pressing a lever, the rat could obtain a reward of a food pellet, or the experimenter could administer a punishment by means of a mild electric shock. In this way, much was learned about the learning process and the most efficient means of modifying the subject's behavior was determined. Skinner summarized his findings in *The Behavior of Organisms* (1938), but within a decade had applied the implication of conditioning principles to society at large in *Walden Two* (1948), a fictional description of a utopian community in which education and social regulation are based on rewarding techniques. Some critics saw in this innovation shades of Aldous Huxley's *Brave New World*, where society was controlled by reward, and greeted the book with fear and dismay. Nevertheless, the Skinner teaching techniques have been widely used for school children, although by use of a teaching machine rather than in a box with food pellets! (Skinner 1979).[27] In addition, by cooperation with drug companies, the effects of certain drugs to aid children with learning difficulties have been studied. Although new understanding has been gained, the whole idea of modifying human

Skinner's baby conditioner in which his daughter spent the first two years of her life being "conditioned". Skinner's attempt to market this device as an "Heir-conditioner" was not successful. (Photograph by Stuart, *People Weekly*)

behavior in a purposeful way has not been an overwhelming success, and the specter of crossing that fine line, from "aid" to "control" of tomorrow's society in today's classroom, has yet to become a total reality.

The vision of behavioral modification still has its enthusiasts. For example, in 1978 Sobell and Sobell reported a program to modify the behavior of a group of twenty gamma alcoholics. In this they used the electric shock "punishment" technique. These researchers believed that behavior therapy would enable hard-core alcoholics to become social drinkers, rather than having to become total abstainers. The experiment was widely reported to be successful, and the United States government began to invest considerable sums of money into this new approach. However, an independent study of the same twenty patients in a ten-year follow-up showed a totally different picture with only one success (Pendery et al. 1982). This is another scandal, and the most charitable conclusion would be that, like Burt and Mead, the theory in the minds of the Sobells assumed greater importance than the facts.

As in the case of biological determinism (nature), behavioral determinism (nurture) also denies the free will, since this says, in effect, that we are simply a product of our environment rather than a product of our genes. Clearly, both factors are important, but even then the human psyche involves far more than mere machine response to a combination of biological and environmental circumstances. It would be extremely difficult for humanistic psychology, however, based as it is on evolution, to acknowledge a spiritual dimension to man; this opens up a philosophical minefield involving the destiny of souls, for instance; as mentioned in the opening chapter, the committed humanist cannot accept such a view.

During the past century a great deal of serious work has been done in the field of psychology, and it would be wrong to leave the reader with the impression that the social sciences are little more than schools for scandal. Nevertheless, it has been necessary here to expose some of these extreme views because of their importance and to give some hint of what constitutes the third leg of the evolutionary structure that supports today's doctrine of secular humanism.

Secular Humanism

In the broadest sense, humanism is any view that recognizes the value and dignity of the individual and seeks to better the human condition; none should fault this noble aspiration. From our brief excursion through history in Chapter One, we saw how the Greek ideals and their rationalism became fused with the Judeo-Christian values, and that from about the time of the Renaissance in the fourteenth century, two basically different types of humanism emerged and persist today. The first is theistic humanism, which holds to a belief in the centrality of God and is characterized by Catholic, including Anglican, thought. Within the spectrum of views held by theistic humanists, Charles F. Potter (1930) very clearly spelled out the destiny of this viewpoint in his *Humanism, a New Religion.*

The second is naturalistic or anthropocentric (man-centered) humanism nourished by the evolutionary thoughts of the nineteenth century and given its biggest impetus by Darwin. It is this second kind of humanism that constitutes secular humanism and is the predominant worldview today. It views mankind as an integral part of nature and thus denies the human soul; it limits values to what has value for humankind, and thus ethics and morals become situational; and it denies the existence of God or relegates him to a non-functional role. In short, secular humanism follows the famous dictum of Protagoras that man is the measure of all things and must create his own life. Natural man thereby replaces the supernatural God and becomes the master of his destiny (Holmes 1983, 16).

The atheistic base of secular humanism can be established precisely from almost any of the humanist literature, but the statement in the preface to the second Humanist Manifesto, published in 1973 (the first was published in 1933), is fully representative:

> As in 1933, humanists still believe that traditional theism, especially faith in a prayer-hearing God, assumed to love and care for persons, to hear and understand their prayers, and to be able to do something about them, is an unproved and outmoded faith. Salvationism, based on mere affirmation, still appears as harmful,

diverting people with false hopes of heaven hereafter. Reasonable minds look to other means of survival (Kurtz and Wilson 1973, 4).

As one of today's leading spokesmen for humanism, Corliss Lamont is more specific; he makes the following statement in his *The Philosophy of Humanism*:

> Humanism believes that Nature itself constitutes the sum total of reality, that matter-energy and not mind is the foundation stuff of the universe....This non reality of the supernatural means, on the human level, that men do not possess supernatural and immortal souls; and on the level of the universe as a whole, that our cosmos does not possess a supernatural and eternal God (Lamont 1977, 116).

Lamont also adds that "since agnostics are doubtful about the supernatural, they tend to be Humanist in practice" (Lamont 1977, 45), precisely the point brought out in the opening statements of Chapter Fourteen. The mere rejection of God, however, does not necessarily produce a humanist since, as it was shown in Chapter Thirteen, there is the counterpart religious requirement of commitment. The commitment, in this case, is to a positive belief in the possibilities of human progress. This belief is supported by, and often results from, the belief in evolution, which is the essential alternative to explaining our material existence, and Lamont dutifully makes his confession of belief:

> Biology has conclusively shown that man and all other forms of life were the result, not of a supernatural act of God, but of an infinitely long process of evolution probably stretching over at least two billion years....With its increasing complexity, there came about an accompanying development and integration of animal behavior and control, culminating in the species man and in the phenomenon called mind. Mind, in short, appeared at the present apex of the evolutionary process and not at the beginning (Lamont 1977, 83).

One of the most marked characteristics of humanism is its amorality as a result of a corrosion of traditional moral values. This may seem like an evolutionary paradox; as implied earlier from the writings of Herbert Spencer, in evolving from the animal, man passed from the amoral to the moral. Spencer believed, as many still do, that ethics, as signified by our legal code, has also evolved into increasing complexity. That being so, we would expect traditional moral offenses to be legislated against ever more severely. Such is not the case, however, because of two overriding humanist mandates. The first argues that since there is no God, the Judeo-Christian principles that form the basis of our legal system were not God given and, consequently, can be changed to fit the situation without fear of divine retribution. This is the root of today's teaching of situation ethics. The second argument follows Rousseau's proposition that man is inherently good and consequently reason dictates that it is simply the historic imposition of harsh laws that has caused man to appear bad. Thus, freed from the metaphysical fetters of Judeo-Christian principles, the humanist then believes that man is free to be his own master. Lamont continues on the theme of man's newfound freedom:

> For Humanism the central concern is always the happiness of man in this existence, not in some fanciful never-never land beyond the grave; a happiness worthwhile as an end in itself and not subordinate to or dependent on a Supreme Deity (Lamont 1977, 30).

Another humanist writer specifically links Darwin and humanist amorality:

> Darwin's discovery of the principle of evolution sounded the death knell of religious and moral values. It removed the ground from under the feet of traditional religion (Chawla 1964).

Taken in their most elemental form, "religious and moral values", whether they be for the Jew, the Christian, or the Moslem, are based on the bibilical ten commandments, the last six of which deal with man's relationship to his fellow man. Many of these commandments apply to areas of man's sexuality. It is, then, not surprising that the humanist movement has been vitally concerned with "liberating" man from restrictive codes of sexual behavior. We have seen that Margaret Mead supplied much support for this notion. For example, the laws forbidding incest, which has been a universal taboo since the days of Moses, have been relaxed in Sweden, thus permitting free violation of the fifth commandment, while it is apparent that our media are attempting to give every encouragement for violation of the seventh. In the past few years, there has been a concerted effort on the part of liberal educators to introduce sex education into the school system, while more recently this has been accompanied by the availability of free and confidential contraceptive services. The justification given is that these services are necessary to combat venereal diseases—particularly Herpes simplex— which have now gone beyond endemic proportions. This rationale is actually a well-worn strategem. Yet, nevertheless, it still works, for the public expectation is to equate authority with integrity. The strategy consists of studied procrastination—a House investigation committee or a Royal Commission are the usual devices. Then, when memories are dim, the early sequence of events is reversed so that the effect is now claimed to be the cause. In this way, the heaping of more coals, rather than less, on the fire is justified. Sex education was extended to even earlier school grades.

The final humanist objective is socialist world government with, of course, the humanist elite in control. To some, this may appear the rational answer to the world's problems, yet a moment's thought on some of the horror stories made public and that are associated with big government should call to mind Lord Acton's warning in 1887: "Power tends to corrupt and absolute power corrupts absolutely" (Acton 1972, 335). Nevertheless, the humanist faith surpasses the historical record, and the humanist vision includes full-scale nationalization of industry and dissolution of national identity as each government becomes subordinate to the supergovernment. The document that expresses this most clearly has only recently been made public and consists of the framework policy for UNESCO, written about 1946 by Julian Huxley and mentioned earlier in this chapter. The UNESCO preparatory commission "withheld sponsorship of the text" of this document, which meant, in effect, that the policy of this public body was restricted to those with a "need to know" for thirty years, by which time it was felt that the climate of public opinion would accept its disclosure; it was finally published by UNESCO in 1976 (J. Huxley 1976, 14). Having established that the philosophy of UNESCO should be "evolutionary in background", Huxley continues:

> From the evolutionary point of view, the destiny of man may be summed up very simply: it is to realize the maximum progress in the minimum time. This is why the philosophy of UNESCO must have an evolutionary background and why the concept of progress cannot but occupy a central position in that philosophy (J. Huxley 1976, 23).

Shades of tautological reasoning may be detected in this statement as it equates evolution with progress, but be that as it may, Huxley cautiously introduces the idea of the one world government:

> The moral for UNESCO is clear. The task laid upon it to promote peace and security can never be wholly realized through the means assigned to it—education, science and culture. It must envision some form of world political unity, whether through a single

The United Nations Educational, Scientific and Cultural Organization
(UNESCO) building in Paris. (Jones, UNESCO)

world government or otherwise, as the only certain means for
avoiding war (J. Huxley 1976, 23).

Finally, after proposing dissolution of national sovereignty, which has
since been attempted with the European Common Market, Huxley's
policy concludes:

> The unifying of traditions into a single common pool of exper-
> ience, awareness, and purpose is the necessary prerequisite for
> further major progress in human evolution. Accordingly,
> although political unification in some sort of world government
> will be required for the definitive attainment of this stage, unifica-
> tion in the things of the mind is not only necessary also but it can
> pave the way for other types of unification (J. Huxley 1976, 30).

The phrase "unification in the things of the mind" is perhaps one of
the key elements in the concept of single world government, and since
"maximum progress in minimum time" is a necessary mandate, unification can most effectively take place in the nation's schoolrooms
beginning at the elementary grades where minds are most receptive.
Skinner's work on behavioral modification has been seen as a vital tool
in unifying young minds, and there are even serious advocates of
modification by pharmacological means (Ladd 1970).[28]

Unification of the Mind in the Schools

The humanist influence has been particularly forceful in the educational field and, in recent years, has received an increasing and universal directive from the UNESCO organization. As an early example of their intention to abolish all ideas of national sovereignty, the following statement appeared in the UNESCO publication entitled "In the classroom with children under thirteen years of age"; it was intended for the teaching profession and, although undated, was issued about 1949:

> As long as the child breathes the poisoned air of nationalism, education in world-mindedness can produce only rather precarious results. As we have pointed out, it is frequently the family which infects the child with extreme nationalism. The school should therefore use the means described earlier to combat family attitudes (UNESCO 1949, 58).

In the United States the humanist element can be traced back as far as Horace Mann, who proposed that removal of the Bible from the schools would greatly increase genuine educational progress. Throughout the nineteenth century, the Bible had been used, especially in elementary classes, as a universally available book from which to teach good English and, at the same time, to impart a code of moral behavior.

John Dewey (1859-1952) picked up Mann's banner and almost singlehandedly reformed the American school system to conform to humanist ideals; the Bible was banished and so, eventually, was school prayer. The present-day, somewhat questionable standards of the American educational system are thus seen by some to be directly attributable to Dewey. Dewey's humanist credentials were established by signing the first Humanist Manifesto in 1933, by contributing regularly to such left-wing periodicals as *New Republic*, and in receiving socialist honors for aiding Trotsky at his Moscow trial, in 1936-37. Dewey was responsible for introducing Darwin's theory into the American school system (Clark 1960).

The steadily increasing humanist influence on education eventually came into conflict with the Christian element at the famous Scopes "monkey" trial in 1926, described in Chapter Eight. The Christian cause was championed by William Jennings Bryan, who placed his faith in the common people and resented the attempt of a few thousand humanists "to establish an oligarchy over forty million American Christians" (Coletta 1969, 230) and dictate what should be taught in the schools. Bryan referred to it as a "scientific soviet" (Levine 1965, 289).

Today, the tables are completely turned, and the evolutionary interpretation of natural science is taught in schools and universities to the exclusion of any other interpretation. This has been brought about by the dedicated efforts of liberal educators following in Dewey's footsteps and the virtual absence of any opposition from the church. In the past decade, however, mounting and effective opposition has been heard from a number of concerned organizations spearheaded by the Institute for Creation Research, California (Numbers 1982). The humanist influence on the American educational system has been thoroughly documented by La Haye (1980) to whom parts of this chapter are indebted.

Unification of the Mind by the Media

Finally, in completing this section on unifying the things of the mind, we must recognize how our thoughts and opinions are molded by the information we receive daily through magazines, newspapers, radio, and television. For that reason there has traditionally been a system of checks and balances whereby all facts that are known may be aired and opposing viewpoints heard. For the past decade or so, however, mere lip service has been paid to this vital freedom as news syndicates have coalesced to a single viewpoint—that of the humanist.

There has, in effect, been a censorship or severe curtailment of news items that do not support either the theory of evolution or the socialist ideals. An example of this type of censorship was the occasion of the catch of the dead creature by the Japanese fishermen in 1977 (described in Chapter Four). The discovery evidently came close to upsetting the foundation for secular humanism, and there was a virtual news blackout in the western hemisphere, even though the museums and the National Geographical Society were fully informed.[29] In contrast, the Japanese press, radio, and television gave this item full coverage and even commemorated the event with a postage stamp depicting the

In 1977 the Japanese celebrated one hundred years of scientific discovery with a National Exhibition and chose the *Plesiosaur* as discovery of the year for the celebration emblem.

creature as a *plesiosaur,* or sea-dwelling dinosaur. Quite evidently, unfortunate incidents such as this discovery must come under full control. As a further step in accomplishing unification of the world's mind, the last item in the humanist manifesto is currently being put into effect. The item reads: "We must expand communication and transportation across frontiers....The world must be open to diverse political, ideological, and moral viewpoints and evolve a worldwide system of television and radio for information and education" (Kurtz and Wilson 1973, 8).

In 1980 the general conference of UNESCO in Belgrade adopted a resolution to include the principles of a New World Information and Communication Order. Since that time there has been a coercive attempt to bring the free-world's television and radio news media under a single beneficent banner, purportedly with the object of maintaining freedom of the press and information. However, the United States government perceived the real motives to be quite the reverse when it was suggested that journalists be licensed "for their protection", and withdrew its membership from UNESCO in December 1983.

Who Are the Secular Humanists?

Not every believer in evolution is a humanist, but it is an essential requirement that every humanist should believe in evolution. The distinction is made by the humanist's having made a commitment to a positive belief in the possibilities of human progress. For this reason, many who believe in the future of humanism now claim humanist credentials, and this cuts across every conceivable barrier. In religion, humanists may be Roman Catholic or Protestant, Jew or Buddhist, while among the professions, humanists are evident from archaeology to zoology. In politics, humanists may be Liberal or Conservative, Republican or Democrat. Knowledge of the personal life and beliefs of political candidates is important, since it is a vital part of leadership strategy to ensure that, regardless of party, every key position is filled by a humanist of proven commitment, thus accomplishing the humanist objective while giving the appearance of a democratic process.

There are now literally hundreds of humanist organizations mostly operating at a local level, but many operate on an international level through the United Nations agencies. The forerunners of these organizations began in the last century and were largely inspired by Marx and Engels. In England, for example, Marxist followers Sidney and Beatrice Webb founded the left-wing Fabian Society in 1884. Notable members were playwright Bernard Shaw and authors H.G. Wells and

Beatrice Webb, 1858-1943; Sidney Webb, 1859-1947; and Bernard Shaw, 1856-1950, founding members of the Fabian Society. (*Daily Herald*, London)

Jack London. The Webbs also founded the Marxist-oriented London School of Economics in 1895, to which many a leading socialist since has paid youthful homage (Caine 1963). In America, Felix Adler laid the ground for the American Ethical Union founded in 1889 in New York City. Since then, each of these Marxist-inspired organizations has spawned special interest groups of which the American Civil Liberties Union (ACLU) and the American Humanist Association (AHA) are perhaps the most visible in North America. The AHA, mentioned earlier in this chapter, began in 1928 with some students at the University of Chicago and the related Meadville Theological School. In 1933 the AHA drew up its first manifesto under the guiding hand of John Dewey, while 1973 saw the publication of the second humanist manifesto containing seventeen objectives and signed by 120 leading humanists identified by name and affiliation. The Unitarian Church was well represented by its ministers, while other names of note included the science author Isaac Asimov; Nobel prize winner (for DNA) Francis Crick; Canadian abortionist Henry Morgentaler; psychologists Hans Eysenck, B.F. Skinner, and Lord Richie-Calder, formerly rector of the University of Edinburgh.

The editorial board of the American Humanist Association (1979) made no secret of the fact that there is a very close connection between their membership and United Nations organizations. This leaves little room to doubt that the objectives of the two organizations, as outlined in the second manifesto, are essentially the same; in the case of Huxley's *Philosophy for UNESCO*, there could be no possible doubt. From among the contributors to the AHA publication, *The Humanist*, we find Brock Chisholm, director general of the World Health Organization (WHO); Lord Boyd Orr, director general of the United Nations Food and Agriculture Organization; U. Thant, director general of the United Nations; and other humanist luminaries, such as U.S. Senator Barry Commoner, medical missionary Albert Schweitzer, and philosopher Bertrand Russell. In 1959 Gerald Wendt retired as head of the natural sciences at UNESCO to become editor of *The Humanist*. Clearly there is a positive link between the humanist organizations and the United Nations.

* * *

Although humanism is surely as old as Cain, an attempt has been made in these chapters to trace its path from the Greek philosophers to the plateau reached at the time of the French Revolution. Orthodox religion, and the Bible in particular, stood in the way of further advancement until the mid-nineteenth century. The humanist philosophy then received its most vital impetus at the unwitting hand of Charles Darwin from which it has been propelled into the twentieth century to become secular humanism, the dominant worldview of today.

The theory of evolution is the platform on which secular humanism stands, yet as we have seen, this is not only a hollow structure with shifting timbers but is in danger of collapsing altogether. Less than a decade ago it would have been virtually impossible to speak out in criticism of Darwin, so closely was his name associated with evolution regardless of the mechanism supposedly responsible. Today, many voices are raised and writers such as Rifkin (1983) and Taylor (1983) have actually entered the secular publishing world and openly exposed the grand delusion to which Darwin had committed his life. Legions of others since have made that same commitment and will find it difficult if not impossible to deny their faith, but for the rest, it is hoped that these pages will have brought some understanding of today's world turmoil.

With the humanist influence felt in virtually all positions of power, secular and sacred, the time is rapidly approaching when the supporting structure of purported evidence can be replaced entirely by fiat. Even now, the mechanism of evolution and contrary evidence is waived aside in deference to the statement that evolution is a fact. We can confidently expect to see Darwin finally buried and forgotten as one of science's embarrassing moments.

The new Darwin will be a marriage of convenience between science and religion and, as in any marriage of this type, will be a disaster for both parties. Nevertheless, even today we can see abundant evidence of this union in the political outworkings of what is left of freedom in Western society; the encroachment of Communism from without and the welcoming hand of secular humanism from within. Democracy has long been an illusion and reality shows that, as in the past, we shall always be under some form of totalitarian rule. Historically, the lesson is clear, and it is well to be reminded that under the rule of man there has been a general decline in prosperity accompanied by rising unemployment; the Socialist solution in the past has been to cull off the excess population by the guillotine, gas chamber, and labor camp. On the other hand, nations truly under God's rule have prospered without these horrors and the old British Empire and North America, at least until a decade or so ago, were the classic examples. This then is the choice before all thinking individuals; it is a choice as old as mankind and offers us rule by an inevitably corrupt humanist elite or rule by a benevolent, all wise, and incorruptible Creator.

APPENDIX A

Malthusian Progression Derived From 1798 Edition of
An Essay on the Principle of Population

PERIOD IN YEARS	POPULATION GROWTH	SUBSISTENCE IN ACRES	POPULATION PER ACRE
25	2	2	1
50	4	3	1+
75	8	4	2
100	16	5	3+
125	32	6	5+
150	64	7	9+
175	128	8	16+
200	256	9	28
225	512	10	51
250	1,024	11	93
275	2,048	12	170
300	4,096	13	315

APPENDIX B

Increasing Estimates of the Age of the Earth

AUTHORITY	YEAR OF DETERMINATION	AGE IN MILLIONS OF YEARS
	1850	25
Kelvin	1862	20
Kelvin	1897	40
J. Joly	1899	90
Rayleigh	1921	1,000
W. O. Hotchkiss	1932	1,600
A. Holmes	1947	3,350
L. Ahrens	1949	2,500
A. Holmes	1956	4,500
Still accepted	1984	4,500

Note the sudden increase in estimated age with the introduction of the radiometric method in 1921. Throughout, the estimated age appears to double about every twenty years, and it would, therefore, seem another increase is imminent.

Uranium 238 to Lead 206 Decay Series

ISOTOPE	HALF-LIFE	EMMISSION
Uranium 238	4.55 x 10⁹ years	Alpha
Thorium 234	24.1 days	Beta
Protactinium 234	1.14 minute	Beta
Uranium 234	235,000 years	Alpha
Thorium 230	80,000 years	Alpha
Radium 226	1,660 years	Alpha
Radon 222	3.85 days	Alpha
Polonium 218	3.05 minutes	Alpha
Lead 214	26.8 minutes	Beta
Bismuth 214	19.7 minutes	Beta
Polonium 214	15 x 10⁻⁵ seconds	Alpha
Lead 210	2.22 years	Beta
Bismuth 210	4.97 days	Beta
Polonium 210	139 days	Alpha
Lead 206	stable	none

APPENDIX D

Velocity of Light. Values Decreasing

AUTHORITY	YEAR OF DETERMINATION	OBSERVED VALUE Km/Sec	PREDICTED VALUE Km/Sec	DIFFERENCE BETWEEN OBSERVED & PREDICTED
Roemer	1675	301,300. ±200	301,422.8	- 122.8
Bradley	1728	301,000.	300,871.5	+128.5
Textbooks	1871	300,400. ±200	299,950.9	+449.1
Cornu-Helmert	1874	299,990.	299,937.7	+ 52.3
Michelson	1879	299,910. ± 50	299,922.1	- 12.1
Newcombe	1882	299,860 + 30	299,911.9	- 51.9
Michelson	1882	299,853. ± 60	299,911.7	- 58.7
Textbooks	1885	299,940.	299,905.0	+ 35.0
Perrotin	1902	299,901. ± 84	299,858.8	+ 42.2
Textbooks	1902	299,895.	299,857.9	+ 37.1
Textbooks	1906	299,880.	299,850.8	+ 29.2
Textbook	1924	299,802. ± 30	299,818.4	- 16.4
Michelson	1926	299,796. ± 4	299,814.9	- 18.9
Mittelstaedt	1928	299,778. ± 10	299,812.9	- 34.9
Pease-Pearson	1932	299,774. ± 11	299,808.1	- 34.1
Anderson	1939	299,771. ± 12	299,801.3	- 30.3
Huttel	1940	299,768. ± 10	299,800.4	- 32.4
Essen	1947	299,797. ±3	299,795.8	± 1.2

Continued on next page

Velocity of Light. Values Decreasing

AUTHORITY	YEAR OF DETERMINATION	OBSERVED VALUE Km/Sec	PREDICTED VALUE Km/Sec	DIFFERENCE BETWEEN OBSERVED & PREDICTED
Aslakson	1949	299,792.4 ±5.5	299,794.9	- 2.47
Bergstrand	1949	299,796. ±2	299,794.9	+ 1.13
Essen	1950	299,792.5 ±1	299,794.4	- 1.95
Bergstrand	1950	299,793.1 ±1	299,794.4	- 1.35
Bergstrand	1951	299,793.1 ±2.5	299,794.1	- 0.97
Aslakson	1951	299,794.2 ±1.4	299,794.1	± 0.13
Froome	1951	299,792.6 ±1.3	299,794.1	- 1.47
Kraus	1953	299,800.	299,793.4	± 6.57
Froome	1954	299,792.75 ±0.35	299,793.2	- 0.41
Florman	1954	299,795.1 ±3.1	299,793.2	+ 1.93
Scholdstrom	1955	299,792.4 ±0.4	299,792.9	- 0.54
Plyler et al.	1955	299,792.0 ±6	299,792.9	- 0.94
Plyler et al.	1955	299,793.0	299,792.9	+ 0.05
Cohen et al.	1955	299,793.0 ±0.3	299,792.9	+ 0.05
Bergstrand	1956	299,793.0 ±0.3	299,792.8	+ 0.23
Wadley	1956	299,792.9 ±2	299,792.8	+ 0.13
Rank et al.	1956	299,791.9 ±2	299,792.8	- 0.86
Edge	1956	299,792.4 ±0.4	299,792.8	- 0.36
Wadley	1957	299,792.6 ±1.2	299,792.6	- 0.02
Bergstrand	1957	299,792.9 ±0.2	299,792.6	+ 0.27
Rank et al.	1957	299,793.7 ±0.7	299,792.6	+ 1.07
Rank et al.	1957	299,793.2	299,792.6	+ 0.57
Mulligan et al.	1957	299,792.8 ±0.6	299,792.6	+ 0.17
Froome	1958	299,792.5 ±0.1	299,792.5	- 0.02
Corson et al.	1962	299,790	299,792.4	- 2.44
Karolus	1966	299,792.1 ±1	299,792.4	- 0.00
Helmberger	1966	299,792.44 ±0.2	299,792.4	- 0.00
Simkin et al.	1967	299,792.6 ±0.11	299,792.4	+ 0.11
I.T.T. Staff	1970	299,793	299,792.4	+ 0.55
Bay et al.	1972	299,792.5 ±0.02	299,792.4	+ 0.02
Evenson	1973	299,792.5 ±0.00	299,792.4	+ 0.01
Blaney	1974	299,792.5 ±0.00	299,792.4	+ 0.01
C.C.D.M. (Fr.)	1975	299,792.5 ±0.00	299,792.4	+ 0.01
A.P.French (txt.)	1976	299,792.5	299,792.4	+ 0.01

Light velocity values taken from the following principal sources:
- (A) 1973. Velocity of light 300 years ago. *Sky and Telescope* 45 (June): 353.
- (B) 1927. The velocity of light. *Science* 66 (30 September): page x in supplement.
- (C) Birge, R.T. 1934. *Nature* 134: 771.
- (D) Froome, K.D., and L. Essen. 1969. *The velocity of light and radio waves.* New York: Academic Press. p.137, Table 1.
- (E) Textbooks: Garside and Phillips. 1953. *A textbook of pure and applied chemistry*; Glasstone, S. 1950. *Sourcebook on atomic energy.*

APPENDIX E

Electron Rest Mass. Values Increasing

AUTHORITY	REFERENCE	YEAR OF DETERMINATION	VALUE x 10^{-31} Kg.
R.T. Birge	*Rev. Mod. Phys.* 1:1	1929	8.994
R.T. Birge	*Science* 75:383	1932	9.035
F.G. Dunnington	*Rev. Mod. Phys.* 11:70	1939	9.1070
R.T. Birge	*Phys. Rev.* 60:785	1941	9.1064
J.D. Ryder	*Electronic Eng. Princ.* p.3	1947	9.1060
G.I. Brown	*Mod. Valence Theory* p.167	1953	9.1066
W.J. Moore	*Physical Chemistry* p.209	1950-56	9.1068
H.H. Sisler	*General Chemistry* p.121	1949-59	9.1070
A.J. Woodall	*Physics* p.1239	1955	9.1078
E.R. Cohen et al.	*Rev. Mod. Phys.* 27:363	1955	9.1083
W.J. Moore	*Physical Chemistry* p.618	1957	9.1085
A.P. French	*Princ. Mod. Physics* p.109	1958	9.1085
Wehr & Richards	*Phy. of the Atom* p.41	1960	9.1084
Cohen & DuMond	*Proc. 2nd Int. Conf. Nuc. Mass*	1963	9.1091

APPENDIX F

Specific Charge or Charge to Mass Ratio
Value Decreasing

AUTHORITY	REFERENCE	YEAR OF DETERMINATION	VALUE q/m (x 10^7 emu/grm)
J.J. Thompson	*Basic Physics*, p.893	1900	1.7 600
Houston	*Intro. to Atom. Phy.* p.337	1927	1.7 600
R.T. Birge	*Rev. Mod. Phys.* 1:1	1929	1.7 60
R.T. Birge	*Science* 75:383	1932	1.7 60
F.G. Dunnington	*Phys. Rev.* 52:475	1937	1.7 597
Houston	*Intro. to Atom. Phys.* p.337	1938	1.7 593
F.G. Dunnington	*Rev. Mod. Phys.* 11:70	1939	1.7 591
R.T. Birge	*Phys. Rev.* 60:785	1941	1.7 592
Ryder	*Elec. Eng. Princ.* p.3	1947	1.7 590
Gardner	*Elec. & Mag.* p.639	1951	1.7 589
Cohen & DuMond	*Rev. Mod. Phys.* 25:706	1953	1.7 592
E.R. Cohen et al.	*Rev. Mod. Phys.* 27:363	1955	1.7 589
P. Fano	*Bas. Phys. At. & Mol.* p.11	1959	1.7 589
Wehr & Richards	*Phys. of the Atom* p.34	1960	1.7 589

APPENDIX G

Plank's Constant. Values Increasing

AUTHORITY	REFERENCE	YEAR OF DETERMINATION	VALUE (x 10^{-27} erg/sec)
M.E. Plank (In J.W. Nicholson)	*R.A.S., Mon. Not.* 72:677/629	1912	6.548
Ryerson Lab.	*Electrons* R.A. Millikan p.242	1904-15	6.260
L.P. Seig	*Sc. Am.* Supp. 1914, 78 (18 July): 46	1914	6.415
R.T. Birge	*Rev. Mod. Phys.* 1:1	1929	6.547
R.A. Millikan (In G.P. Thompson)	*Sc. Am.* 1930, 143 (30 July):38	1930	6.550
F.G. Dunnington	*Rev. Mod. Phys.* 11:70	1939	6.610
R.T. Birge	*Phys. Rev.* 60:785	1941	6.624
R.A. Millikan	*Electrons* p.242	1946	6.560
Martin & Connor	*Basic Physics* p.929	1951	6.622
G.I. Brown	*Mod. Valence Theory* p.16, 23	1953	6.624
E.R. Cohen et al.	*Rev. Mod. Phys.* 27:363	1955	6.6251
W.J. Moore	*Physical Chemistry* p.618	1957	6.6252
A.P. French	*Principles of Mod. Phys.* p.109	1958	6.6252
Wehr & Richards	*Physics of the Atom* p.65	1960	6.6253
Cohen & DuMond	*Proc. 2nd Int. Conf. on Nuc. Mass*	1963	6.6256
T. Barnes	*C.R.S. Quarterly* 1980, 17:46	1980	6.6262

APPENDIX H

Gyromagnetic Ratio. Values Decreasing

AUTHORITY	REFERENCE	DATE	g VALUE (rad/sec/gauss)
Thomas, Driscoll & Hipple	*Phys. Rev.* 78:787	1950	267 53.00
Cohen using the 1950 result	*Fund. Const. Phys.* p.269	1957	267 53.00
Driscoll & Bender	*Phys. Rev. Lett.* 1:413	1958	267 52.20
Vigoreux	*Proc. Roy. Soc.* A270:72	1962	267 52.03
Yagola, Zingermann, & Sepetyi	*Fund. Atom. Con.* p.45	1963	267 51.34
Yanovskii & Studentov	*Izmerit. Tekh.* 5:24	1963	267 51:30
Cohen & DuMond	*Proc. 2nd Int. Conf. Nuc. Mass*	1963	267 51.92
Taylor, Parker, & Langenberg	*Rev. Mod. Phys.* 41:375	1969	267 51.96
Wertz & Bolton	*Elec. Spin. Res.* Table A	1972	267 51.00

Note: The first determination was carried out in 1946 but only reported to three figures.

Half-lives of Some Radioactive Elements Increasng

AUTHORITY	DATE	IONIUM (x 10⁴ years)	RADIUM A (mins.)	RADIUM F (days)	PROTOACTINIUM (x 10⁴ years)	ACTINIUM (years)	ACTINIUM X (days)	ACTINIUM C (mins.)	THORIUM C (mins.)	CARBON 14 (years)
Soddy	1904	—	2.77	—	—	—	—	—	—	—
Rutherford	1904	—	—	—	—	—	—	—	55.	—
Rutherford	1913	7.0	3.00	136.0	—	—	10.5	3.47	60.0	—
Rutherford	1930	7.6	3.05	136.3	1.25	13.4	11.2	4.76	60.5	—
Crowther	1936	7.6	3.05	136.5	1.20	20.0	11.2	4.71	60.8	—
Hoyle	1947	—	—	—	—	—	—	—	—	5550
Libby	1949	—	—	—	—	—	—	—	—	5568
Libby	1950	—	—	—	—	—	—	—	—	5580
Glasstone	1950	8.0	3.05	140.0	3.20	21.7	11.2	4.76	60.5	—
Korsunsky	1958	8.3	3.05	140.0	3.20	—	11.4	4.76	60.5	5720
Rev. Mod. Phys.	1958	8.0	3.05	138.4	3.43	21.6	11.7	4.79	60.5	—
Upsala	1963	—	—	—	—	—	—	—	—	5685
AWRE, Eng.	1963	—	—	—	—	—	—	—	—	5760
NBS, U.S.A.	1963	—	—	—	—	—	—	—	—	5780
Gregory	1966	—	—	—	—	—	—	—	—	5760
Lammerts	1970	—	—	—	—	—	—	—	—	5760

APPENDIX J

Carbon 14 Dates Reported in *Radiocarbon Journal*

SAMPLE DESCRIPTION	LOCATION	LAB. IDENTITY	RADIOCARBON (volume year)		AGE (Years)
Crude oil from 1,100 ft.	California	C-631	*	1952	24,000
Pleistocene wood	La Brea	LJ-55	1	1959	14,400
Petrified wood	Italy	Pi-75	3	1961	10,090
Neanderthal mandible	Libya	GrN-2022	5	1963	40,700
Neanderthal skeleton	Iraq	Grn-1495	5	1963	50,600
Mylodon dung	Chile	Sa-49	6	1964	10,200
Mammoth vertebra	Wyoming	A-372	6	1964	9,600
Mastodon bones	Ohio	M-1254	7	1965	10,700
Diprotodon molar	New Zealand	NZ-1	7	1965	11,100
Broken Hill man	Rhodesia	UCLA-630	7	1965	9,000
Coal	—	MO-334	8	1966	1,680
Fossil wood & coal	Spain	G1F-198 to	8	1966	3,930
Fossil wood & coal	Spain	G1F-278	8	1966	5,025
Natural gas	Mississippi	I-1149	8	1966	34,000
Neanderthal bones	Morocco	NY-73	10	1968	32,000
Sabre-tooth tiger femur	La Brea	UCLA-1292	10	1968	28,000
Pleistocene wood	La Brea	UCLA-1325	11	1969	8,550
Mammal bones associated with *Zinjanthropus boisei*	Africa	UCLA-1321	11	1969	10,100

*Reported in Libby, W.F. 1952. *Radiocarbon dating*. University of Chicago Press.

APPENDIX K

Earth's Magnetic Field. Values Decreasing.

AUTHORITY	YEAR	MAGNETIC MOMENT (amp per meter^2) x 10^{22}
Gauss	1835	8.558
Adams	1845	8.488
Adams	1880	8.363
Neumayer	1880	8.336
Fritsche	1885	8.347
Schmidt	1885	8.375
Vestine et al.	1905	8.291
Vestine et al.	1915	8.225
Dyson-Furner	1922	8.165
Vestine et al.	1925	8.149
Vestine et al.	1935	8.088
Jones-Melotte	1942-43	8.009
Vestine et al.	1945	8.065
Afanasieva	1945	8.010
U.S.C. & G.S.	1945	8.066
Fanselau-Kautzleben	1945	8.090
U.S.C. & G.S.	1955	8.035
Finch-Leaton	1955	8.067
Nagata-Oguti	1958-59	8.038
Cain et al.	1959	8.086
Fougere	1960	8.053
Adam et al.	1960	8.037
Jensen-Cain	1960	8.025
Leaton et al.	1965	8.013
Hurwitz et al.	1965	8.017

439

APPENDIX L

POPULATION EXPLOSION

$$P_n = \frac{2}{C-1} \left[C^{n-x+1} \right] \left[C^x - 1 \right]$$

P_n= World population after n generations

n = Number of generations found by dividing total time by number of years per generation

x = Number of generations alive. If people live to see their grandchildren, x equals 3.

C = Half the number of children in the family. Zero population growth occurs when all children live to parenthood, and each set of parents has two children, C then equals 1.

The calculations are very simple and "ballpark" figures can be found quickly with a pocket calculator, while for the larger exponents, a set of common logarithm tables will be required.

Example 1. Assuming Archbishop Ussher was right and the earth was created about 4004 B.C., this would put the Genesis Flood at about 4,300 years ago. Although 4 couples survived, with insignificant error we can begin with 1 couple and take C equals 1.23, which means that throughout the total time, the average family has less than 2.5 children. This will take into account loss of population by disease, starvation, war, etc. Suppose people only lived for 43 years to simplify the calculation, and they lived to see their grandchildren so that there were 3 generations alive at any one time, thus x equals 3. n is found by dividing 4,300 by 43 equals 100 generations.

$$P_n \text{ today} = \frac{2}{1.23-1} \left[1.23^{100-3+1} \right] \left[1.23^3 - 1 \right]$$

$$P_n \text{ today} = 8.70 \left[1.23^{98} \right] \left[0.86 \right]$$

P_n today = Approximately 4.8 billion

By imposing these very severe restrictions on population growth, and bearing in mind that historical records show large families until relatively recent times which allows even greater depopulation by natural disaster, it is seen that the world population derived is just about the actual world population for today. The time frame of 4,300 years would, therefore, seem reasonably correct.

Example 2. Suppose that the conditions were exactly as in Example 1 except that the time frame was expanded to 1 million years. In this case, n would be given by 1,000,000 divided by 43 equals 23,256 generations. C remains at 1.23 and x equals 3.

$$P_n \text{ today} = \frac{2}{1.23-1} \left[1.23^{23256-3+1}\right] \left[1.23^3-1\right]$$

$$P_n \text{ today} = 7.48 \left[1.23^{23254}\right]$$

$$P_n \text{ today} = 7.48 \text{ x antilog} \left[23254 \text{ x log } (1.23)\right]$$

$$P_n \text{ today} = 7.48 \left[4.50 \text{ x } 10^{2090}\right]$$

$$P_n \text{ today} = 3.37 \text{ x } 10^{2091}$$

Mathematicians have given thought to the largest number possible, and, to have any meaning, the total number of electrons in the universe has been considered as a candidate. By computation this number is 10^{90}, a mere drop in the bucket compared to 10^{2091}! In other words, if mankind had been multiplying at this very modest rate for a million years, the population would by now be so great that when packed shoulder to shoulder, it could not be accommodated within the entire universe!

Notes

Chapter One

1 The account of Er is in Plato (1974 ed, 447) or line 614b in the universal Stephanus notation. The reader should be aware that the chapter headings and the italicized notes in the dialogues have been added by the commentator and, therefore, are to be regarded as opinions. The account of Er, for example, is found under the heading of "myth", but Plato does not regard it as such and specifically says, "It is not like Odysseus' tale to Alcinous" (p. 448).

2 Bible resuscitations: 2 Kings 4:18-37; 2 Kings 13:20-21; Matthew 9:18-26; Luke 7:11-18; John 4:46-53; John 11:11-46; Acts 9:36-43; and Acts 20:9-12.

3 Belief in the supernatural presents no problem to children, a fact well recognized by the adult population, which is seemingly dedicated to filling the child's mind with unlikely stories of tooth fairies, ghosts, and goblins. The unlikeliness of these stories is crucial. Taken as representing the supernatural, the stories have to lose all credibility, say, before high school, so that allusion to dimensions beyond the natural can be met then with the greatest skepticism. Nevertheless, people have an amazing resilience, and many still manage to retain a childlike curiosity for things beyond the natural world.

4 In his biography of Socrates, A.E. Taylor (1975) says: "Socrates had heard a divine 'voice' since childhood and experience showed him that neglect of its warnings commonly led to unpleasant consequences" (p. 45). "Convinced of the soul's immortality, Socrates believed he had a mission to preach to all men the single duty of 'tending the soul' and 'making it as good as possible'" (p. 146).

5 Plato's phrase (p. 420, line 592b) reflects his ideas of ideal forms in heaven and was expressed four hundred years later by the writer of Hebrews (9:23).

6 The translator (Plato 1974 ed., 41) comments that the Republic is the temporal and only a shadow of the eternal. This same thought is found in 2 Corinthians 4:18.

7 In his introduction to *The Republic* (1974 ed.) the translator agrees that "Plato was not a good nineteenth century liberal" (p. 51).

8 The humanist Blackham (1976) writes, "The thinking of Plato and Aristotle proved congenial to the eventual triumphant Christian theologians established by the Roman State. The tradition established by Democritus and Protagoras was anathema to the Christians....

From the humanist point of view Plato is the enemy and Democritus...is the champion" (p. 105). The book is dedicated to Democritus and Protagoras.

9 Young (1974) shows that historians Lynn White and Arnold Toynbee have added the weight of scholarship to the accusation that the Christian church is responsible for today's pollution. Young comments that White's paper, presented to the American Association for the Advancement of Science in 1966, may have been welcome to divert the blame for our ecological crises from science to the church, but shows that the claims are unfounded. Toynbee blames Judeo monotheism and specifically Genesis 1:28 for the world's ills and suggests the remedy lies in reverting from the Weltanschauung of monotheism to the Weltanschauung of pantheism! Young points out that, in the first place, polytheism and pantheism are not the same thing.

10 Constantine, when preparing his troops for the key battle for Rome at Milvian Bridge in A.D. 312, saw the cross of Jesus superimposed over the evening sun. A voice, such as the one heard by Socrates and by Saul on the road to Damascus spoke, saying, *"In hoc signo vinces"*—In this sign you will conquer. He went into battle with the sign, the cross, painted on the shields and won. The initial letters of the Latin have been contracted to IHS and are often found appended to the crucifix.

11 Shotwell (1923) exposed Origen (A.D. 185-254) as an early liberal among the fathers of the Church: "Interpretation of the Scriptures by allegory is not, in Origen's eyes, an unwarranted liberty.... He not only denied the literal truth of much of Genesis and...was a modern among the moderns—many a sermon upon the reconciliation of science and religion...might be taken bodily from Origen" (p. 292).

12 Leonardo Bigollo Fibonacci was perhaps the greatest mathematician of the Middle Ages. His name is associated principally with the numerical sequence in which each succeeding term is the sum of the two immediately preceding. Born in 1179, he traveled to Algiers and from the Arabs learned the Hindu system of numerals from 1 to 9. He is credited with having introduced these to Europe, where calculations were still being made by the clumsy Roman numerals and Greek letters. The zero was, however, purely an Arab device and was introduced

to Europe as part of the "Arabic" numeral system we use today.

13 Thomas Aquinas wrote *Summa Contra Gentiles*, (1258-60) as a theological defense of Christian doctrine against the Jewish and Arab philosophers of the day. Aquinas wrote *Summa theologica* (1265-74) as a grand summary of all Christian doctrine. In it he claimed it was necessary to subject Christian wisdom to the discipline of "the Philosopher", by which he meant Aristotle. An English version of both works in summary form may be found in Magill (1963).

14 Wyclif (or Wycliffe) followers, known as Wycliffites or Lollards—which may mean "mutterer" or "mumbler"—had by 1395 become an organized and well-supported group. They spread across Europe, and a revival began in Czechoslovakia under Jan Hus. Persecution was directed from Rome, and in England many Lollards were burned at the stake; Hus met the same death at Constance in 1415.

15 Campanella (1963) gives eleven arguments for and against Galileo but finishes by refuting the idea that the earth moves around a stationary sun. He cites the following Scriptures that were seen to be violated by Galileo: Joshua 10:13; Judges 5:20; Psalm 93:1, Psalm 104:5; Ecclesiastes 1:4-6; and Isaiah 38:8.

16 Dante Alighieri's *Divine Comedy*, written about 1300, consists of three parts: Inferno, Purgatorio, and Paradiso. The latter-day Roman doctrine of Purgatory was fixed in the medieval mind by Dante's poetic and imaginative capture of Latin scriptural interpretation, and then secured visually in the Victorian mind by the Gustave Doré engravings made in the 1860s to illustrate a republished edition of Dante's work.

17 The Dutch spectacle makers had invented the "spy-glass" in 1608 and by means of a "newsletter", Galileo then constructed several instruments of his own. He began observations in 1610 and studied the movement of sunspots and the moon and discovered the four largest moons of Jupiter. He reported these observations in *The starry messenger* (1611), which is today regarded as a classic piece of scientific reporting. Continuing his observations, Galileo published *The assayer* in 1623, in which he pointed out that the three comets that had caused so much controversy in 1618 had passed effortlessly through one "crystalline sphere" and into the next, so that it was evident that the "spheres" were purely imaginary. The hollow spheres had originally been conceived as a means of enabling the planets, but principally the fixed stars, to rotate in unison about a stationary earth. Even so, Galileo had only disproved the presence of the spheres but had offered no proof for his argument for heliocentricity. Interestingly, to this day, since there is no known stationary reference

point in space, absolute motion cannot be determined. Thus Galileo's and subsequently our own view of the solar system is based less on fact and more on what seems most rational. *The assayer* expressed Galileo's more rational view in a very complete way. It was this aspect that came into conflict with the Church's theological view of the universe.

18 Gutenberg's printing press was developed about 1460. By 1480 the process was becoming "commercial", and the first recorded biblical text to be printed was a Pentateuch in Hebrew at Bologna in 1482. By 1497 a small "porn" market had evolved in the printing trade, since it is on record that Savonarola introduced a feature to Florence's religious festival that year to collect and burn "souvenirs of regretted wickedness"—cards, dice, nude pictures, and spicy books such as the *Decameron*; Savonarola was burned at the stake for his efforts by a fanatical mob the following year.

19 Hermes Trismegistus of ancient Egypt set out the philosophy that there is a harmony and correspondence among all different kinds of manifestations in the universe—the circling of the planets, the tides of the earth, the growth of vegetation, the lives of animals and people. Discovery of the periodicities in nature was said to indicate certain ratios found to be in harmony and believed to be under the divine control of a universal music. These ratios lead, for example, to a "sacred geometry" used by the Greek architects so that their temples would resonate with the life forms of the universe and thus enhance life. Some of the "dark practices" involved music based on the harmonies constructed from the "sacred ratios" in order to receive knowledge of the secrets of the universe.

20 The classic work of Michelson and Morley to measure the speed of light was carried out in 1887. D.C. Miller repeated this work many times from 1902-26, confirming the work of 1887 and showing that this does not support Einstein's theory of relativity reported in 1905. Miller presented the results to the American Physical Society on December 1925, but from that day to this nothing has been done, and Polanyi (1955) points out that every standard textbook continues the myth that the speed of light experiments confirm the theory of relativity.

21 Webster (1924, 120) shows that Francis Bacon had an influence among the Rosicrucians and was associated with freemasonry. At that time, in the 1620s, both organizations were involved in some "dark practices" not approved of by the church, and, as head of the church and a strong Christian, James I would have had little choice but to terminate Bacon; bribery was possibly the lesser charge.

22 Brown (1977) states "the famous *Cogito ergo*

sum of Descartes was not a logical deduction that the person actually exists from the fact of thinking, since the premise of the argument already contained the conclusion. At its best it is an affirmation of personal existence but not strictly proof. The argument is really saying the same thing twice over in different words" (p. 488).

23 The Greek Anaxagoras (about 500 B.C.) is said to be the originator of the doctrine of dualism, which holds that mind and matter exist as two distinct entities. Following its reintroduction by Descartes and an understanding of the laws of conservation of mass, of energy, and of momentum, the chief drawback of dualism is seen to be the problem of how a non-physical entity, the soul, which has no mass, can influence the body, which does have mass. Psychology has proposed a number of alternative theories such as radical behaviorism, logical behaviorism, and central-state identity, all of which totally rule out the existence of the soul or spirit within man.

24 Details of Rousseau's sordid sex life including his exhibitionism are in Vol. 1 of his *Confession*, while the abandonment of his children at the Paris Foundling Hospital is mentioned in Vol. 2, pp. 74 and 89.

25 The seven day week, so closely identified with the first chapter of Genesis, has always been a source of irritation to atheistic governments. The governments of France in 1793, of Russia in 1918, and that of Sri Lanka during the 1960s all unsuccessfully tried to change the seven day week.

Chapter Two

1 In fairness to Alfonso, King of Castille, he made this remark after studying the earth-centered Ptolemaic solar system, which was later shown by Copernicus and Galileo to be fundamentally wrong.

2 Eighth line of the preface to the poem "Milton".

3 A mechanical device found in 1902 by marine archaeology at Antikythera, Greece, was discovered by gamma-ray techniques in 1973 to be a mechanism of unbelievable sophistication containing an epicyclic differential gear system. The mechanism was dated at 87 B.C. and, thus, the differential gear that we find in the back axle of the automobile today and which was believed to have been invented during the Industrial Revolution for textile machines was actually known to the Greeks eighteen centuries earlier.

4 Remains of wet batteries were discovered in 1939, by Wilhelm Konig, near Baghdad. It is believed that the batteries were used for electroplating gold onto jewelry and were more than two thousand years old; rediscovery of this process was not made until the eighteenth century A.D.

5 The extensive article by Wertime (1973) deals with the controversy regarding the beginnings of iron smelting from ores. Iron artifacts have been found which date as early as 2500 B.C. but this is disturbing for the usual textbook sequence of Stone Age, Bronze Age, and Iron Age. The author points out that the Black Sea coast is lined with self-fluxing sands containing 77 percent magnetite, which could permit smelting to be carried out at the unusually low temperature of 900°C.

6 A 1967 investigation showed that a sophisticated casting technique had been employed which it was believed had been developed in the fourteenth century A.D. Although the horse had been dated at 470 B.C., because of the use of this casting technique, it was declared to be a fake. In 1973 another investigation, using a recently developed thermoluminescence technique for dating, showed without doubt that the horse was very ancient; it has since been reinstated as genuine. The Greek casting technique was evidently lost and only rediscovered in the fourteenth century. From Zimmerman et al. (1974).

7 According to Raven (1942), John Ray had a distant though important influence on Charles Darwin. One of Ray's most significant works was *The Wisdom of God manifested in the works of Creation* published in 1691 and republished in at least ten editions. This work departed from the then traditional view of God held by the church in that although Ray gave great respect to design in nature and to a Designer, he could not accept the miraculous or the Genesis Flood (Raven p. 450). The theologian William Paley borrowed extensively from Ray's *Wisdom of God* and incorporated it into his *Natural theology* (1802), which Darwin read and enjoyed so much as a student at Cambridge (see Chapter Five). Raven concludes about Ray's *Wisdom of God*: "More than any other single book it initiated the true adventure of modern science, and is the ancestor of the *Origin of Species* or of *L'Évolution Creatrice*." (See Chapter Fourteen.)

8 This is Osborn's (1929, 187) translation of the Latin from Linnaeus's *Philosophia botanica*, 1751. Other authors translate slightly differently although with the same meaning, e.g. Barber (1980, 52) and Himmelfarb (1968, 170).

9 Himmelfarb (1968, 170) quotes Knut Hagberg's *Carl Linnaeus* (London: 1952, 197) who in turn quotes from Linnaeus's *Dissertation on Perloris* (1744) to show that Linnaeus conceded that it was "possible for new species to arise", and Himmelfarb adds that Linnaeus was held suspect by orthodox Christians for saying so.

10 Linnean Society. This spelling in preference to Linnaean was officially adopted in 1802.

11 Eulogy to Lamarck delivered to the French Academy in 1832 by Cuvier: "A system resting on such foundations may amuse the imaginations of a poet...but it cannot for a moment bear the examination of anyone who has dissected the hand, the viscera, or even a feather" (p. 47).

12 In a footnote Weismann (1891) mentions Jewish circumcision, then adds, "Among nations which practice circumcision as a ritual, children are sometimes born with a rudimentary prepuce [foreskin], however rather extensive statistical investigation has shown that this does not occur more frequently than in other nations in which circumcision is not performed" (1:447).

13 Gorczynski and Steele (1981) were experimenting with mice and observed some apparently inherited reactions to certain drugs. The article aroused editorial comments such as "too soon for the rehabilitation of Lamarck" and "biological heresy". (See also *Science 81* May issue.)

14 Weismann (1891) describes the classic experiment started in 1887 with white mice, beginning with seven females and five males. A total of 901 mice were produced in five generations. All had their tails removed before breeding and all had been born with normal tails (1:444).

15 Coleman (1964) says of Cuvier, "His system was, if anything, 'extinctive', eliminating by catastrophe, and not 'progressive', creating (through God) new and higher creatures as an aftermath of catastrophe. There had been a succession of discrete populations, each more or less complete, and each neatly perishing by the action of some remote catastrophe" (p. 51).

16 Nordenskiold (1928) states: "The assertion that so often occurs in literature that, in his (Cuvier's) view, life had been created anew after each catastrophe is utterly incorrect; on the contrary he points out that isolated parts of the earth may have been spared on each occasion when it was laid waste, and that living creatures had propagated their species anew from these cases, which indeed he expressly applies to the human race" (p. 338).

Chapter Three

1 French historian Halévy (1937-8) writing in the nineteenth century clearly saw that the presence of the Evangelical movement in England prevented a socialist revolution such as had occurred in France. "We shall explain by [the Evangelical revival] the extraordinary stability which English society was destined to enjoy throughout a period of revolution and crises; what we may truly term the miracle of modern England, anarchist but orderly, practical and businesslike, but religious, and even pietist" (p. 10). Halévy saw this as providential; left-wing historians have labelled this a conservative prop for an economically oppressive society.

2 Richie-Calder (1982) exposes just some of the connections between the French revolutionaries and the Lunar Society. Richard Edgeworth, a member of the Lunar Society, was on visiting terms with Rousseau, while Benjamin Franklin was a friend of Matthew Boulton of Birmingham and frequently visited Paris to meet his friends Voltaire and Rousseau. Voltaire lived for some years in exile in England (p. 142).

3 Webster (1924) comments on J.G. Findel's *History of Freemasonry* (1866, 131): "Findel frankly admits that the *New Atlantis* contained unmistakable allusions to Freemasonry and that Bacon contributed to its final transformation" (p. 120). Webster pointed out that one of the earliest and most eminent precursors of Freemasonry is said to have been Francis Bacon, who is also recognized to have been a Rosicrucian; the Rosicrucian and Freemason orders were closely allied and may have had a common source.

4 Letter from C. Darwin to J.D. Hooker, July 1860. Found in F. Darwin 1887, 2:324.

5 In 1782 Joseph Priestley published *An history of the corruptions of Christianity*. By "corruptions" Priestley was referring to the New Testament miracles. Priestley's output of theological works from the Unitarian viewpoint was phenomenal, considering that at the same time he was a notable scientist. Schofield (1963) estimates that he published eleven volumes of religious history, fourteen volumes of polemical theology, seven volumes of sermons, as well as numerous tracts and Unitarian hymns. In his *History of early opinions* (1786), he tried to demonstrate that the earliest Christians had not held the view that Jesus was the eternal Son of God but that this had been introduced later. Priestley's disbelief in the Bible miracles was no doubt quite sincere, but he actively promoted his ideas and thus generated unbelief in others. The Bible-believing public was enraged, and when he showed his sympathies to the French socialist revolutionaries in 1791, they burned his house to the ground. He left England and died in America in 1804.

6 This passage discovered by Himmelfarb (1968, 387) was penned by Darwin in October 1873 and reveals the completely irreligious nature of the man. Passages such as this have not been generally made available to the public and are part of a vast body of correspondence which, to this day, remains unpublished, confined to the archives of the Cambridge University Library.

7 Although *Zoönomia* was placed on the Index in 1817, none of Charles Darwin's works, including *The Descent of Man* (1871), were ever placed on the Catholic Index. The *Index librorum prohibitorum* (Index of Forbidden Books) was initiated at the Council of Trent in 1557, revised under Benedict (1757) and Leo (1900), reevaluated at Vatican II, and abolished in 1966.

8 According to Simpkins (1974) and most commentaries, Malthus received his inspiration from three sources: Godwin, W. 1793. *An enquiry concerning political justice and its function on general virtue and happiness.* London. Godwin, W. 1797. *The enquirer: Reflections on education, manners and literature.* Dublin-London. Condorcet, ed. 1795. *Outlines of an historical view of the progress of the human mind.* Translated from the French. London.

9 Polanyi (1957) quotes extensively from Joseph Townsend 1786. *Dissertation on the poor law.* Beginning with a story of goats and dogs from Condorcet, which was at most apocryphal, Malthus had elevated it to the status of a scientific principle, later expressed by Herbert Spencer as "survival of the fittest", a principle that became the coincident inspiration for both Wallace and Darwin's theory of evolution by natural selection.

10 Playfair's work (1970) is the only biography of Hutton, but readers should be aware that Playfair was very sympathetic to Hutton's views and deals in a most cursory manner with such matters as the charge of atheism. Others were also sympathetic to Hutton's rather socialist views, including the Edinburgh Review, an organ of Edinburgh University.

11 Lyell (1830-33) assumed that events in the past had taken place at the same rate as are observed today. He then argued that for the many small and necessarily disconnected unusual events (minor catastrophes) to have occurred all at the same time (thereby resulting in a single major catastrophe) would be a coincidence far beyond all chance of ever happening (1:80). This argument is pure sophistry since it is based on the assumption that uniformitarianism is true.

12 A worldwide distribution of volcanic ash was reported by Kennett et al. (1975) from 320 deep-sea sections drilled during the Deep Sea Drilling Project. The results indicated that there has been a much higher rate of volcanism in the past than has previously been expected.

13 Brian Sullivan of *The Philadelphia Inquirer* (2 January 1981) reported that at the 147th national meeting of the American Association for the Advancement of Science held in Toronto, evolution was "voted-in" as a scientific law.

14 In a letter to Joseph Dalton Hooker, Darwin referred to Lyell and Hooker's conspiracy as the "delicate arrangement". Brackman (1980, xi) took this as the title for his revealing book.

15 Colp (1977) draws from several unpublished

papers and letters of Charles Darwin at the university library, Cambridge, to show that during March and April 1851, while being treated by Dr. Gully at Malvern, Darwin consulted a clairvoyant. She told Darwin that "the mischief" was in his stomach and lungs and described to him "a most appalling picture of the horrors which she saw in his inside" (p. 44). Darwin had witnessed many forms of the occult during the journey of the *Beagle.* In the Indian Ocean, among the Cocos Islands, he had attended a black magic ritual which, however, he contemptuously described as a "foolish spectacle" (footnote in Brackman 1980, 279). Wallace had a disagreement with Darwin centered on this area of spiritism. Wallace was convinced that man had a soul or spirit; Darwin was evidently not at all convinced. The argument ran that since animals do not possess a soul, then at some point in the supposed ancestral lineage of man, the belief in the soul required God to have given it. Wallace, for all his irreligion, considered this to have been necessary. Darwin was opposed and thus by implication denied the existence of the human soul.

16 Brackman (1980) has quoted this now famous moment of revelation from Wallace's *The wonderful century,* written in 1898. However, there seem to be a number of versions: Bronowski (1973, 306) has another version but no reference, while Himmelfarb (1968, 246) quotes from Wallace's *My life* (1905, 1:362) with a third version. Each version contains the expression, "suddenly flashed upon me the idea". Brackman (1980) makes the interesting observation that at the time of his revelation Wallace had malarial fever which leaves the victim temporarily "high" (p. 198).

17 This line appears in Tennyson's (1974) *In memoriam A.H.H.* (Canto 56): "Man...who trusted God was love indeed/ and love Creation's final law—/ Tho' nature, red in tooth and claw,/ with ravine, shriek'd against his creed" (p. 105).

Chapter Four

1 In his letter to Mantel, 29 October 1841. Lyell states the purpose of his first visit to Niagara: "As I shall send a paper on the proofs of their [Niagara Falls] recession to the Geological Society, I will not dwell on them now" (in K. Lyell 1881, 2:58).

2 In his letter to Horner 13 June 1842. During his second visit to Niagara, Lyell says: "I have found some additional evidence of value to my mind, in favour of recession of the Falls" (in K. Lyell 1881, 2:60).

3 In the tenth edition of his *Principles,* Lyell (1867) states: "But after the most careful enquiries which I was able to make during my visit to the spot in 1841-2, I came to the conclusion that the average of one foot a year would be a much more probable conjecture. In that case it would have required 35,000 years for the retreat of the Fall" (1:361).

4 The biased nature of Lyell's estimate is entirely lost from view in Bailey's (1962, 149) biography.

5 In the Royal Ontario Museum Publication, Tovell (1979, 16) gives a summary of the published rates of recession of Niagara Falls from 1842 to 1927. The average value is 4 feet (1.2 m) per year. Discounting four very low values, the average becomes 5 feet (1.5 m) per year. Footnote to the table indicates that the falls have now been "stabilized" and recession in recent years is reduced to 1 foot (0.3 m) per year.

6 Ronov (1959) states: "The quantity of carbonate sediments [limestone] deposited in a given post pre-Cambrian epoch was directly proportional to the intensity of volcanism and to the area of distribution of inland seas" (p. 497).

7 Both papers report surveys by depth sounder and piston cores in the tropical Pacific revealed a layer of white ash evidently laid down rapidly and believed to be volcanic in origin. The layer is correlated with white ash in other locations and is believed to have been caused by worldwide volcanism.

8 HMS Challenger, a corvette of 2,306 tons, was fitted out with laboratories and a scientific team. In three and a half years, from 1873-76, it traveled 69,000 miles taking samples from the ocean bottom around the world. For a delightful summary of this massive work see Schlee (1971).

9 Pettersson (1950, 44) reports the thickest ocean bottom sediment found was thirteen thousand feet in the Atlantic.

10 Brues (1951) presents a series of photographs of insects trapped in gum from pine trees, which are thus perfectly preserved. Alleged to be thirty to ninety million years old, the insects appear to be identical to those found today.

11 Andrews (1926) makes the following statements: "These eggs were in a great deposit full of dinosaur skeletons" (p. 229). "Most interesting of all was the fact that in two eggs that had been broken in half we could plainly detect the delicate bone of the embryonic dinosaurs" (p. 231).

12 Miller (1841) points out that in Britain over an area of ten thousand square miles fish remains are found bearing "unequivocally the marks of violent death. The figures are contorted, contracted, curved; the tail in many instances is bent around the head; the spines stick out; the fins are spread to the full, as in fish that die in convulsions" (p. 232).

13 George C. Page museum information sheet: "Specimens have thus far been found of some 3,000 individual wolves. The remains of approximately 2,500 saber-tooths [tigers] rank second" (p. 4).

14 The discovery in 1914 of a human skeleton of modern appearance among Pleistocene animals at six to ten feet below the surface sparked heated controversy. Boule and Vallois (1957, 478) cite professor Merriam's explanation, which relies more on imagination than fact, to totally discount the evidence.

15 The discovery by Irving (1973) of the jawbone of a teenage child among Pleistocene animals in North America caused a dilemma. A variety of radiocarbon test dates taken from associated pieces of wood were available. However, the investigators were uncertain whether to choose the ages of about 40,000 years to satisfy the geologists, or choose the ages about 10,000 years to satisfy the archaeologists, who surmise that man arrived in North America relatively recently. An age of 27,000 years was selected. Interestingly, in the footnote to reference 5 it is noted that repeat radiocarbon tests were carried out but, "when it became apparent that the radioactivity was equivalent to a date of about 4,000 years, the counting was stopped" (see Chapter Twelve). The discovery in text and picture for general public consumption was reported in *National Geographic* 1979, 156 (September): 330-363.

16 Laverdière (1950) describes the most recent whale discovery in 1947 at between 275 and 300 feet (84-92 m) above sea level. This paper is a convenient summary of seventeen other fossil whales previously reported and found in the hills surrounding the St. Lawrence River valley. Hills in Vermont (U.S.) rise to 500 feet above sea level, and a whale fossil was discovered there in 1907.

17 Hallam (1963) gives five examples to show what he believes to be cyclic changes in Jurassic sedimentation caused by cyclic rising and falling of sea level. No mechanism is given, and the explanation does not explain ancient sedimentations and beaches tilted from the horizontal. This paper is only one of many that require multiple vertical movements over vast lengths of time. A typical presentation of the rising and falling of continents and sea levels is found in Dunbar 1960, 395.

18 Doumanai and Long (1962) write, "The most striking testimony to the richness of this [fossil] record are the numerous coal beds as much as 13 feet thick.... Large petrified tree trunks as much as 24 feet long and 2 feet in diameter...are embedded in the sandstone. Coal measures...have been known in Antartica since 1901" (p. 175).

19 In the discussion to this lengthy and detailed presentation by Whitley (1910), Sir Henry

Howarth said that many of the facts were to be found in his book *The mammoth and the flood* (1887). Howarth's book is today a rarity and Whitley's paper is likely to be more readily available; both speak of many thousands of buried mammoths.

20 Farrand (1961) presents a typical Lyellian argument to explain the frozen mammoths, saying that those found were victims of tundra life, i.e. fell into a bog, and thus no catastrophe is admitted. The author downplays the number of mammoth specimens found claiming only "about 39". In his letter reply to Farrand (1961), Lippman (1962) reports: "Lydekker reports in the Smithsonian Reports for 1899, that about 20,000 pairs of tusks in perfect condition were exported for the ivory trade in the few decades preceding 1899. 'Buried ivory' was apparently a world-trade even in Aristotle's time" (p. 361).

21 Early in 1859 Darwin bought a billiard table for himself (Colp 1977, 65).

22 The massive and highly documented work of Dillow (1981) provides more details than will be found in the older works and should be more readily available.

23 Hertz (1904) soberly describes the erect genital: "In the afternoon we succeeded in exposing...the protruded male genital, 86 centimeters long above and 105 centimeters long below; 10 centimeters above the urinary meatus; the diameter of the flattened-out penis is 19 centimeters" (p. 623). See also Digby 1926, 132.

24 Gow (1972) took ice core samples from nine Antarctic glaciers; cores were 7,100 feet long. He found more than two thousand individual volcanic ash falls interbedded with the ice, which suggests to some that volcanic eruptions brought about the Ice Age. On the other hand, this does not preclude the possibility that the proximity of a comet caused simultaneous volcanic activity.

25 Sears reports that more than 1,300 meteorites have been found in Antarctica. This is very unusual, since the world's museums only boast of 2,000 collected throughout the rest of the world, their occurrence being quite rare. There may be meteorites at the sea bottom of the Arctic. This would indicate that the source of the ice was extraterrestrial as was the source of the meteorites. (See Chapter Twelve.)

26 A series of ocean-bottom core samples described by Hough (1950) showed that ice was absent from Antarctica's Ross Sea six thousand years ago and only extended to its present limit four thousand years ago.

27 The famous Heart Mountain thrust fault in Wyoming has perplexed geologists for years. According to fossil dating, "old" rock 1,500-1,800 feet thick and thirty by sixty miles is situated on top of "younger rock". It is argued that the "old" rock was uplifted and pushed across the "new" rock, but Pierce (1957) admits this orthodox explanation is fantastic and is at a loss to provide an alternative explanation.

28 Corliss (1978) has fully documented more than four hundred articles from orthodox scientific journals, published in English since about 1850 to the most recent, relating to discoveries of ancient man either as actual skeletons or artifacts found in geologically unexpected places. At 786 pages this is a massive confrontation to today's geological and anthropological sciences.

29 The petrified human skull was found in the coal deposit at the Freiberg (East Germany) mine; a complete chemical analysis was reported, and it was noted how the organic matter had been completely replaced by iron and manganese oxides and hydrates. The skull was given brief mention by Otto Stutzer (1940, 271) *Geology of coal*. Chicago.

30 O'Rourke (1976) concludes: "The charge of circular reasoning in stratigraphy can be handled in several ways. It can be *ignored*, as not the proper concern of the public. It can be *denied*, by calling down the Law of Evolution. Fossils date rocks, not vice-versa, and that's that. It can be *admitted*, as a common practice...or it can be *avoided* by pragmatic reasoning" (p. 54. Emphasis in original.)

31 Students sometimes have held before them the example of pitch at room temperature. Although very brittle under a rapidly applied load (struck with a hammer), it will bend easily even under its own weight over a period of several days. This analogy is seldom found in print, however, as it is quite false: pitch is an amorphous solid whereas rock has a crystalline structure.

32 Mackal (1980) gives details of a number of "fossil" creatures found to be living, such as the Paleozoic coelacanth in 1938 and the Miocene Okapi (giraffid) in 1901.

33 Apart from brief mention in newspapers during late July 1977, this article by Koster (1977) was the only full and objective published report in the English-speaking press. (See also Chapter Fifteen.)

34 Alvarez and others (1980) propose an extraterrestrial cause for dinosaur extinction. Commented on in *Science News*, 1979, 115:356.

35 Vertebrate paleontologist Roland Bird (1939) of the American Museum of Natural History describes dinosaur and human-like tracks at the Paluxy River.

36 Roland Bird (1954) describes removal of the dinosaur tracks from the Paluxy riverbed and installation at the American Museum of Natural History.

37 Paluxy River. June 1982. More than one

hundred people representing the press and school teachers were invited as witnesses while TV cameras recorded the removal of tons of rock from the Paluxy riverbed following a trail of existing dinosaur tracks. The excavation revealed thirty-six fresh dinosaur prints together with twelve human-like footprints and a human-like handprint. Any possibility of fraud under these conditions was completely ruled out.

38 Human-like tracks appear in limestone of the Carboniferous era—that is, long before the appearance of mammals! They have been found from Virginia and Pennsylvania through Kentucky, Illinois, Missouri, and into the Rocky Mountains. Ingalls (1940) points out that they cannot all be carvings and even if they were made by an ancestor of man then modern geology is completely wrong.

39 Derek Ager (1973) spends more than one hundred pages giving evidence that refutes Lyellian geology yet he cannot accept special Creation and the Noachian Flood. The result is an interesting attempt to be honest to science on the one hand while being loyal to the creed of evolution on the other.

40 Cowen's (1975) book is an attempt to be honest to science but loyal to evolution. Such books as this and Ager's (1973) must eventually bring about the realization that there is something fundamentally wrong with Lyellian geology.

41 Here Lyell (1845, 2:155) describes the fossil trees at South Joggins, Nova Scotia.

Chapter Five

1 Francis Darwin's (1887) *The life and letters of Charles Darwin* contained the autobiography of Charles Darwin, but until the publication of Lady Barlow's restored version in 1958, it was not generally known just how much of Darwin's irreligious nature had been edited out of the 1887 version.

2 Brackman (1980, 32) provides details of Leonard G. Wilson's discovery of seven of Lyell's notebooks at Kinnordy House, Kirriemuir, Scotland, in 1961. It is clear that within forty-eight hours of receiving Wallace's Sarawak Law in 1856, Lyell began to keep his own "transmutation notebook".

3 The context of Darwin's note given in Barlow (1958, 30) that his father was a Freemason is in reference to the blood rites of initiation to that organization. There is no evidence that Charles Darwin had followed his grandfather Erasmus or his father Robert into Freemasonry.

4 Expanded to four volumes in the third edition in 1801, Erasmus Darwin's *Zoönomia* was a massive work, which Darwin admitted in

his *Autobiography* was full of speculation.

5 Charles Darwin had this biography translated from German into English by W.S. Dallas. He wrote a very lengthy introduction and, in a footnote (p. 61), mentions that his grandfather Erasmus had two illegitimate daughters.

6 The footnote in Barlow (1958, 22) is Francis Darwin's note that both Charles and his brother Erasmus were christened and intended to belong to the Church of England.

7 Henrietta Litchfield (1915) wrote: "Kitty Wedgwood...died in 1823. Dr. Darwin used to say that she was the only woman he ever knew who thought for herself in matters of religion" (1:164). This has clearly been edited by either Emma (or her daughter Henrietta), because Himmelfarb (1968:11) points out that the original letter, held at Cambridge, states, "Dr. Darwin used to say that...so clear-sighted a woman could not be a believer."

8 Cambridge University Calendar for 1824 specifies that the ordinary B.A. course embraced three fields: (a) Natural Philosophy including Euclid's Elements, the principles of Algebra, plane and sphere trigonometry, mechanics, hydrostatics, optics, astronomy, and Newton's Principia (calculus); (b) Theology and Moral Philosophy covered by Beausobre's Introduction, Doddridge's and Paley's Evidences, Butler's Analogy, Paley's Moral Philosophy, Locke's Essay, Duncan's Logic, and the Greek New Testament; (c) Belles Lettres covered by "the most celebrated Greek and Latin classics". The Bible, as such, was not included. Darwin received the M.A., as was customary, two years after receiving the B.A.

9 As an eighteenth century theologian, Paley did not have to face such problems as trying to reconcile Genesis with geology, which was the major concern in the nineteenth century. However, T.H. Huxley was able to claim that he "proleptically accepted the modern doctrine of evolution" (F. Darwin 1887, 2:202). Here Huxley was referring to a paragraph in Paley's *Natural theology* (1972, 314). Although the central theme of Paley's work is acknowledgment of an intelligent designing author, careful reading shows that he was inclined towards a liberal view in which having once created life God then retired to let matters develop by chance processes.

10 Keynes (1933) recognized Paley's merits when he classed him with Locke, Hume, Adam Smith, Bentham, Darwin, and Mill as belonging to a tradition of humane science "marked by a most noble lucidity, by a prosaic sanity free from sentiment or metaphysic, and by an immense disinterestedness and public spirit" (p. 120).

11 The well-referenced account by Eiseley (1959)

of developments of evolutionary biology before 1859 reproduces in full the papers of Edward Blyth published in 1835 and 1837. See also H.M. Vickers 1911. *Nature* 85:510.

12 Galton's (1869) thesis is summed up in his statement, "to give the more suitable races or strains of blood a better chance of prevailing speedily over the less suitable... the word eugenics would sufficiently express the idea" (p.24).

13 The conspiracy to obtain priority for Darwin is fully outlined following p.58 of Brackman (1980). Central to Brackman's thesis is the Darwin to Gray Letter of 5 September 1857. However, having got this far, he then misses the point. So far, all the published versions of this letter are of Darwin's edited copy and contain item six, which deals with the vital divergence principle, but the question is, Did the copy received by Gray contain this item? Gray's correspondence for this period was also missing, and the published version is again taken from Darwin's edited version.

14 Gray's widow, Jane (1939), partially reproduced a letter from Darwin to Gray of 5 September 1857, but it is from Darwin's edited version and not the original received by Asa Gray. The abstract states, "enclosed six principles of Natural selection, in another handwriting" (p.10).

15 Sarton's (1930) article contains facsimile copies of:
1.) Darwin's unpublished sketch of 1839, copied in 1844.
2.) Abstract of Darwin to Gray letter of 5 September 1857 (edited version).
3.) Wallace's Ternate paper of February 1858.

16 Published the year he died, Keith (1955) had evidently revealed a little too much of Darwin for the time, and his book *Darwin revalued* never appeared on publishers' lists; it is something of a rarity today. The information on Darwin's finances appear in the chapter "The man of business" (p.231).

17 Charles Darwin's influence on psychology is expressed by Zusne (1975): "To psychology, his books *The Origin of Species* (1859), *The Descent of Man* (1871) are of particular importance. They spell out the basic assumption underlying psychology, namely that man is on a continuum with the rest of the animal world, and that, since animals can be studied by the scientific method, so can man.... The evolutionary viewpoint concerning the development of both structure and function, including the mental processes, is now the accepted and pervasive point of view in psychology" (p.112).

18 Darwin (1965) describes sneering defiance in man and the uncovering of the canine teeth on p.247 ff.

19 Bell (1844) actually calls the *Levator labii proprius* that uncover the canine teeth in man the "muscles of snarling" (p.131). However, as acknowledged by Darwin, Bell believed that they had been specially created for the sake of expression.

20 One of the most recent articles on this theme appeared under the title "Darwin went home to the Bible" in the tabloid *The National Educator* (Fullerton, Calif.) for July 1975. This article in turn sparked off a number of religious tracts distributed by well-meaning but misled individuals.

21 Lady Hope: Recent correspondence has revealed that Elizabeth Reid Stapleton-Cotton married Adm. Sir James Hope. Although she remarried after his death, she preferred to be known as Lady Hope until her death. However, there is no evidence that she ever visited Darwin, and none of this changes the evidence of the Darwin correspondence.

22 A footnote in Barlow (1958, 93) consists of a letter from Darwin's widow, Emma, to his son, Francis, dated 1885 and refers to a passage in his autobiography in which he equates the child's belief in God with the monkey's instinctive fear and hatred of a snake. Emma requested that this passage be removed to "avoid giving pain to your father's religious friends". Only time will tell how many other irreligious statements of this sort made by Darwin remain in the Cambridge University Library Archives.

Chapter Six

1 The four separate origins of man are depicted monumentally in Frederick Hart's "The Creation" unveiled on October 1982 at Washington Cathedral (Episcopalian). The sculpture is eighteen feet tall and twenty-four feet wide and conveys the instant when humankind emerged from a swirl of dust or smoke. This is at complete variance with the biblical description of the creation of Adam and yet still appeals to the miraculous.

2 The work of observation (not breeding experiments) was conducted in 1939 and first reported by David Lack in 1947. A summary by Lack may be found in *Scientific American*, 1953, 88 (April): 67.

3 Darwin's (1845) only mention of the finches was as follows: "Seeing this gradation and diversity of structures in one small, intimately related group of birds one might really fancy, that from an original paucity of birds in this archipelago, one species had been taken and modified for different ends" (p.380).

4 Darwin confessed to the absence of transition fossils in the *Origin* (1859): "Why then is not every geological formation and every stratum full of such intermediate links? Geology assuredly does not reveal any such finely graduated organic chain; and this, perhaps, is the most obvious and gravest objection which can be urged against my theory. The explanation lies, as I believe, in the extreme imperfection of the geological record" (p. 280).

5 Paleontologist Kitts (1974) makes the confession: "Despite the bright promise that paleontology provides a means of 'seeing' evolution, it has presented some nasty difficulties for evolutionists, the most notorious of which is the presence of 'gaps' in the fossil record. Evolution requires intermediate forms between species and paleontology does not provide them" (p. 467).

6 Typical of the many theories put forward to explain the extinction of the dinosaur, Russell (1982) suggests that a huge meteorite changed the earth's climate 63 million years ago.

7 In his Sarawak law (1855), Wallace cites the case of the "scaly flapper of the penguin". Found in Brackman (1980, 325).

8 From this review of literature on reptile to mammal jawbone transition (Manley 1972), the reader may gain some insight into the monumental amount of effort expended on this hypothetical notion.

9 In Darwin's copy of *Vestiges of creation* was pinned a slip of paper with the memorandum: "Never use the word(s) higher and lower" (found in F. Darwin and A.C. Seward 1903, 1:114).

10 Mayr (1972) explains Darwin's memorandum to himself on the basis of chance variation which can sometimes result in what can be interpreted as progress. The reader should be aware that this is simply playing with words, because without progress there would be no evolution.

11 "Die Mutationstheorie" of Hugo de Vries was not accepted by European or English biologists of the day. Hugo de Vries introduced it to America in 1904 in a lecture at the University of California. Prof. MacDougal of the Carnegie Institution then became the apostle of the new gospel of mutation and evangelized the notion. By 1914 it was being taught in U.S. schools and colleges, and, despite refutation by Jeffrey (1914) in the U.S. and Bateson in England, the idea that mutation is responsible for one species to diverge to become another is still taught as dogma today.

12 Nobel Prize winner Szent-Gyoryi (1977) acknowledges that the Second Law of Thermodynamics is a great obstacle to synthetic evolution and he proposes "syntropy" or negative entropy to explain evolution from the simple to the complex.

13 Interestingly, Gould (1977b) refused the author permission to quote his statements in full from this revealing article.

14 Often misquoted, Darwin's letter to Asa Gray

of 3 April 1860 is found in the following context: "It is curious that I remember well times when the thought of the eye made me cold all over but I have got over this stage of the complaint, and now small trifling particulars of structure often make me uncomfortable. The sight of a feather in a peacock's tail whenever I gaze at it, makes me sick" (F. Darwin 1887, 2:296).

15 Spencer introduced his phrase "survival of the fittest" in his *Principles of Biology* (1865): "It cannot but happen...that those will survive whose functions happen to be most nearly in equilibrium with the modified aggregate of external forces....This survival of the fittest implies multiplication of the fittest" (1:164).

16 Darwin (1872) acknowledged Herbert Spencer as the father of the phrase "survival of the fittest": "I have called this principle...by the term Natural Selection....But the expression often used by Mr. Herbert Spencer of the Survival of the Fittest is more accurate, and is sometimes equally convenient" (p. 49).

17 Everett (1978) has assembled a collection of reproductions from such painting masters as John Gould, showing forty-two types of bird of paradise. The full-page color pictures of these brilliantly colored birds with their unique breast fan and spiral-tipped tail decorations stand in mute defiance of any attempt to explain their origin by evolutionary concepts.

Chapter Seven

1 Haeckel (1879) gives the first phylogenetic chart of the "Pedigree of Man" depicted as an actual tree in 2:189. See also Wendt 1972, 78.

2 James A. Jensen's discovery of *Paleopteryx thomsoni*, the world's oldest bird dated at 140 million years, was announced in *The New York Times* 15 November 1981:39. See also *Science News* 24 September 1977, 112:198.

3 A wonderful confession by Gould and Eldredge (1977) states: "Smooth intermediates between *Baupläne* are almost impossible to construct, even in thought experiments; there is certainly no evidence for them in the fossil record (curious mosaics like *Archaeopteryx* do not count)", p. 147.

4 The "organized element" reproduced as a drawing on p. 88 of Pfeiffer's (1964) volume in the Time-Life Science Library series was taken from the photograph on p. 45 of Mason (1963). Mason had explained that this supposed elemental life-form found in the Orgueil meteorite resembles nothing more than an hexagonal crystal of troilite or iron sulphide. Further details may be found in Mason's book *Meteorites*. 1962. New York: John Wiley, p. 95.

5 Referring to a 1961 report by B.S. Nagy et al.,

Mason (1963) reports: "These authors found similar spectra to those of the hydrocarbons in butter and in recent terrestrial sediments" (p. 45).

6 Typically, the press reported to the public only the most newsworthy aspects of the meteorite controversy and headline: "Space life on earth: bacteria-like cells from meteorites". In *Science Newsletter*, 1961, 79 (15 April): 227, and in *Science Digest*, 1961, 49 (June): 13. All these claims are now discounted, but it is hardly newsworthy now to correct the false impression left in the public mind. See also *Scientific American* 208 (March 1963): 43.

7 Bolsche (1906), a thoroughgoing Haeckelean, glossed over, omitted, and even denied the seamier aspects of Haeckel's life. The biography makes no mention of Haeckel's five-year love affair.

8 In his letter to F. von Altenhausen, 22 February 1898, Haeckel explains how he began as a Christian but after studying evolution became a freethinker and pantheist (p. 28; see note 10).

9 Plate 1 of Gasman (1971) has been reproduced from Klemm's (1968) *Der Ketzer'* and shows a Berlin lecture hall complete with a huge backdrop of charts and skeletons for Haeckel's Sunday evening public lecture.

10 Haeckel's mistress is given as Franziska von Altenhausen, but this was simply to conceal her real identity, which was Frida von Uslar-Gleichen. In Werner (1930).

11 Haeckel (1868) occupied seventy-three pages of a prestigious scientific journal with pure speculation, including more than thirty figures of his imaginary Monera. Pages 104-7 show the *Protamoeba primitivia*, which he claimed reproduced itself by a process of fission. All these elementary life particles were entirely nonexistent.

12 T.H. Huxley (1868): "I propose to confer upon this new 'Moner' the generic name of *Bathybius*, and to call it after the eminent Professor of Zoology in the University of Jena, *B. haeckelii*" (p. 210). An illustration is given in plate 4.

13 Haeckel's most popular work, *The history of creation* (1876), reproduced in both German and English for more than half a century, was built on the supposition that the Monera existed and led in the final chapters to the evolution of man.

14 The moment of truth for *Bathybius haeckelii* was reported by Murray (1875-76): "Mr. Buchanan [the chemist] determined that the flocculent matter was simply the amorphous sulphate of lime precipitated by spirit from the sea-water" (p. 530).

15 Buchanan (1875, 604) gives the complete analytical procedure. The amorphous sulphate of lime was actually a clear, jelly-like substance, and suspended within this mass were small discoidal shapes; these were later found to be the exoskeletons of minute sea creatures.

16 Rupke (1971, 178) cites the French paper by A. deLapparent in *Revue des questions scientifiques III*, 1878, pt. 1, p. 67, and gives an English translation of critical comments.

17 Concerning the X club, Bibby (1972, 3) shows that the X club aimed at making worldwide disciples. Bibby (p. 58) lists the nine members as: Busk, Frankland, Hirst, Hooker, Huxley, Lubbock, Spencer, Spottiswoode, and Tyndall.

18 Haeckel was still stoutly defending his *Bathybius* in 1877, two years after it had been exposed as gypsum by Buchanan (1875). Pictures of *Bathybius* continued to appear in Haeckel's popular *History of Creation* (1876) until the final edition in 1923.

19 Footnote 13 of Hoyt (1976, 338) shows that Lowell's evolutionary thinking came from Ernst Haeckel's (1906) *Last words on evolution* (London), a copy of which, autographed to Lowell from Haeckel, was found in Lowell's library.

20 Pickering (1896, 113) points out that Schiaparelli wrote in Italian, which was little understood by English-speaking people, but the French astronomer Flammarion translated it into French, and Pickering's paper comments on the version in *L'Astronomie* 1882, 1:217.

21 Serviss (1901) gives an English translation of the French version of Schiaparelli's paper on the Martian "canali", which appeared in *L'Astronomie*, 1882, 1:217.

22 The Wellsian theme of life on other planets was carried forward by Edgar Rice Burroughs, who began a series of science fiction novels in 1912 and was joined later by a host of other writers. The television and film media have more recently exploited this theme, while its popularity is undoubtedly due to fulfilling Haeckel's need to provide an explanation for the origin of life without appeal to the miraculous.

23 Pioneer 10 was the first spacecraft to leave our solar system, in 1972. The Sagans and Drake (1972) first point out the high probability of there being intelligent life in the universe, then describe the message carried on the Pioneer to would-be extraterrestrial discoverers. Carl Sagan is carrying Percival Lowell's banner today.

24 Barnard's star has been observed to have an irregularity which, it is speculated, may be due to a "dark companion", that is, a planet. However, it would have to be an immense planet, and there is no direct evidence that it exists.

25 The authors Crick and Orgel (1973) acknowledge that the Swedish scientist Svente Arrhenius had first proposed the idea of panspermia in his book *Worlds in the making* in

1908. However, it was not then generally accepted because science was too ignorant of the complexity of the "simple" cell, and Darwinism demanded spontaneous generation of life on earth. Crick has since published the panspermia proposal in his *Life itself: Its origin and nature.* New York: Simon and Schuster, 1981. See also *Time* (New York), 1973, 102 (10 September): 53.
26 Clark (1968, 144 and 283) describes the Oparin-Haldane connection and their Communist sympathies.
27 Emile Borel (1962) was one of the world's foremost experts on mathematical probability. In chapter three he explores those circumstances in which remote theoretical probability becomes a practical impossibility, and he attaches numerical values to these transitions: "Probabilities which are negligible on the Cosmic Scale. A phenomenon with a probability of 10^{-50} will therefore never occur, or at least never be observed" (p.28). This probability value may be expressed as one chance in one followed by fifty zeroes.
28 In his abstract, Yockey (1977) says: "Geological evidence for the 'warm little period' is missing." He concludes that, "belief in currently accepted scenarios of spontaneous biogenesis is based on faith, contrary to conventional wisdom" (p.377).
29 Dr. Murray Eden (1967) of M.I.T.: "Without such a biological and deterministic mechanism the process of recombination would almost always lead to nonsense" (p.9). Eden is saying that without intelligent design, random combinations of biological elements could not produce complex organisms. On p.110 Eden emphasizes that the Darwinian notion of random chance must be reduced to a non-crucial role in any evolutionary model.
30 Salisbury (1969) points out the contradiction in modern biology that if life really depends on each gene being as unique as it appears to be, then it is too unique to come into being by chance mutations. In other words, there will be nothing for natural selection to act on.

Chapter Eight

1 In this edition of Hesiod (1948), lines 106-201, entitled by the editors "The five ages of man", trace the gradual increase of evil through successive stages in the decline of man (p.104).
2 The text of West (1978) is in Greek but the extensive English commentary is well worth reading. The commentary on the Pandora story (lines 47-105) is on p.165 while the commentary on the Gold, Silver, Bronze, Heroic, and Iron ages, where the life span of man decreases as moral integrity breaks down and life becomes harder (lines 106-201) is on p.172. The editor entitles this section "The myth of ages", but

Hesiod relates the episode historically.
3 Paraphrase of Plato's (1933 ed.) *The Statesman* (p.23): It is said that there was once an earthborn race that the Deity himself tended and watched over. They had fruit in abundance from many different trees, not grown by tilling, but given spontaneously by the earth. They lived, too, for the most part naked—the temperament of the seasons not being painful to them. Theirs were soft beds of grass, springing up without grudging from the soil. The men of that time were ten thousand fold happier than those of the present.

Written about 370 B.C., this is remarkably similar to the first four chapters of Genesis. The Fall of Man from the Age of Innocence is described on p.24.
4 Unlike the Greek and Roman works, *Paradise Lost* is mainly concerned with theological aspects such as the Fall of Satan and eternal punishment for the unredeemed. Nevertheless, the overall theme is of the Fall of Man. A modern edition of Milton's *Paradise Lost* is by Eberhart (1969).
5 Ellegard (1958, 303) relates the discussions held at the British Association meetings of 1867 and 1869, in which the one camp, led by the Duke of Argyll and including A.R. Wallace, proposed that early man was civilized morally in spite of material backwardness. The opposing Darwinian camp was led by Sir John Lubbock, a member of the X club (see Bibby 1972). The reader should be aware that Ellegard's publication was funded by a humanist foundation and is thereby antithetical to the orthodox Christian position.
6 Boule and Vallois (1957, 201, 213, and 241) give all the details pertinent to the La Chapelle-aux-Saints fossil and Boule's reconstruction of Neanderthal man.
7 Brace (1979, 21) states that the earlier view of Neanderthal man by Boule was incorrect
8 Buettner-Janusch (1973) clearly states "...all Neanderthals are best considered representatives of an allopatric, allochronic species—*Homo sapiens*" (p.253); on p.259 he explains that there is as great a variation in Neanderthal skulls as in modern man.
9 The 1908 date of the discovery of a Neanderthal skeleton in armor is not particularly early and it was well authenticated, but it is evidence that does not support the current evolutionary ideas of Neanderthal man and so never appears in modern textbooks.
10 The skull and body proportions of the living Neanderthal individual were carefully measured and reported by a responsible anatomist, who further reports that the Tay Tay people of the Philippine Islands also display distinctive Neanderthaloid features.

11 Whitney (1880) had been faithfully reporting his work in the *American Journal of Science* for almost twenty years prior to this date; however, this thirty-page report on the human remains gives some idea of the controversy surrounding the issue and explains why such an important discovery as the Calaveras skull was reported in the relative obscurity of the *Memorandum of the Museum of Harvard College.*

12 Keen (1977) repeats the explanation offered by the religious press in 1876 that the Calaveras skull was a hoax, but characteristically fails to mention its mineralization indicating great age or the stone bowls and dozens of other human artifacts found in the same strata.

13 Professor Thom (1971) has shown by actual measurements at the numerous sites that the builders of these megalithic observatories at least four thousand years ago were extremely well accomplished in the astronomical and mathematical arts.

14 The "mother and daughter" picture found on page 151 of *Cro-Magnon man* is acknowledged to have been taken from *Art in the ice-age* by H-G. Bandi and J. Maringer, New York: Praeger 1953:131. Bandi and Maringer in turn acknowledge their source of this picture simply as "after Breuil" and describe it as having been found in a cave at Minateda, Spain. Breuil, a well-respected authority on ancient man, published *Les roches peintes de Minateda* in Paris in 1920.

15 Keith (1911) has provided a summary and comments on the Selenka-Trinil expedition reported in German in 1911; no English translation is available.

16 In his introduction to the centennial edition of the *Origin*, Professor Thompson (1958) said: "The success of Darwinism was accompanied by a decline in scientific integrity." Thompson then mentions as examples the reckless statements of Haeckel; the shifting, devious, and histrionic arguments of T.H. Huxley; the Piltdown fraud; and Dubois' *Pithecanthropus*, p. xxi.

17 Much of the information on Piltdown man has been taken from Reader (1981).

18 Gould (1979) makes out a very convincing case for Teilhard de Chardin's being the culprit. Bowden (1977) had earlier drawn the same conclusion.

19 Although discovered in 1921, the Rhodesian man caused some difficulties in interpretation and was not reported by the British Museum until 1928.

20 Far from the present reckoning of 30,000-40,000 years, Klein (1973) points out that from the associated fauna and radiometric dating it should be closer to 125,000 years.

21 It can most charitably be said of Osborn that he was deceived himself before he deceived others. Nevertheless, the reader should be aware that deception was a natural outcome of his particular worldview. He had strong Marxist leanings and an atheistic outlook evident from the preface to his *The Origin and evolution of life*: "In truth, from the period of the earliest stages of Greek thought man has been eager to discover some natural cause of evolution, and to abandon the idea of supernatural intervention in the order of nature" (Osborn 1918, ix).

22 An article in *Science* 122 (1 July 1955):23 comments that although the Scopes trial was instigated by the American Civil Liberties Union, when it came time to pay for the defense, this had to be raised by an appeal to the American Association for the Advancement of Science. The same article quotes from *The New York Herald Tribune*, which pointed out that the issue in the Scopes trial was "the right to think versus the right of State to make laws prohibiting discussion". Exactly that situation exists today! Davidheiser (1971) corrects the false view of the trial imposed upon the public by the popular press and the movie "Inherit the Wind" by presenting the facts according to the stenographic record. Scopes (1967, 60) confessed in his autobiography that the trial was an arranged affair in which he had agreed to say that he had taught evolution although he wasn't sure that he ever had! This confession, made forty-two years after the trial, completely negates the popular image of Scopes as a crusader of the truth.

23 The living peccary was named *Catagonus ameghino* but was admitted to be of the same species as the extinct Pleistocene peccary *Catagonus wagneri*.

Chapter Nine

1 T.H. Huxley (1901): "No one is more strongly convinced...etc" (7:153). Interestingly, this passage has been omitted from the Huxley essay reprinted in the *Encyclopaedia Britannica*'s *Gateway to the Great Books* (1963, 8:204).

2 Ralph von Koenigswald (1956, 63) describes how he found the fossil teeth in a Peking drugstore, but it is not necessary to go to China to contribute to the heady science of paleoanthropology. At the time of writing, the author found "Dragon's teeth" (ask for Loong nhar) in a downtown Toronto Chinese herbal center where the going price was five dollars an ounce. The Chinese use the fossil teeth ground to powder with herbs in a medicinal decoction as a cure for insomnia.

3 As is so often the case, Hood (1964, 33) records that a single book read during Black's early manhood set the goal for his life.

4 Teilhard de Chardin's (1965) first impression of the Peking man skull: "Viewed from the

back...the *Sinanthropus* skull has a roughly triangular shape like that of the simians [apes] rather than an ovoid one like that of present day men. Zoologically *Sinanthroepus* deserves a species to himself" (p.65). First published in *Revue des questions scientifiques* (Louvain, Belgium) 98 (20 July 1930).

5 Weidenreich (1943) gives a description of all the fossil finds at Chou K'ou Tien to 1943. There were said to be fourteen skulls, but other authorities speak of sixteen or even forty.

6 Teilhard de Chardin's (1965) previous view (note 4 above) that *Sinanthropus* was an ape is now abandoned, and, far from disagreeing with Black's estimate of 964 cubic centimeters, he is now prepared to accept 1,200 and assign the creature to the status of "hominian". First published in *Études* (Paris) 92 (5 July 937).

7 For the first time in a modern and semipopular article, these Chinese authors admit to the existence of an ash heap six meters deep (1983, 93).

8 Dunbar (1960, 447) begins by saying that about forty individuals were recovered, when in fact Weidenreich (1943) had only reported fourteen.

9 Weidenreich (1938) refuted Dubois' (1935) confession that the Java man skullcap was that of a large ape. To this day Java man remains in museums and textbooks as part of the canon of faith.

10 The first section of Breuil's (1932) paper describes the fire at Chou K'ou Tien.

11 Bowden (1977, 93) shows how Breuil's paper in *L'Anthropologie* (March 1932) was not mentioned in the formal report by Black and Teilhard of May 1933.

12 Boule and Vallois (1957) play down the extent of the fire by their statement, "*Sinanthropus* kindled fire and did so frequently" (p.144).

13 Referring to Dart's claim that the Taung is in the Lineage of Man, Keith (1925a) flatly said "The claim is preposterous" (p.11).

14 Reader (1981) quotes newspaper headlines of the day: "Missing Link 5,000,000 years old"; "Missing-link that could speak"; "Birth of Mankind"; etc. (p.89).

15 Reader (1981, 157) discovered that the 600,000 years claimed at first for *Zinjanthropus* was a guess made by G. Mortelmans, a science writer. I am indebted to John Reader for many such details included in his book.

16 This work for Leakey et al. (1961) introduced the potassium-argon radiometric dating method to paleoanthropology.

17 This paper by Leakey et al. (1968) contains a table summary of the ages for each of the Olduvai Gorge beds.

18 Reck reported his find in a German scientific paper in 1914. Bowden (1977) gives the reference (actually, footnote 135 in Bowden's notation and not 136) and a summary in English.

19 Authors Straus and Hunt (1962) say that until all the contradictory dates and the existence and duration of the geological unconformities are resolved, the dates are of doubtful value in formulating hypotheses about the rates of evolution of man and his culture.

20 For further articles on *Zinjanthropus* see *National Geographic*, 1961, 120 (October): 564, 590.

21 *Homo habilis*. Various ages are reported according to the rock samples submitted for radiometric analysis, but the consensus is that since these remains were found in the same stratigraphic level as the *Zinjanthropus*, they must be the same age, that is, about 1.7 million years. See Leakey et al., 1968.

22 *Homo habilis*—handyman—is announced in this paper by Leakey et al. (1964).

23 Payne (1965, 215) says *Homo habilis* is the same age as *Zinjanthropus boisie*. See also *Time* magazine 110 (7 November 1977): 36.

24 Louis Leakey (1961) describes a "rich living floor" twenty feet higher than the level of his *Zinjanthropus* discovery, but still in bed I.

25 Fitch and Miller (1970) reported an age of 2.6 million plus or minus 260,000 years.

26 Richard Leakey (1971) declares his belief that two distinct hominids, the *Australopithecus* and the *Homo habilis*, lived at the same time in East Africa. The *Australopithecus* became extinct and the *Homo habilis* went on to become man.

27 The age of "Lucy" is given as 3.0-3.4 million years by Johanson and Edey (1981, 187). Bowden (1977, 185) notes that there are considerable discrepancies in the ages obtained for "Lucy". Given a choice of figures, there would be a natural tendency to select the larger number and thus claim the distinction of having discovered the oldest missing link.

28 Pilbeam (1970b) points out that a living baboon today, *Theropithecus galada*, found in Ethiopia, has "man-like" features and dentition just like *Ramapithecus*. He adds that there is no need to suppose that *Ramapithecus* was a hominid, but that in all probability it was simply an ape like the *T. galada*.

29 In *The first American*, Ceram (1971b, 282) gives a good account of the Laguna-girl discovery in California in 1933. Carbon 14 analysis indicated it to be seventeen thousand years old. References given.

30 Coon's (1965) plates 1, 6, and 66 are photographs of living individuals having massive eyebrow ridges (supraorbital torus) characteristic of Neanderthal man.

31 T.H. Huxley's (1901) essay "On the relations

of Man to the lower animals" is an excellent summary of the anatomical similarities and differences between man and ape (7:77).

32 Terrace (1979) exposes many of the experimental procedures in which it is claimed that apes have communicated with humans and vice versa. In the same issue, J.V. Sebek (p. 78) explains the "Clever Hans" effect whereby performing animals appear to communicate.

Chapter Ten

1 Haller's (1971) book is one of a number of important books documenting what has long been suspected: the ingrained, firm, and almost unanimous racism of North American men of science during the nineteenth and into the twentieth century.

2 Photographs of the Weidenreich reconstruction appear in virtually every book concerned with fossil man. It should be borne in mind that the reconstruction leaves an impression of *Sinanthropus* being "near human" but the early descriptions were of its being "near ape". None of the original fossil pieces now exist, so it is not possible to refute or confirm the reconstruction and acceptance of this as evidence of man's evolution thereby becomes a matter of faith.

3 In the first edition of the *Origin*, Darwin spoke of rudimentary, atrophied, or aborted organs in the sense of their being regressive; that is, they had at one time been fully functional but through disuse had become smaller or even absent. Later researchers, such as Wiedersheim, realized that a small and useless organ might, in fact, be progressive or nascent—that is, might be on the evolutionary road to becoming fully functional. This led then to the difficulty of knowing when a seemingly useless organ was either regressive or progressive.

4 This modern school biology textbook contains the amazing statement, "There are more than 100 such vestigial organs including appendix, the coccyx, wisdom teeth, nictitating membrane of the eye, body hair, muscles that move the ears and nose" (p. 773). Incredibly, this author includes an illustration of male nipples. As a final insult to the reader's intelligence a reproduction of Haeckel's fraudulent drawings of the embryos of the fish, chick, pig, and human is shown on p. 776.

5 Darwin (1871) claimed that the human male nipples were rudimentary rather than nascent, and states: "These in several instances have become well developed, and have yielded a copious supply of milk" (1:31).

6 Concerning the so-called vestigial human ear muscles compared to the horse, Darwin (1871) actually said, "Consequently we ought

frankly to admit their community of descent" (1:32).

7 The Lamarckian overtones in Darwin's (1859) thinking can frequently be seen in such statements as: "...bearing in mind how strong is the principle of inheritance..." (p. 457).

8 Carpenter et al. (1978) begins with the presupposition, "The vestigial posterior appendages (spurs or claws)...", and goes on to describe how the male snakes use these retractable spurs in combat. Since they have a useful function, how can they be vestigial?

9 *Biological Sciences Curriculum Study: A molecular approach* (1980, 238) cites the yolk sac of the human embryo as vestigial. *Biological Sciences Curriculum Study: An enquiry into life* (1980, 279): cites the human appendix as vestigial while on p. 282 a redrawn version of Haeckel's embryos of dog, bat, rabbit, and man taken from Romanes (1892) is given as evidence of the long-discredited Biogenetic Law.

10 Metchnikoff (1907), the great medical authority, made the following incredible statements: "Some very large parts of our alimentary canal must be regarded as useless inheritances, bequeathed to us by our animal ancestors" (p. 69).

11 The perceived problems of bacteria in the human intestine are discussed on p. 248ff. and Metchnikoff concludes that removal of this bacteria, if necessary by the removal of the intestine, would greatly lengthen the human life span!

12 Interestingly, like Rudolph Virchow in Germany, Lane became involved in socialist issues in his later years. In 1926 he gave up a successful practice to found the New Health Society (Tanner 1946, 126)

13 It was the rise of Mendelian genetics that caused Haeckel's Biogenetic law to be abandoned early in this century. Gould's (1977c) book on the history of the subject and its ramifications to the social sciences is said to be the first published in fifty years.

14 Drawings of the dog and human embryo appear in Haeckel's (1868) *History of creation*. 1:309-11.

15 The now familiar engraving of the development of the embryos of a dog, bat, rabbit, and man taken from Haeckel's *Anthropogenie* (1874) appear on p. 153 of Romanes (1892).

16 In Winchester's (1971, 83) school biology textbook, Haeckel's fraudulent illustration of embryos has been reproduced as evidence of evolution and enhanced by color tinting. The author makes no mention that the theory was discredited half a century earlier.

17 In a step-by-step manner, Rifkin (1983, 111-56) exposes the faulty logic of the theory of evolution.

Chapter Eleven

1　Shakespeare's (1599) line given to Rosalind addressing Orlando in *As you like it* (4, 1:90) was an unquestioned truth in the sixteenth century.

2　Referring to Genesis 1:26 Lightfoot (1825) says, "Man created by the Trinity about the third hour of the day, or nine of the clock in the morning" (2:335). A man of great scholarly ability, John Lightfoot's (1602-75) over-enthusiastic exegesis has been far from "harmless" in its latter-day use by critics who have taken the "nine of the clock" statement out of context to use it to discredit the Ussher date for the time of Creation.

3　Having given the figures for the rate of sediment deposition, Dunbar (1960) then assures his readers that "these deposits are only a surface veneer of the great delta built by the Nile" (p. 18). However, this cannot be true since Lyell (see 1914, 29) states that the highest point on the delta is only seventy-two feet above sea level.

4　Lyell (1914) describes the work of measuring sediment thickness in the Nile delta and the human artifacts that were continually brought up by the boring tools on pp. 26-30. Lyell concludes, "In a boring 72 feet deep, being 2 or 3 feet below the level of the Mediterranean, in the parallel of the apex of the [Nile] delta...M. Rosière had estimated the mean rate of deposit of sediment in the delta at 2¼ inches in a century; were we to take 2½ inches, a work of art [a brick] 72 feet deep must have been buried more than 30,000 years ago" (p. 29).

5　Joly (1922) was long occupied with finding the age of the earth by the concept of "denudation of the continents"—that is, measuring the salts in the oceans and the rate of addition; as well as measuring sediments. He concluded the earth to be no more than 200 million years and in this paper gives a valuable criticism of the radiometric methods, which, at that time, were giving ages ten times as long. On p. 482 he gives a lengthy argument to show that the halo phenomenon does not support the long radiometric ages.

6　During the past few decades Israel's National Water Carrier and Jordan's Ghor canal have siphoned off about eight hundred cubic meters of water daily from the River Jordan. The result is that with continuing evaporation, the level of the Dead Sea is dropping and the salt, which is at the saturation point (28 percent), is beginning to precipitate out.

7　Koczy (1954) concludes: "2 x 10⁻¹⁴ grams of uranium is added each year to each millilitre of sea water. Therefore, if no uranium is removed from sea water, its uranium content should be doubled in the course of 60,000 years, which is an improbably short time from a geo-logical point of view" (p. 126).

8　University of Toronto's Macallam (1903) explains: "... the proportions [of salts] in plasma are an ancestral feature derived from a form which had its habitat in the ocean in the earlier geological periods when the ocean water was very much less rich in salts of magnesia than it is now" (p. 234).

9　Immanuel Kant published his *Allgemeine Natürgeshichte und Theorie des Himmels* in 1756. In it he expressed an evolutionary system of cosmology. This system was given authority when in 1796 Pierre-Simon, marquis de Laplace, defended it in his *Exposition du système du monde*. Laplace expanded on this theme in 1825 in his *Traité de Méchanique Céleste* while Robert Chambers's *Vestiges* (1844) popularized the notion among the English-speaking people. On page 17 of *Vestiges* Chambers gives his translation of a key passage from the *Traité*: "Planets all move nearly in one plane.... Motions of all their axes are in one direction—namely, from west to east." This statement lent great support to the theory of an evolved solar system but is factually incorrect. Of the nine planets in our solar system, three revolve in a retrograde direction and the remainder in the prograde direction. Of the forty-four satellites (moons) it is known that twelve revolve in a retrograde direction and twenty-one in a prograde direction. The direction of rotation of the remainder is at present unknown.

10　In his letter to J. Croll, 31 January 1869, Darwin writes: "I am greatly troubled at the short duration of the world according to Sir William Thomson for I require for my theoretical views a very long period before the Cambrian formation" (F. Darwin and A.C. Seward 1903, 2:163).

11　Concerning the lack of randomness found for cobalt 60 and cesium 137 decay, Anderson and Spangler (1973) conclude: "The evidence is inconsistent with the thesis of decay independence" (p. 3120).

12　In his abstract Anderson (1972) states: "The inconsistency...of radioactive decay raises serious questions relative to the generality of the independence of radioactive decay."

13　Anderson and Spangler (1974) were free to express their views more explicitly in the journal *Pensée*, which is now defunct. The same authors writing in *American Physical Society, Bulletin*, 1971, 10:1180 had presented their data in cautiously worded terms to show that the gamma emission rate of cobalt 60 was significantly influenced by electrical fields. They concluded that, in this case, radioactive decay is not independent.

14　Radioactive decay. The terms used in expressing rate of decay are as follows:

1.) *Particle count.* A sample of known weight is exposed to a Geiger counter for a known period of time, perhaps two days, and the total number of (alpha) particles emitted counted.

2.) *Specific decay rate.* The particle count is divided by the sample weight and by the time to reduce the figure to i) the number of counts or atoms per milligram per hour in the case of the uranium/lead method or, ii) atoms per gram per minute in the case of the carbon 14 method.

3.) *Decay constant.* This is formed mathematically from the specific decay rate:

$$\lambda = -\frac{1}{N}\frac{\delta N}{\delta T}$$

where lambda, λ, is the decay constant, N is the number of radioactive atoms of a particular kind in a sample at a given moment and $\delta N/\delta T$ is the rate of decay of those atoms at that moment. Potassium 40, for example, has a decay constant of 0.58×10^{-10} per year.

4.) *Half life.* This is derived from the decay constant and is the time required for a large number of radioactive atoms of a particular kind in a sample to decay to half the original number.

$$\tau = \frac{\log 2}{\lambda} = \frac{0.693}{\lambda}$$

where the half-life is usually denoted by tau, τ, and lambda, λ, is the decay constant.

15 Rutherford writes referring to Aston's (1929) work and concludes, "The uranium in our earth has its origin in the sun.... It has been decaying since the separation of the earth from the sun...The earth cannot be older than 3.4×10^9 years" (*Nature* 1929, 123:313).

16 Cosmic rays are shown to be very high energy protons, some exceeding the mass of helium nuclei by thirteen times. Since the nuclei of argon 36 are only nine times that of helium, some of these cosmic rays are, therefore, themselves the nuclei of argon. Moreover, cosmic bombardment of argon 40 produces argon 36, so that throughout time, argon 36 has been increasing.

17 Potassium-argon ages of 3.3 billion years were reported by Funkhouser and Naughton (1968) for lava thought to be less than one million years old.

18 Emiliani (1958) was one of the first to estimate ancient ocean temperatures by measuring the oxygen 18 content of oyster shells taken from drill cores. The results also bore a relationship to age and caused a significant downward revision of the times for the ice ages. (See Chapter Twelve, note 4).

19 Eldridge (1982, 104) categorically states the age of moon rocks to be 4.5 billion years, yet, typically for this type of publication, no references to this source are given.

20 Ages of moon rock samples quoted by S.R. Taylor (1975) range between 3.16 and 4.6 aeons, where the "aeon" is defined as a billion years (p. 64, 180 and 263). Same reference sources used as quoted in Whitcomb and DeYoung (1978, 99-100).

21 Whitcombe and DeYoung (1978, 99) cite the following sources for the dating of moon rocks and in their Table IV-4 summarize all the radiometric ages reported. Proceedings of the second, third, and fourth Lunar Science Conference; *Earth and Planetary Science Letters* for 1972-77; *Science* 1970, 167:462-555.

22 Professor of nuclear medicine Dudley's (1975) criticism of this most sacred aspect of the dogma of uniformitarianism, i.e. a constant decay rate, was not acceptable to the mainline scientific journals but appeared in the *Chemical and Engineering News* and in full (in English) in the Italian journal *Letters al Nuovo Cimento* 1972, 5:231.

23 Hynek's (1983) short article with a diagram shows how Roemer made his measurements in 1668 by observing the time between eclipses of Jupiter's moons from opposite positions of the earth's orbit around the sun.

24 Goldstein et al. (1973) refrain from giving the actual and corrected velocity but simply conclude by saying that "the velocity of light did not differ by 0.5% in 1668 to 1678 from the current value." 0.5 percent beyond the current value turns out to be 301,300 km per second.

25 Strong (1957) asks the question, "Does c change with the passage of time?" (p. 126).

26 Steidl (1982) gives a four-page summary of the monographs produced by Barry Setterfield, which at the time this book was going press were not generally available in North America.

27 Moon and Spencer (1953) make the following remarkable statement: "The acceptance of Riemannian space allows us to reject Einstein's relativity and to keep all the ordinary ideas of time and all the ideas of Euclidean space out to a distance of a few light years. Astronomical space remains Euclidean for material bodies, but light is considered to travel in Riemannian space. In this way, the time required for light to reach us from the most distant stars is only 15 years" (p. 635).

Chapter Twelve

1 Loren Eiseley (1961, 239) in *Darwin's century*, uses this quote as an example of Huxley's sophistry, that is, his deceptive argument that appears to be correct but is actually invalid; in this case because it assumes evolution to be proven.

2 An excellent descriptive paper of the halo phenomenon was produced by Joly (1917) in which he refers to the early work conducted in the latter part of the nineteenth century.

3 Gentry's (1967, 78) statement, acceptable to *Medical Opinion and Review*, is the obvious implication of Gentry's work but could not be expressed in such terms in the mainline journals such as *Science* (organ of the American Association for the Advancement of Science).

4 Emiliani (1956) comments on the results obtained by the oxygen 18 dating method applied to oyster shells taken from seabed core samples: "This chronology is considerably shorter than the chronologies usually suggested in the literature. If correlation between core stages and continental stratigraphy is correct, the Pleistocene time since beginning of the Günz age appears to be only about 300,000 years" (p.924). Loren Eiseley (1961) in his *Darwin's century* (New York: Doubleday) refers to Emiliani's work and cautiously adds, "The million-year age of the Pleistocene period may be shortened by new studies" (p.139). It was shortened by more than half, and so another article in the canon of yesterday's faith quietly became discredited. (See also Chapter Eleven, note 18).

5 One of the unsolved mysteries of Antarctica is the mummified bodies of crab-eater seals found thirty miles in-land and up to three thousand feet above sea level in ice-free areas. Described by Dort (1971), their age is unknown. Further details by L. Péwé and N. Rivard in *Science* 1959, 130 (18 September): 716.

6 In explaining the delayed introduction of the new high-energy spectrometry, Grootes (1980) said: "For C_{14} counting by accelerator...it is not yet exactly known where the background counts come from." He suggested that "background counts originate in the accelerator in parts of the system that are not occasionally cleaned or changed" (p.793). The sequel to this little insight into the heady workings of nuclear physics passed from the ridiculous to the bizarre when the new high-energy accelerator was installed at a well-known Canadian university (1983). The C_{14} results obtained using previously analyzed samples again gave ages that were too young, i.e., more C_{14} was found than expected from the alleged age; furthermore, there could be no question of contamination. Rather than question the long ages demanded by Lyellian uniformitarianism, the physicists in charge seriously believed that some new particle mimicking C_{14} had been generated! (Private discussion with author.)

7 In 1952 Kulp described the carbon 14 method: "There are two basic assumptions in the carbon 14 method. One is that the carbon 14 concentration in the carbon-dioxide cycle is constant. The other is that the cosmic ray flux has been essentially constant" (p.261). These sweeping assumptions established the method in the 1950s but have since been modified significantly.

8 By 1965 it was being recognized that the production of C_{14} was not uniform and Suess (1965) states: "The oceans as a whole cannot, of course, be considered a well-mixed reservoir" (p.5947).

9 Stansfield (1977): "It now appears that the C_{14} decay rate in living organisms is about 30 percent less than its production rate in the upper atmosphere.... Creationists argue that since C_{14} has not yet reached its equilibrium rate, the age of the atmosphere must be less than 20,000 years" (p.83). Stansfield obtained the 30 percent figure from the work of R. Lingenfelter, 1963. *Reviews of Geophysics* (Washington) 1:1.

10 According to Dillow (1981, 146) the surface atmospheric pressure of the pre-flood world was 2.18 atmospheres of 32 pounds per square inch.

11 The *pterosaur* fossil was found in non marine rock of flat topography and Lawson (1975) suggests that in some way the creature had to be capable of powered flight since it could not soar from clifftops. See also G.G. Shor, *Science*, 1975, 188 (16 May): 677.

12 Jueneman (1972) points out the inconsistencies in results when C_{14} is calibrated against the bristle-cone pine and suggests something is radically wrong. The situation has led to divided schools of opinion. For the European school, see G.W. Pearson et al. 1977. *Nature* 270 (3 November): 25. For the American school, see H.E. Suess. 1976. *Antiquity* 50 (March): 61.

13 Helmholtz (1856, 506) sets forth the question of the contracting sun and all the pertinent calculations in the appendix to his article.

14 Yockey (1977) boldly exposes the whole problem of the absent neutrinos and points out that "the neutrino was originally an *ad hoc* assumption [by Wolfgang Pauli in 1931] to save the principle of conservation of energy in decay" (p.395). His statement "the measured flux is less than one fifth of the predicted value and may be zero" was derived from the published data of Bahcall and Davis (1976). Bahcall and Davis (1976) state: "The Ar_{37} production rate...is 0.13...atoms per day.... The cosmic ray production rate...is 0.09 Ar_{37} per day....There is no evidence for a solar neutrino capture rate of 1.5 units [per day]" (p.266).

15 Wittmann (1980) provides additional data to indicate a shrinking sun, while the July 1980 issue of *Sky and Telescope* (p.10) contains a diagram showing all of Eddy and Boornazian's data. Although there is scatter, there seems little doubt of their downward trend.

16 Parkinson (1980) takes the data obtained between 1836 and 1954 and points out that there were six observers and two telescopes, which introduced bias. He admits the absence of

neutrinos is a problem but cannot accept that the sun is shrinking.

17 Stephenson (1982) wants an open-ended beginning for our solar system and states: "The data provide fairly strong evidence that the diameter of the sun oscillates. The period of oscillation is some 80 years and its amplitude is about 0.025 percent" (p.172). Eddy and Boornazian's (1979) conclusion of secular decrease was discounted but the same data is used by Stephenson to justify oscillation!

18 Thwaites and Awbury (1982) explain: "If one extrapolates back in time 4.6 billion years with the accepted estimate of 0.005 second per year per year, one gets a fourteen-hour day" (p.19). With further explanation, the authors show how one second per year corrections need to be made at the 20th, 28th, 35th, 40th, 45th, 49th, 53rd, and 57th years, and so on (continuing to two second per year corrections starting at the 214th year after the correction system is begun). The system used today was actually back-dated to 1900, but the authors failed to mention why two second a year corrections have been made since 1981. See *The Astronomical Almanac.*

19 Challinor (1971) studied data from 1956 to 1969 and concluded there were three types of variation in the rate of rotation of the earth: seasonal, irregular, and long-term.

20 Table B5 of *The Astronomical Almanac* (1983) shows leap seconds have always been added, never subtracted, on the following dates: January 1, July 1, 1972; every January 1 from 1973 to 1980; then January 1 and July 1, 1981, 1982, and 1983.

21 Oort's notion for the origin of comets is dismissed by Brady (1970) in the statement: "With this sort of evidence it seems unnecessary to reopen the question of interstellar origins [of comets] and the view established by Strömgren (1914) and now generally accepted that these comets all approach the planetary system in elliptical orbits of a very long period, is still unassailable" (p.1064).

22 The Australian tektites have given rise to a lot of controversy since they are found in a stratigraphic horizon near the Pleistocene-Holocene boundary which is dated at 7,000 to 20,000 years B.P. However, potassium-argon and fission track radiometric methods have given dates of 700,000 years and older. No one wants to give up the stratigraphic dating, and no one wants to give up the radiometric method! See also R.O. Chalmers et al. *Geological Society of America: Bulletin* Part 1 1979. 90 (May): 508, where the argument still rages.

23 Gold (1955) speculates, "From the nickel content of the deep ocean deposits...the quantity of material currently deposited on the Earth is...one million tons per year. This esti-

mate would imply that the Moon is acquiring a layer one centimeter in thickness every 10^7 years" (p.598). (In 4.5 billion years this would amount to eighteen inches.) Gold continues, "Fine dust particles on the [Moon's] surface...move only at such a speed that the maria can be filled to an average depth of perhaps a thousand feet in a period that may be three thousand million years" (p.599). Lyttleton (1956), a British enthusiast, predicted a layer of dust on the moon "several miles in thickness" (p.72).

24 Bender et al. (1973) say: "The lunar laser ranging measurements...have an accuracy of 1 nsec in round trip travel time. This corresponds to 15 cm in the one-way distance" (p.237). Writing in 1975, S.R. Taylor in *Lunar science: A post-Apollo view* (New York: Pergamon) added that "further improvements have enabled the distance to be measured to within 2 to 3 cm" (p.3).

25 Baldwin (1965) frankly confesses that the origin of the moon is a mystery: "There is no existing theory of the origin of the moon which gives a satisfactory explanation of the earth-moon systems as we now have it. The moon is not an optical illusion or mirage. It exists and is associated with the earth. Before 4.5 billions of years ago the earth did not exist. Somehow, in this period of time, the two bodies were formed and became partners. But how?" (p.42).

26 William Thomson (1865) opposed Darwin's long ages in three fundamental areas: (1) The luminosity of the sun, (2) the rotation of the earth, and (3) the heat of the earth. The rate of heat flow through the surface of the earth is given in the statement: "The increase of temperature downwards may be taken as roughly averaging 1 degree Centigrade per 30 meters" (p.513).

27 Curie temperatures are: pure iron, 750°C; haematite, Fe_2O_3, 675°C; magnetite, Fe_3O_4, 578°C.

28 Lamb (1883) was an extremely able scientist yet in his biography in the *Encyclopaedia Britannica* or Scribner's *Dictionary of scientific biography*, no mention is made of Lamb's classic work on terrestrial magnetism. Jacobs (1967) says of Lamb's work: "H. Lamb showed in 1883 that...this time is of the order of 10^5 years, whereas the age of the earth is more than 4×10^9 years" (p.430).

29 Gauss (1834) was instrumental in forming the Magnetic Association in 1835 to which workers submitted their results. Magnetic measuring stations were located at Greenwich (U.K.), Dublin, Capetown, Hobart (Tasmania), Toronto, St. Helena Island, and other stations throughout the East India Company. (Gauss adopted the name Charles as the French equivalent of his given name Karl for this French publication.)

30 McDonald and Gunst (1967) conclude that the earth's magnetic field is decaying "5 percent per one hundred years" (p. 1), while their Table 3 lists the magnetic moment measurements made from 1835 to 1965 (reproduced in Appendix K).

31 The data from the 1979/80 satellite showed that the overall intensity of the earth's magnetic field was declining at a rate of twenty-six nanoteslars per year with a half-life of just 830 years. Extrapolation of the data shows that the magnetic field will have entirely disappeared in 1,200 years.

32 Earth's heat. The power (P) consumed by electrical devices is rated in terms of watts where this is given by the electrical resistance (R) multiplied by the current (I) squared: $P=RI^2$. The resistance (R) of the hot rocks within the earth will be essentially constant, but as the current (I) increases in the past, as indicated by the greater magnetic field, the power (P) and thus the heat generated will increase as the square of the current. For example, if R is constant at 10 and I increaes arithmetically 2, 4, 6, 8, etc., then P will increase as follows: 40, 160, 360, 640, etc. The total power produced by the current in the earth beneath us is given by multiplying P by the constant 8.13×10^8, which gives a colossal number of megawatts. However, to go back only ten thousand years in the past would mean increasing this figure millions of times and at this point the heat generated would be too great for life to exist on the earth's surface.

33 Carrigan and Gubbins (1979) complain, "No one has developed an explanation of why the sign reversals take place. The apparently random reversals of the earth's dipolar field has remained inscrutable" (p. 125).

34 In *New Scientist* 1964, 24 (3 December): 631, the anonymous author cautiously points to a beginning of "no more than a few million years ago" and asks the question "where is the earth's radiogenic helium?"

35 A photograph appears in this *National Geographic* article showing a bat entombed in a stalagmite, clearly indicating that growth during this period must have been over a few days, or weeks at most.

36 Dickey et al. (1968) have noted that evolutionary theory requiring millions of years cannot explain the enormous pressure differences which exist in adjacent rock strata: "The significance of this observation to structural geology is very great. It means that pore water has been able to move across the bedding planes of shale hardly at all in spite of a pressure gradient exceeding ten pounds per square per foot during scores of millions of years. Obviously shales have small but appreciable permeability

to water; otherwise how could compaction occur?" (p. 612).

37 Books and articles continue to appear containing extrapolated ventures into frightening population statistics. Two examples are Vogt (1960) and Hauser (1970).

38 Langer (1964) shows that between A.D. 1348 and 1350 at least a quarter of the population of Europe died of the plague; however, within three hundred years, the normal rise in population had been resumed.

39 Stansfield (1977) gives a typical evolutionary explanation: "The size of a population may fluctuate over various lengths of time, but the long-term picture is one of stability" (p. 82). This author appeals to an oscillating population in order to leave an open-ended past.

Chapter Thirteen

1 This little book, which records Keith's 1925 Conway memorial lecture, gently draws aside the veil that hides the inner sanctum of the human mind to reveal the altar upon which we place our most treasured and secret offerings of belief.

2 Darwin had used this same passage from Marcus Aurelius in the second edition (1874) of his *Descent of Man* (p. 123). A parallel passage written a millenium earlier than Marcus Aurelius appears in Proverbs 23:7.

3 Westfall (1981) has written what is regarded to be the definitive work on Newton. A less voluminous work is by B.J.T. Dobbs. 1976. *The Foundation of Newton's Alchemy.* New York: Cambridge University Press.

4 Cohen (1955) writes, "Newton had essayed a linguistic analysis of theology in an attempt to find the corruptions that had been introduced to Christianity. Newton was not an orthodox Trinitarian" (p. 72).

5 Strauss (1835) gained notoriety in the German academic community and the church by his *Das leben Jesu*, in which he dismissed the Gospel of John, stripped the other accounts of the miraculous, and gave prime place to Matthew.

6 Twelve of these enormous folio volumes ordered by Napoleon contain some of the finest hand-coloured engravings ever produced and capture in the imagination the splendor that was once Egypt. See also notes to Denon (1803).

7 Roberts (1846-49) spent 1838-39 in Egypt and Palestine making very accurate drawings of the ancient buildings and monuments. He considered the French work *Description de l'Égypt* grossly inaccurate. Roberts noted that the Egyptian temples and monuments had been maintained in good order by the Christian church until about A.D. 700 when they were abandoned to Islam. Most of the destruction had been wrought since that time. Denon (1803), renowned mostly for a series of pornographic etchings, was an intrepid artist-adventurer, both in the deserts of Egypt and in the bedrooms of Paris. His remarkable illustrations of former Egyptian decadence produced in these volumes together with those of François Jomard and others in the famous *Déscription de l'Égypt* spawned numerous magazine articles. The more truthful artistic renditions of Egypt by David Roberts of England and Carl Lepsius of Germany also did much to promote public interest in ancient Egypt during the early 1800s.

8 Ceram (1971a) had taken his information on Champollion from a German biography of 1906. There is, however, a more recent biography of Champollion by M. Pourpoint 1963. *Champollion et l'enigme égyptienne: le roman d'une découverte.* Paris. Other than Ceram's chapter (pp. 88-116), there appears to be no biography in English.

9 In a footnote, Libby (1963) says: "The Egyptian historical dates beyond 4,000 years ago may be somewhat too old, perhaps 5 centuries too old at 5,000 years ago" (p. 278). It is of interest to note that Libby's reference to this statement was not a publication but a private communication with an authority (I.E.S. Edwards) on Egyptian dating. This confession completely vindicates Velikovsky's (1952) thesis and brings biblical events and Egyptian history into line, but so far as is known, nothing has yet been openly published to this effect.

10 Champollion's dating was evidently questioned from the beginning as indicated by the title of historian William Mure's (1829) document held in the British Museum Library archives.

11 Broken pillars. Sedgwick and Buckland were not only great geologists but also pillars of the Anglican Church. It appears that they began by believing in the literal interpretation of Genesis but, when faced with evidence that seemed to be explained more rationally by Lyell's uniformitarianism, slipped slowly away from the biblical account and in later years became virtual Darwinians. Others, such as Agassiz of Harvard University, remained believers to the end, although their understanding changed over the years. Murchison in England had little belief and less understanding of the Bible in the first place and was thus a good candidate for Lyell's geology.

12 The moment of capitulation to Lyell, if not Darwin, by Smith's Bible dictionary appeared in the 1884 edition under "Noah": "The language of the books of Genesis does not compel us to suppose that the whole of the surface of the globe was actually covered with water if the evidence of geology requires us to adopt the hypothesis of a partial deluge" (p. 453).

13 Monsignor Manning (1865-74) of the Roman Catholic diocese of Westminster, London, was of the conservative school and founded the "Academia" in 1861 to combat "science falsely so-called", while he preached against the new "brutal philosophy" of nature where "there is no God and the ape is our Adam" (p. 51).

14 An abridged version of Henry Layard's 1849 classic *Nineveh and its remains* has recently been made available under the same title, edited by H.W.F. Saggs. 1970. London: Routledge and Paul.

15 Brackman's (1978) thoroughly readable and highly informative modern work recounts the discoveries at Nineveh and Babylon and their confirmation of the biblical accounts.

16 Bradley (1975) evaluates the impact of Evangelicalism on the Victorian period. Habershon (1909) and Thompson and Hutchinson (1929) describe the evangelical upsurge accompanying Layard's discoveries.

17 In his letter to E. Haeckel, 23 November 1868, Charles Lyell said that six editions of his *Principles* had prepared the way for Darwin. In K. Lyell 1881, 2:436.

18 Robert Chambers was elected to the Fellowship of the Royal Society of Edinburgh in 1840. Within a year, he began to write *Vestiges.* The first edition (1844) was anonymous. The second, in 1846, contained a sequel in which his name was mentioned. Although he was widely suspected to have been the author, this was not acknowledged until the 1880s.

19 Gosse (1907) explains, "It was the notion of Lyell himself a great mover of men that before the doctrine of natural selection was given to the world...a certain bodyguard of sound and experienced naturalists...should be privately made aware of its tenor" (p. 116).

20 The biographer, Edmund Gosse (1907), refers to his father's book of the title *Omphalos*, published in 1857, which used an argument based on Adam's navel to counter Lyell and Darwin's belief in the transmutation of species; the key to this strange contortion is given: "For instance Adam would certainly... display an omphalos [navel], yet no umbilical cord had ever attached him to a mother" (p. 121).

21 Remarking to his friend Rev. F.D. Maurice on the circumstances under which *Water babies* was written, Kingsley (1904) writes, "Remember that the physical science in the book is not nonsense but accurate earnest as far as I dare speak yet" (p. 245).

22 This well-documented review by Lucas (1979) of what must surely be all the recorded facts leaves Wilberforce as a reasonable and well-informed contender. See also letter in *Nature*

1980, 287 (9 October): 480.

23 In a letter to C. Darwin dated 2 July 1860, J.D. Hooker describes how T.H. Huxley could not make himself heard at the Wilberforce debate and Hooker himself rose to defend Darwin. In L. Huxley 1918, 1:525.

24 Letter from C. Darwin to J.D. Hooker, July 1860. Found in F. Darwin 1887, 2:324.

25 Patriarchs acknowledged by Christ are in the following passages:

Moses: Matthew 8:4; 19:8; Mark 1:44; 7:10; 10:3; 12:26; Luke 16:31; 20:37; 24:27; John 5:45; 6:32 and 7:19.

Abel: Matthew 23:35; Luke 11:51.

Noah: Matthew 24:37; Luke 17:26.

26 Bozarth (1978) puts his finger on the central conflict between evolution and Christianity: "It becomes clear now that the whole justification of Jesus' life and death is predicated on the existence of Adam....Without the original sin, who needs to be redeemed?' (p.30).

27 Ramm (1954) has produced a useful survey of the many theories to harmonize Scripture with geology, but the reader is warned that Ramm writes from the evolutionary viewpoint.

28 Helena Blavatsky founded the spiritualist Theosophical Society in 1875, and Pember's book was intended to shed some light on this activity. The 1876 edition of this popular work was entitled *Earth's earliest ages and their lesson for us, including a treatise on spiritualism*. The title of subsequent editions was changed slightly.

29 Undoubtedly the definitive work on the Gap theory, Custance (1970) nevertheless uses some very strained interpretations for its support. Field's (1976) *Without form and void* was written specifically to counter every argument used by A.C. Custance (1970), one of the last proponents of the Gap theory.

30 Numbers (1982) presents a fair and well-documented history of the Creation movement, from the early 1920s when they tried to keep evolution out of the schools to the 1980s when they tried to get Creation in.

Chapter Fourteen

1 Details of the situation in 1888 in which agnosticism had become a national issue with T.H. Huxley furiously defending his views are given in L. Huxley 1900, 1:217; 2:221.

2 Francis Darwin (1887, 1:317) commented in a footnote on his father's interview with Edward Aveling. The note adds that Aveling (1883) wrote on Charles Darwin and atheism in *The religious views of Charles Darwin*. Aveling (1897) countered this footnote by his article *Charles Darwin and Karl Marx* in *New Century Review*.

3 Dupree (1959, 182) points out that both Gray and Darwin were married to Unitarians and, interestingly, Gray's wife was continually in ill health. Gray himself likened Jane's miseries—dyspepsia, headaches, dizziness, and so on—to those of Charles Darwin.

4 Letter from C. Darwin to A. Gray, 26 November 1860. In F. Darwin 1887, 2:146.

5 This statement, which lays out the foundation for modern theistic evolution, is a letter from A. Gray to G.F. Wright 14 August 1875, reported in J.L. Gray 1893, 2:656.

6 Published by A. Gray in *Atlantic Monthly* for July, August, and October 1860.

7 Letter from C. Darwin to C. Lyell, 2 August 1861. Found in F. Darwin and A.C. Seward 1903, 1:191. Natural selection to Darwin had become sacred (he always wrote the words as a proper noun) and in a letter to Asa Gray, 8 May 1868, it is clear he would not allow any other mechanism for evolution to be considered: "If the right variations occurred, and no others, Natural Selection would be superfluous" (in F. Darwin 1887, 3:85).

8 Aristotle (1961 ed.) in his Book B., lines 198b-199a, describes the end purposes within natural processes and concludes that there must be some guiding principle, since chance or luck alone would not produce what is found. In contrast, Darwin claimed that luck or chance alone is responsible for natural selection.

9 Some commentators attempt to redress Darwin's irreligious views by quoting his reference to the Creator in the last paragraph of the *Origin*. The fact is the first edition (1859) contained no reference to the Creator while the addition of the words "by the Creator" were made as an afterthought to the penultimate paragraph in the second and subsequent editions. This was surely only a sop to mollify the Christian community. The paragraph reads: "To my mind it accords better with what we know of the laws impressed on matter by the Creator, that the production and extinction of the past and present inhabitants of the world should have been due to secondary causes" (1860, 488).

11 Acknowledgment of the first eleven chapters of Genesis found in: Matthew 19:4-5; 24:37-39; Mark 10:6; Luke 3:38; 11:51; 17:26-27; Romans 5:12; 1 Corinthians 6:16; 11:8-12; 15:21-45; 2 Corinthians 11:3; Ephesians 5:31; 1 Timothy 2:13; Hebrews 11:7; 1 Peter 3:20; 2 Peter 2:5; 3:4; 1 John 3:12; Jude 11,14; Revelation 14:7.

12 Humanist writer Bozarth (1978) makes the following revealing statement: "Christianity has fought evolution...because evolution destroys utterly and finally the very reason Jesus' earthly life was supposedly made necessary. Destroy Adam and Eve and the original sin, and in

the rubble you will find the sorry remains of the son of god" (p. 30).

13 Although employed by Harvard, Gray (1880) delivered his new gospel to Yale, which he found to be less committed to orthodoxy, and it was here that he converted James Dana.

14 Although a Baptist by training, Fosdick (1956) was asked to take the First Presbyterian Church, New York City. After preaching a particularly fiery sermon, "Shall the fundamentalists win?" in May 1922, he was forced to resign. The Presbyterians at that time were fundamentalist and fully accepted Special Creation and the Flood.

15 John Henry Newman published his *Essay on the development of Christian doctrine* in 1845. He conceded that the Scriptures were given by inspiration, but argued that it had taken eighteen centuries for man to come to an understanding and to "their full elucidation". The theory of development is clearly based on the evolutionary supposition of man's ascent, rather than on the Fall.

16 Henri Bergson's standing in the scientific and intellectual circles of Paris suffered for the same reason that Alfred R. Wallace was excluded from the London circles. Both were deeply involved in the study of occult phenomena, and in 1913 Bergson became president of the Society for Psychical Research.

17 The doctrine of theistic evolution is summed up by the statement in Teilhard de Chardin's *Christianity and evolution*: "On the one side there is an innate, tumultuous upsurge of cosmic and humanistic aspiration...that upsurge is the new faith in the world. And on the other side...the anticipation of a transcendent and loving pole of the universe; it is unswervingly upheld by Christian dogma...this is the ancient faith in God....Surely the two terms—faith in the world and faith in God—so far from being antagonistic, are structurally complementary?" (p. 175).

18 The Teilhard Centre for the Future of Man, London, lists its executives as: historian Dr. Joseph Needham, Anglican Bishop George Appleton, Canon David Jenkins, anthropologist Dr. Margaret Mead (deceased 1978), Professor Roger Garaudy, Professor Bernard Towers, and Lady Collins.

19 A translation of the *Monitum* is as follows: There are now widely available certain works of Fr. Teilhard de Chardin, published even after the author's death, which are enjoying considerable popularity. Leaving aside all judgment on purely scientific matters, it is sufficiently clear that in the areas of philosophy and theology the aforementioned works abound in such ambiguities and even serious errors as to offend against Catholic teaching. Therefore the Father of the Sacred Congregations of the Holy Office urges bishops and superiors of religious institutes to effectively protect the minds, especially of the young, against the dangers in the works of Fr. Teilhard de Chardin and his followers. Dated Rome, 30 June 1962.

20 Originally published in 1961 in Germany, this English translation of J.V. Kopp's *Teilhard de Chardin: A new synthesis of evolution* (1964) was published less than two years after the papal *monitum* banning Teilhard's works. Kopp's work promotes Teilhardian evolution yet is given the Imprimatur of Cardinal Spellman to assure the Catholic reader that it is free of doctrinal or moral error!

21 Garaudy (1968) is the leading French Communist philosopher and is on the executive board of the Teilhard Centre for the Future of Man. His vision for the future of Christianity is contained in his statement: "The synthesis of the (Christian) God of the Above and the (Marxist) God of the Ahead: this is the only God whom we shall in the future be able to adore in spirit and in truth" (p. 54).

22 Marx's manuscript of his *Critique* contained neither title nor date while his subject refers to paragraphs 261-313 of Hegel's major work in political theory. The familiar quotation appears on p. 131 in Marx's introduction, which is actually at the end of the book.

23 Letter from C. Kingsley to C. Darwin, 18 November 1859. In F. Darwin 1887, 2:287.

24 Powell (1857) not only dismissed the whole of the Old Testament, which of course included the Creation account and the Flood, but, in a series of papers *On the study of the evidences of Christianity* published in 1860, also dismissed all the New Testament miracles. One might wonder what there was left in Powell's theology!

25 Frederick Temple's 1860 essay *Education of the world* was considered too liberal by many since it denied miraculous Creation, and he was eventually obliged to withdraw it from later editions of the popular *Essays and reviews*. Nevertheless, by that time, in 1865, the book had already run to twelve editions. Temple's son, William (1881-1944), carried the liberal banner more successfully. William's theological position was Hegelian Idealist which linked God with nature, while his left-wing political aspirations linked church with state. He also became Archbishop of Canterbury in 1942 and was responsible for the founding of the leftist British Council of Churches and the World Council of Churches.

26 Marx had just finished reading Darwin's *Natural selection* and commented to his friend Engels in his letter of 19 December 1860, "Although it is developed in a crude English way, this is the book that contains the natural

history foundation for our viewpoint" (p. 139).

27 Nietzsche (1882) said: "God is dead, but considering the state the species of Man is in, there will perhaps be caves, for ages yet, in which his shadow will be shown" (3:108).

28 Marx and Engels were commissioned to prepare the manifesto at a secret Congress of the Communist League held in London in 1847. The first draft was drawn up in German while a French translation was quickly prepared for the abortive Paris uprising of June 1848. There were subsequently many translations and revisions.

30 Professor Harrison's (1969) refutation of the Documentary hypothesis has been greatly expanded recently by the conservative scholar V.P. Hamilton. 1982. *Handbook on the Pentateuch*.

31 This classic work of Driver (1891) formed volume one of the International Theological Library and more than any other work served to liberalize theological students. The evolutionary ideas of Wellhausen were thus carried across the English Channel and into British pulpits by the efforts of Professor S.R. Driver.

32 Ceram's (1971a, 276) account is recommended since it contains the complete translated poem of Ut-napishtim giving the account of the Flood.

33 Lindsell (1976) gives a well-documented record of the battle between liberal and conservative scholars from the nineteenth century to the present day.

34 Kitchen (1978, 26) argues from a mass of historical and archaeological evidence that the early narratives in Genesis are firmly rooted in the normal life and literature of the second millenium B.C. and not in the dating scheme of the Graf-Wellhausen school. G.J. Wenham (1978) *Vetus Testamentum* 28:347 also points out the illogic of the Documentary hypothesis.

35 Radday et al. (1982) conclude: "We are fervent in our belief that the Documentary hypothesis in Genesis should be rejected or at least thoroughly revised" (p. 481).

36 Magnusson's (1977) book followed from the BBC television series and is a recent example of the popularization of the liberal view.

37 All the Creation and Flood material of Frazer (1918) is in Vol. 1. An abridged single volume was published in 1923, but much of the Creation and Flood material was omitted.

38 The author is indebted to the extensive work of Custance (1979); however, for all his research showing the universality of the Flood traditions, the reader should be warned that he concludes by saying that the Flood was local!

39 The first edition of Frazer (1890) was in two volumes, but by the third edition, in 1910, the work had expanded to twelve volumes. A single volume abridgement was published in 1922 and

is the version still being reprinted today.

40 Montgomery's (1972) otherwise excellent, well-documented historical review loses some credibility by the inclusion of the "Navarra wood'. Said to be from the ark and five thousand years old (footnote on p. 129), it has since been shown to be only a few hundred years old by carbon 14 dating and, as evidence, must be totally rejected.

41 Heidel (1963) is a conservative scholar and author of *The Babylonian Genesis*, which also appeared in the second edition in 1963.

42 Sayce (1893) was originally a supporter of the Developmental Hypothesis but in the light of archaeological evidence he abandoned this view for the traditional account. He was then forced to use the Religious Tract Society as the medium for his scholarly work. In his work on races he showed (p. 61) that there was a linguistic as well as racial relationship between the early inhabitants of Chaldea and the early Chinese.

43 Tax and Callender (1960) record: "The Chinese did not invest the person of the monarch with the attributes of divinity. Above the king, who was not a god, was T'ien, 'Heaven', or Shang-Ti, the 'Supreme Ancestor' and the earthly sovereign was but his deputy" (3:13).

44 Harper (1979), an English evolutionist, refers to evolution as a "metaphysical belief".

45 Bird (1979) cites "Torcaso v. Watkins" while the footnote identifies this as "367 U.S. 488, 495 and n.11 (1961)", p. 178.

46 Tax and Callender (1960) record the words of Julian Huxley: "I am an atheist in the only correct sense, that I don't believe in the existence of a super-natural being who influences natural events" (3:46).

Chapter Fifteen

1 Humanists Kurtz and Wilson (1973) declare: "We have reached a turning point in human history where the best option is to transcend the limits of national sovereignty and move towards the building of a world community" (p. 4). These ideas began with Karl Marx in 1848 where the central objective of the Communist Manifesto was and still is to eliminate national sovereignty by "the abolition of private property".

2 This is a condensed version of the original seventy-four-page document by Huxley published in 1948 entitled *UNESCO: Its purpose and philosophy*. A further condensed version will be found in *The Humanist* 1979, 39 (March/April): 35. Huxley (1976) sets the theme of the philosophy with Attlee's words: "Since wars begin in the minds of men, it is in the minds of men that the defences of peace must be constructed" (p. 14).

3 Irving (1955) speaking of Spencer: "He produced a treatise on sociology without reading

Comte, and a treatise on ethics without apparently reading anybody. Clubs provided Spencer with an excellent substitute for reading" (p. 237).

4 Vorzimmer (1963) shows how Darwin lifted Spencer's Lamarckian "physiological units" from the *Principles of biology* (Spencer 1864, 1:289) and called them "pangenes" in his *Variation* (Darwin 1868, 2:357). Blending inheritance works against natural selection by tending to bring a reversion back to the original stock rather than allow the supposed divergence to a new species. The Lamarckian aspect of blending inheritance is that acquired characteristics are supposed to be inherited; this results in a reduction of the power of natural selection. Lamarckian thinking was long ago discredited and, in deference to Darwin, it has never been considered "proper" to mention his 1868 excursion into Lamarckism by commentary on his "Hypothesis of Pangenesis".

5 Change and Progress. The empty and often fraudulent promises of political candidates and especially the advertising agencies have led us to equate the word "change" with progress. However, when optimal conditions already exist any change can only result in regression.

6 The first statement of Galton's "Law" appeared in his *Natural inheritance* (London) 1889, 134.

7 The system of dividing railway passenger cars into first and second class has been carried over into the twentieth century and subsequently adopted by the airlines.

8 Concerning civilization's future, humanist Bertrand Russell (1951) confidently makes this prediction: "Ultimately less than 30 percent of the female population will be used for breeding purposes. Reproduction will be strictly limited to the type and numbers required to fill the needs of the State" (p. 49).

9 The reviewer in *Nature* 1981, 291 (21 May): 267 scathingly refers to Lumsden and Wilson's (1981) work as "gibberish". In 1983 a simplified version of this gibberish was offered to the public entitled *Promethean fire*.

10 Cowan's (1969) studied conclusion of Galton's work on heredity: "Rarely in the history of science has a generalization been made on the basis of so little concrete evidence, so badly put, and so naively conceived" (p. 9).

11 The hookworm, *Uncinaria necator americanus*, present in human feces was found to be transmitted through the bare feet of the victim. The heroic work of Charles Wardell Stiles in 1902 was responsible for tracking down the hookworm and promoting universal use of the flush toilet. In Williams (1969).

12 For the want of a better word, Binet (1908) spoke of "general intelligence". Stern (1914) gave this scientific respectability by dividing the

mental age by the actual age of the subject and multiplying the result by 100 to round out the numbers. Stern called this the Intelligence Quotient (I.Q.).

13 Inspired by Havelock Ellis, with whom she had a long-continued extra-marital relationship, Sanger was an active advocate of birth control from 1915 to 1961. Editor of the left-wing *The Woman Rebel*, which was succeeded by *Birth Control Review*, she founded the Planned Parenthood Federation.

14 Chase (1980) includes an enormous wealth of detail concerned with scientific racism to which this chapter is indebted. The names of the notables have been included to alert the reader of the philosophical ideals of yesterday's leaders— a little digging into the background of today's leaders will prove equally as revealing.

15 Originally a Ph.D. dissertation, Gasman (1971) brings together a wealth of documented detail and is recommended to the reader further interested in the Darwin to Hitler connection.

16 In 1918 Darwin apostle Ernst Haeckel became a member of the *Thule Gesellschaft*, a secret, radically right-wing organization that played a key role in the establishment of the Nazi movement; Rudolf Hess and Hitler attended the meetings as guests (Phelps 1963).

17 Keith (1949) forthrightly states: "The German Fuhrer...has consciously sought to make the practice of Germany conform to the theory of evolution" (p. 230).

18 Van Evries' (1868) work is a fine example of scientific racism in which from anatomical studies of the brain he claimed that the Negro is inferior to the Caucasian. The work was quoted as "science" for the next half century. In contrast, a work of real science had been reported thirty-two years earlier by Frederick Tiedemann of Heidelberg University in the *Royal Society of London: Philosophical Transactions* 1836, 126:497, showing that the brains of Negroes and Europeans were no different.

19 After saying "no intellectual discoveries are more painful than those which expose the pedigree of ideas" (p. 373), Carmichael (1954) traces the genesis of modern scientific naturalism to its ultimate fruition in Fascism and Communism.

20 The title of the twenty-five-year anniversary issue "In the minds of men" is taken from the central purpose of UNESCO, as stated by Huxley (see Huxley 1976). After giving a history of the organization, the publication surveys the two principal objectives: The human rights movement and the peace movement. Early in 1982 the U.S. Congressional Committee on Intelligence heard an updated report on Soviet front groups; the World Peace Council (WPC) headed the list as the umbrella organization for all various peace movements and operates under the sponsorship of UNESCO.

21 Fest (1974) has presented one of the best biographies of Hitler and in 844 pages documents, point by point, similarities between Hitler's Fascism and Lenin's Communism, the former freely borrowing from the latter.

22 Nolte (1966) observed: "Fascism is anti-Marxism which seeks to destroy the enemy by the evolvement of a radically opposed and yet related ideology and by the use of almost identical and yet typically modified methods" (p.20).

23 Mahoney (1976), a psychologist, "invented" a research paper on child psychology. He reproduced it fifty-seven times and reversed the conclusions in half of them by reversing the data. The rejection rate at journal publishers showed that there was a distinct bias towards behavioural modification. In other words, the research paper was accepted if it validated the current belief in behavioural modification and rejected when it invalidated this belief. The author wrote up the results of this experiment designed to show the effect of bias among peer reviewers and tried to get it published in the profession's journals. It was rejected. He finally published it as a book. Mahoney exposes the harm done to real science by the rivalry between the behavioral and the biological determinist schools. The latter is fighting to maintain a position with investigations on identical twins. See *Science* 1980, 207 (21 March): 1323.

24 Eysenck (1981) is the biological determinist of the nature school; Kamin is the behavioral determinist of the nurture school.

25 Boas's view of the Judeo-Christian ethic can be gleaned from his statement: "The psychological origin of the implicit belief in the authority of religion which was so foreign to my mind...became a problem...in fact, my whole outlook upon social life is determined by the question: How can we recognize the shackles that tradition has laid upon us? For when we recognize them, we are able to break them." From Kardiner 1961, 139.

26 Mead's demise. Margaret Mead was a vice-president of the Teilhard Centre for the Future of Man (see Chapter Fourteen, note 18), but when her time came to face death in 1978, she sought comfort and assurance from the shaman, which she evidently had not found in Teilhard de Chardin's theistic evolutionary philosophy. Further details of Mead's belief in the paranormal have been given by Martin Gardiner in the *Skeptical Enquirer* (Buffalo), Fall issue 1983:13.

27 The idea may be farfetched but Skinner's daughter, Deborah, spent her first two-and-a-half years in a "Baby box" under controlled conditions; this caused some public outcry in 1945. Contrary to rumors, she did not commit suicide nor sue her father. Skinner's attempt to market the "Baby box" under the name of "Heir Conditioner" was a failure. See also *People Weekly* (New York), 1979, 11 (11 June): 73.

28 Controversy arises when it comes to deciding when a child is hyperactive. Children with a strong Judeo-Christian background, for example, may well be in conflict and considered hyperactive when taught that ethics are not hard and fast but situational. Some would advocate drug therapy to help the child conform and thus resolve the conflict.

29 The Japanese scientists who had examined the evidence (pictures, witnesses, and fin samples) thought the dead creature was a *plesiosaur* said to be extinct more than 100 million years ago; see *The New York Times* 24 July 1977. However, Western scientists, far removed from most of the evidence, dismissed the idea that it was a *plesiosaur*, and this view was reflected in the Western press when it was reported at all; see *Nature* 1977, 75 (28 July): 225.

References

ACKERKNECHT, Erwin Heinz. 1953. *Rudolf Virchow, doctor, statesman, anthropologist.* Madison: University of Wisconsin Press.

ACTON, John E.E. Dalberg. [1887] 1972. Letter of Lord Acton to Bishop Mandell Craighton 5-April 1887. *Essays on freedom and power* by Lord Acton. Selected by Gertrude Himmelfarb. Reprint. Gloucester, Mass.: Peter Smith.

ADLER, J. 1980. Is man a subtle accident? *Newsweek* 96 (3 November): 95.

AGER, Derek. 1973. *The nature of the stratigraphic record.* London: Macmillan.

ALDRICH, L.T. and A.O. Nier. 1948. Argon 40 in potassium minerals. *Physical Review* (New York) 74 (15 October): 876.

ALVAREZ, L.W., W. Alvarez, F. Asaro, and H.V. Michel. 1980. Extraterrestrial cause for the Cretaceous-Tertiary extinction. *Science* 208 (6 June): 1095.

Ancient skulls discovered near Santa Barbara. 1923. *Nature* (London) 112 (10 November): 699.

ANDERSON, J.L. 1972. Non-Poisson distribution observed during counting of certain C_{14} labelled organic (sub) monolayers. *Journal of Physical Chemistry* (Washington) 76: 3604.

ANDERSON, J.L. and G.W. Spangler. 1973. Serial statistics: Is radioactive decay random? *Journal of Physical Chemistry* (Washington) 77: 3114.

ANDERSON, J.L. and G.W. Spangler. 1974. Radiometric dating: Is the "decay constant" constant? *Pensée* (Portland, Ore.) 4 (Fall): 31.

ANDREWS, Roy C. 1926. *On the trail of ancient man.* New York: Putnam.

ARISTOTLE. 1961 ed. *Aristotle's physics.* Translated by Richard Hope. Lincoln, Neb.: University of Nebraska Press.

ARISTOTLE. 1965 ed. *Historia animalium.* Loeb Classical Library, nos. 437-39. 3 vols. Translated by A.L. Peck. Cambridge: Harvard University Press.

ASHTON, E.H. and S. Zuckerman, 1950. Some quantitative dental characters of fossil anthropoids. *Philosophical Transactions of the Royal Society* (London) ser.B, 234: 485.

ASIMOV, Isaac. 1959. 14 million tons of dust per year. *Science Digest* (New York) 45 (January): 33.

ASTON, F.W. 1929. The mass-spectrum of uranium lead and the atomic weight of protactinium. *Nature* (London) 123 (2 March): 313.

AUGUSTA, Joseph and Z. Burian. 1961. *Prehistoric reptiles and birds.* Translated by Margaret Schierl. London: Paul Hamlyn.

AVELING, Edward B. 1883. *The religious views of Charles Darwin.* London: Free Thought Publishing Co.

AVELING, Edward B. 1897. Charles Darwin and Karl Marx. *New Century Review* (London) 1: 323.

BACON, Francis. [1620] 1876. Novum organum. In *The physical and metaphysical works of Lord Bacon.* Edited by Joseph Devey. Reprint. London: George Bell.

BAHCALL, J.N. 1969. Neutrinos from the sun. *Scientific American* 221 (July): 91.

BAHCALL, J.N. and R. Davis. 1976. Solar neutrinos: A scientific puzzle. *Science* 191 (23 January): 264.

BAILEY, Edward. 1962. *Charles Lyell.* London: Nelson.

BALDWIN, Ralph Belknap. 1965. *A fundamental survey of the moon.* New York: McGraw-Hill.

BALME, D.M. 1970. Aristotle: Natural history and zoology. In *Dictionary of Scientific Biography.* Edited by Charles Gillispie. 1: 258-66. New York: Charles Scribner's Sons.

BARBER, Lynn. 1980. *The heyday of natural history.* London: Jonathan Cape.

BARLOW, Nora, ed. 1958. *The autobiography of Charles Darwin, 1809-1882.* London: Collins.

BARNES, Thomas G. 1971. Decay of the earth's magnetic moment and the geochronological implications. *Creation Research Society Quarterly* (Ann Arbor, Mich.) 8 (June): 24.

BARRETT, Paul. 1982. *Concordance to Charles Darwin's origin of species.* New York: Cornell University Press.

BEECHER, Henry Ward. 1885. *Evolution and religion.* 2 vols. New York: Fords.

BEER, Gavin de. 1958. Darwin and embryology. In *A century of Darwin.* S.A. Barnett ed. London: Heinemann.

BEER, Gavin de. 1972. Jean Jacaues Rousseau and his world. London: Thames and Hudson.

BELL, Charles. 1844. *Anatomy and philosophy of expression as connected with the fine arts.* 3rd ed. London: John Murray.

BENDER, P.L., D.G. Currie, R.H. Dicke, et al. 1973. The lunar laser ranging experiment *Science* 182 (19 October): 229.

BEREANO, P.L. 1969. The scientific community and the crisis of belief. *American Scientist* (New Haven, Conn.) 57 (Winter): 484.

BERGSON, Henri. [1907] 1911. *L'evolution creatrice*. Paris. Translated by A. Mitchell as *Creative evolution*. London: Macmillan.

BIBBY, Cyril. 1972. *Scientist extraordinary: T.H. Huxley*. New York: St. Martin's Press.

BINET, A. and T. Simon, [1908] 1973. *The development of intelligence in children (the Binet-Simon scale)*. Translated by E.S. Kite. Reprint. New York: Arno Press.

Biological Sciences Curriculum Study. 1980. *Biological science: A molecular approach*. Toronto: D.C. Heath.

Biological Sciences Curriculum Study. 1980. *Biological science: An enquiry into life*. New York: Harcourt Brace Jovanovich.

BIRCH, L.C. and P. Ehrlich, 1967. Evolutionary history and population biology. *Nature* (London) 214 (22 April); 349

BIRD, Roland T. 1939. Thunder in his footsteps. *Natural History* (New York) 48 (May): 254.

BIRD, Roland T. 1954. We captured a "live" brontosaur. *National Geographic* 105 (May): 707.

BIRD, Wendel. 1979. Freedom from establishment and unneutrality in public school instruction and religious school regulation. *Harvard Journal of Law and Public Policy* (Cambridge, Mass.) 2:125.

BISCHOFF, T.L.W. 1845. *Entwicklungsgeschichte des hunde eies*. Braunschweig. Germany: F. Vieweg.

BISHOP, J.A. and L.M. Cook, 1975. Moths, melanism and clean air. *Scientific American* 232 (January): 90.

BJORKSTEN, Johan. 1963. Aging: Primary mechanism. *Gerontologia* (Basel, Switzerland) 8:179.

BLACK, D., P. Teilhard de Chardin, W.C. Pei, and C.C. Young 1933. Fossil man in China. *Memoirs of the Geological Survey of China* (Peking) Ser. A, no. 11 (May).

BLACK, David. 1979. *Carl Linnaeus: travels*. New York: Charles Scribner's Sons.

BLACKHAM, H.J. 1976. *Humanism*. England: Harvester Press.

BLAKE, William. [1804-8] 1966. Milton, a poem in two books, In *The complete writings of William Blake*. Edited by Geoffrey Keynes. Reprint. London: Oxford University Press.

BÖLSCHE, Wilhelm. 1906. *Haeckel, his life and work*. Translated by J. McCabe. London: Fisher and Unwin.

BOAS, Franz. 1892. The growth of children. *Science* 19 (6 May): 256; 19 (20 May): 281; and 20 (23 December): 531. See also B. Kaplan Environment and human plasticity. *American Anthropologist* (1954) 56: 789.

BOAS, Franz. 1912. Changes in the bodily form of descendants of immigrants. *American Anthropologist* (Washington, D.C.) 14 (no. 3): 530.

BOAS, Franz. 1916. Eugenics. *The Scientific Monthly* (Washington, D.C.) 3: 471.

BOLTWOOD, B.B. 1907. On the ultimate disintegration products of the radioactive elements. *American Journal of Science* (New Haven, Conn.) Ser. 4, no. 23, 173 (February): 77.

BONOMI, Joseph. 1847. On the site of Memphis and the colossal statue of Ramses II. *Royal Society for Literature: Transactions* (London) 2nd ser., 2:304.

BOREL, Émile. [1943] 1962. *Probabilities and life*. Translated by Maurice Baudin. Reprint. New York: Dover Publications.

BOTTA, M.P.F. and M.E. Flandin, 1849-50. *Monument de Ninive*. 5 vols. Paris: Imprimerie Nationale.

BOULE, Marcellin and H.V. Vallois [1921] 1957. *Fossil men*. Translated by M. Bullock. Reprint. London: Thames and Hudson.

BOURDIER, Franck. 1971. George Cuvier. In *Dictionary of Scientific Biography*. Edited by Charles Gillispie. 3: 521-28. New York: Charles Scribner's Sons.

BOWDEN, M. 1977. *Ape-men: Fact or fallacy?* Bromley, U.K.: Sovereign Publications.

BOWKER, R.R. 1983. *Bowker's subject guide to books in print for 1983-1984*. 4 vols. New York: R.R. Bowker.

BOZARTH, G.R. 1978. The meaning of evolution. *The American Atheist* (Austin, Tex.) 20 (September): 19.

BRACE, Loring C., H. Nelson, N. Korn, and M. Brace. 1979. *Atlas of human evolution*. New York: Holt, Rinehart and Winston.

BRACE, Loring C. 1979. *The stages of human evolution*. 2nd ed. Englewood Cliffs, N.J.: Prentice-Hall.

BRACKMAN, Arnold C. 1978. *The luck of Nineveh*. New York: Van Nostrand Reinhold.

BRACKMAN, Arnold C. 1980. *A delicate arrangement*. New York: Times Books.

BRADLEY, Ian. 1975. *The call to seriousness*. New York: Macmillan.

BRADY, J.L. 1970. Influence of the planetary system on 143 long-period comets. *The Astronomical Journal* (New York) 75 (November): 1052.

BRAMWELL, C.D. and G.R. Whitfield. 1976. Biomechanics of Pteranodon. *Royal Society of London. Philosophical Transactions* Section B, 267 (11 July): 564.

BREADY, J.W. 1926. *England before and after John Wesley*. London: Hodder and Stoughton.

469

BREUIL, H. 1932. Le feu l'industrie de pierre et d'os dans le gisement du "Sinanthropus" à Chou K'ou Tien (The fire and the industry of stone and bone in the layer of Sinanthropus at Chou K'ou Tien). *L'Anthropologie* (Paris) 42 (March): 1-17

British Museum (Natural History). 1928. *Rhodesian man and associated remains.* London: British Museum (Natural History) Publication. (March): 1-17.

BROAD, W.J. 1980. Bank for Nobel sperm. *Science* 207 (21 March): 1326.

BROAD, W.J. 1981. Fraud and the structure of science. *Science* 212 (10 April): 137.

BROCA, Paul. 1864. *On the phenomena of hybridity in the genus homo.* Edited with permission of the author by C. Carter Blake. London: Green, Longman and Roberts.

BRONOWSKI, Jacob. 1973. *The ascent of man* Boston: Little, Brown.

BROOM, R. 1936. A new fossil anthropoid skull from South Africa. *Nature* (London) 138 (19 September): 486.

BROOM, R. 1938. More discoveries of *Australopithecus. Nature* (London) 141 (7 May): 828.

BROWN, Colin. 1977. Reason and unreason. *Eerdman's handbook of the history of Christianity.* Edited by T. Dowley. Grand Rapids: William B. Eerdman.

BROWN, Theodore M. 1971. Descartes: Physiology. In *Dictionary of scientific biography.* Edited by Charles Gillispie. 4: 61-65. New York: Charles Scribner's Sons.

BRUES, Charles T. 1951. Insects in amber. *Scientific American* 185 (November): 56.

BUCHANAN, J.Y. 1875-76. Preliminary report of H.M.S. Challenger. *Proceedings of the Royal Society of London* 24:593.

BUETTNER-JANUSCH, John. 1973. *Physical anthropology: A perspective.* New York: John Wiley.

BUFFON, Georges. [1753] 1857. *Histoire naturelle.* 10 vols. Paris. Translated and abridged as *Buffon's natural history.* 2 vols. Reprint. New York: Leavitt and Allen.

BURCHFIELD, Joe D. 1975. *Lord Kelvin and the age of the earth.* New York: Science History Publications.

BURLINGAME, Leslie J. 1973. Jean Baptiste Pierre Antoine de Monet de Lamarck. In *Dictionary of scientific biography.* Edited by Charles Gillispie. 7: 584-94. New York: Charles Scribner's Sons.

CAINE, Sidney. 1963. *The history of the foundation of the London school of economics and political science.* London: G. Bell.

CAMPANELLA, Tommaso. [1639] 1963. Defense of Galileo. In *Gateway to the great*

books. Edited by Robert M. Hutchins and Mortimer J. Adler. Chicago: Encyclopaedia Britannica, Inc. 8 (Natural Science): 359.

CARLEN, Claudia, ed. 1981. *The papal encyclicals 1939-1958.* Washington, D.C.: McGrath Publishing.

CARMICHAEL, Leonard. 1954. Science and social conservatism. *The Scientific Monthly* (Washington, D.C.) 78 (June): 373.

CARPENTER, C.C., J.B. Murphy, and L.A. Mitchell. 1978. Combat bouts with spur use in the Madagascan boa (Sanzinia madagascariensis). *Herpetologica* (Kansas) 34 (June): 207.

CARRIGAN, C.R. and D. Gubbins, 1979. The source of the earth's magnetic field. *Scientific American* 240 (February): 118.

CASKEY, Marie. 1978. *Chariot of fire: Religion and the Beecher family.* New Haven: Yale University Press.

CATACOSINOS, P.A. 1975. Do decay rates vary? *Geotimes* (Falls Church, Va.) 20:4.

CERAM, C.W. 1971a. *Gods, graves and scholars.* 2nd ed. rev. Translated from the German by E.B. Garside and S. Williams. London: Victor Gollancz.

CERAM, C.W. 1971b. *The first American.* New York: Harcourt Brace Jovanovich.

CHALLINOR, R.A. 1971. Variations in the rate of rotation of the earth. *Science* 172 (4 June): 1022.

CHALMERS, Thomas. 1857. Natural theology. Vol. 5 of *Select works of Thomas Chalmers.* 12 vols. Edited by William Hanna. Edinburgh: Thomas Constable.

CHAMBERS, Robert. [1844] 1887. *Vestiges of the natural history of creation.* Reprint. London: George Routledge.

CHASE, Allan. 1980. *The legacy of Malthus.* Chicago: University of Illinois Press.

CHAWLA, S.S. 1964. A philosophical journey to the West. *The Humanist* (San Francisco) 24 (September/October): 151.

CHESTERTON, G.K. 1925. *The everlasting man.* London: Hodder and Stoughton.

CLARK, Robert E.D. 1948. *Darwin: Before and after.* London: Paternoster Press.

CLARKE, M.L. 1974. *Paley: Evidences for the man.* University of Toronto Press.

CLARK, Ronald W. 1968. *The life and work of J.B.S. Haldane.* New York: Coward-McCann.

CLARK, W.E. le Gros. 1967. *Man-apes or apemen?* London: Holt Rinehart and Winston.

CLARKSON, E.N.K. and R. Levi-Setti. 1975. Trilobite eyes and the optics of Descartes and Huygens. *Nature* 254 (24 April): 663.

CLARK, Gordon H. 1960. *Dewey.* Philadelphia: The Presbyterian and Reformed Publishing Co.

COHEN, Bernard I. 1955. An interview with Einstein. *Scientific American* 193 (July): 33.

COLBERT, Edwin. 1949. The ancestors of mammals. *Scientific American* 180 (March): 40.

COLEMAN, W. 1964. *Georges Cuvier: Zoologist*. Cambridge: Harvard University Press.

COLENSO, John W. 1862-71. *The Pentateuch and the book of Joshua critically examined*. 6 pts. London: Longman.

COLETTA, Paolo E. 1969. *William Jennings Bryan*. Lincoln: University of Nebraska Press.

COLP, Ralph. 1977. *To be an invalid*. Chicago: University of Chicago Press.

COOK, Melvin A. 1957. Where is the earth's radiogenic helium? *Nature* (London) 179 (26 January): 213.

COOK, Melvin A. 1966. *Prehistory and earth models*. London: Max Parrish.

COON, Carlton S. 1965. *The living races of man*. New York: Alfred A. Knopf.

CORLISS, William R. 1978. *Ancient man*. Glen Arm, Md.: Source Book Project, P.O. Box 107, Glen Arm, MD, 21057.

COWAN, Ruth L.S. 1969. Sir Francis Galton and the study of heredity in the nineteenth century. Ph.D. diss. University of Toronto, Toronto.

COWEN, Richard and J.H. Lipps. 1975. *Controversies in the earth-sciences*. New York: West Publishing.

COWLING, T.G. 1934. The magnetic field of sunspots. *Royal Astronomical Society of London: Monthly Notices* 94:39.

COX, George W. 1888. *Life of John William Colenso*. 2 vols. London: Ridgway.

CRICK, Francis H. and Leslie E. Orgel. 1973. Directed panspermia. *Icarus* (London) 19 (July): 341.

CROSLAND, Maurice. 1983. Explicit qualifications as a criterion for membership of the Royal Society: A historical review. *Royal Society of London, Notes and Records* 37 (March): 167.

CURTIS, G.H., R. Drake, T.E. Cerling, and J.E. Hampel. 1975. Age of KBS tuff in Koobi Fora formation, east Rudolf, Kenya. *Nature* (London) 258 (4 December): 396.

CUSTANCE, Arthur C. 1970. *Without form and void*. Brockville, Canada: Privately published.

CUSTANCE, Arthur C. 1979. *The flood: Local or global?* Vol. 9 of The Doorway Papers. Grand Rapids, Michigan: Zondervan.

CUVIER, Georges. [1812] 1836. *Recherches sur les ossemens fossiles des quadrupedes*. 10 vols. Paris: Deterville.

CUVIER, Georges. [1817] 1978. *Essay on the theory of the earth*. Translated by G. Cuvier. Reprint. New York: Arno Press.

DALRYMPLE, G.B. and J.G. Moore. 1968. Argon 40: Excess in submarine pillow basalts from Kilavea volcano, Hawaii. *Science* 161 (13 September): 1132.

DALRYMPLE, G. Brent and Marvin A. Lanphere. 1969. *Potassium-argon dating*. San Francisco: W.H. Freeman.

DART, R. 1925. *Australopithecus africanus*: the man-ape of South Africa. *Nature* (London) 115 (7 February): 195.

DARWIN, Charles. 1839. *Journal and remarks. Narrative of the surveying voyage of HMS Adventure and Beagle between 1826 and 1836*. 3 vols. London: John Murray. This was later revised, edited, and republished as:

DARWIN, Charles. 1845. *Journal of the researches into the natural history and geology of the countries visited during the voyage of HMS Beagle round the world*. 2nd ed. London: John Murray.

DARWIN, Charles. 1859. *On the origin of species by means of natural selection*. 1st ed. London: John Murray.

DARWIN, Charles. 1860. *On the origin...* 2nd ed. London: John Murray.

DARWIN, Charles. 1868. *The variation of animals and plants under domestication*. 2 vols. London: John Murray.

DARWIN, Charles. 1869. *On the origin...* 5th ed. London: John Murray.

DARWIN, Charles. 1871. *The descent of man and selection in relation to sex*. 2 vols. New York: D. Appleton.

DARWIN, Charles. 1872. *On the origin...* 6th ed. London: John Murray.

DARWIN, Charles. [1872] 1965. *The expression of the emotions in man and animals*. Reprint. London: John Murray. Chicago: University of Chicago Press.

DARWIN, Charles [1872] 1971. *On the origin...* 6th ed. Reprint. Introduction by L. Harrison Matthews. London: J.M. Dent.

DARWIN, Erasmus. 1794-96. *Zoönomia or the laws of organic life*. 2 vols. London: St. Paul's churchyard.

DARWIN, Francis, ed. 1887. *Charles Darwin, life & letters*. 3 vols. London: John Murray.

DARWIN, Francis, and A.C. Seward, eds. 1903. *More letters of Charles Darwin*. 2 vols. London: John Murray.

DARWIN, George H. 1879. On the bodily tides of viscous and semi-elastic spheroids, and on the ocean tides on a yielding nucleus. *Philosophical Transactions of the Royal Society* (London) 170:1.

DARWIN, George H. 1880. On the secular changes in the orbit of a satellite revolving around a tidally disturbed planet. *Philosophical Transactions of the Royal Society of London* 171:713.

471

DARWIN, George H. 1903. Radioactivity and the age of the sun. *Nature* (London) 68 (24 September): 496.

DAVIDHEISER, Bolton. 1971. The Scopes trial. In *A symposium on creation No. 3*. Edited by D.W. Patten. Grand Rapids: Baker Book House.

DAY, Michael H. 1977. *Guide to fossil man*. 3rd ed. Chicago: University of Chicago Press.

DeGRAZIA, A. 1966. *The Velikovsky affair*. New York: University Books.

DENON, Dominique V. [1802] 1803. *Voyage dans la basse et la haute Egypte*. 2 vols. Paris. Translated as *Travels in upper and lower Egypt*. Reprint. London: T. Longman and O. Rees.

DEWEY, John. [1910] 1951. *The influence of Darwin on philosophy and other essays in contemporary thought*. New York: H. Holt. Reprint. Gloucester, Mass: Peter Smith.

DICKEY, P.A., C.R. Shiram, and W.R. Paine. 1968. Abnormal pressure in deep wells in southern Louisiana. *Science* 160 (10 May): 609.

DIGBY, Bassett. 1926. *The mammoth and mammoth hunting grounds in northeast Siberia*. London: H.F. Witherby.

DILLOW, Joseph C. 1981. *The waters above*. Chicago: Moody Press.

DORT, W. 1971. Mummified seals of Southern Victoria land. *Antarctic Journal of the United States* (Washington) 6: 210.

DOSTAL, K.P., M. Nagel, and D. Pabst. 1977. Variations in nuclear decay rates (in English). *Zeitschrift für Naturforschung* (Tübingen, W. Germany). Series A, 32 (April): 345.

DOUGLAS, Emily Taft. 1970. *Margaret Sanger: Pioneer of the future*. New York: Holt Rinehart and Winston.

DOUMANAI, G.A. and W.E. Long. 1962. The ancient life of Antarctica. *Scientific American* 207 (September): 169.

DRIVER, S.R. 1891. *An introduction to the literature of the Old Testament*. Edinburgh: T and T Clark.

DUBOIS, Eugene. 1920. The proto-Australian fossil man of Wadjak, Java (in English). *Koninklijke Akademie van Wetenschappen; proceedings* (Amsterdam) 13:1013.

DUBOIS, Eugene. 1935. On the gibbon-like appearance of *Pithecanthropus erectus* (in English). *Koninklijke Akademie van Wetenschappen; proceedings* (Amsterdam) 38:578.

DUBOS, René J. 1976. *Louis Pasteur: freelance of science*. Reprint. New York: Charles Scribner's Sons.

DUDLEY, H.C. 1975. Radioactivity re-examined. *Chemical and Engineering News* (Washington) 53 (7 April): 2.

DUNBAR, Carl O. 1960. *Historical geology*. 2nd ed. New York: John Wiley.

DUPREE, Hunter A. 1959. *Asa Gray*. Cambridge: Harvard University Press.

DURANT, Will. 1954. Our oriental heritage. Vol. 1 of *The story of civilization*. 11 vols. New York: Simon and Schuster.

EBERHART, Richard, ed. 1969. *John Milton: paradise lost, paradise regained*. New York: Doubleday.

ECKER, A. 1851-59. *Icones physiologicae*. Leipzig: L. Voss.

EDDINGTON, Arthur S. 1926. The source of stellar energy. *Nature* (London) 117 (1 May): 25 in supplement.

EDDY, John A., and A.A. Boornazian. 1979. Secular decrease in solar diameter. *Bulletin of the American Astronomical Society* (New York) 11: 437.

EDEN, Murray. 1967. Inadequacies of neo-Darwinian evolution as a scientific theory. *Mathematical challenges to the neo-Darwinian interpretation of evolution*. Edited by P. Moorhead and M. Kaplan. Monograph No. 5. Philadelphia: The Wistar Institute Press.

Editorial Board of the American Humanist Association. 1979. Fifty years of Humanist publication. *The Humanist* (San Francisco) 39 (January/February): 16.

EDWARDES, Michael. 1971. *East-West passage: The travel of ideas, arts and inventions between Asia and the Western world*. New York: Taplinger Press.

EISELEY, Loren C. 1959. Charles Lyell. *Scientific American*. 201 (August): 98.

EISELEY, Loren C. 1959. Charles Darwin, Edward Blyth, and the theory of natural selection. *Philosophical Society* 103:94.

EISELEY, Loren C. 1961. *Darwin's century*. New York: Doubleday.

ELDREDGE, Niles. 1982. *The monkey business*. New York: Washington Square Press.

ELDREDGE, N. and S.J. Gould. 1972. Punctuated equilibria: an alternative to phyletic gradualism. *Models in paleobiology*. Edited by J.T. Schopf. San Francisco: Freeman Cooper.

ELGIN, Suzette. 1973. *What is linguistics?* Englewood Cliffs, N.J.: Prentice-Hall.

ELLEGARD, Alvar. 1958. *Darwin and the general reader*. Stockholm: Göteborg Press.

EMILIANI, Cesare. 1956. Note on absolute chronology of human evolution. *Science* 123 (25 May): 924.

EMILIANI, Cesare. 1958. Ancient temperatures. *Scientific American* 198 (February): 54.

ENGEL, A.E.J. 1969. Time and the earth. *American Scientist* (New Haven, Conn.) 57 (Winter): 458.

ENGLER, A. and K. Prantl. 1915. *Die natür-lichen pflanzenfamilien. Ergänzungsheft III.* Leipzig: Wilhelm Englemann.

ERNLE, Lord. 1923. Victorian memoirs and memories. *The Quarterly Review* (London) 239 (475): 224.

EVERETT, Michael. 1978. *The birds of para-dise.* New York: Putnam.

EYLES, V.A. 1972. James Hutton. In *Dictionary of scientific biography.* Edited by Charles. Gillispie. Vol. 6, 577-89. New York: Charles Scribner's Sons.

EYSENCK, Hans J. and Leon Kamin. 1981. *The intelligence controversy.* New York: John Wiley.

FARRAND, William R. 1961. Frozen mam-moths and modern geology. *Science* 133 (17 March): 729.

FEDUCCIA, A. and H.B. Tordoff. 1979. Asymmetric vanes indicate aerodynamic function. *Science* 203 (9 March): 1021.

FEST, Joachin C. 1974. *Hitler.* Translated by R. Winston and C. Winston. New York: Harcourt Brace Jovanovich.

FIELDS, Weston W. 1976. *Unformed and un-filled.* Phillipsburg, N.J.: Presbyterian and Reformed Publishing Company.

FISHER, Arthur. 1973. The riddle of the leap second. *Popular Science* (New York) 202 (March): 110.

FITCH, J.F. and J.A. Miller. 1970. Radioistopic age determinations of Lake Rudolf artifact site. *Nature* (London) 226 (18 April): 226.

FITCH, J.F. and J.A. Miller. 1976. 1973 Nairobi: Conventional potassium-argon and argon-40/argon-39 dating of volcanic rocks from East Rudolf. In *Earliest man and envi-ronments in the Lake Rudolf basin.* Edited by Yves Coppens, F.C. Howell, G.L. Isaac, and R.E.F. Leakey. Chicago: University of Chi-cago Press.

FODOR, Jerry A. 1981. The mind-body prob-lem. *Scientific American* 244 (January): 114.

FOSDICK, Harry E. 1956. *The living of these days.* New York: Harper.

FRAZER, James. 1890. *The golden bough: A study in magic and religion.* London: Mac-millan.

FRAZER, James. 1918. *Folklore in the Old Testament.* 3 vols. London: Macmillan.

FREEMAN, Derek. 1983. *Margaret Mead and Samoa: The making and unmaking of an anthropological myth.* Cambridge: Harvard University Press.

FREEMAN, Richard. 1965. *The works of Charles Darwin, an annotated bibliograph-ical handlist.* London: Dawsons of Pall Mall.

French Government. 1809-22. *Description de l'Égypte—ou-recueil des observations et des recherches qui ont été faites en Égypte pendant l'expédition de l'armée française.* 21 vols. Paris: French Government.

FUNKHOUSER, J.G. and J.J. Naughton. 1968. Radiogenic helium and argon in ultrafamic inclusions from Hawaii. *Journal of Geo-physical Research* (Washington) 73 (15 July): 4606.

GALILEO. 1960. The Assayer. In *The contro-versy of the comets of 1618.* Galileo Galilei, Horatio Grassi, Mario Guiducci, and Johannes Kepler. Translated by Stillman Drake and C.D. O'Malley. Philadelphia: University of Pennsylvania Press.

GALTON, Francis. 1869. *Heredity genius.* London: Macmillan.

GALTON, Francis. 1897. The average contri-bution of each several ancestor to the total heritage of the offspring. *Proceedings of the Royal Society* (London) 61 (31 July): 401.

GARAUDY, Roger. [1966] 1968. *From ana-thema to dialogue: A Marxist challenge to the Christian churches.* Reprint. New York: Random House.

GARTNER, S., and J.P. McGuirk. 1979. Ter-minal Cretaceous extinction: scenario for a catastrophe. *Science* 206 (14 December): 1272.

GASMAN, Daniel. 1971. *The scientific origins of national socialism.* New York: American Elsevier.

GAUSS, Charles. Frederic. 1834. Mesure absolue de l'intensité du magnétisme terrestre. *Annales de Chimie et de Physique* (Paris). 2nd ser. 57:5-69.

GENTRY, Robert V. 1967. Cosmology and earth's invisible realm. *Medical Opinion and Review* (New York) 3 (October): 65.

GENTRY, Robert V. 1974. Radio-halos in a radiochronological and cosmological per-spective. *Science* 184 (5 April): 62.

GILL, Edmund D. 1970. Age of Australite fall. *Journal of Geophysical Research* (Richmond, Va.) 75 (10 February): 996.

GLÉNARD, Frantz. 1899. *Les ptoses viscérales (estomae, intestin, rein, foie rate) diagnostic et nosographie (enteroptose hépatisme).* Paris: Alcan.

GLICK, Thomas F. 1976. Teilhard de Chardin, Pierre. In *Dictionary of scientific biography.* Edited by Charles Gillispie. 3:274. New York: Charles Scribner's Sons.

473

GLOCK, W.S. and S. Agerter. 1963. Anomalous patterns in tree rings. *Endeavor* (London) 22 (January): 9.

GODDARD, Henry H. 1914. *Feeble-mindedness: Its causes and consequences.* New York: Macmillan.

GOLD, Thomas. 1955. The lunar surface.... *Royal Astronomical Society of London: Monthly Notices* 115:585.

GOLDSCHMIDT, Richard. 1940. *The material basis for evolution.* New Haven: Yale University Press.

GOLDSTEIN, S.J., J.D. Trasco, and T.J. Ogburn. 1973. On the velocity of light three centuries ago. *The Astronomical Journal* (New York) 78 (February): 122.

GOLDSTEIN, Thomas. 1980. *Dawn of modern science.* Boston: Houghton Mifflin.

GORCZYNSKI, R.M. and E.J. Steele. 1981. Simultaneous yet independent inheritance of somatically acquired tolerance to two distinct H-2 antigenic haplotype determinants in mice. *Nature* (London) 289 (19 February): 678.

GOSSE, Edmund. 1907. *Father and son: a study of two temperaments.* London: Heinemann.

GOULD, S.J. 1977a. The return of hopeful monsters. *Natural History* (New York) 86 (June/July): 22.

GOULD, S.J. 1977b. Evolution's erratic pace. *Natural History* (New York) 86 (May): 12-16.

GOULD, S.J. 1977c. *Ontogeny and phylogeny.* Cambridge: Harvard University Press.

GOULD, S.J. 1978. Morton's ranking of races by cranial capacity. *Science* 200 (5 May): 503.

GOULD, S.J. 1979. Piltdown revisited. *Natural History* (New York) 88 (March): 86.

GOULD, S.J. 1981a. A most chilling statement. *Natural History* (New York) 90 (April): 14.

GOULD, S.J. 1981b. *The mismeasure of man.* New York: W.W. Norton.

GOULD, S.J. and N. Eldredge. 1977. Punctuated equilibria: The tempo and mode of evolution reconsidered. *Paleobiology* (Chicago) 3:115-51.

GOW, Anthony J. 1972. Glaciological investigations in Antartica. *Antartic Journal of the United States* (Washington) 7:100.

GRANT, Madison. 1918. *The passing of the great race.* Rev. ed. New York: Charles Scribner's Sons.

GRAY, Asa. 1861. *Natural selection not inconsistent with natural theology. A free examination of Darwin's treatise on the origin of species and of its American reviewers.* London: Trübner.

GRAY, Asa. 1880. *Natural science and religion: Two lectures delivered to the theological school of Yale College.* New York: Charles Scribner's Sons.

GRAY, H. and C.M. Goss., eds. 1973. *Anatomy and the human body.* 29th ed. Philadelphia: Lea & Febiger.

GRAY, Jane L., ed. [1893] 1939. *Calendar of the letters of Charles Robert Darwin to Asa Gray.* Reprint. Boston: Historical Record Survey.

GRAY, Jane L. ed. 1893. *Letters to Asa Gray.* 2 vols. Boston and New York: Houghton Mifflin.

GRENE, M. 1959. The faith of Darwinism. *Encounter* (London) 13 (November): 48.

GROOTES, P.M. 1980. Discussion of a paper by Gove et al. *American Journal of Science: Radiocarbon Supplement* (New Haven, Conn.) 22 (3): 793.

HABERSHON, Ada R. 1909. *The Bible and the British Museum.* London: Morgan and Scott.

HAECKEL, Ernst. 1866. *Generelle Morphologie der Organismen.* 2 vols. Berlin: G. Reimer.

HAECKEL, Ernst. 1868. Monographie der Moneren. *Jenaische Zeitschrift für Medicine und Naturwissenschaft* (Leipzig) 4:64.

HAECKEL, Ernst. [1868] 1876. *Natürliche schöpfungsgeschichte.* Berlin. Translation revised in 1876 by E. Ray Lankester under the title *The history of creation.* 2 vols. New York: D. Appleton.

HAECKEL, Ernst. 1877. Bathybius und die Moneren. *Zeitschrift für einheitliche Weltanschauung auf Grund der Entwickelungslehre* 1:293.

HAECKEL, Ernst. [1874] 1879a. *Anthropogenie oder Entwicklungsgeschichte des Menschen.* Leipzig: W. Englemann. Translated in 1879 under the title *The evolution of man: A popular exposition of the principal points of human ontogeny and phylogeny.* 2 vols. New York: D. Appleton.

HAECKEL, Ernst. 1879b. *Freedom in science and teaching.* New York: D. Appleton.

HAECKEL, Ernst. 1904. *The wonders of life.* New York: Harper.

HAECKEL, Ernst. 1911. My church departure. Being reasons as stated by himself for his late withdrawal from the free evangelical church. *Truth Seeker Co., Inc.* (San Diego). 2.

HALÉVY, Élie. 1937-38. Religion and culture. Vol. 3 of *A history of the English people in 1815.* 3 vols. Translated by E.I. Watkin. London: Penguin Books, Pelican Series.

HALLAM, A. 1963. Eustatic control of major cyclic changes in Jurassic sedimentation. *Geological Magazine* (England) 100:44.

HALLER, John S., Jr. 1971. *Outcasts from evolution: Scientific attitudes of racial inferiority, 1859-1900.* Urbana: University of Illinois Press.

HAMMOND, A.L. 1974. Exploring the solar system (III): Whence the moon? *Science* 186 (6 December): 911.

HARDING, J.T. 1981. No fair hearing. *Liberty* (Washington) 76 (July-August): 11.

HARDY, G.H. [1908] 1959. Mendelian proportions in a mixed population. In *Classic Papers in Genetics*. Edited by James A. Peters. Reprint. Englewood Cliffs, N.J.: Prentice-Hall.

HARPER, G.W. 1979. Alternatives to evolution. *School Science Review* (Hatfield, U.K.) 51 (September): 16.

HARRISON, Roland K. 1969. *Introduction to the Old Testament*. Grand Rapids, Mich.: William B. Eerdmans.

HARRISON, Roland K. 1970. *Old Testament times*. Grand Rapids, Mich.: William B. Eerdmans.

HAUSER, P. 1970. What to do as population explodes, implodes and displodes, *Smithsonian* (Washington) 1 (December): 20.

HEARNSHAW, L.S. 1979. *Cyril Burt, psychologist*. New York: Cornell University Press. See also *Science* 1979, 205 (17 August): 673; and 206 (21 December): 1392.

HEIDEL, Alexander. 1963. *The Gilgamesh epic and Old Testament parallels*. 2nd ed. Chicago: University of Chicago Press.

HELMHOLTZ, Herman L.F. von. 1856. On the interaction of natural forces. *Philosophical Magazine* (London) 4th ser., 11:489.

HENNELL, Michael. 1977. The evangelicals. In *Eerdmans' handbook to the history of Christianity*. Edited by Tim Dowley. Grand Rapids, Mich.: William B. Eerdmans.

HERZ, O.F. 1904. Frozen mammoths in Siberia. In *Smithsonian Institution annual report for the year ending June 30, 1903*. Washington, D.C.: U.S. Government printing office.

HESIOD, 1948 ed. Works and days. In *Greek literature in translation*. Edited by George Howe and Gustave A. Harrer, translated by C.A. Elton, revised by P.H. Epps. New York: Harper and Row.

HESSE, Mary. 1970. Francis Bacon. In *Dictionary of scientific biography*. Edited by Charles Gillispie. New York: Charles Scribner's Sons. 1:372.

HIMMELFARB, Gertrude. 1955. Men and ideas: Malthus. *Encounter* (London) 5:53.

HIMMELFARB, Gertrude. [1959] 1968. *Darwin and the Darwinian revolution*. Reprint. New York: W.W. Norton.

HINDLEY, Keith. 1977. Fallen stars by the tonne. *New Scientist* (London) 75 (7 July): 20.

HIS, Wilhelm. 1874. *Unsere Körperform*. Leipzig: C.W. Voegel.

HITLER, Adolf. [1924] 1941. *Mein kampf*. Annotated edition by John Chamberlain et al. New York: Reynal and Hitchcock.

HOFFMANN, Banesh. 1972. *Albert Einstein: Creator or rebel?* New York: Viking Press.

HOFSTADTER, Richard. 1944. *Social Darwinism in American thought*. Philadelphia: University of Pennsylvania Press.

HOLMES, A. 1956. How old is the earth? *Transactions of the Edinburgh Geological Society* (Edinburgh) 16: 313.

HOLMES, Arthur F. 1983. Studies in a Christian world view. Vol. 1. In *Contours of a world view*. Edited by Carl F. Henry. Grand Rapids, Mich.: William B. Eerdmans.

HOLT, Anne D. 1931. *A life of Joseph Priestley*. London: Oxford University Press.

HOOD, Dora. 1964. *Davidson Black: A biography*. Toronto: University of Toronto Press.

HOOYKAAS, Reijer. 1972. *Religion and the rise of modern science*. Reprint. London: Chatto and Windus.

HORACE. [1911] 1931. Ode To Torquatus. In *The complete works of Horace*. Translated by John Marshall. Reprint. London: J.M. Dent.

HOROWITZ, Norman H. 1977. The search for life on Mars. *Scientific American* 237 (November): 52.

HOUGH, Jack. 1950. Pleistocene lithology of Antarctic Ocean bottom sediments. *Journal of Geology* (University of Chicago) 58:254.

HOWARD, Robert. 1975. The rotation of the sun. *Scientific American* 232 (April): 106.

HOWSE, Ernest M. [1953] 1976. *Saints in politics*. Reprint. London: George Allen and Unwin.

HOYLE, Fred. 1981. The big bang in astronomy. *New Scientist* (London) 92 (19 November): 521.

HOYLE, Fred and C. Wickramasinghe. 1981. *Evolution from space*. London: J.M. Dent.

HOYT, William G. 1976. *Lowell and Mars*. Tucson: University of Arizona Press.

HUBER, B. 1958. Recording gaseous exchange under field conditions. In *The physiology of forest trees*. Edited by K.V. Thimann. New York: Ronald.

HUTTON, James. [1795] 1972. *The theory of the earth*. Reprint. New York: Stechert-Hafner.

HUXLEY, Julian. 1976. A philosophy for UNESCO. *The UNESCO Courier* (Paris) 29 (March): 14.

HUXLEY, Leonard, ed. 1900. *Life and letters of Thomas Henry Huxley*. 2 vols. London: Macmillan.

HUXLEY, Leonard, ed. 1918. *Life and letters of Sir Joseph Dalton Hooker*. 2 vols. London: John Murray.

HUXLEY, Thomas H. [1857] 1901. On some fossil remains of man. In *Man's place in* nature. Vol. 7 of *Collected essays*. 9 vols. Reprint. London: Macmillan.

HUXLEY, Thomas H. [1863] 1901. On the relations of man to the lower animals. In *Man's place in nature*. Vol. 7 of *Collected essays*. 9 vols. Reprint. London: Macmillan.

HUXLEY, Thoms H. 1868. On some organisms living at great depths in the North Atlantic Ocean. *Quarterly Journal of Microscopical Science* (London) n.s. 8:204.

HUXLEY, Thomas H. 1869. Anniversary address. *Quarterly Journal of the Geological Society of London* 25: xlviii.

HUXLEY, Thomas H. 1871. Discussion of a paper presented by Capt. Shepard Osborn. *Proceedings of the Royal Geographical Society* (London) 15: 38.

HUXLEY, Thomas H. 1882. Joseph Priestley. In *Science and culture*. New York: D. Appleton.

HUXLEY, Thomas H. 1893. *Darwiniana: essays*. London: Macmillan.

HYNEK, J. Allen. 1983. Other suns, other worlds. *Science Digest* (New York) 91 (February): 44.

INGALLS, Albert G. 1940. The Carboniferous mystery. *Scientific American* 162 (January): 14.

INGERSOLL, Leonard R., Otto Zobel, and A.C. Ingersoll. 1954. *Heat conduction: With engineering, geological and other applications*. Rev. ed. Madison, Wis.: University of Wisconsin Press.

IRVING, William. 1955. *Apes, angels and Victorians*. New York: McGraw-Hill.

IRVING, William N., and C.R. Harington. 1973. Upper Pleistocene radiocarbon-dated artefact from the northern Yukon. *Science* 179 (26 January): 335.

ISRAEL, H. 1973. Age factor and pattern of change in craniofacial structures. *American Journal of Physical Anthropology* (New York) 39: 111.

IVANHOE, F. 1970. Was Virchow right about Neanderthal? *Nature* (London) 227 (8 August): 577.

JACOBS, John A. 1967. The earth's magnetic field. *Society of Exploration Geophysicists: Mining Geophysics* (Tulsa) 2: 426.

JACOBS, John A. 1963. *The earth's core and geomagnetism*. New York: Macmillan.

JAKI, Stanley L. 1978. *The road to science and the ways to God*. Chicago: University of Chicago Press.

JAMES, William. 1902. *The varieties of religious experience*. New York: Modern Library.

JANUS, Christopher and William Brashler. 1975. *The search for Peking man*. New York: Macmillan.

JEFFREY, Edward C. 1914. The mutation myth. *Science* 39 (3 April): 488.

JEFFRIES, Harold. 1929. *The earth: Its origin, history and physical constitution*. 3rd ed. Cambridge, U.K.: University Press.

JENSEN, Arthur R. 1969. How much can we boost I.Q. and scholastic achievement? *Harvard Educational Review* (Cambridge) 39 (Winter): 1.

JENSEN, James A. 1977. Bone Bonanza: Early bird or mastodon. Anonymous article. *Science News* (Washington) 112 (24 September): 198.

JOHANSON, D.C. 1976. Ethiopia yields first "family" of early man. *National Geographic Magazine* (Washington) 150 (December): 790.

JOHANSON, D.C. 1979. A systematic assessment of early African hominids. *Science* 203 (26 January): 321.

JOHANSON, D.C. and M.A. Edey, 1981. *Lucy: The beginnings of humankind*. New York: Simon and Schuster.

JOLY, J. 1901. An estimate of the geological age of the earth. In *Smithsonian Institution Annual report for the year 1899*. Washington, D.C.: U.S. Government Printing Office.

JOLY, J. 1917. The genesis of pleochroic haloes. *Royal Society of London: Philosophical Transactions* Series A, 217 (29 January), 51.

JOLY, J. 1922. The age of the earth. *Nature* (London) 109 (15 April): 480.

JOYCE, C. 1981. When the cheating has to stop. *New Scientist* (London) 90 (9 April): 68.

JUENEMAN, Frederic B. 1972. Editorial comment. *Industrial Research* (New York) 14 (August): 13.

KANG, C.H. and Ethel R. Nelson, 1979. *The discovery of Genesis*. St. Louis, Mo.: Concordia.

KARDINER, Abram and Edward Preble. 1961. *They studied man*. Cleveland: World Publishing.

KARSTEN, C.J.B. 1842. About a human skull changed into brown iron ore and bitumen. *Archive für Mineral Geognosie und Hüttenkunde* (Berlin) 16:372.

KEEN, Myra A. 1977. Paleontological hoaxes. *Natural history* (New York) 86 (May): 24.

KEITH, A., G.E. Smith, A.S. Woodward, and W.J.H. Duckworth. 1925. The fossil anthropoid from Taungs. *Nature* (London) 115 (14 February): 234.

KEITH, Arthur. 1911. The problems of Pithecanthropus. *Nature* (London) 87 (13 July): 49.

KEITH, Arthur. 1925a. The Taungs skull. *Nature* (London) 116 (4 July): 11.

KEITH, Arthur. 1925b. The nature of man's structural imperfections II. *Nature* (London) 116 (12 December): 867.

KEITH, Arthur. 1925c. *The Religion of the Darwinist*. London: Watts.

KEITH, Arthur. 1948. *A new theory of human evolution*. London: Watts.

KEITH, Arthur. 1949. *Evolution and ethics*. New York: G.P. Putnam.

KEITH, Arthur. 1950. *An autobiography*. New York: Philosophical Library.

KEITH, Arthur. 1955. *Darwin revalued*. London: Watts & Co.

KEITH, M. and G. Anderson. 1963. Radiocarbon dating: fictitious results with mollusk shells. *Science* 141 (16 August): 634.

KELLY, Alfred. 1981. *The descent of Darwin: The popularization of Darwinism in Germany*. Chapel Hill, N.C.: University of North Carolina.

KENNETT, James P. and Robert C. Thunell. 1975. Global increase in quarternary explosive volcanism. *Science* 187 (14 February): 497.

KERMACK, D.M. et al. 1968. The Welsh pantothere *Kuehneotherium praecursoris*. *Zoological Journal of the Linnean Society* (London) 47 (April): 407.

KERMACK, D.M., F. Mussett, and H.W. Rigney. 1973. The lower jaw of *Morganucodon*. *Zoological Journal of the Linnean Society* (London) 53 (September): 157.

KETTLEWELL, H.B.D. 1959. Darwin's missing evidence. *Scientific American* 200 (March): 48.

KETTLEWELL, H.B.D. 1973. *The evolution of melanism: The study of a recurring necessity*. Oxford: Clarendon Press.

KEYNES, John M. 1933. *Essays in biography*. Toronto: Macmillan.

KIMBALL, John W. 1965. *Biology*. Reading, Mass.: Addison-Wesley.

KIMURA, Motoo. 1979. Neutral theory of molecular evolution. *Scientific American* 241 (November): 98.

KING-HELE, Desmond. 1977. *Doctor of revolution: The life and genius of Erasmus Darwin*. London: Faber and Faber.

KINGSLEY, Charles. [1863] 1979. *Water babies*. London. Reprint facsimile edition. New York: Mayflower Books.

KINGSLEY, Francis E., Ed. [1883] 1904. *Charles Kingsley: His letters and memories of his life*. 2nd ed. London: Macmillan.

KITCHEN, Kenneth A. 1978. *The Bible in its world*. Downers Grove, Ill.: InterVarsity Press.

KITTS, David. 1974. Paleontology and evolutionary theory. *Evolution* (University of Kansas) 28 (September): 458.

KLEIN, R.G. 1973. Geological antiquity of Rhodesian man. *Nature* (London) 244 (3 August): 311.

KLEMM, Peter. 1968. *Der Ketzer von Jena*. Leipzig: Urania Press.

KLUCKHOHN, Clyde. 1949. *Mirror for man*. New York: McGraw-Hill.

KNOPF, Adolph. 1957. Measuring geologic time. *The Scientific Monthly* (Washington) 85 (November): 232.

KOCZY, F. Friedrich. 1954. Geochemical balance in the hydrosphere. In *Nuclear Geology*. Edited by H. Faul. New York: John Wiley.

KOENIGSWALD, G.H.R. von and F. Weidenreich. 1939. The relationship between *Pithecanthropus* and *Sinanthropus*. *Nature* (London) 144 (2 December): 926.

KOENIGSWALD, G.H.R. von. 1956. *Meeting prehistoric man*. London: Thames and Hudson.

KONIG, Charles. 1814. On a fossil human skeleton from Guadeloupe. *Philosophical Transactions of the Royal Society* (London) 104:107.

KOPP, Joseph V. 1964. *Teilhard de Chardin: A new synthesis of evolution*. Ramscy, New Jersey: Paulist Press.

KOSTER, John. 1977. Creature feature. *Oceans* (Oceanographic Society, San Francisco) 10 (November-December): 56.

KRAUSE, Ernst L. 1879. *Erasmus Darwin*. Translated by W.S. Dallas. London: J. Murray.

KRISTOF, L.K. 1969. Teilhard de Chardin and the Communist quest for a space age world view. *Russian Review* (Stanford, Calif.) 28: 277.

KROPOTKIN, P.A. [1902] 1939. *Mutual aid: A factor of evolution*. Reprint. Harmondsworth (U.K.): Pelican Books.

KUHN, Thomas S. 1962. *The structure of scientific revolutions*. Chicago: University of Chicago Press.

KULP, J.L. 1952. The carbon 14 method of age determination. *The Scientific Monthly* (Washington) 75 (November): 259.

KURTZ, P. and E.H. Wilson, eds. 1973. Humanist manifesto II. *The Humanist* (San Francisco) 33 (September/October): 4.

LaHAYE, Tim. 1980. *The battle for the mind*. New Jersey: Fleming H. Revell.

LACK, David L. [1947] 1968. *Darwin's finches*. Reprint. Gloucester, Mass.: Peter Smith.

LACK, David L. 1953. Darwin's finches. *Scientific American* 88 (April): 67.

LADD, E.T. 1970. Pills for classroom peace? Controversy over use of drugs to improve school performance by controlling hyperactivity. *Saturday Review* (New York) 53 (21 November): 66.

LAMARCK, Jean B. [1809] 1914. *Philosophie zoologique*. Translated by Hugh Elliot, under the title *Zoological philosophy*. Reprint. London: Macmillan.

LAMB, Horace. 1883. On electrical motions in a spherical conductor. *Philosophical Transactions* (London) 174: 519.

LAMB, Horace. 1883-84. On the induction of electrical currents in cylindrical and spherical conductors. *Mathematical Society: Proceedings* (London) 15: 139.

LAMBERT, Edward C., M.D. 1978. *Modern medical mistakes*. Toronto: Fitzhenry and Whiteside.

LAMONT, Corliss. 1977. *The philosophy of humanism*. New York: Frederick Ungar.

LANGER, William L. 1964. The black death. *Scientific American* 210 (February): 114.

LANGMAN, Jan. 1975. *Medical embryology*. 3rd ed. Baltimore: Williams and Wilkins.

LANGSTON, W. 1981. Pterosaurs. *Scientific American* 244 (February): 122.

LASH, Nicholas. 1975. *Newman on development*. Shepherdstown, W.Va.: Patmos Press.

LAVERDIÈRE, J.W. 1950. Baleine fossile de la Daveluyville, Québec. *Naturaliste Canadien* (Laval University, Quebec) 77 (September-October): 271.

LAWLESS, J.H. et al. 1972. Organic matter in meteorites. *Scientific American* 226 (June): 38.

LAWSON, D.A. 1975. Pterosaur from the Cretaceous of west Texas: Discovery of the largest flying creature. *Science* 187 (14 March): 947.

LAYARD, Henry A. 1849. *Nineveh and its remains*. 2 vols. London: John Murray.

LAYTON, T.B. 1956. *Sir William Arbuthnot Lane, Bt*. London: Livingstone.

LEAKEY, L.S.B. 1928. The Oldoway skull. *Nature* (London) 121 (31 March): 499.

LEAKEY, L.S.B. 1959. A new fossil skull from Olduvai. *Nature* (London) 184 (15 August): 491.

LEAKEY, L.S.B. 1960a. From the Taung skull to "Nutcracker man". *Illustrated London News* 236 (9 January): 44.

LEAKEY, L.S.B. 1960b. Finding the world's earliest man. *National Geographic Magazine* (Washington) 118 (September): 420.

LEAKEY, L.S.B. 1961. New finds at Olduvai Gorge. *Nature* (London) 189 (25 February): 649.

LEAKEY, L.S.B., J.F. Evernden, and G.H. Curtis. 1961. Age of bed I, Olduvai Gorge, Tanganyika. *Nature* (London) 191 (29 July): 478.

LEAKEY, L.S.B., P.V. Tobias, and J.R. Napier. 1964. A new species of the genus *Homo* from Olduvai Gorge. *Nature* (London) 202 (4 April): 5.

LEAKEY, L.S.B., R. Protsch, and R. Berger. 1968. Age of bed V, Olduvai Gorge, Tanzania, *Science* 162 (1 November): 559.

LEAKEY, R.E.F. 1971. Further evidence of lower pleistocene hominids from east Rudolf, North Kenya. *Nature* (London) 231 (28 May): 241.

LEAKEY, R.E.F. 1973. Skull 1470. *National Geographic Magazine* (Washington) 143 (June): 819.

LEAKEY, R.E.F. 1979. *The illustrated origin of species*. New York: Hill and Wang.

LECKY, William Edward Hartpole. 1888-91. Great Britain: History to the eighteenth century. Vol. 2 of *History of England in the eighteenth century*. 8 vols. New York: D. Appleton.

LEDLEY, Fred. 1982. Evolution and the human tail: Case report. *The New England Journal of Medicine* (Boston) 306 (20 May): 1212.

LEE, Robert E. 1981. Radiocarbon: Ages in error. *Anthropological Journal of Canada* (Ottawa) 19 (3): 9.

LEPSIUS, Carl R. 1849. *Denkmaeler aus Aegypten und Aethiopien*. 13 vols. Berlin: Nicolai.

LEVINE, Lawrence W. 1965. *Defender of the faith: William Jennings Bryan*. New York: Oxford University Press.

LEWIN, R. 1980. Evolutionary theory under fire. *Science* 210 (21 November): 883.

LEWIS, C.S. 1948. *The problem of pain*. New York: Macmillan.

LIBBY, Willard F. 1955. *Radiocarbon dating*. 2nd ed. Chicago: University of Chicago Press.

LIBBY, Willard F. 1963. Accuracy of radiocarbon dates. *Science* 140 (19 April): 278.

LIGHTFOOT, John. [1642] 1825. A few and new observations on the book of Genesis, the most of them certain, the rest probable, all harmless, strange, and rarely heard of before. Reprinted in *The whole works of the Rev. John Lightfoot D.D.* Edited by John Rogers Pitman. 13 vols. London: J.F. Dove.

LINDROTH, Stern. 1973. Carl Linnaeus. In *Dictionary of scientific biography*. Edited by Charles Gillispie. 8: 374-81. New York: Charles Scribner's Sons.

LINDSELL, Harold. 1976. *The battle for the Bible*. Grand Rapids, Mich.: Zondervan.

LIPPMAN, Harold E. 1962. Letter to editor. *Science* 137 (10 August): 449.

LISCHER, Richard. 1979. *Marx and Teilhard: Two ways to the new humanity*. Maryknoll, N.Y.: Orbis.

LITCHFIELD, Henrietta, ed. 1915. *Emma Darwin: A century of family letters 1792-1896*. 2 vols. London: John Murray.

LITHERLAND, A.E. 1980. Ultrasensitive mass spectrometry with accelerators. *Annual*

478

Review of Nuclear Particle Science (Palto Alto, Calif.) 30: 437.

Living Neanderthal man. 1910. *Nature* (London) 85 (8 December): 176.

LONG, George, trans. 1869. *The thoughts of the Emperor Marcus Aurelius Antoninus.* 2nd rev. and cor. ed. London: Bell and Daldy.

LONGWELL, C.R., A. Knopf, and R.F. Flint. 1950. *Outlines of physical geology.* 2nd ed. New York: John Wiley.

LOVELL, Bernard. 1979. *In the centre of immensities.* London: Hutchinson.

LOWELL, Percival. [1888] 1911. *The soul of the far East.* New York: Macmillan.

LOWELL, Percival. 1894. *Occult Japan.* Boston: Houghton Mifflin.

LOWELL, Percival. 1906. *Mars and its canals.* New York: Macmillan.

LOWELL, Percival. 1909. *The evolution of the worlds.* New York: Macmillan.

LUCAS, J.R. 1979. Wilberforce and Huxley: Legendary encounter. *The Historical Journal* (Cambridge, UK) 22 (June): 313.

LUCRETIUS. 1951 ed. *On the nature of the universe.* Translated by R.E. Latham. England: Penguin Classics.

LUKAS, Mary and Ellen Lukas. 1977. *Teilhard.* London: Collins.

LULL, Richard S. 1935. *Fossils.* New York: University Society.

LUMSDEN, Charles J. and Edward O. Wilson. 1981. *Genes, mind and culture: The co-evolutionary process.* Cambridge: Harvard University Press.

LYELL, Charles. 1830-33. *Principles of geology.* 3 vols. London: John Murray.

LYELL, Charles. 1845. *Travels in North America in the years 1841-42.* 2 vols. New York: Wiley & Putnam.

LYELL, Charles. [1863] 1914. *The geological evidence of the antiquity of man.* Reprint. London: J.M. Dent.

LYELL, Charles. 1867. *Principles of geology.* 10th ed. 3 vols. London: John Murray.

LYELL, Kathryn M., ed. 1881. *Life, letters and journals of Sir Charles Lyell.* 2 vols. London: John Murray.

LYNE, C.W. 1916. The significance of the radiographs of the Piltdown teeth. *Proceedings of the Royal Society of Medicine* (London) 9 (Odontological section): 33

LYTTLETON, R.A. 1956. *The modern universe.* New York: Harper and Brothers.

MACALLAM, A.B. 1903. On the inorganic composition of the *Medusae, Aurelia flavidula* and *Cyanea artica. The Journal of Physiology* (London) 29: 214.

MacBETH, Norman. 1971. *Darwin retried: An appeal to reason.* Ipswich, Mass.: Gambit.

MACKAL, Roy P. 1980. *Searching for hidden animals.* New York: Doubleday.

MAGILL, Frank N., ed. 1963. *Masterpieces of Christian literature in summary form.* New York: Harper and Row.

MAGNUSSON, Magnus. 1977. *BC: The archaeology of the Bible lands.* London: Bodley Head.

Magsat down: Magnetic field declining. 1980. *Science News* (Washington) 117 (28 June): 407.

MAHONEY, Michael. 1976. *Scientists as subject.* Cambridge, Mass.: Ballinger.

MAISEL, Albert Q. 1966. The "useless" gland that guards our health. *Reader's Digest* (Canadian edition) 89 (November): 212.

MALTHUS, Thomas R. [1798] 1878. *An essay on the principle of population as it affects the future improvement of society.* Reprint. London: Reeves and Turner.

MANLEY, G.A. 1972. A review of some current concepts of the functional evolution of the ear in terrestrial vertebrates. *Evolution* (University of Kansas) 26 (December): 608.

MANNING, Henry E., ed. 1865-74. *Essays on religion and literature.* London: Longman.

MARSHACK, Alexander. 1972. *The roots of civilization.* London: Weidenfeld and Nicholson.

MARTIN, Malachi. 1978. *The final conclave.* New York: Stein and Day.

MARTIN, Malachi. 1981. *The decline and fall of the Roman church.* New York: G.P. Putnam's Sons.

MARX, Karl. [1843] 1970. *Critique of Hegel's "Philosophy of Right".* Translated by Annette Jolin and Joseph O'Malley. Reprint. Cambridge: The University Press.

MARX, Karl. 1850. *The manifesto of the communist party.* Translated by H. Macfarlane. London: Red Republican.

MASALA, Sebastianus. 1962. Actass Congregationum: Suprema Sacra Congregatio S. Officii. Monitum. *Acta Apostolicae Sedis* (Vatican) 54 (6 August): 526.

MASER, Werner. 1970. *Hitler's Mein Kampf: An analysis.* London: Faber and Faber.

MASON, Brian. 1962. *Meteorites.* New York: John Wiley.

MASON, Brian. 1963. Organic matter from space. *Scientific American* 208 (March): 43.

MASURSKY, H., R.M. Batson, J.F. McCauley, et al. 1972. Mariner 9 television reconnaissance of Mars and its satellites. *Science* 175 (21 January): 294.

MATTHEW, William D. 1915. *Climate and evolution.* New York: The Academy.

MATTHIAE, Paolo. 1981. *Ebla: an empire re-*

discovered. New York: Doubleday.

MAYR, Ernst. 1950. Taxonomic categories in fossil hominids. *Cold Spring Harbour Symposia on Quantitative Biology* 15: 109.

MAYR, Ernst. 1963. *Animal species and evolution.* Cambridge, Mass.: Harvard University Press.

MAYR, Ernst. 1972. The nature of the Darwinian revolution. *Science* 176 (2 June): 987.

McDONALD, K.L. and R.H. Gunst. 1967. *An analysis of the earth's magnetic field from 1835 to 1965.* ESSA Technical Report IER 46-IES. Washington, D.C.: U.S. Government Printing Office.

McNAUGHTON, N.J. and C.T. Pillinger. 1980. Comets and the origin of life. *Nature* (London) 288 (11 December): 540.

MEAD, Margaret. [1928] 1973. *Coming of age in Samoa.* Reprint. New York: William Morrow.

MEDAWAR, Peter. 1961. Book review: The Phenomenon of Man. *Mind* (Oxford) 70 (January): 99.

MEDAWAR, Peter. 1967. Remarks by the chairman. In *Mathematical challenges to the neo-Darwinian interpretation of evolution.* Edited by Paul Moorhead and Martin Kaplan. Monograph No. 5. The Wistar Institute Press, Philadelphia.

MENDEL, Gregor. [1865] 1959. Experiment in plant-hybridization. In *Classic papers in genetics.* Edited by J.A. Peters. Reprint. Englewood Cliffs, N.J.: Prentice-Hall.

METCHNIKOFF, Élie. [1903] 1907. *The nature of man.* Translated by P.C. Mitchell. Reprint. London: G.P. Putnam's Sons.

MIKAYA, Adam. 1978. The politics of Ebla. *Biblical Archaeology Review* (Washington, D.C.) 4 (Sept./Oct.): 2. See also H. Shanks. 1979. Syria tries to influence Ebla scholarship. *Biblical Archaeology Review* 5 (March/April): 37.

MILANO, Paolo, ed. 1981. *The portable Dante.* England: Penguin Books.

MILLAR, Ronald. 1974. *The Piltdown men.* St. Albans, U.K.: Paladin.

MILLER, Hugh. 1841. *The old red sandstone; or, new walks in an old field.* Edinburgh: J. Johnstone.

MILLER, Hugh. 1849. *Footprints of the creator; or, the Asterolepis of Stromness.* London and Edinburgh: Johnstone and Hunter.

MILLER, Hugh. 1857. *The testimony of the rocks.* Boston: Gould and Lincoln.

MILLER, Stanley L. 1953. A production of amino-acids under possible primitive earth conditions. *Science* 117 (15 May): 528.

MILLOT, J. 1955. The coelacanth. *Scientific American* 193 (December): 34.

MIVART, St. George J. 1873. *Man and apes: An exposition of structural resemblances and differences bearing upon questions of affinity and origin.* London: R. Hardwicke.

MIVART, St. George J. 1890. *Dogs, jackals, wolves and foxes: A monograph of the Canidae.* London: R.H. Porter.

MONTGOMERY, John W. 1972. *The quest for Noah's ark.* Minneapolis, Minn. Bethany Fellowship.

MOON, P. and D.E. Spencer. 1953. Binary stars and the velocity of light. *Optical Society of America Journal* (New York) 43 (August): 635.

MORRISON, P. et al., eds. [1977] 1979. *The search for extra-terrestrial life.* Reprint. Originally published as NASA publication SP-419. New York: Dover Publications.

MORTON, Glen R. 1982. Fossil succession. *Creation Research Society Quarterly* (Creation Research Society, Ann Arbor, Mich.) 19 (September): 103.

MORTON, Samuel G. 1839. *Crania Americana.* Philadelphia: J. Dobson.

MOULTON, Forest Ray. 1956. *An introduction to celestial mechanics.* New York: Macmillan.

MUNK, W.H. and G.J.F. MacDonald. 1960. *The rotation of the earth.* London: Cambridge University Press.

MURE, William. 1829. *Brief remarks on the chronology of the Egyptian dynasties, showing the fallacy of the system laid down by Messrs. Champollion in two letters on the museum of Turin.* London.

MURRAY, John. 1875-76. Preliminary report on the scientific results of the voyage of HMS Challenger. *Proceedings of the Royal Society of London* 24: 471.

MURRAY, John, ed. 1880-95. *Report on the scientific results of the voyage of HMS Challenger...* 50 vols. Edinburgh: HM Stationary Office.

MUSSON, A.E. and E. Robinson. 1969. *Science and technology in the industrial revolution.* England: Manchester University Press.

Neanderthal in armour. 1908. *Nature* (London) 77 (23 April): 587.

NIER, A.O. 1939. The isotropic constitution of radiogenic leads and the measurement of geologic time. *Physical Review* (New York) 55 (15 January): 153.

NIETZSCHE, Friedrich. 1882. *Die Fröhliche Wissenschaft.* 3 vols. (Chemnitz).

NOBLE, C. and J. Naughton. 1968. Deep ocean basalts: Inert gas content and uncertainties in age dating. *Science* 162 (11 October): 265.

NOERDLINGER, P.D. 1977. An examination of an interstellar hypothesis for the source of comets. *Icarus* (New York) 30: 566.

NOLTE, Ernst. 1966. *Three faces of Fascism.* New York: Rinehart and Winston.

480

NORDENSKIOLD, Erik. 1928. *The history of biology.* New York: Tudor Publishing.

NUMBERS, Ronald L. 1982. Creationism in 20th-century America. *Science* 218 (5 November): 538.

O'ROURKE, J.E. 1976. Pragmatism versus materialism in stratigraphy. *American Journal of Science* (Yale University) 276 (January): 47.

OGDEN, J. 1977. The use and abuse of radiocarbon. *Annals of the New York Academy of Science* 288: 167.

OORT, J.H. 1950. The structure of the clouds of comets surrounding the solar system and a hypothesis concerning its origin. *Bulletin of the Astronomical Institutes of the Netherlands* (Haarlem) 11 (13 January): 91.

OPARIN, A.I. [1936] 1953. *Origin of life.* Translated by S. Morgulis. Reprint. New York: Dover Publications.

OSBORN, Henry F. 1918. *The origin and evolution of life.* New York: Charles Scribner's Sons.

OSBORN, Henry F. 1929. *From the Greeks to Darwin.* New York: Charles Scribner's Sons.

OTTAWAY, J.H. 1973. Rudolph Virchow: An appreciation. *Antiquity* (Cambridge, U.K.) 47: 101, 106.

OWEN, Richard. 1855. Of the anthropoid apes and their relation to man. *Royal Institution of Great Britain. Proceedings 1854-1858* (London) 3:26.

OWEN, Robert. [1813-14] 1969. *A new view of society.* Reprint. Introduction by V.A.C. Gatrell. Baltimore: Penguin Books.

OXNARD, Charles F. 1975. *Uniqueness and diversity in human evolution: Morphometric studies.* Chicago: University of Chicago Press. See also C.F. Oxnard. 1975. *Nature* (London) 258 (4 December): 389.

PADOVER, Saul K. 1979. *The letters of Karl Marx.* Englewood Cliffs, N.J.: Prentice-Hall.

PAGE, George C. Museum Publication. 1983. Rancho La Brea tar pits: 5081 Wilshire Boulevard. Los Angeles, CA 90036.

PARKINSON, John. 1980. What's wrong with the sun? *New Scientist* (London) 86 (24 April): 201.

PASTEUR, Louis. 1861. Mémoire sur les corpuscles organisés qui existent dans l'atmosphère. Examen de la doctrine des générations spontanées. *Annales des sciences naturelles (partie zoologique)* (Paris) 4th ser. 16: 5.

PATTERN, Donald W. 1966. *The biblical flood and the ice epoch.* Seattle: Pacific Meridian Publishing.

PATTERSON, Colin. 1981. Evolution and creation. Paper read at the American Museum of Natural History, New York, 5 November.

PAYNE, M.M. 1965. Family in search of prehistoric man. *National Geographic Magazine* (Washington) 127 (February): 194.

PECKHAM, Morse, ed. 1959. *The origin of species by Charles Darwin: a variorum text.* Philadelphia: University of Penn. Press.

PEMBER, George H. 1884. *Earth's earliest ages and their connection with modern spiritualism and theosophy.* London: Hodder and Stoughton.

PENDERY, M.L. et al. 1982. Controlled drinking by alcoholics? *Science* 217 (9 July): 169.

PETERS, D.P. and S.J. Ceci. 1980. A manuscript masquerade. *The Sciences* (New York) 20 (September): 16.

PETTERSSON, Hans. 1950. Exploring the ocean floor. *Scientific American* 183 (August): 42.

PETTERSSON, Hans. 1960. Cosmic spherules and meteoritic dust. *Scientific American* 202 (February): 123.

PETTINATO, Giovanni. 1976. The royal archives of Tell Mardikh-Ebla. *Biblical Archaeologist* (Cambridge, Mass.) 39 (May): 444; 39 (September): 94.

PETTINATO, Giovanni. 1981. *The archives of Ebla: An empire inscribed in clay.* New York: Doubleday.

PFEIFFER, John. 1964. *The cell.* New York: Time Inc., Life Science Library Series.

PFIZENMAYER, E.W. [1926] 1939. *Siberian man and mammoth.* Translated by M. Simpson. Reprint. London: Blackie.

PHELPS, Reginald. 1963. Before Hitler came: Thule society and Germenen Orden. *Journal of Modern History* (University of Chicago) 25: 245.

PICKERING, William H. 1896. Schiaparelli's latest views regarding Mars. In *Smithsonian Institution Annual Report for 1894.* Washington, D.C.: U.S. Government Printing Office.

PIERCE, William G. 1957. Heart mountain and South Fork detachment thrusts of Wyoming. *American Association of Petroleum Geologists: Bulletin* 41: 591.

PILBEAM, David. 1970a. *The evolution of man.* London: Thames and Hudson.

PILBEAM, David. 1970b. *Gigantopithecus* and the origins of hominidae. *Nature* (London) 225 (7 February): 516.

PLATO. 1933 ed. The statesman Part 2. In *Works of Plato.* Translated by George Burgess. New York: Tudor Publishing.

PLATO. 1937 ed. *The Timaeus.* In *Plato's cosmology: The Timaeus of Plato.* Translated and commented on by Francis M. Cornford. New York: Harcourt Brace.

PLATO. 1970 ed. *Protagoras and Meno*. Translated by W.K.C. Guthrie. England: Penguin Classics.

PLATO. 1974 ed. *The republic*. 2nd ed., rev. Translated by Desmond Lee. England: Penguin Classics.

PLAYFAIR, John. [1803] 1970. Biographical account of the late Dr. James Hutton, F.R.S. Edin. *Transactions of the Royal Society of Edinburgh*. 5:39. Reprint in *Contributions to the History of Geology* (New York) 5: 141-203.

POLANYI, Karl. 1957. *The great transformation*. Boston: Beacon Press.

POLANYI, Michael. 1955. The origin of ideas. *Encounter* (London) 5 (September): 61.

POPENOE, Paul. 1934. The German sterilization law. *Journal of Heredity* (Washington, D.C.) 25: 257.

POTTER, Charles F. 1930. *Humanism: A new religion*. New York: Simon and Schuster.

POTTER, Charles F. 1951. *The preacher and I: An autobiography*. New York: Crown.

POWELL, Baden. 1857. *Christianity without Judaism*. London: Longman.

PRICE, Derek de Solla. 1975. *Gears from the Greeks*. New York: Science History Publications.

PRICE, J.L. and T.I. Molleson. 1974. A radiographic examination of the left temporal bone of Kabwe Man, Broken Hill Mine, Zambia. *Journal of Archaeological Science* (London) 1: 285.

PRIDEAU, T. ed. 1973. Cro-Magnon man. In The Emergence of Man series. New York: Time Life Books.

PRIESTLEY, Joseph. 1782. *An history of the corruptions of Christianity*. 2 vols. Birmingham: Percy and Jones.

PROTSCH, R. 1974. Age and position of Olduvai hominid I. *Journal of Human Evolution* (London) 3 (September): 379.

RADDAY, Yehuda T., et al. 1982. Genesis, Wellhausen and the computer. *Zeitschrift für Alttestamentliche Wissenschaft* (Berlin) 94 (4): 467.

RAMM, Bernard. 1954. *The Christian view of science and scripture*. Grand Rapids, Mich.: William B. Eerdmans.

RAUP, David. 1979. Conflicts between Darwin and paleontology. *Field Museum of Natural History Bulletin* (Chicago) 50: 22.

RAVEN, Charles. 1942. *John Ray naturalist: His life and works*. Cambridge, England: The University Press.

RAVETZ, Jerome R. 1971. *Scientific knowledge and its social problems*. Oxford: Oxford University Press.

RAWLINGS, Maurice. 1978. *Beyond death's door*. New York: Thomas Nelson.

REED, Douglas. 1978. *The controversy of Zion*. South Africa: Dolphin Press.

READER, John. 1981. *Missing links*. London: Collins.

RECK, H. 1914. A man of 150,000 years ago. *Illustrated London News* 144 (4 April): 562. See also *Scientific American* 1914, 108 (27 June): 523.

REDI, Francesco. 1668. *Esperienze intorno alla generazione degl'insetti*. (Experiments about the spontaneous generation of insects.) Firenze: All'insegna della Stella.

REGAL, P.J. 1975. Evolutionary origin of feathers. *Quarterly Review of Biology* (New York) 50 (March): 35.

REUSCH, Franz H. [1862] 1886. *Bibel und Natur*. Freiburg: Herder. Translated by K. Lyttelton under the title *Nature and the Bible; Lectures on the Mosaic history of Creation in its relation to natural science*. 2 vols. Edinburgh: T. and T. Clark.

RIFKIN, Jeremy. 1983. *Algeny*. New York: Viking Press.

RITCHIE-CALDER, Lord. 1982. The Lunar Society of Birmingham. *Scientific American* 247 (June): 136.

ROBERTS, David. 1846-49. *Egypt and Nubia from drawings made on the spot by David Roberts, R.A. With historical descriptions by William Brockedon, F.R.S.; drawn on stone by Louis Haghe*. 3 vols. London: F.G. Moon.

ROBLE, Raymond G. 1977. The auroras. *Natural History* (New York) 86 (October): 60.

ROGER, Jacques. 1970. Georges-Louis Leclerc, Compte de Buffon. In *Dictionary of scientific biography*. Edited by Charles Gillispie. 2: 576-82. New York: Charles Scribner's Sons.

ROMANES, George. 1878. *A candid examination of theism*. London: English and Foreign Philosophical Library.

ROMANES, George. 1892. *Darwin and after Darwin*. London: Longmans.

RONOV, A.B. 1959. On the post pre-Cambrian geochemical history of the atmosphere and hydrosphere. *Geochemistry* (the Geochemical Society translation of the Russian journal of the same name) no. 5: 493.

ROSEN, S. 1968. Cosmic rays. *Science and Technology* (New York), 83 (November): 22.

ROUSSEAU, Jean J. [1770] 1904. *The confession of Jean Jacques Rousseau*. 2 vols. Reprint. English translation privately published (banned in the U.S.A. in 1929).

RUKANG, W. and L. Shenglong. 1983. Peking man. *Scientific American* 248 (June): 86.

RUNCORN, S.K. 1955. The earth's magnetism. *Scientific American* 193 (September): 152.

RUPKE, N.A. 1971. Summary of the monera fallacy. In *Scientific studies in Special Creation.* Edited by W.E. Lammerts. Philadelphia: Presbyterian and Reformed Publishing.

RUSCH, Wilbert. 1969. Ontogeny recapitulates phylogeny. *Creation Research Society Quarterly* (Ann Arbor, Mich.), annual issue, June.

RUSH, J.H. 1955. The speed of light. *Scientific American* 193 (August): 62.

RUSSELL, Bertrand. [1927] 1957. *Why I am not a Christian and other essays on religion etc.* Edited by Paul Edwards. Reprint. London: Allen and Unwin.

RUSSELL, Bertrand. 1929. *Marriage and morals.* New York: Garden City Publishing.

RUSSELL, Bertrand. 1949. *Practice and theory of Bolshevism.* London: Allen and Unwin.

RUSSELL, Bertrand. 1951. *The impact of science on society.* New York: Columbia University Press.

RUSSELL, Dale. 1982. The mass extinction of the late Mesozoic. *Scientific American* 246 (January): 58.

SAGAN, Carl, Linda S. Sagan, and Frank Drake. 1972. A message from earth. *Science* 175 (25 February): 881.

ST. JAMES-ROBERTS, I. 1976. Cheating in science. *New Scientist* (London) 72 (25 November): 446.

SALISBURY, Frank. 1969. Natural selection and the complexity of the gene. *Nature* (London) 224 (25 October): 342.

SALM, Walter G. 1964. Babylon battery. *Popular Electronics* (New York) 21 (July): 51.

SANDERSON, I.T. 1960. Riddle of the frozen giants. *Saturday Evening Post* 232 (16 January): 39.

SANTAYANA, George. [1905] 1954. *The life of reason.* 2 vols. Reprint, single vol. New York: Charles Scribner's Sons.

SARTON, George. 1930. Discovery of the theory of natural selection. *Isis* (Philadelphia. University of Pennsylvania) 14: 133.

SAYCE, A.H. 1893. *The races of the Old Testament.* London: Religious Tract Society.

SCADDING, S.R. 1981. Do vestigial organs provide evidence for evolution? *Evolutionary Theory* (University of Chicago) 5 (May): 173.

SCHILLER, Ronald. 1971. Those mysterious cave paintings. *Reader's Digest* (Canadian edition) 98 (March): 68.

SCHLEE, Susan. 1971. Her majesty's fauna on the bounding main. *Natural History* (New York) 80 (October): 76.

SCHOFIELD, R.E. 1963. *The lunar society of Birmingham.* London: Oxford University Press.

SCHOOLCRAFT, Henry R. 1822. Remarks on the prints of human feet, observed in the secondary limestone of the Mississippi valley. *The American Journal of Science and Arts.* (New Haven) 5: 223.

SCHUCHERT, Charles and Carl O. Dunbar. 1950. *Outlines of historical geology. 4th ed.* New York: John Wiley.

SCOPES, J.T. and James Presley. 1967. *Centre of the storm: Memoirs of John T. Scopes.* New York: Holt, Rinehart and Winston.

SCOTT, Walter. 1827. *Life of Napoleon Buonaparte.* 9 vols. Edinburgh: Ballantyne. 2: 306.

SEARS, Derek. 1979. Rocks on the ice. *New Scientist* (London) 81 (22 March): 959.

SERVISS, Garrett P. 1901. *Other worlds: Their nature, possibilities and habitability in the light of latest discoveries.* New York: D. Appleton.

SEWARD, A.C., ed. 1909. *Darwin and modern science.* Cambridge, England: University Press.

SHACKLETON, E.H. 1909. *The heart of the Antarctic.* 2 vols. London: W. Heinemann.

SHAPIRO, H.L. 1971. The strange unfinished saga of Peking man. *Natural History* (New York) 8 (November): 8.

SHAPLEY, Harlow, ed. 1960. *Science ponders religion.* New York: Appleton-Century-Crofts.

SHAWVER, L.J. 1974. Trilobite eyes. *Science News* 105 (2 February): 72.

SHOTWELL, James T. [1922] 1923. *An introduction to the history of history.* Reprint. New York: Columbia University Press.

SIMPKINS, Diana M. 1974. Thomas Robert Malthus. In *Dictionary of scientific biography.* Edited by Charles Gillispie. 6: 67-71. New York: Charles Scribner's Sons.

SINGER, Fred S. 1954. The origin of meteorites. *Scientific American* 191 (November): 36.

SKINNER, B.F. 1938. *The behavior of organisms: An experimental analysis.* New York: Appleton-Century-Crofts.

SKINNER, B.F. 1948. *Walden two.* New York: Macmillan.

SKINNER, B.F. 1979. My experience with the baby-tender. *Psychology Today* (New York) 12 (March): 28.

SMITH, G. Elliot. 1922. Hesperopithecus: The ape-man of the western world. *Illustrated London News.* 160 (24 June): 944.

SMITH, William. [1884] 1967. *Smith's Bible dictionary.* Rev. ed. by F.N. and M.A. Peloubet. Grand Rapids, Mich.: Zondervan.

SMUTS, Jan C. 1926. *Holism and evolution.* London: Macmillan.

SOBELL, M.B. and L.C. Sobell. 1978. *Behavioural treatment of alcohol problems.* New York: Plenum Press.

SPEAIGHT, Robert. 1967. *Teilhard de Chardin: A biography*. London: Collins.

SPENCER, Herbert. 1865. *Principles of biology*. 2 vols. London: Williams and Norgate.

SPENCER, Herbert. 1904. *An autobiography*. 2 vols. London: Williams and Norgate.

STANSFIELD, William D. 1977. *Science of evolution*. New York: Macmillan.

STEIDL, Paul M. 1982. Panorama of science: The velocity of light and the age of the universe. *Creation Research Society Quarterly* (Ann Arbor, Mich.) 19 (September): 128.

STEPHENSON, Richard F. 1982. Historical eclipses. *Scientific American* 247 (October): 170.

STERN, William. 1914. *The psychological methods of testing intelligence*. Translated by Guy M. Whipple. Baltimore: Warwick and York.

STRAUSS, David F. [1835] 1846. *Das leben Jesu*...Tübingen, Germany: C.F. Osiander. Translated by George Eliot under the title *The life of Jesus, critically examined by Dr. David Friedrich Strauss*. London: Chapman.

STRAUSS, David F. [1872] 1873. *Der alte und der neue Glaube*. Leipzig. 2nd ed. Translated by M. Blind under the title *The old faith and the new; a confession*. London: Asher.

STRAUS, W.L. and A.J.A. Cave. 1957. Pathology and the posture of the Neanderthal man. *Quarterly Review of Biology* (New York) 32: 348.

STRAUS, W.L. and C.B. Hunt. 1962. The age of *Zinjanthropus*. *Science* 13 (27 April): 293.

STRONG, C.L., ed. 1975. Amateur scientist: A.A. Michelson's apparatus. *Scientific American* 233 (October): 120.

STRUTT, R.J. 1910. The accumulation of helium in geologic time III. *Proceedings of the Royal Society* (London) Series A, 83: 298.

STUCKENRATH, R. 1977. Radiocarbon: Some notes from Merlin's diary. *Annals of the New York Academy of Sciences* 288: 188.

STUIVER, M. and Hans E. Seuss. 1966. On the relationship between radiocarbon dates and true sample ages. *American Journal of Science: Radiocarbon Supplement* (New Haven, Conn.) 8: 534.

SUESS, Hans F. 1965. Secular variations of the cosmic ray produced carbon 14 in the atmosphere and their interpretations. *Journal of Geophysical Research* (Richmond, Va.) 70 (1 December): 5937.

SUTHERLAND, Mason. 1953. Carlsbad caverns in colour. *National Geographic Magazine* (Washington) 104 (October): 433.

SUTTON, Antony. 1976. *Wall Street and the rise of Hitler*. Suffolk, U.K.: Bloomfield Books.

SUTTON, C. 1980. Neutrinos: Do they rule the universe? *New Scientist* (London) 86 (19 June): 308. See also *New Scientist* 1980, 86 (24 April): 201, and 1981, 92 (5 November): 371.

SZENT-GYORGYI, Albert. 1977. Drive in living matter to perfect itself. *Synthesis I* (New York) 1: 14.

TANNER, W.E. 1946. *Sir W. Arbuthnot Lane: His life and work*. London: Baillière, Tindall & Cox.

TARR, W.A. 1932. Meteorites in sedimentary rocks? *Science* 75 (1 January): 17.

TAX, Sol and Charles Callender, eds. 1960. *Evolution after Darwin*. 3 vols. Chicago: University of Chicago Press.

TAYLOR, Alfred Edward. [1932] 1975. *Socrates*. Reprint. Westport, Conn.: Greenwood Press.

TAYLOR, Gordon Rattray. 1983. *The Great Evolution Mystery*. London: Collins.

TAYLOR, Stuart Ross. 1975. *Lunar science: A post Apollo view*. New York: Pergamon Press.

TEILHARD DE CHARDIN, Pierre. [1955] 1959. *The phenomenon of man*. Translated by Bernard Wall. London: Collins.

TEILHARD DE CHARDIN, Pierre. [1956] 1965. *The appearance of man*. Translated by J.M. Cohen.

TEILHARD DE CHARDIN, Pierre [1969] 1971. *Christianity and evolution*. Translated by René Hague. London: Collins.

TEMPLE, Frederick. 1860. The education of the world. In *Essays and reviews*. Edited by J.W. Parker, London: Longman.

TENNYSON, Alfred. [1850] 1974. *In memoriam and other poems*. Reprint. Edited, with an introduction by John D. Jump. London: Dent.

TERRACE, H.S. 1979. How Nim Chimpsky changed my mind. *Psychology Today* (New York) 13 (November): 65.

THOM, A. 1971. *Megalithic lunar observatories*. Oxford: Clarendon Press.

THOMPSON, R. Campbell and R.W. Hutchinson. 1929. *A century of exploration at Nineveh*. London: Luzac Publishers.

THOMPSON, W.R. 1958. Introduction. In *The origin of species* by Charles Darwin. Reprint. Everyman Library Series, No. 811. London: J.M. Dent.

THOMSON, Arthur J. 1932. *The great biologists*. London: Methuen.

THOMSON, William. 1865. The doctrine of uniformity in geology briefly refuted. *Royal Society of Edinburgh: Proceedings* 5 (18 December): 512.

THOMSON, Wyville. 1875. Letter to T.H. Huxley, June 1875. Reported in *Quarterly Journal of Microscopical Science* n.s. 15: 390.

THWAITES, William M. and Frank T. Awbrey. 1982. As the world turns. *Creation/evolution* (San Diego State University, Calif.) 9 (Summer): 18.

TOBIAS, P.V. 1970. Brain size, grey-matter and race—fact or fiction? *American Journal of Physical Anthropology* (New York) 32: 3.

TOLLES, H.F. 1980. Observations on the speed of light. *Ham Radio* (Greenville, N.H.) 13 (January): 62. See also letter reply in 13 (April): 6.

TOVELL, Walter M. 1979. *The Niagara River*. Toronto: Royal Ontario Museum Publication.

TREDENNICK, Hugh. 1962. *The last days of Socrates*. England: Penguin Classics.

TRIMBLE, V. and F. Reines. 1973. The solar neutrino problem—a progress (?) report. *Review of Modern Physics* (New York) 45 (January): 1.

TURNER, Samuel H. 1841. *Companion to the book of Genesis*. London and New York: Wiley and Putnam.

UNESCO. 1949. *In the classroom with children under thirteen years of age*. Brooklet 5 in the series Towards World Understanding. Paris.

UNESCO Contributors. 1972. *In the minds of men: UNESCO 1946-1971*. Paris: UNESCO publications.

UPTON, A.C. 1957. Ionizing radiation and the aging process. *Journal of Gerontology* (St. Louis, Mo.) section A, 12 (July): 306.

U.S. Naval Observatory. *The astronomical almanac: 1982*. Washington, D.C.: U.S. Government Printing Office.

VALLOIS, H.V. 1962. The social life in early man: The evidence of skeletons. In *The social life of early man*. Edited by S.L. Washburn. London: Methuen.

VAN EVRIE, J.H. 1868. *White supremacy and Negro subordination, or Negroes a subordinate race, and (so-called) slavery its normal condition*. 2nd ed. New York: Van Evrie Horton.

VAN FLANDERN, T.C. 1977. Evidence for a recent origin of comets and asteroids. *American Physical Society: Bulletin* (New York) 22 (4): 538.

VELIKOVSKY, I. 1952. *Ages in chaos*. New York: Doubleday.

VELIKOVSKY, I. 1955. *Earth in upheaval*. New York: Doubleday.

Velocity of light 300 years ago. 1973. *Sky and Telescope* (Cambridge, Mass.) 45 (June): 353.

VILLEE, Claude A. 1977. *Biology*. 7th ed. Toronto: W.B. Saunders.

VOGT, William. 1948. *The road to survival*. New York: William Sloane Associates.

VOGT, William, 1960. *People! challenge to survival*. New York: William Sloane Associates.

VORZIMMER, Peter. 1963. Charles Darwin and blending inheritance. *Isis* (Philadelphia, Pa.) 54: 371.

WADE, Nicholas. 1980. Dinosaur battle erupts in British Museum. *Science* 211 (2 January): 35.

WADE, Nicholas and William Broad. 1983. *Betrayers of the truth: Fraud and deceit in the halls of science*. New York: Simon and Schuster.

WALKER, A.C. and R.E.F. Leakey. 1978. The hominids of east Turkana. *Scientific American* 239 (August): 43.

WALLACE, Alfred Russel [1855] 1980. On the law which has regulated the introduction of new species. Reprinted in *A delicate arrangement* by Arnold Brackman, 311-25. New York: Times Books.

WALLACE, Alfred Russel [1858] 1980. On the tendency of varieties to depart indefinitely from the original type. Reprinted in *A delicate arrangement* by Arnold Brackman, pp. 326-37. New York: Times Books.

WALLACE, Alfred Russel. 1875. *Miracles and modern spiritism*.

WALLACE, Robert. [1809] 1969. *A dissertation on the numbers of mankind*. Reprint. New York: Augustus M. Kelley.

WATTS, A.E. 1980. *The metamorphoses of Ovid: An English version*. San Francisco: North Point Press.

WEBSTER, N.H. [1924]. *Secret societies and subversive movements*. Reprint. Hawthorne, Calif.: Christian Book Club of America.

WEBSTER, Nesta H. [1919] 1969. *The French revolution*. Reprint. Hawthorne, Calif.: Christian Book Club of America.

WEBSTER, Noah. 1799. *A brief history of epidemic and pestilential diseases*. 2 vols. Boston: Hartford, Hudson and Goodwin.

WEBSTER, Robert. 1970. *Gems*. London: Butterworths.

WEIDENREICH, F. 1938. *Pithecanthropus* and *Sinanthropus*. *Nature* (London) 141 (26 February): 378.

WEIDENREICH, F. 1939. On the earliest representation of modern mankind recovered on the soil of East Asia. *Peking Natural History Bulletin* 13: 161.

WEIDENREICH, F. 1943. The skull of *Sinanthropus pekinesis*: A comparative study on a primitive hominid skull. *Geological Survey of China (Paleontologica Sinica.)* (Peking), Whole Series 127, n.s.D, 10: 1-484.

WEIDENREICH, F. 1965. *Apes, giants and men*. Chicago: University of Chicago Press.

WEINER, J.S., K.P. Oakley, and W.E. Le Gros Clark. 1953. The solution of the Piltdown problem. London: *Bulletin of the British Museum (Natural History). Geology*. 2 (3): 139.

WEISMANN, August. 1891. *Essays upon heredity and kindred biological problems*. 2nd ed. 2 vols. Translated and edited by E.B. Poulton, S. Schönland, and A.E. Shipley. Oxford: Clarendon Press.

WEISMANN, August. 1893. *The germ-plasm: A theory of heredity*. Translated by W.N. Parker. London: Walter Scott.

WELLS, H.G. 1898. *War of the worlds*. London: W. Heinemann.

WENDT, Herbert. 1968. *Before the deluge*. New York: Doubleday.

WENDT, Herbert. 1972. *From ape to Adam*. New York: Bobbs-Merrill.

WERNER, Johannes, ed. 1930. *The love letters of Ernst Haeckel written between 1898 and 1903*. New York: Harper and Brothers.

WERTIME, Thoedore A. 1973. The beginnings of metallurgy. *Science* 182 (30 November): 875.

WESSON, Paul S. 1979. *Cosmology and geophysics*. London: Oxford University Press.

WEST, M.L., ed. 1978. *Hesiod: Works and days*. Oxford: Clarendon Press.

WESTFALL, Richard S. 1981. *Never at rest: A biography of Isaac Newton*. New York: Clarendon Press.

WETZEL, R.M., et al. 1975. *Catagonus*, an "extinct" peccary, alive in Paraguay. *Science* 189 (1 August): 379.

WHIPPLE, Fred L. 1974. The nature of comets. *Scientific American* 230 (February): 37.

WHITCOMB, John C. and D.B. DeYoung. 1978. *The moon: Its creation and significance*. Winona Lake, Ind.: BMH Books.

WHITCOMB, John C. and Henry M. Morris. 1961. *The Genesis flood*. Philadelphia: Presbyterian and Reformed Publishing.

WHITELAW, Robert L. 1970. Time, life and history in the light of 15,000 radiocarbon dates. *Creation Research Society Quarterly* (Ann Arbor, Mich.) 7 (June): 56.

WHITLEY, D.G. 1910. The ivory islands of the Arctic ocean. *Journal of the Transactions of the Victorian Institute*. Title since changed to *Faith and Thought*. (London) 42: 35.

WHITNEY, J.D. 1880. Human remains and works of art in the auriferous gravel series. In The auriferous gravels of the Sierra Nevada of California. *Memorandum of the Museum of Harvard College* 6 (pt 1, sec. 5): 258.

WIEDERSHEIM, Robert. 1895. *The structure of man*. Translated by H. Bernard and M. Bernard. London: Macmillan.

WILBERFORCE, S. 1860. [Review of] On the origin of species by means of natural selection by Charles Darwin. *The Quarterly Review* (London) 180 (July): 225.

WILLIAMS, Greer. 1969. *The plague killers*. New York: Charles Scribner's Sons.

WILLOUGHBY, David P. 1974. *The empire of Equus*. San Diego: A.S. Barnes.

WILSON, Edward O. 1975. *Sociobiology: The new synthesis*. Cambridge: Harvard University Press.

WILSON, Edward O. 1978. *On human nature*. Cambridge: Harvard University Press.

WILSON, Leonard. 1973. Charles Lyell. In *Dictionary of scientific biography*. Edited by Charles Gillispie. 8: 563-76. New York: Charles Scribner's Sons.

WINCHESTER, A.M. 1971. *Modern biological principles*. 2nd ed. New York: Van Nostrand Reinhold.

WINSLOW, J.H.A. and Meyer. 1983. The perpetrator at Piltdown. *Science 83* (Washington) 4 (September): 33.

WISEMAN, Nicholas. 1836. *Twelve lectures on the connection between science and revealed religion delivered in Rome*. 2 vols. London: Catholic Bookselling and Publishing.

WITTMANN, Axel. 1980. Letters. *Sky and Telescope* (Cambridge, Mass.) 60 (September): 190.

WORZEL, Lamar J. 1959. Extensive deep-sea sub-bottom reflections identified as white ash. *National Academy of Sciences: Proceedings* (New York) 45: 349.

WRIGHT, D.J.M. 1971. Syphilis and Neanderthal man. *Nature* (London) 229 (5 February): 409.

YATES, Frances A. 1964. *Giordano Bruno and the Hermetic tradition*. Chicago: University of Chicago Press.

YOCKEY, Hubert P. 1977. A calculation of the probability of spontaneous biogenesis by information theory. *Journal of Theoretical Biology* (London) 67: 377.

YOUNG, A.T. 1971. Seeing and scintillation. *Sky and Telescope* (Cambridge, Mass.) 42 (September): 139.

YOUNG, R.V. 1974. Christianity and ecology. *National review* (New York) 26 (20 December): 1454.

ZIMMERMAN, D.W., et al. 1974. Thermoluminescence authenticity measurements on core material from the bronze horse of the New York Metropolitan Museum of Art. *Archaeometry* (Oxford, U.K.) pt 1, 16 (February): 19.

ZUCKERMAN, Solly. 1971. *Beyond the ivory towers*. London: Weidenfeld and Nicholson.

ZUSNE, Leonard. 1975. *Names in the history of psychology*. Washington, New York: John Wiley.

Index

Boldface numbers refer to the page numbers of illustrations.

review, 467 n 23; by drugs, 424, 467 n 28; work of B.F. Skinner, 418-19; work of Sobels with alcoholics, 419

Bell, Charles, 134

Bent rocks, 104-5, **104**, 448 n 31

Bergson, Henri: occult involvement, 464 n 16; work, 375

Bible: dating sequence in, 284; fixity of kinds, 39; Latin version, 16; resuscitations, 442 n 2; societies founded, 345

Biddle, John: Unitarian Church, 116

Big-bang theory, 4

Binet, Alfred: craniometry dismissed, 406; measures intellect, 407

Biogenesis, 180. *See also* Spontaneous generation

Biogenetic law: condemned by Gavin de Beer, 274; description, 274-77

Biometrika, journal, 405

Birds of Paradise, 174, 451 n 17

Biston betularia. See Moth, peppered

Boa constrictor: claim for vestigial legs, 270-71

Boas, Franz: geography and human features, 144, 414; influence on Margaret Mead, 416; life and work, 413-14, 416; nurture and intelligence, 405; opposed to eugenicists, 414; worldview, 467 n 25

Boise, Charles, 243, 247

Bore-hole project, 286-87, 457 n 3, 457 n 4

Borel, Emil: on probability, 201, 453 n 27

Botta, Emil: discovery of Babylon, 353

Boule, Marcellin: Neaderthal man, 211-12; Peking man, 235-40; position, 53

Boulton, Matthew, 55

Bowel movements: frequency of, 273

Bozarth, G.R.: recognizes the importance of Adam, 463 n 12, 463 n 26

Black, Davidson: Peking man, 235-40

Black death: effect on population, 338

Blythe, Edward: natural selection, 125-26

Brain capacity: man's use of, 263

Branchial clefts. *See* Pharyngeal arches

Breuil, Henri: Minateda woman and child, 220, 454 n 14; Peking, 238

Bristle-cone pine tree: carbon 14, calibration, 321

British Council of Churches, 379, 464 n 25

British museum: discovery of Nineveh, 352; Guadaloupe fossil, 218; Piltdown hoax, 228

Broca, Paul: brain size and intellect, 258, 402

Broken Hill man. *See* Rhodesian man

Bronowski, J: quote, 198-99; Vatican archives, 22

Bronze age, 208

Bronze Greek horse, 38, 444 n 6

Broom, Robert: discovery at Makapansgat, 243

Bruno, Giordano: victim of Inquisition, 24

Bryan, William Jennings, 425. *See also* Scopes trial

Buckland, William, 66, 110, 350

Buffalo and cow cross, 142

Buffon, Compte de: life and works, 42-48, **42**;

planet theory, 44

Burke, Edmund: denounced Lunar society, 56

Burt, Cyril: fraudulent work on twins, 411-12

Calaveras skull: American human fossil, 253; discovery, **216**, 217; Whitney's work, 454 n 11

Cambridge University, 120

Camel and dromedary cross, 142

Campanella and Galileo, 443 n 15

Canidae. See Dog family

Carbon 14 dating, 313-15; accelerator method, 459 n 6; assumptions, 317, 459 n 7, 459 n 8, 459 n 9; calibration, 320-22; correction factors, 320; early results, 315-16; earth's magnetic field, 318; Egyptian chronology, 462 n 9; half-life, 314-15; production and decay rates, 314, 317-18; vapor canopy, 319; Whitelaw's statistical analysis, 320; young earth indicated, 459 n 4, 459 n 9

Cat and rabbit cross, 142

Catagonus ameghino. See Peccary

Catholic *Index of forbidden books*, 21, 30, 58, 375; Darwin books, 132; history of, 445-46 n 7

Cave paintings, 219-20. *See also* Cro-Magnon man

Cenozoic Research Laboratory, 236

Censorship in the media, 359, 426-27

Chagas' disease, 128

Challenger, H.M.S.: *Bathybius haeckelii*, 187-90; scope and work, 87, **188**, 447 n 8

Chalmers, Thomas: gap theory, 362-63, **363**

Chambers, Robert: *Vestiges of Creation*, 58, 354, 462 n 18

Champollion, Jean-François: biography, 462 n 8; dating, 462 n 10; life and work, 347-48; 347

Chicago Field Museum Conference, 166

Chickadee, 146, **146**

Chinese ideograph, 391-92, **392**

Chondrite, 184. *See also* Meteorite

Chou K'ou Tien: Lucy discovery, 248; Peking man, 235-40

Christ, Jesus: object of worship, 341; resurrection of, 342; Son of God, 360

Christianity: best means of attack, 57; first converts, 14; persecution of, 14, 16, 20

Chrysalis, the: image in Potter's church, 372

Churchill, Winston: eugenics, 408

Circumcision: foreskin not vestigial, 269-70; Weismann's statistics for, 48, 445 n 12

Civil War, American: racial origins, 262

Cladistics, 147, 164

Coalbeds in the Antarctic, 97, 447 n 18

Coal mines: temperature rise in, 292, 460 n 26

Coccyx. *See* Tailbone, vestigial

Coelacanth, 106, 175

Colectomy, 273

Colenso, John: life and work, 378-80, **378**; publicity given to, 353

Columba livia. See Pigeons

Comet: Halley's, 202; origins, 326-27

Communist: Fascist objectives similar, 467 n 22; Manifesto history, 465 n 28; party, religious aspects of, 341

Condorcet, Marquis of: vision of utopia, 61

Constantine I, emperor: at Milvern, 16, 442 n 10

Continents sinking, 93-94

Contracting sun, 322-24, 459 n 13

Copernicus, Nicholas: 23-24, **24**

Cosmic rays and carbon 14 production, 313-19

Council of Trent, 21

Counter Reformation, 21

Craniometer, 406, **406**

Creation: as alternative to evolution, 279; belief in, 344-45, 364; evidence for, 312; not falsifiable, 393; religious aspects, 341; the sculpture portraying, **141**; vestigial organs, 265

Crick, Francis: opposed to spontaneous generation, 393; signature to Humanist Manifesto, 428; theory of directed panspermia, 195, 327

Cro-Magnon man: 219-21; Les Cambarelles, 219; Minateda, **220**

Curie temperature, 331, 460 n 27

Custance, Arthur: gap theory, 364, 463 n 29

Cuvier, Georges: brain weight, 259; life and work, 46, 49-53, **49**; paleontological techniques developed by, 50; theory of the earth, 51, 53, 65, 445 n 15, 445 n 16

Cynodont. See Transition fossils

Cyphanthropus. See Rhodesian man

Dana, James: life and work, 370-71, **370**

Dante (Alighieri), 23, 443 n 16

Dart, Raymond: Taung skull, 241-42

Darwin, Charles: Aristotle misquoted, 368-69; Bible knowledge, 119-22, 367; billiards, 98; Biogenetic law, 275; biographies, 115; Cambridge curriculum, 449 n 8; Christianity challenged by, 344; "delicate arrangement", 130, 446 n 14; *Descent of man*, 207; Edinburgh University, 118; evolution of the eye, 167, 451 n 14; evolution theory, 52, 58, 182, 279-81; *Expression of the emotions in men and animals*, 134; family, immediate, 126-27, **128**; greeted as an atheist, 366; house, **129**; Hitler inspired by, 409-11; illness, 127-30; inherited baldness, 48; irreligious nature concealed, 450 n 22; *Journal of Researches*, 148; Kelvin, 457 n 10, 460 n 26; Lady Hope, 450 n 20, 450 n 21; Lamarckism, 127, 399-400, 466 n 4; laws of nature inviolable, 4; letter to A. Gray, 13-15; life and works, 117-37; Lyell prepared ground for, 353; man of faith, 168; man of wealth, 133; Marx corresponds with, 381; multiple species of man, 262; murder of God, 126; natural selection, 158-59, 399-400; object of worship, 341; occult experience, 75, 446 n 15; on the soul, 446 n 15; *Origin*, publication of, 130-33, 354-56; perfection, problem of, 451 n 14; personification of nature, 9; pigeons, 130, 138, 148-50; plagiarism, 125; psychology, 134, 450 n 17;

secular humanism, foundation for, xii; statute of, **135**; transition fossils, 150; Unitarian Church influence, 116; unpublished works, 115, 445 n 6; *Variation of plants and animals*, 369, 400. *See also Origin.*

Darwinism: Marxism aligned with, 411; religious aspects, 394; rise of in Germany, 409

Darwin's finches: classified by Lack, 147, **148**; mentioned by C. Darwin, 148, 450 n 2, 450 n 3

Darwin-Wallace theory, 73

Darwin, Emma, 136-37, **136**

Darwin, Erasmus (the elder): Edinburgh University, 121; Lunar Society, 55, **58**; racey lifestyle, 118, 120, 449 n 5; *Zoönomia*, 58, 120

Darwin, Francis, 115

Darwin, George: fission theory for origin of moon, 44, 330; radioactivity suggested to measure age of earth, 294; radioactivity supplies sun's energy, 323

Darwin, Leonard, 408

Darwin, Robert: Freemason, 119, 449 n 3; opposed to Bible, 120

Date of Creation: according to scholars, 283; appended to Bibles, 284

Dawson, Charles, 227-28

Day-age theory, 362

Dead Sea dating from salt, 289-90, **289**

Decay constants not constant, 307-08

Declaration of Independence. *See* American Revolution

"Delicate arrangement", 130, 450 n 13, 450 n 14, 450 n 15

Democracy: vox populi, vox dei, 16

Democritus, 10, 206

Dental arcade of man and ape, **251**

Descartes, René: Christianity challenged by, 344; Fall of man, 207; life and works, 28-30, **29**; mind and brain, 258; on the soul, 30

Descent of man, 133, 134, 159; not placed on Catholic *Index*, 373

Design in nature, 40, 139, 266

Development. *See* Evolution

Developmental hypothesis. *See* Documentary hypothesis

De Vries, Hugo: mutation theory, 161, 451 n 11, **162**

Dewey, John: signer of first Humanist Manifesto, 425, 428; U.S. education, 425

Dinosaur: eggs, 89, 447 n 11; extinction of, 107; museum collections, 150-51; tracks, 108; tracks with human tracks, 448 n 36, 449 n 37; tracks with wheel tracks, 280

Divine right of kings, 7

Documentary hypothesis, 383-87; archaeology refutes, 387; Chinese history refutes, 392; computer refutes, 386; Ebla discovery refutes, 390-91; Hegelian evolution basis for, 384; work of S.R. Driver, 465 n 31

Dog family, 142, **143**

Doré, Gustave, 443 n 16, **37**

Down house, 129-30, **129**
Doyle, Arthur Conan: occult involvement, 75; Piltdown affair, 228
Dripstone, 335-36, **336**
Drosophila melanogaster. See Fruit fly mutation experiments
Dubois, Eugene, 221-25, **223**; confesses skull cap is ape, 238, 455 n 9; Wadjak skulls, 222-24. *See also* Java man
Dynamo theory, 331

Earth: internal heat, 461 n 32; magnetic field, 331-34, 461 n 30; Magsat, 461 n 31; rotation, 325-26; rotation corrections, 460 n 18, 460 n 19, 460 n 20
Ebla discovery, 389-91; Creation account, 391
Eddington, Arthur: thermonuclear sun, 323
Eddy and Boornazian: contracting sun, 324
Eden, Murray: chance and design, 453 n 29
Edinburgh University: and Darwin, 118; and Hutton, 67; Lunar Society members, 56
Education: humanist influence in, 425
Egypt: dating and carbon 14 calibration, 320, 349, 462 n 9; destruction of temples, 461 n 7; and the Greeks, 348; hieroglyphics deciphered, 346-48; and the Israelites, 348; Napoleon conquers, 346; on the soul, 2, **2**, 3, **3**; pictorial records of, 461 n 6
Einstein, Albert: relativity, 28; velocity of light, 443 n 20; view of God, 397
Eldredge and Gould: punctuated equilibria, 164-66
Ellis, Havelock, 416
Embryo, 274-77. *See also* Biogenetic law
Emerson, Ralph Waldo, 117
Empedocles: Darwin cites, 368; five human senses, 9
Eoanthropus dawsoni. See Piltdown man
Eohippus. See Horse
Epicurus: ascent of man, 206; philosophy, 11
Episcopius. *See* Gap theory
Equus caballus. See Horse
Erect genital of mammoth, 98, **99**, 448 n 23
Eugenics: coined by F. Galton, 450 n 12
Evangelical movement: cause of opposition to Darwin, 54; prevents socialist revolution, 54, 445 n 1
Evolution: declared a law, 73, 446 n 13; involves miracle, 393-94; neither provable nor refutable, 392-93; reasons for maintaining, 280-81; religious aspects, 341, 393-95
Ex nihilo Creation, ix, 312-13
Exodus, date of, 384
Extinction of life forms, 172-76
Extraterrestrial origin of life theme, 184, 190-96, 202-03, 452 n 22, 452 n 23
Eysenck and Kamin, 414

Fabian Society, 427-28
Fascism, 411, 467 n 21, 467 n 22

Fall of man theme, 204-08
Fantasia, x
Faraday, Michael, 359, **359**
Feuerbach, L., 382
Fibonacci, Leonardo: Arab numerals, 442 n 12
Finches. *See* Darwin's finches
FitzRoy, Robert: H.M.S. Beagle, 122; suicide, 124, 129
Fontechevade skull, 215. *See* Neanderthal man
Fosdick, Harry Emerson: funded by Rockefeller, 372; opposed to fundamentalists, 372, 464 n 14; promoter of liberal theology, **385**, 386
Fossil: absence of, 150, 450 n 4, 450 n 5; abundance of, 92; anomolous, 105-9; bat, **173**; clams, 90; coelacanth, 106, 175; dinosaur eggs, 89; feather, 153; fish, **89**, 90, 447 n 12; flesh reconstructions, 209, 261; formation, 85-87, **87**; horse evolution, 152-53; human jaw, 91, **91**; human skull, 91, 447 n 14, 102, **216**, 217, 230-31, **230**, 244-45, **244**, 455 n 18, 246-47, 253; ichthyosaur, 88-89, **89**; insects, 89, 447 n 10; living, 448 n 32, 448 n 33; plesiosaurus, **86**; polystrate tree, 114, **114**; sabre-tooth tiger, 91, 447 n 13; teeth, 88, 454 n 2; transitions, 150-58; whales, 93, 447 n 16 *See also Archaeopteryx*
"1470" man, 246-47
France, Anatole, **258**, 259
Franco, General: object of worship, 340
Franklin, Benjamin, **32**, 55-56, **55**
Frazer, James, 387-88, **89**
Free love: scientific sanction for, 416-18
Freeman, Derek: exposes Margaret Mead, 417
Freemasonry: and Francis Bacon, 443 n 21, 445 n 3; in Darwin family, 119, 449 n 3
Freiberg skull, 102-3
French Revolution, 31-55; cause of, 34; Christianity challenged by, 344; English hostile to, 54; goddess of Reason, 34; Lord Acton quoted, 34; Lunar Society, 56; metric system, 34; socialist humanism, 36; Statue of Liberty, **35**
Fruit fly mutation experiments, 162-63, **163**

Galapagos islands, 147
Galen, 17
Galileo (Galilei): biblical arguments, 443 n 15; comets controversy, 443 n 17; life and work, 22-25, **25**; sun-spots, 325; telescope, 443 n 17; Vatican archives, 22
Gall, Franz Joseph, **401**
Galley Hill man, 215. *See* Neanderthal man
Galton, Francis, 127; coins eugenics, 450 n 12; life and works, 402-8, **403**
Gap theory, 363-64, 463 n 29
Gauss, Karl: brain weight, 259; magnetic field of earth, 331-33, **333**, 460 n 29
Genesis: affirmed by N.T. writers, 370, 463 n 11; two accounts of creation, 180
Genesis Flood, 49, 57, 58, 65, 70, 71, 123, 125; acknowledged by Catholic and Protestant church until recently, 344-45, 366; acknowl-

edged by Christ, 360; atmospheric pressure, 459 n 10; Babylon account of, 384-85; in Chinese records, 391-92; difficulties of, 110; and Egyptian dating, 348; fossils as evidence for, 218, 350, 362; legends of, 387-88, 465 n 37, 465 n 38, 465 n 39; Mosaic account, 383; object of skepticisim, 343; and population growth, 339; reproductive-repopulation model, 111-13; unacceptable to many, 365; Whitcomb and Morris model, 111

Genesis kinds, **138**, 139

Gentry, Robert: radio-halos, 311-12

Geological Society, 66, 227-28

Geospizinae. See Darwin's finches

Germ theory: and Pasteur, 181; and Weismann, 48

German National Socialist Party, 408, 411. *See also* Nazi Party

Gigantopithecus blacki, 234

Gill-slits in human embryo alleged, 277, **278**

Glénard, Frantz: viseroptosis, 272

Goddard, Henry, 407, 408

Gorilla: discovery of, 142

Gosse, Edmund: contrived acceptance of *Origin*, 355, 462 n 19

Gosse, Philip: and Adam's navel, 462 n 20; encounter with Darwin, **354**, 355

Gould, S.J.: paraphrased, 165; re-analysis of S. Morton's work, 263

Gould and Eldredge: punctuated equilibria, 165; reject *Archaeopteryx*, 178. *See* Eldredge and Gould

Graf-Wellhausen hypothesis. *See* Documentary hypothesis

Graham, Robert: human sperm bank, 415

Grand Canyon, 100

Grant, Madison, eugenicist, 408, 409

Gray, Asa: Darwin's letter to, 131, 450 n 13, 450 n 14, 450 n 15; promoter of theistic evolution, 367-71, **367**

Gray, Jane: Unitarian influence on Asa, 367, 463 n 3

Greek technology: Antikythera device, 444 n 3; architecture, 32, **33**; bronze horse, **38**, 444 n 6

Guadaloupe fossils, 215-18, **216**, **218**, 253

Gutenberg, Johann, 21, **21**, 443 n 18

Haeckel, Ernst: *Bathybius haeckelii*, 187-90, 452 n 12, 452 n 14, 452 n 15, 452 n 16, 452 n 18; Biogenetic Law, 274-77; branded a fool, 184; fraudulent embryos, **275**, 276-77, **277**, 456 n 4, 456 n 9, 456 n 16; euthanasia advocated, 409; evolution elitist, 411; family tree, **177**, 178; Frida von Uslar-Gleichen, 185-87, **187**, 452 n 8, 452 n 10; life and works, 184-86, **185**, **187**, 190, **222**, 276, 408-9; *monera*, 187-90, 196; pantheist, 184; *Pithecanthropus alalus*, 221; public lectures, **186**; Thule Gesellschaft Society, 466 n 16. *See also* Java man

Haldane, J.B.S., 197. *See* Oparin-Haldane theory

Haley's comet, 327

Hammond, A.L.: earth and moon system, 330

Ham's son: descendants of, 262

Handy man, 245-47, 455 n 21, 455 n 23, 455 n 26

Hardy-Weinberg law, 406

Harvard University: Unitarian stronghold, 367

Heads of the famous: sizes of, 259

Hegel, Georg: absolute spirit, 381-82, **382**; Christianity challenged by, 344; Marx influenced by, 381; philosophy supported by Darwin, 386

Helium: lack of in earth's atmosphere, 334-35

Helmholtz, Herman von, 322, **323**, 324

Hermetic tradition, 25, 443 n 19

Herpes simplex, 422-23

Hesiod: ages of man, 205, 453 n 1, 453 n 2; Fall of man, 207

Hesperopithecus harold cooki. See Nebraska man

His, Wilhelm, 276

Hitler, Adolf: inspired by Darwin, 409; object of worship, 340; objectives, 409, 467 n 21, 467 n 22

Holmes, A: age of the earth, 299-300

Hominid/Hominoid: definition of, 249

Homo antiquus. See Neanderthal man

Homo erectus. See Java man

Homo erectus pekinensis. See Peking man

Homo habilis. See Handyman

Homo neanderthalensis. See Neanderthal man

Homo rhodesiensis. See Rhodesian man

Homo sapiens, 41, 210; interfertility, 145

Homo sapiens neanderthalensis. See Neanderthal man

Homo troglodytes, 41

Homology. *See* Design in nature

Hooker, Joseph, **131**, 135, 142; in "delicate arrangement", 74, 355; in Oxford debate, 358

Hookworm: flush toilet eradicates, 466 n 11; germ of laziness, 405

Hopeful monster theory, 164-65

Horace: ascent of man, 207; ode, 12

Horse: evolution of, 152-53; family, 139, **140**

Howard, Robert: rotation of sun, 325

Hoyle, Fred: rejects spontaneous generation, 202-3

Human fossils: Calaveras, **216**, 217, 253, 454 n 11; documentation of, 102, 448 n 28; foot tracks, 108-9, **109**, 449 n 38; Freiberg skull in coal, 102, 448 n 29; Galley Hill, 215; Gaudaloupe specimens, 215-18, **216**, **218**; Laguna, 253, 455 n 29; Rancho La Brea, 91, 447 n 14; Reck's, 244-45, 455 n 18; Rhodesian skull, 229-31, **230**; Santa Barbara skulls, 217; Wadjak, 222, 224; Yukon jaw, 91, 447 n 15

Human interfertility, 144-45

Humani Generis, 373-74

Humanist influence in the media, 426-27

Humanist Manifesto: aims, 397; first, 428; second, 420-21

491

Hume, David, 26, 59, 344
Hutton, James: charged with atheism, 446 n 10; Edinburgh University, 121; theory of the earth, 66-67, **67**
Huxley, Aldous: *Brave new world*, 411, 418
Huxley, Julian: atheist, 394, **397**, 465 n 46; synthetic theory, 163; on unification, 424; UNESCO policy, 398, 423-24; world government, 423-24
Huxley, Thomas H: agnostic, 365; ape to man, **256**; Bible respected, 365; embryos, 275; Haeckel's *monera*, 186-89; horse fossils convince, 152; Kingsley confessed to, 365; *Origin* convinces, 159; *Origin* reviewed, 358; Oxford debate, 358-59, **359**; sophistry in, 458 n 1
Hymen, 270
Hyracotherium. *See* Horse
Hyrax. *See* Rock badger

Icaronycteris index. See Bat
Ice age, 95-97; date for, 458 n 18
Ice caves, 100
Ileosigmoidostomy, 272. *See also* Metchnikoff
Index Librorum Prohibitorum. See Catholic *Index of forbidden books*
Indian (N. american): intellect measured, 262; skulls, **269**
Industrial melanism, 171-72
Industrial Revolution, 36, 53, 55
Ingersoll's reworking of Kelvin's heat data, 294
Inquisition, 21
Institute for Creation Research, 426
Intelligence Quotient, 407. *See also* Binet, Alfred
Intestine: thought to be vestigial, 456 n 10, 456 n 11
Iron: age, 208; early smelting of, 444 n 5
Isotopes: of argon, 300-1; of helium, 335; of lead, 299-300; of oxygen, 302
Israel: Dead Sea chronometer, 289-90, **289**; Dead Sea level falling, 457 n 6
Ivory from frozen mammoths, 97

James, William: and Lowell, 190; the "sixth" sense, 10
Japanese "plesiosaur", 106-7, **107**, 426-27; postage stamp, 426, **426**
Java man, 221-25; classification, 252; Dubois' confession, 225, 455 n 9
Jesus, 13, 14
Jeffrey, Edward: discredits mutation, 161
Jeffries, Harold: earth/moon dynamics, 330
Jensen, James: discovers early bird, 155
Jesuit: Marxist influence in, 376; promotion of theistic evolution 374-77, **377**
Jews: divine right of kings, 7; Mosaic law, 12. *See also* Circumcision
Johanson, Donald: Lucy, 243, 247-49, 455 n 27; rift valley, 289
Joly, John: work on sea salts, 288
Joule heating of the earth, 333, 461 n 32

Keir, James: Lunar Society, 56
Keith, Arthur: classification by brain size, 249; Piltdown hoax, 226-30, **226**; Taung skull, 242, 455 n 13; vestigial organs, 267-68
Kelvin, Lord: age of the earth, 292-94, **292**; giant of science, 359
Kettlewell, H.B.D., 171-72. *See also* Industrial melanism
Keynes, John M., 59
Kingsley, Charles: Darwin admirer, 355-57, **356**; Father God to Mother Nature, 382; theistic evolution, 377-78; *The Water Babies*, 356-57
Koczy, Friedrich: uranium salts in sea water, 290-91, 457 n 7
Koenigswald, Ralph von: Java, 225; Peking, 234, 236
Krakatoa, volcano, 68
Kropotkin, P.A.: animal mutual aid, 79
Krstolich restoration of Neanderthal man, 213
Kruegar, Ivar, 235
Kuehneotherium, 156-57. *See also* Transition fossils

La-Chapelle-aux-Saints fossil, 211-12. *See also* Neanderthal man
Lady Hope: and Darwin's last days, 136-37
Laguna girl. *See* Human fossils
Lamarck, Jean B: eulogy to, 46, 445 n 11; hymen, unfamiliarity with, 270; life and works, 44-47, **46**
Lamarckism: defined, 47; examples, 46, 279; inherited capacity for intellect, 259-60; recent revival of, 48, 445 n 13; in Russia, 48, 52, 260
Lamb, Horace: free decay theory, 331, **332**
Lamont, Corliss, 421-22
Lane, William A: autointoxication, 272-73; colectomy, 273; New Health Society, 456 n 12
Language: more complex in the past, 255
Laplace, Pierre S. de: Nebular theory, 292-93, 457 n 9
Laughlin, Harry, eugenicist, 408
Layard, Austen H: discovery of Nineveh, 352-53, **352**; Documentary hypothesis, 384
Leakey, Louis: Nutcracker man, 243-46
Leakey, Richard: 1470 skull, 246-47; *Homo habilis*, 252; promotes Biogenetic law, 274, 276; transitions claimed, 157, 165; work, 255
Leap second, 326, 460 n 18, 460 n 20. *See also* Earth
Ledley, Fred: reports human tail, 278-79
Leucippus: atomistic philosophy, 10
Lewis, C.S., author, 23
Libby, Willard: carbon 14 dating, 314; Egyptian and Bible concordance, 349, 462 n 9
Liberal theologians control institutions, 385
Lightfoot, John: time of creation, 284, 457 n 2
Linnaeus, Carolus: archetypes, 42; classification system, 138-39; life and work, 38-43, 49
Linné, Carl von. *See* Linnaeus, Carolus
Linnean Society, 43, 66, 74, 130, 445 n 10

Locke, John, philosopher and unitarian, 116
London, Jack, author and Fabian member, 428
London School of Economics, 428
Lord's Day Observance Society founded, 345
Lovell, Bernard, astronomer, 201
Lowell, Percival, 190-94, **191**; Haeckel, influence of, 190, 452 n 19; preconception, 194, 242; 700 Martian canals, 193
Lucretius (Carus): ascent of man, 207; chance can be creative, 369; *On the nature of the universe*, 11; *The nature of things*, **13**
Lucy: discovered by Johanson, 248, 455 n 27
Lumpers, defined, 145
Lunar laser-ranging experiment, 329-30. *See also* Moon
Lunar receiving laboratory, 195
Lunar Society, 55, 57, 59, 445 n 2
Luther, Martin, 20, **20**
Lyell, Charles: assumptions in theory, 78-80; Christianity challenged by, 72, 344-45, 350; Cuvier's theory defeated by, 360; Darwin influenced by, 57, 341; "delicate arrangement, 74, **131**; expanded time frame, 57, 69, 104, 166, 285; geologic column, 71,-72, 102-4; life and work, 52, 66, **69**, 135; Miller opposed to, 360; Niagara Falls visit, 81-84, **82**, **83**, 286, 446 n 1, 446 n 2, 446 n 3, 447 n 4; Owen opposed to, 270; and Prévost, 66; *Principles of geology*, 58, 68, 76, 124, 133, 285, 383; promotes *Origin*, 355; uniformitarianism, 68, 446 n 11
Lysenko, Trofim, 52, 260

Macallam, A.B.: salt in living matter and oceans, 291
Magnetic field of the earth, 331-34. *See also* Earth
Magsat, 332, 334, 461 n 31. *See also* Earth
Mahoney, Michael: bias in peer review, 412, 467 n 23
Malthus, Thomas R: contraception objected to, 62; *Essay on the principle of population*, 59; goats and dogs, account, 59-61; inspired by, 59, 446 n 8; Keynes, opinion of, 63; life and work, 59, **60**; Marx, opinion of, 64; population, theory of, 61-65; summary of thesis, 78
Mammoth, frozen: Beresovka, 98-100; erect genital, 98, **99**, 448 n 23; source of ivory since Aristotle's day, 97, **97**, 448 n 20
Man: and ape, **207**; appendix, **268**; interfertility of, 141, 144-45, 262; multiple origins of, **141**, 262, 450 n 1
Mann, Horace, early U.S. educator, 425
Manning, Henry E.: opposed to evolution, **351**, 352, 462 n 13
Mars: and Percival Lowell, 190-94, **192**; Viking Lander, 193
Marsh, Othniel C.: fossil horses, 152
Marx, Karl: abolition of private property, 465 n 1; Aveling, son-in-law of, 137; Communist Manifesto, 383; Darwin, opinion of, 381, 464

n 26; Darwin receives *Das capital*, 381; Fabian Society inspired by, 427; London citizen, 76, **381**; new world order, 376; object of worship, 341
Marxism: rule by the elite, 411
Mason, Brian, 183-84. *See also* Meteorite
Matterhorn: fossils in reverse order, 114
Matthew, Patrick: inspired Darwin, 125
Matthew, William: inspired Davidson Black, 235
Matthews, Harrison: evolution is a faith, 394
Matthiae, Paolo: on Ebla, 390
Maxwell, James C., giant of science, 359
Mead, Margaret: death, circumstances of, 417, 467 n 26; Freeman unmasks, 417; life and work, 416-18, **417**; sex liberator, 422
Medawar, Peter: critique of Teilhard de Chardin's *Phenomenon of man*, 375-76; neo-Darwinian theory, 164
Medicinal herbs, 39, **41**
Mendel, Gregor: Darwin challenged by, 161; Galton refuted by, 402-4; genetics understood, 48; Lamarckism refuted by, 260; life and work, 160-61
Memphis: discovery of Ramses II statue, 286-87, **287**. *See also* Bore-hole project
Meteorite: in Antarctica, 448 n 25; Australian tektite controversy, 328, 460 n 22; carriers of life, 196, 202; dust of, 327-29; organized elements in, **183**, 451 n 4; Orgueil, 183-84
Metchnikoff, Elie, **273**: alimentary canal vestigial, 272, 456 n 10, 456 n 11; on the hymen, 270
Methodist revival, 54
Michelangelo: Sistine chapel ceiling, 377, **377**. *See also* Adam
Miller, Hugh, **361**: Mosaic day-age theory, 362; opposed to *Vestiges*, 360-61; suicide of, 350; works, 360-61
Miller, Stanley: experiment, 199, **199**
Milton, John: ages of man, 206; Fall of man 206, 453 n 4; Unitarian beliefs, 116
Mohammed: object of worship, 341
Mohenjo-daro, India, 338
Monera, 187, 189
Monitum: condemns Teilhard de Chardin, 375; English translation of, 464 n 19
Monogenists, 141, 144
Moon: age of, 303-4, 330, 458 n 19, 458 n 20, 458 n 21; dust on, 329, 460 n 23; lunar laser ranging experiment, 329-30, 460 n 24; origin a mystery, 460 n 25
Moore, Hugh: crusade to curb population, 337
Morganucodon. See Transition fossils
Morgentaler, Henry: signer of the Humanist Manifesto, 428
Morton,. Samuel, **261**: skulls, examples, **269**; work, 261-64
Moses: Christ refers to, 463 n 25; Documentary hypothesis regards as myth, 383-84; Ebla evidence indicates high education, 390; Miller

and Mosaic days, 362, patriarch of the Jews, 12

Moth, peppered, 171-72.

Mouse-tail experiments of Weismann, 48, 445 n 14

Mule, 139, **140**

Muller, Herman J.: Repository for Germinal Choice, 415

Museum d'Histoire Naturelle, 46, 49, 51, 53

Museum displays, 88

Mutability. *See* Evolution

Napoleon I (Bonaparte), **346**; conquest of Egypt, 286, 348, **349**

Napoleon III (Louis): and Pasteur, 179

National Geographic magazine: ape-man image promoted by, 243-45; censorship of information, 108, 426

National sovereignty: elimination of, 397

Natural history: decline of public interest in, 350

Natural theology. *See* Natural history

Nature-nurture controversy, 402-20

Nazi Party: Fascist motives, 411; gas chambers, 410; sterilization, 410; *See also* German National Socialist Party

Neanderthal man, 209-15: in armor, 215, 453 n 9; burial rites, 4, 215; Field Museum reconstructions, 212-13; living specimens, 215, 453 n 10; possible longevity, 214; skull capacity, 212; supra-orbital torus, **214**; syphilis, 214; vitamin B deficiency, 213

Nebraska man, 231-33, **232**

Needham, Joseph: English Jesuit, 15, 180

Negro: intellect and racism, 262-63

Neo-Darwinian theory. *See* Synthetic theory

Neo-Lamarckism, 48

Neutrinos: solar output of, 323

Newman, John Henry, **372**: development theory, 373, 464 n 15; Oxford Movement, 373

Newton, Isaac, 29, 43, 66, 135, **342**; Bible miracles unaccepted, 342, 365, 461 n 3, 461 n 4; Unitarian beliefs, 116

Niagara Falls: age of, 94-95, 285; Lyell visits, 81-83, **82**, **83**; rates of recession, 82-83, 447 n 5

Nietzsche, Friedrich: Christianity challenged by, 344; declares God dead, 383

Nineveh: Christian response to, 353, 462 n 14, 462 n 15, 462 n 16; discovery by Layard, 352, **352**; Documentary hypothesis seen to be supported by, 385

Noah, ark of: accommodation of species, 142, 145; alleged discovery, 388-89; in Chinese ideographs, 392; Christ acknowledges, 360, 463 n 25; necessity to build, 362

Nobel prize winners' sperm bank, 415

Nuclear waste storage, 337

Nuremberg trials: eugenics movement affected by, 410

Nutcracker man: age of, 243-44, 455 n 16; associated with Reck's fossil, 244-45; with evidence of a stone shelter, 246

Occult, involvement in by: H. Bergson, 375, 464 n 16; Communist Party, 395; C. Darwin, 75, 446 n 15; C. Doyle, 75; liberal church, 395; Nazi Party, 395; J. Ruskin, 75; A. Tennyson, 75; A.R. Wallace, 75, 446 n 16

O'Hair, Madalyn Murray: object of worship, 341

Oil wells: high pressure, 336-37

Olduvai Gorge, 243-46. *See also* Leakey, Louis: Nutcracker man

Olympic games, religious aspects, 341

Oparin-Haldane theory, 196-203: amino acid formation, 197; Miller experiment, 199; photosynthesis, 200; protein formation, 197

Orgel, Leslie: coworker with Francis Crick, 195

Orgueil meteorite, 183-84. *See also* Meteorite

Origen, early liberal theologian, 16, 442 n 11

Origin of moon: George Darwin's fission theory for, 44, 330

Origin of species (On the): Biogenetic law hinted at, 275; Catholic *Index* does not censure, 373; concordance to, 138; Creator mentioned, 369, 463 n 9; definition of species not given, 145; difficult to read, 132; and Haeckel, 184; Hegel's philosophy supported by, 383, 386; introduction by Thompson, 454 n 16; promotion of, 354-55; publicity given to, 353, 380; reason's alternative to miracle, 380; reception of, 130-33; racism caused by, 403; review by T.H. Huxley, 358; review by B. Powell, 378

Orohippus. See Horse

Osborn, Henry F: eugenicist, 408; horse fossils, 153; Marxist worldview, 454 n 21; Nebraska man examined by, 231-32

Os coccyx. See Tailbone, vestigial

Os penis, 254

Ovid: ages of man, 205; Fall of man, 207

Owen, Richard, **210**: ape and man differences, 209-10, 221; opposed to Darwin, 210

Owen, Robert, English socialist, 57

Oxford debate: meeting of the British Association, 357

Oxford Movement, 373. *See also* Anglo-Catholicism, Newman

Oxnard, Charles: multivariate analysis, 253-54

Oxygen 18 method of dating, 302, 315, 458 n 18, 459 n 4. *See also Radiometric dating methods*

Paleotragus, 175

Paley, William, **121**: clockmaker argument, xi; Darwin influenced by, 121, 444 n 7; opposed to David Hume, 344; religious views exposed, 449 n 9; works, 121

Paluxy River, Texas: dinosaur tracks, 108, 448 n 35, 448 n 36, 448 n 37

Pandora, 205, **205**

Panspermia theory, 327

Papyrus Ipuwer: Egyptian and biblical concordance, 349

Parus atricapillus. See Chickadee

Parus carolinus. See Chickadee

Pasteur, Louis: attempt to discredit, 183; bacteria discovered, 198; life and work, 179-84, **179**, **182**; opposition to, 161; spontaneous generation dealt blow by, 181

Patterson, Colin: declares evolution is anti-knowledge, 393

Pearson, Karl: mathematician with Francis Galton, 404

Peccary, 233, 454 n 23

Peking man, 234-41, **239**; classification of, 252; decapitated apes, 238; human fossils found with, 240; reconstruction of skull, 237, 261, 454 n 4, 454 n 6; upper cave, 240; use of fire, 238-39

Pember, George: and the Gap theory, 364

Penguin flipper cited by Darwin, 154-55

Persistence of facies discussed by Ager, 113

Pettersson, Hans: measures meteoritic dust in fall, 328-29

Pettinato, Giovanni: work at Ebla, 390-91

Pharaoh's tomb: carbon 14 calibration, 320-21, 462 n 9

Pharyngeal arches, 277. See Gill-slits

Photosynthesis in Oparin-Haldane theory, 200

Phrenology: craniometer, use of, 406, **406**; popularized by F J Gall, **401**

Phylogenetic chart, 177

Pigeons: Darwin's experiments, 148-50; oil gland in, 264; variations of, **148**

Pilbeam, David: on Peking man, 239; on *Ramapithecus*, 252, 455 n 28

Piltdown man, 225-229; filed teeth, 229; reconstruction of skull, 261

Pineal gland: seat of the soul, 258; vestigial, 269

Pithecanthropines, classification of, 243, 249-51

Pithecanthropus alulus. See Java man

Pithecanthropus erectus. See Java man

Pithecanthropus pekinensis. See Peking man

Pituitary gland, vestigial, 267

Pius XII, Pope: condemns evolution, 373

Plague: effect of on population, 338-39, **339**

Planets: rotation refutes Laplace 293, 457 n 9

Plato: aware of a sixth sense, 9; on Creation, 11; Er's account, 1, 4, 442 n 1; heaven is an ideal pattern, 7, 442 n 5; ideas developed by others, 32; not a liberal, 7; Paradise before man's Fall, 453 n 3; Pythagoreans visited by, 6; *The Republic*, a model for socialism, 1, 6, 7; and the Sophists, 7; utopia, 6

Pleochroic halos. See Radio-halos

Plesiosaur: fossil, **86**; Japanese and Western opinions, 467 n 29; Japanese fishermen catch, 106-7, **107**, 426-27; possibly still living, 175; reconstruction, **86**

Polygenists, 141, 144, 262

Pongo, 41

Poor Law: and Townsend, 60

Population growth, 337-39, **339**, 461 n 39

Potassium-argon dating method: applied to: 1470 man, 247, 455 n 25; Lucy, 248, 455 n 27;

Nutcracker man, 243, 455 n 16; argon contamination, 301, 458 n 16; description of, 300

Potter, Charles: Chrysalid, statue of, 372; humanism declared a religion, 420

Powell, Baden: review of *Origin*, 378

Pressure differentials in oil wells, 366-67, 461 n 36

Priestley, Joseph, **56**; Darwin's family influenced by, 126; Edinburgh University graduate, 121; exiled, 56; Malthus influenced by, 59; Unitarian Church evangelist, 56, 117, 445 n 5

Probability, 200-2, 453 n 27

Prodigy: ancestral brain, 264; Myron Romano, 206

Protagoras: atheistic view, 11; Christian view challenged by, 442 n 8; early secular humanist, 420; opposed to Socrates, 8

Protsch, R.: determines age of Reck's fossil, 245

Pterosaur: evolution of flight, 178; size evidence of vapor canopy, 319, 159 n 11

Ptolemy of Alexandria, 22-24

Punctuated equilibria: description of, 164-66; and theistic evolution, 366

Pyramid of power found in elitist organizations, 33, 51

Racism among men of science, 260, 456 n 1

Radday, Yehuda: Developmental hypothesis refuted by computer, 386

Radioactive decay: assumption, 303; constancy questioned, 296, 304-5, 307-8, 317-19, 457 n 11, 457 n 12, 457 n 13; explained, 295-98; mathematical relationships, 297, 457 n 14; as source of earth's heat, 294; as source of sun's energy, 323

Radio-halos, 310-12; evidence for *ex nihilo* Creation, 312

Radiometric dating: assumptions summarized, 303; calibration, 320-22; concordance of, 302; principles, 295; radio-halos invalidate the assumptions, 312

Radiometric dating methods: carbon 14, 313-15; oxygen 18, 302, 315, 458 n 18, 459 n 4; potassium/argon, 300-1; uranium/lead, 295 300

Raised beaches, 93

Ramapithecus punjabicus, 249, 251-52, 455 n 28

Ramses II; statue, 286-87, **287**

Rancho La Brea tar pit, 90-92, **91**; human skull discovered in, 91, 447 n 14; wolf and sabertooth tigers, 91, 447 n 13

Raup, David: confesses absence of transition fossils, 151

Rawlings, Maurice: clinical resuscitation, 1

Ray, John: classification based on biblical fixity of kinds, 39, 139; influence on Paley and Darwin, 444 n 7

Recapitulation theory. See Biogenetic law

Reck, Hans: human fossil discovery, 244-45, **244**

Redi, Francesco: disproves abiogenesis, 180

Renaissance, 32, 33; defined, 25

Reproductive-repopulation model, 111-13
Reptile to mammal transition, 156-57
Resurrection: a stumbling block to belief, 13, 365
Resuscitation: biblical cases of, 5, 442 n 2
Reusch, Franz: German theologian, 351
Revolution. *See under* American, French, Industrial, Russian
Rhodesian man, 229-31, **230**; age, 231, 454 n 20; Mair's opinion of hole, 231; Rigg's disease, 230-31
Rift Valley, Ethiopia, 248
Riverside Church, New York, 372. *See also* Fosdick, Harry Emerson
Rock badger, 152
Rockefeller Foundation, funding for: eugenicist H. Goddard, 407; Fosdick's Riverside Church, 372; Peking man, 235-36
Roemer, Olaus: velocity of light measurement, 305, 458 n 23
Rosetta Stone, **347**, 348
Rosicrucian order: and Francis Bacon, 443 n 21
Rousseau, Jean J.: children abandoned, 31; Christianity challenged by, 344; education of children, 31; exhibitionism, 444 n 24; friend of Malthus family, 59; life and work, **30**, 31-32, **32**; Lunar Society connections, 56, 57; secular humanism supported by, 422; *Social contract*, 31; Wilson's *Sociobiology* supported by, 413
Royal Society: governed by T.H. Huxley, 189; haven for radicals, 345; Lunar Society founders, 55; vision of Francis Bacon, 28
Ruin-restoration theory. *See* Gap theory
Runcorn, S.K.: dynamo theory, 331
Ruskin, John: occult involvement, 75
Russell, Bertrand: Margaret Mead's work used to justify worldview, 416; proposes controlled human breeding, 466 n 8; pro-Soviet view, 6
Russian Revolution, 7, 444 n 25

Saber-tooth tiger, 19, 447 n 13
St. Helen's volcano, 84
Saltation theory. *See* Hopeful monster theory
Salts in: blood plasma, 291, 457 n 8; Dead Sea, 289-90; sea water, 288, 457 n 5
Sanger, Margaret, advocate of birth control, 408, 466 n 13
Sanskrit, a complex ancient language, 255
Savonarola: burned at the stake, 443 n 18
Schiaparelli and Mars, 191-92, **192**, 452 n 20, 452 n 21
Scofield Reference Bible promotes Gap theory, 364
Scopes trial, 232, 425; publicity given to, 232, 353; staged by ACLU, 454 n 22
Sea serpent, **106**
Second law of thermodynamics, 204, 305
Secular humanism: definition, 420; prospects for mankind, 429-30; religious aspects, 394
Secular humanists' strategies for world leadership, 427

Sedimentary rocks: absence of meteorites in, 327-28; classification of, 101-2; in Grand Canyon, 100; volcanic ash produces, 70, 84-85. *See also* Volcanic ash
Seven day week, 34-35, 444 n 25
Sex education in schools: results of, 422-23
Sexual selection, 158
Selenka expedition and Java man, 224
Semi-lunar fold of the eye said to be vestigial, 268
Setterfield, Barry: investigates the constancy of constants, 306, 458 n 26
Shackleton, E.H.: Antarctic coal, 97
Shakespeare, William: language deteriorated since, 255; quote, 282, 457 n 1
Shang-Ti, heavenly emperor, 392, 465 n 43
Shapley, Harlow, x, **xi**, 312
Shaw, Bernard: founding member of the Fabian Society, 427-28, **428**; quoted, 382
Shrinking sun. *See* Contracting sun
Simpson, George G.: work on fossil horses, 153
Sinanthropus pekinensis. See Peking man
Sistine Chapel ceiling, 377
Situational ethics opposed to Bible ethics, 422
Skinner box, 418; for human use, **419**, 467 n 27
Skinner, B.F: signer of the Humanist Manifesto, 428; works, 418
Skulls, Indian: from S. Morton's collection, **269**
Smith's Bible dictionary denies worldwide Flood, 351
Smith, George: deciphers Nineveh tablets, 384
Smith, Grafton Elliot, involved with: Nebraska man, 232; Peking man, 235-36; Piltdown man, 227-29; Taung skull, 241-42
Smith, William: "Strata" Smith, 69
Smith, William R., editor of *Encyclopaedia Britannica*, 385-86
Smuts, Jan Christiaan: holism, 242; Taung skull, 242
Sobell and Sobell: treatment of alcoholics, 419
Socialist network of organizations, 427-28
Social Darwinism: basis of, 403; Lowell's associates practitioners of, 190
Society for Psychical Research, 75, 464 n 16
Socrates: death of, 5, **6**; Divine Voice heard by, 5, 442 n 4; immortality of the soul, belief in, 8, 9; teaching method of, 5
Spallanzani, Lazzaro: supported biogenesis, 180
Spearman, C.E.: victim of Cyril Burt's plagiarism, 412
Species, 139-47: archetypes, 146-47; cladistics, classification by, 147; Darwin avoided definition of, 145; textbook definition, 146; typological concept, 146; word origin, 39
Speed of light. *See* Velocity of light
Spencer, Herbert: amorality justified by, 421; lauded by Christian press, 401; life and work, 398-401, **399**; situational ethics based on, 422; survival of the fittest, 132, 169, 451 n 15; X Club member, 189
Sperm bank. *See* Muller, Herman J.

Spiritism. *See* Occult
Splitters, 145
Spontaneous generation, 179-82
Stalactites. *See* Dripstone
Stalagmite containing fossil bat, 461 n 35
Stalin, Joseph: object of worship, 340
Starlight: time to reach earth, 306, 458 n 27
Stegosaurus, 151
Sterilization laws in: America, 408; Germany, 409-10
Stone age, 208
Stone mortars found with Calaveras skull, 217
Straus and Cave on Neanderthal man, 212-13
Strauss, David, German theologian, 343, **343**
Sun: contraction of, 322, **324**, 459 n 15, 459 n 16, 460 n 17; energy source, 322-25; neutrino problem, 323, 459 n 14; rotation of, 325
Survival of the fittest: a tautology, 169-70. *See also* Spencer, Herbert
Survival of the least fittest, 174
Swanscombe skull, 253
Swift, Johnathon. brain capacity of, 259
Syllabus of Errors, 373
Symbiosis: a major problem for Oparin, 200
Syncline. *See* Bent rocks
Synthetic theory, 163, 170
Syntropy proposed as mechanism for evolution, 164, 451 n 12

Tail, reported on human, 278-79
Tailbone, vestigial, 268, 277
Taoism in China, 392
Taung skull, 242-42; an *Australopithecine*, 245; Keith rejects, 242, 455 n 13; Smith accepts, 242; Smuts involved with, 242
Teilhard de Chardin, Pierre: Communist use of, 376; incomprehensible language, 376; inspired by H. Bergson, 375; Peking man, 235-41, 454 n 4, 455 n 6; Piltdown man suspect, 226-29, **229**; reconciles Christianity and evolution, 374-76, **374**, 464 n 17; reports Rhodesian man, 231
Tektite. *See* Meteorite
Teleology: Aristotle believed in, 9; prodigy example questions, 206
Tell El-Amarna evidence of Egyptian and Bible concordance, 349
Tell Mardikh. *See* Ebla discovery
Temple, Frederick: archbishop, **379**, 380; forced to withdraw eassy, 464 n 25
Temple, William: archbishop, 379, **379**; founder of the World Council of Churches, 464 n 25
Tennyson, Alfred: occult involvement, 75; quoted, 79, 446 n 17
Terrace, H.S.: ape to man communication exposed, 254
Theistic evolution, 366-80: Anglican Church adopts, 377-80; Communist Party finds useful, 376, 464 n 21; Darwin rejects, 369, 463 n 7; Genesis denied, 366; Gray promotes, 367-68;

Roman Church adopts, 372-77, **377**; a stepping-stone to secular humanism, 395; supported by punctuated equilibria, 366
Theistic humanism: defined, 420
Theropithecus galada, 252. *See also Ramapithecus punjabicus*
Thirty-nine articles. *See* Anglican Church
Thom, A.: on megalitic monuments, 220, 454 n 13
Thomism. *See* Aquinas, Thomas
Thompson, W.R.: comments on Java man, 225, 454 n 16
Thomsen, Christian, Danish archaeologist, 208
Thomson, William. *See* Kelvin, Lord
Thyroid gland, vestigial, 267
Tonsils, vestigial, 267
Toynbee, Arnold: condemns Christianity, 15, 442 n 9
Transcendental Meditation form of worship, 341
Transition fossils, 150-58: reptile to mammal, 156-57. *See also Archaeopteryx*
Transmutation. *See* Evolution
Trilobite eye: evolution of, 168-69, **168**
Trinity, doctrine of: rejected by Isaac Newton, 343
Trismegistus, Hermes. *See* Hermetic tradition
Tse-tung, Mao: object of worship, 340
Turgenev, Ivan: brain capacity, **258**, 259
Turner, Samuel, American theologian, 351

Uniformitarianism, 309
Unitarian Church: in America, 117, 367; Emma Darwin, influence on Charles, 122, 126-27, 137, 463 n 3; history of, 116-17; Humanist Manifesto subscribed to by, 428; Jane Gray, influence on Asa Gray, 367, 463 n 3
United Nations and population policies, 337
UNESCO: Humanist Association connections, 429; media censorship, 427; peace movements sponsored by, 411, 466 n 20; policy of, 423-24, **424**, 465 n 2
Universal constants: relatedness, 304-5
Uranium/lead dating method, 295-300; lead contamination, effect of, 299; mineral formation, 298. *See also* Radiometric dating
Uranium salts in sea water, 290-91, 457 n 7
Uslar-Gleichen, Frida von: affair with Haeckel, 186, **187**
Ussher, James: Creation, date of, 283-85, **284**; Egyptian dating not concordant with, 348; 9 o'clock statement wrongly ascribed to, 284, 457 n 2
Utopia, 6, 33. *See also* Plato

Van Evrie, J.H., early scientific racist, 410, 466 n 18
Vapor canopy: evidence for, 319
Velikovsky, I.: Right on Egyptian dating, 349; wrong on other issues, 109

Velocity of light: constancy in question, 305-6; cosmological implications, 306; Roemer's measurements, 305, 458 n 23; Setterfield's work, 306, 458 n 26

Vestiges of Creation: Darwin's *Origin* aided by, 353, 462 n 18; Hugh Miller opposes, 361; Baden Powell adopts, 378

Vestigial organs, 264-79; Boa constrictor hind legs, 270-71; Chinese foot-binding refutes, 270; circumcision refutes, 269-70; Darwin's reasoning Lamarckian, 266; Flat-head Indians' head binding refutes, 270; homology as the basis for, 266; medical practices based upon, 272-73; regressive or progressive, 264, 456 n 3; Scadding refutes, 267; textbooks still use as examples, 265, 272, 456 n 4, 456 n 9; whale, hind legs, 270, **271**

Vestigial organs of man, claims for: appendix, 267, 273; coccyx, 268, 277-79; hymen, 270; male nipples, 265, 456 n 5; pineal gland, 269; pituitary gland, 267; semi-lunar fold of the eye, 268 thyroid, 267; tonsils, 267

Villee, Claude (textbook author): claims one hundred human organs vestigial, 265; includes male nipples, 267

Virchow, Rudolph, **211, 213**: Boas taught by, 413; German race type sought for, 406; Haeckel taught by, 184; Neanderthal man examined by, 210-11

Virgin birth, object of a divided view, 116, 360, 365

Vogt, William. *See* Moore, Hugh

Volcanic ash: Antarctic preserves past record, 100, 448 n 24; extensive in the past, 84, 447 n 6, 447 n 7; forms sedimentary rock, 85; world-wide distribution of, 70, 446 n 12

Voltaire: denies Fall of man, 207; free-thinker, **26**, 32; Lunar Society, **55**, 57; quoted, 15

Vox populi, vox dei, 16

Wakefield, Gilbert: influence on Malthus, 59

Wallace, Alfred R.: birds of paradise, 174; "delicate arrangement", victim of, 130, 446 n 14; life and works, 74-76, **73**, **76**; occult involvement, 75-76, 446 n 15; pension, 75; revelation, moment of, 77-78, 446 n 16; Sarawak law, 77, 130; summary of thesis, 78-79; tautology exposed, 80; Ternate paper, 78, 130-31

Wastefulness of nature, 169

Webb, Sidney and Beatrice, founders of: Fabian Society, 427; London School of Economics, 428, **428**

Weber, Wilhelm, coworker with Karl Gauss, **333**

Wedgwood, Josiah: Lunar Society member, 55; Unitarian Church member, 117, **118**, 126

Weidenreich, Franz: reconstructs Peking man, 237-40, 456 n 12

Weiner and Oakley: expose Piltdown man, 228

Weismann, August: Darwin's tautology defend-ed, 167; mouse-tail experiments, 48, 266, 445 n 14; statistical work on circumcision, 48

Wellhausen, Julius: work on the Documentary hypothesis, 383-86

Wells, H.G.: Fabian Society member, 427; inspired by Lowell for life on Mars, 193, **193**

Wenner-Gren Foundation to seek ape to man evidence, 374

Wesley, John: brought evangelical revival to English-speaking people, 54, **54**, 344

Westminster Abbey, repository for unbelief: C. Darwin, 135, 380; J. Hooker, 135; C. Kingsley, 357; C. Lyell, 135; I. Newton, 135

Whale: pregnant, 89; Quebec hill discovery, 94, **94**; vestigial hind legs claimed, 270-71, **271**

White, Lynn: historian blames Christianity, 15

Whitelaw, Robert: statistical analysis of carbon 14 data, 320

Whitney, J.D.: report on Calaveras skull, 217

Wickramasinghe, C. *See* Hoyle, Fred

Wiedersheim, Robert: definitive work on vestigial organs, 264-65

Wilberforce, Samuel: Darwin's opinion of, 358; Oxford debate, **357**, 358

Wilkinson, John, Lunar Society member, 55

Wilson's bird of paradise, **175**

Wilson, Edward O.: altruism, 413; ethics and free-will, effect of, 413; C. Lumsden, coworker, 405; *Sociobiology*, 412

Wiseman, Nicholas, Catholic cardinal, **351**

Wistar Institute Symposium, 164, 170, 201

Woman and child of Minateda, 200, 454 n 14

Woodward, Arthur S., work with: Piltdown man, 227-29; Rhodesian man, 230

World Council of Churches, 379

World government: socialist objective, 423

Worship: a universal practice, 340-41

Wyclif, John: caused early evangelical revival, 19, 443 n 14

X Club: members listed, 452 n 17; Royal Society controlled by, 189

Xenophon, disciple of Socrates, 5

Yale University: J. Dana converts to evolution, 371

Young, Robert: concordance lists Creation dates, 283

Zdansky, Otto: initiates work on Peking man, 235

Zeno and his mathematical paradox, 201

Zero: introduced by Arabs, 17, 442 n 12

Zinjanthropus boisei. See Nutcracker man

Zoönomia: Catholic *Index* condemns, 58; C. Darwin influenced by, 120, 121

Zoroastrian belief in resurrection, 2, 3

Zuckerman, Solly: multivariate analysis, 254; quoted, 255